Smoking in dreamland

Wondrous weapons

Steeplejack

Waxed floor show

Labor Day

Christmas Eve

Thanksgiving Day

July 4th

D1309130

PROPERTY OF CENTRAL HIGH SCHOOL OF COMMERCE

THE AUTHORS

HAROLD S. DIEHL is Dean of the Medical Sciences and Professor of Preventive Medicine and Public Health at the University of Minnesota. He was formerly President of the American Student Health Association; Health Consultant to the American Youth Commission; member, Health Advisory Council to the Boys Clubs of America; and member of the Executive Council of the American Public Health Association.

ANITA DUNCAN LATON is retired Professor of Health and Hygiene, San Jose State College, California. She was formerly Assistant Professor of Education and Supervisor of the Teaching of Science, University of California, Berkeley; and Research Associate, Bureau of Educational Research in Science, Teachers College, Columbia University, New York.

The drawings are by STEPHEN ROGERS PECK. Statistical charts on pages 12, 13, 19, 20, 21, 33, 36, 154, 155, 210, 305, 402, 408, 412, 433, and 470 are by HAROLD K. FAYE.

HEALTH

McGRAW-HILL BOOK COMPANY, INC.

New York   Chicago   San Francisco   Dallas   Toronto   London

No. 34505
CENTRAL H. S. OF COMMERCE
LIBRARY
DEPT.

HAROLD S. DIEHL

ANITA D. LATON

and SAFETY

for YOU

1957 Edition

HEALTH AND SAFETY FOR YOU

Copyright © 1957 by the McGraw-Hill Book Company, Inc.
Copyright, 1954 by the McGraw-Hill Book Company, Inc. Printed
in the United States of America. All rights reserved. This book, or
parts thereof, may not be reproduced in any form without permission of the publishers.

Library of Congress Catalog Card Number: 57-9464

Photograph on page ii, courtesy of Moses Brown School.
Photograph on page viii, Pinny from Monkmeyer. Photograph on page x, courtesy of Library of Congress.

PREFACE

Today, as never before in our history, we are concerned with the need for a strong America. The strength we look for cannot be legislated or dictated. It can come only as informed and responsible individuals direct their lives in terms of their own well-being and that of other people. Education in our democracy is concerned with developing understanding as a basis for attitudes and action, not with teaching rules and obedience to higher authority. In our democracy we formulate our own rules and choose our own authorities.

Health and Safety for You is designed to fit into the pattern of American education at its best, to give young people reliable information, and to help them use this knowledge in safeguarding their health and solving their own health problems. This is not a book of rules; it is a guide to enable the student to make his own rules. The material is drawn from many fields—anatomy and physiology, psychology, nutrition, and medicine, to mention a few of the most important —and it is organized as a basis on which students can act with confidence in meeting their problems of health and safety.

Three factors make teaching in the field of health more complicated in this second half of the twentieth century than it has ever been before. One is the increase in information about human beings, how they function, and what ills may befall them. Research has progressed so far and fast that even specialists cannot keep up with all the new

material that is being discovered and described in scientific publications.

A second factor is the complexity of modern living. Whether or not the well on grandfather's farm contained pure or contaminated water was important to only a few persons; the water supply for a modern city makes the difference between health and sickness, even life and death, to thousands. The automobile has brought great convenience to all of us; but it brings death and disaster to thousands every year. Air pollution is a new and serious health menace. And many people live under increasing tension and strain.

A third factor results from the new techniques of communication and their use for putting pressures on everybody's thinking and behavior. The itinerant peddler of a few decades ago used a winning smile and an ingratiating manner to sell his pills and potions, but he reached one family at a time. The modern advertiser uses radio, television, newspapers, magazines, and posters to reach millions of potential buyers. He employs artists, musicians, psychologists, and orators to prepare scripts and layouts which will entice these buyers to spend their money for his product.

The first two chapters of *Health and Safety for You* introduce the field of health especially as it concerns young people, and show the special advantages and problems of adolescents as compared with those of younger and older persons.

The third and fourth chapters deal with safety and first aid. Year after year, accidents stand at the top of the list of causes of death among young people. Automobile accidents and drownings claim the lives of thousands. It seems logical that an early place in this book should be given to thoughtful consideration of how young people can further their chances of staying alive and safe.

The fifth chapter gives an overview of the structure and functioning of the human body with emphasis on living, acting, thinking, feeling human beings. The seventeen chapters which follow deal with the various functions of the body, how each may be maintained at a high level of efficiency, and the common malfunctions and diseases sometimes associated with them. Modern knowledge allows no separation between physical hygiene and mental hygiene. Each chapter includes ideas which are properly related to mental hygiene; Chapter 19, entitled "Mental Health and Personality," summarizes and organizes these ideas.

Chapters 20 and 21 deal with environmental factors which influence health. Chapter 22 covers hormones and endocrine glands. Chapter 23 discusses light, air, and other physical factors, and desirable methods of managing these. Chapters 24 and 25 are concerned with the control of microorganisms and the prevention of communicable diseases. Certain communicable diseases are discussed in earlier chapters where they logically seem to belong, colds in relation to noses, for example, and poliomyelitis in relation to nerves. Chapters 24 and 25 bring out the general principles underlying the control of groups of diseases. Cross references direct students to related material in previous chapters.

Chapters 26 and 27 have a personal application to the life of every student. Chapter 26 returns to a theme presented earlier in the book, the necessity for a health inventory that will give each individual a better idea of his own physical status, his special assets and limitations. Chapter 27 points out the vocational opportunities in the field of health, the training necessary, and the rewards in personal satisfactions and community standing. Young people are giving serious thought to a vocation. In this chapter are concrete suggestions that they will find useful.

The final chapter rounds out the picture of individual health care. It describes the health agencies in modern communities and how they assist individuals, families, and the community as a whole. The aim of the chapter is to inform students about available health services in such a way that each student will want to help develop, support, and use these services.

The vocabulary used in *Health and Safety for You* has been checked against studies of vocabularies of teenagers. Technical terms are defined when first used, and found again in the Glossary. Definitions have been developed in harmony with standard and medical dictionaries. Usefulness for ordinary people rather than for specialists is the aim.

Readability is at the student's level; the presentation is designed for the student's understanding and learning. We, however, do not "talk down" to our readers. When a common problem demands complex ideas for its understanding, we have provided the information in simple terms as clearly as possible.

A variety of learning aids is given at the end of each chapter. "So What" summarizes the high points of the chapter and sets these in relation to everyday living. The sections entitled "So What?" are not to be memorized but to be thought about. "Checking Up" includes questions for review and drill; "Things to Do" suggests projects, topics for discussion, and other activities that involve reflection and action by students. The bibliography at the end of the book lists reading materials from many sources and acquaints students with organizations and interests other than schools and textbooks.

The book may be adapted to courses of varying length by making more or less use of these suggestions for additional work. In a one-semester course, only a few of the "Things to Do" can be carried out by the class as a whole. More advanced students or those with special interests may do additional reading and make special reports on individual projects. In a full year's course, more of the activities can be engaged in by the whole class. The number and variety of activities suggested in this text make it easy for the teacher to provide for individual differences among students.

A series of motion pictures prepared to accompany *Health and Safety for You* are listed on page iv. These films extend the text into fields of special interest and importance to young people.

The writing of this book was a cooperative venture of the two authors. However, Julia Mills Diehl, graduate in home economics and wartime instructor in nutrition for the American Red Cross, prepared most of the material for the two chapters dealing with nutrition and foods. The chapter on mental health was prepared with the advice and guidance of Dr. Reynold A. Jensen, Professor of Child Psychiatry, University of Minnesota.

Dr. Edna W. Bailey, Professor Emeritus of Education at the University of California, read the manuscript in all stages of its preparation and made valuable criticisms and suggestions. Miss Margaret Twombly, Professor and Head of the Department of Health and Hygiene, San Jose State College, California, read a number of chapters and helped to shape their wording and scope. Dr. Margaret Hudson of the San Jose Public Schools checked the vocabulary of several chapters. Others who gave valuable counsel and advice are Dr. Ruth Boynton, Professor of Preventive Medicine and Public Health, University of Minnesota; Dr. Ruth Grout, Professor of Health Education, University of Minnesota; Dr. Stewart Thomson, Professor of Preventive Medicine and Public Health, University of Minnesota; Dr. Dorothy Nyswander, Professor of Health Education, University of California, Berkeley; Miss Mattie Dell Webb of the Dallas Public Schools; and Miss Marjorie L. Craig, Director, School Health Bureau, Metropolitan Life Insurance Company. Many other individuals deserve credit.

Portions of the manuscript were checked for accuracy and method of presentation by members of interested groups: the National Tuberculosis Association, the Arthritis and Rheumatism Foundation, the National Foundation for Infantile Paralysis, the American Dental Association, and the American Red Cross.

To all of these the authors are grateful. While taking full responsibility for the book, they feel that its worth has been enhanced by the generous help their friends and professional associates have given them.

HAROLD S. DIEHL
ANITA D. LATON

CONTENTS

Preface　　　　　　　　　　　　　　　　　　　v

1. Life's Greatest Treasure　　　　　　　　　1

2. The Best Years of Our Lives　　　　　　　7

3. You Bet Your Life　　　　　　　　　　　18

4. What to Do in Emergencies　　　　　　44

5. Wonderfully Made　　　　　　　　　　71

6. The Body's Framework and Power Plant　92

7. Keep Physically Fit and Like It　　　　110

8. Nutrition and You　　　　　　　　　　133

9. What Will You Have to Eat?　　　　　149

10. Skin Deep　　　　　　　　　　　　165

11. Your Life Blood　　　　　　　　　　188

12. Your Heart and Circulation　　　　　199

13. Sneezes and Sniffles　　　　　　　　215

14. The Breath of Life　　　　　　　　232

15. Attractive Teeth 245

16. Digestion 259

17. Getting Rid of Body Wastes 280

18. Brain and Nerves 288

19. Mental Health and Personality 311

20. Seeing and Hearing 333

21. Stimulants and Narcotics 354

22. Chemical Regulators of the Body 368

23. Environment and Health 376

24. How We Resist Disease 398

25. Controlling the Spread of Disease Organisms 416

26. Your Health Inventory 438

27. Opportunities for Service in the Field of Health 453

28. Health Services for All People 466

For Further Reading 479

Glossary 486

Index 503

CENTRAL HIGH SCHOOL OF COMMERCE

LIST OF CHARTS

Death Rates for Various Ages	12
Why Young Men Are Rejected for Military Service	13
Accidents—The No. 1 Killer	19
Deaths by Accidents for All Ages	20
Most Dangerous Accidents for Children and Young People	21
The Most Dangerous Jobs	33
Student Accidents by Grades	36
Growth Chart—Boys	152
Growth Chart—Girls	153
Changes in Death Rates from Certain Diseases	210
Poliomyelitis	305
Temperature (Fahrenheit)	402
Immunity	404
Diphtheria Deaths	408
Production of Diphtheria Antitoxin	409
Progress in Control of Five Diseases	412

The Conquest of Disease   433

Physicians in Relation to Population   467

Hospitals and Hospital Beds   469

What People Spent Their Money for   470

Dentists in Relation to Population   471

Nurses in Relation to Population   472

LIST OF TABLES

1. Cancer Deaths in the United States   88

2. Functions of Nutrients   136

3. Daily Calory Requirements   151

4. Calories Needed for Various Activities   154

5. Nutrients Supplied by the Basic Seven Food Groups   155

6. Servings of Food for Different Kinds of Work   157

7. Tobacco Smoking and Length of Life   357

8. Usual Amount of Alcohol in Various Beverages   358

BODY DIAGRAMS

The Skeleton   93

Skeletal Muscles, Tendons, and Ligaments   99

Circulatory System   203

The Lymphatic System   211

Respiratory System   236

Digestive System   263

The Urinary System   281

Central Nervous System   296

Autonomic Nervous System   297

Endocrine Glands   369

PROPERTY OF
CENTRAL HIGH SCHOOL OF COMMERCE

TEXT-FILMS: The following is a list of the McGraw-Hill Text-Films—16-mm sound motion pictures—specially made for use with *Health and Safety for You.*

The Heart—How It Works

Sniffles and Sneezes

Community Health

Your Body during Adolescence

Parents Are People **Too**

CHAPTER 1   Life's Greatest Treasure

People usually think of "treasures" as heaps of gold or silver money, or diamonds and rubies that can be sold for money. They sometimes forget that health is one of our greatest treasures.

In some ways, health is like money. Its value lies not in itself but in what people do with it. Health does not make a person happy. It does make it easier for him to be happy, because he is more able to do what he wants to do. Health does not make a person useful. It does make it more possible for him to be useful.

WHAT IS HEALTH?

This is a book about health, which is not the same as a book about not being ill. It is easy to describe a sick person. He has a toothache; he has measles; he is sick in bed. It is not so easy to define health or to describe a healthy person. He does not have a toothache; he does not have measles; he is able to walk about and to do his work. But when we have said this, we have not really described a healthy person. What else is there?

For one thing, a healthy person generally gets fun out of life. He wakes up rested, feeling that the day will be full of interesting things. He enjoys what he does; he enjoys seeing things, going places, knowing people.

The healthy person usually makes a good impression on other people. His eyes are bright, his hair shines, he stands straight, his skin is clear and pink. He looks as if he finds life enjoyable. Other people think they would like to know him.

The healthy person can play and work hard; he can go places; he can do things. He is likely to be successful—successful in studying, in making a living, in taking care of his children when he has a family of his own. Other people can count on him. He is independent. He can take care of himself and help take care of other people.

Mental health and physical health. In talking about health, we do not limit ourselves to talking about bodily health. People used to think you could consider your body all by itself. Now

1

we have come to understand that you are *you* in everything you are or do or feel. You do not have a body that has no relationship to your mind. Nor do you have a mind unrelated to your body.

All our bodily strengths and weaknesses influence what we do and how we think and feel. A person with a hearing defect may feel lonely and afraid of being laughed at. He may not be able to play games or to sing with other people. A person with a toothache may feel cross and unhappy and annoyed about little things that usually do not bother him. A person with strong muscles may be admired because he can run and play games, and in turn he may feel friendly and confident because he knows that people admire him. These are examples of how physical characteristics affect feeling and thinking.

But feeling and thinking have their influence on how our bodies work. When a person worries a great deal, it may keep him from sleeping and eating properly. It may interfere with his digestion. In fact, there seems to be a good deal of proof that worry and *feeling* upset may cause something as "physical" as stomach ulcers.

Scientists use a long word, *psychosomatic*, to express this idea. It means mind-body. By putting the two together, scientists try to show that mind and body influence each other. We sometimes use the terms *mental hygiene*, meaning care of the mind, and *physical hygiene*, meaning care of the body. In this book, we shall not try to separate them.

SUCCESS WITHOUT GOOD HEALTH

There have been happy and useful people who did not have good health. Beethoven, one of the world's great composers of music, was deaf before he reached middle age and never heard some of his finest music. John Milton was blind when he wrote the great English poem *Paradise Lost*. President Franklin D. Roosevelt was so badly crippled that he could not walk alone.

People like these men make us realize how fortunate we are to have good health. They also remind us that it is possible, but not easy, to live successful lives even if we are not completely healthy.

We should not worry about ourselves. On the other hand, we should make sure that we are doing what we can to keep ourselves healthy. Very few people can be perfectly healthy. Everyone can be more healthy than he is now, if he works at it.

WHERE DO WE FIND HEALTH?

There is a famous story of a man who sold his farm in India and went to hunt for diamonds. He wandered over the whole world but never found the diamonds he was seeking. But the farm he left became one of the greatest diamond mines in the world.

This story applies to many people who desire good health. They try to find this great treasure outside of themselves. They listen to the radio, read advertisements, and take the advice of friends and acquaintances.

Healthy people look as if they enjoy life. Health makes it easier to have fun, to do work you are interested in, and to make friends. (Courtesy *Scholastic Magazines*)

They believe that health can be had by buying this, that, or the other thing. Pay your money and take your choice! It is supposed to be just as simple as that.

Thousands of people today are relying on drugstore vitamins to improve their well-being. Vitamins are better purchased at the grocery store in fruits, vegetables, cereals, milk, and meat. Again, a large number of people take pills to "pep" themselves up, then take "sleeping" pills to help them

sleep. Others follow every food fad they hear of, trying to lose weight or to gain weight. Some eat themselves groggy every day and shorten their lives; others half-starve themselves. Still others bury themselves deep in armchairs and *read* their exercises in the sports pages of the newspaper, then stop at the store next day for a bottle of tonic.

The know-how of health. We do not know all there is to know about keeping healthy. However, our knowledge has grown by leaps and bounds in the last 75 years. It has grown so fast that people in general have not been able to learn all that the scientists have discovered.

Most people care about their health. Many do wrong things and are half-sick only because they do not know the right things to do.

The purpose of this book is to help you understand yourself and what you need to do to keep in good health. It is not a book of rules— "Do this," "Don't do that." Rather, it is a book that explains why your doing certain things will improve your health.

It is not easy to understand human beings. Sometimes you must ask advice of people who know more than you. This book should help you to know when to ask advice and how to use the advice you get.

Fortunately for most of us, the diamond mine of health lies within ourselves. There is no substitute for daily exercise; for the right kind of food, for sleep, for fresh air, and for keeping worry and fear under control. Really intelligent men and women know this and mine their own health diamonds. How about you?

SO WHAT?

Health of body and of mind is one of the greatest treasures a person can have; and

All too often we do not appreciate this priceless treasure until we have lost it; and

We cannot take health for granted;

So, it is just plain good sense to understand the game that we all must play and that means so much to each and every one.

CHECKING UP

1. Describe a healthy person.
2. What does psychosomatic mean?
3. What is meant by mental hygiene? by physical hygiene? How are they related?
4. What is the relationship of health to happiness and usefulness?
5. Tell how a person with a serious bodily handicap, such as crippling or blindness, can still be a successful person.
6. Tell why most of us could not be perfectly healthy even if we worked intelligently at the problem. What should be our aim as far as health is concerned?

Droopy reads about sports but never takes any exercise himself.

7. Who had (or has) the best chance to learn how to keep well —your grandparents, your parents, or you?
8. What are the advantages and disadvantages of vitamin pills? of "pep" pills? of "sleeping" pills?
9. What is the purpose of this book?

THINGS TO DO

1. This may be the beginning of a new subject for you. Take a little time to discuss with your classmates what you would like to learn from it. Collect from each person in the class ten (or more) questions that he or she would like to have answered. Look at these every 2 or 3 weeks to see which ones you can answer.

Poor Fatty dreams of a beautiful figure but keeps on eating candy.

2. Make a list of the health problems you think are most important for students in your school; for the people living in your community; for people in the United States. Ask your family and friends to help make these lists. Keep the lists until the end of this course.

3. Ask five people why they think good health is important. Ask them to describe a healthy person.

4. Give special reports on the lives of people who have been successful in spite of physical defects or poor health, for example, Beethoven, Milton, Franklin D. Roosevelt, Helen Keller, Steinmetz.

5. Give examples of how illness or pain affects the way you feel about things; of how your feelings affect your digestion, posture, or sleep.

CHAPTER 2   The Best Years of

Our Lives

Older people think of youth as a wonderful time of life. Looking backward, Joseph Conrad wrote: "I remember my youth . . . and the feeling that I could last forever, outlast the sea, the earth and all men . . . the triumphant conviction of strength . . . the glow of the heart."[1]

Youth is the age of warm friendships and exciting romance. New interests are developing; knowledge, adventure, and opportunity lie just ahead. Air castles and dreams are built. Pleasures are many and life's cares, for the most part, are light. It is with reason that some people call these "the best years of our lives."

Even though all this is true, young people have their own difficulties. Many of these difficulties are related to the ways their bodies are growing and developing. Others are connected

[1] Joseph Conrad. *Youth and Two Other Stories*, p. 41. Doubleday & Co., New York, 1920.

with leaving childhood behind and taking on the responsibilities of being grown up. Young people between the ages of 12 and 20 choose jobs, decide whether they are going to stay in school, make their own circles of friends, look forward to their own homes, find their places in church, in politics, and in the community. At 12 they have hardly thought of these things; at 20 many of them are settled. And this growing up takes place during a period when young people are apt not to feel sure of themselves and often do not know what to expect of their friends and families.

ADOLESCENCE

We used to think that children were like Topsy; they "just growed." Now some of the wisest scientists in the world have spent years trying to find out how human beings grow and what they are like at different ages. There has been special interest in adoles-

7

Adolescents make plans for the rest of their lives. (From the "Adolescent Development" Series. McGraw-Hill Text-Films)

cence. This period includes roughly the years between 12 and 20. At 12 most people are children. At 20 most people are adults. What happens in these middle years when children are growing into adults? How does such a change come about?

Growing in size. Most young people have a spurt of growth sometime between 12 and 18 years. They outgrow their clothes. They shoot up to be as tall as, and even taller than, their mothers and fathers.

Growing in size does not seem important to many people. This is true because they lack imagination to see what is going on inside a rapidly growing boy or girl. Bones and muscles, for example, are growing in size,

but it may be several years before they are strong enough for heavy lifting and carrying. Building muscle, skin, nerves, lungs, bones, stomach, intestines, and all the other parts of the body takes energy; the adolescent needs extra food and extra rest while he is growing.

Unequal growth. Arms and legs may outgrow other parts of the body for a time. A boy or girl may become clumsy, although it is probably true that he (or she) never looks as awkward as he feels. Sometimes hormones, the chemicals that regulate growth and development, are not in balance for a time. As a result, the individual may become overweight or underweight. His skin may develop

Skin blemishes usually look worse to the person who has them than to anyone else. (From the "Adolescent Development" Series. McGraw-Hill Text-Films)

acne (pimples). He may become irritable and "nervous." He may blush when he is confused and, thus, become more confused and unhappy. Usually, these difficulties disappear in a few months.

Different people grow differently. A sudden spurt of growth means a great deal to some young people in the way they feel about themselves. Mary grew 4 inches during the year she was 12. She was taller than all her friends and felt that she looked odd when she was with them. She began holding her head down and stooping her shoulders. She thought everyone looked at her when she went out on the street. She became shy and disliked going among other people.

Bob, on the other hand, did not grow as rapidly as his friends. At 15 he was still short. He worried for fear he was not "normal." His classmates called him "Shorty" without thinking that they were hurting his feelings. He could not run as fast as the others; he could not reach as far as they. He became gloomy and shy and did not play with the other boys. He was resentful and unhappy at home and did not do good work at school.

Both Mary and Bob needed to know that growing rapidly is something to be expected during adolescence, but that it does not happen to all young people at the same time. Bob might grow to be a taller man than his friends. Mary would find the other girls catching up with her in

These girls and boys are all the same age. They are healthy, normal young people, but they differ in size because each one is growing at his own rate. Each one is probably "just right" for himself. Some are in the middle of their spurt of growth; some have not started to grow rapidly; and others have almost finished growing.

height in a very few years (see Chapter 19).

Boys and girls. This spurt of growth is one of the ways in which boys and girls differ. The average age at which this growth spurt occurs in girls is 2 years earlier than in boys. For most girls, it begins around the age of 12; for most boys, around 14 or 15. But it may happen at 10 or 11 or at 16 or 17 for individual girls or boys.

Between 11 and 14, most girls are taller and heavier than most boys. This is likely to be embarrassing to both boys and girls and may interfere with their having good times together. After 14, however, the boys usually catch up with the girls and keep on growing for a longer period of time.

Along with changes in size, a number of other changes occur during adolescence. New chemicals (hormones) are found in the blood, and these chemicals cause changes all over the body. Voices become deeper and heavier, especially in boys. Sometimes boys are not sure just what their voices will be like when they speak, and this makes them self-conscious. Hair grows at several places on the body. Hair growing on the face is an important milestone in the lives of boys. The shape of the body changes somewhat, owing to growth of bones and to a deposit of fat under the skin. We call these changes secondary sexual characteristics.

From now on, boys and girls feel themselves to be more nearly grown up. The future seems closer, and they make plans about what they are going to be and the families they hope to have. They make their own friends. Other people treat them more and more like adults.

Adolescents and their families. Growing up does not happen all at once. It may be a slow process. It may have setbacks. A boy or girl may feel grown up at one time and just a little later may again feel like a child. Families, too, change from day to day, or even from minute to minute. They treat the adolescent as if he were an adult and expect more of him than they should. Then they go to the other extreme and treat him as they did when he was 7 or 8. It is easy to see that a boy or girl who feels grown up may resent being treated as a child. It is equally true that parents feel discouraged, when they are thinking of a boy or girl as grown up and responsible, to find that he or she is acting like a child (see Chapter 19). But this is all part of growing up. Adolescents who know something of what is happening to them have a better chance of growing up comfortably and also of understanding their parents.

ADOLESCENTS ARE HEALTHY

Adolescence is a very healthy time of life. The death rate is lower than at any other age. In 1954, among the 15-year-olds in the United States, only one person in 1360 died. Among the 30-year-olds, the rate was twice as great, one person dying in every 660. At the age of 2, the rate was almost as great, with one child dying in every 860.

Adolescents have fewer diseases

Girls usually grow up more rapidly than boys. Notice the differences in height of boys and girls at various ages. (Courtesy Metropolitan Life Insurance Co.)

DEATH RATES FOR VARIOUS AGES

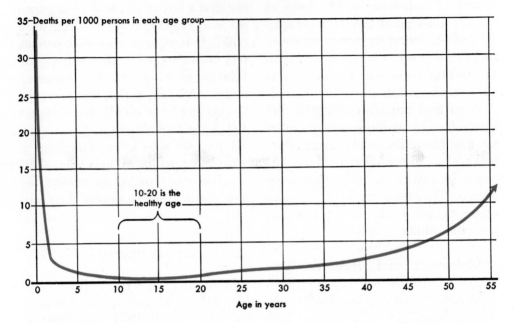

The death rate among babies is high, and it is high again in later life. The curve on the graph goes steadily upward after the age of 55. There are fewer deaths among 10–20-year-olds than for any other 10-year period in the human life span.

than they had when they were children or than they will have when they are grown. Measles, mumps, chicken pox, and other children's diseases are over with, and the diseases of adult life are not yet of much importance.

THE OTHER SIDE OF THE PICTURE

These low rates of death and disease are comforting to adolescents and their parents. However, there is another side to the picture. The chief cause of death in the 10- to 19-year-old group is accidents. Another important cause of death is tuberculosis. Together, accidents and tuberculosis account for almost half of the deaths

each year among adolescents. Most accidents are preventable (see Chapter 3). Tuberculosis is preventable and is curable in the early stages (see Chapter 25). In other words, approximately half of the deaths among adolescents are preventable. If adolescents are to improve their health, they may well start with simply staying alive by avoiding accidents and tuberculosis.

Many of the illnesses of adolescents are not necessary. Most of them are communicable; that is, they spread from one person to another. When a communicable disease spreads rapidly to many people, there is said to be an epidemic of that disease. A little intelligent care will often prevent epidemics of communicable diseases. Usually you can stay away from people with these diseases, if you put your mind on it.

In addition to communicable diseases, adolescents have their share of what we call minor ailments—stomachaches, headaches, cuts and bruises, toothaches, allergies, acne (pimples), constipation. Taken together, these probably cause more loss of fun and work and more general unhappiness than all other diseases. Sometimes these ailments are warning signs, or symptoms, of serious disease. However, most of them result from one or more of the following: eating the wrong kinds of foods, straining the eyes, waiting too long to visit the dentist or the doctor, worry, not enough exercise, too little sleep, and other mistakes in daily living. They seem a high price to pay for ignorance and carelessness.

TAKING INVENTORY OF YOUNG PEOPLE'S HEALTH

Before Pearl Harbor, the Army examined approximately 2 million men but took only about 1 million. In other words, almost one-half of our young men between the ages of 18 and 35

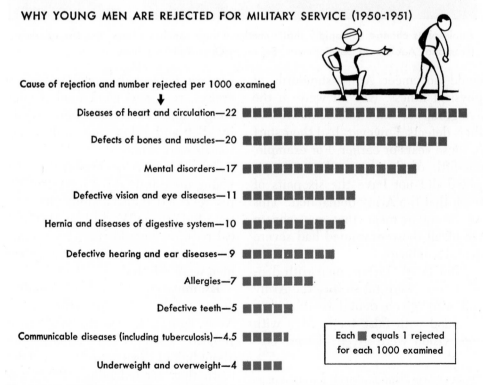

WHY YOUNG MEN ARE REJECTED FOR MILITARY SERVICE (1950-1951)

Cause of rejection and number rejected per 1000 examined

Diseases of heart and circulation—22

Defects of bones and muscles—20

Mental disorders—17

Defective vision and eye diseases—11

Hernia and diseases of digestive system—10

Defective hearing and ear diseases—9

Allergies—7

Defective teeth—5

Communicable diseases (including tuberculosis)—4.5

Underweight and overweight—4

Each ■ equals 1 rejected for each 1000 examined

How many of these conditions could have been prevented if the men had had good health care while they were growing up?

Adolescents change so rapidly that sometimes their families cannot understand them. (From the "Adolescent Development" Series. McGraw-Hill Text-Films)

could not meet Army standards of physical fitness. Not all were in the age group we call adolescent. Most of their defects, however, had their start in those years or earlier. For example, one-fifth of the men who were rejected did not have the six pairs of teeth that the Army demanded.[2] This works out to mean that one man in ten of all those examined had severe dental handicaps.

After Pearl Harbor, men with dental defects were taken into the Army and were given dental treatment or provided with false teeth. Men with poor vision were given glasses. Pos-

ture was corrected through special exercises, rest, and good food. Underweight and overweight were treated by diet and other means. Diseased tonsils were removed.

Selective Service examinations of young men drafted for service in Korea revealed defects similar to those reported during World War II. Physical requirements for military service, however, were reduced; hence, fewer men were rejected.

Examination of school children gives results as impressive as the Army figures. In one study of nearly 100,000 students in Philadelphia, about half of them were found to have teeth that needed filling, straightening, or cleaning. Twenty-three of every 100 were overweight or under-

[2] Present Army standards call for eight pairs of teeth. In a complete set of teeth, there are sixteen pairs.

weight. Twenty-two had flat feet or poor posture. Fourteen had diseased tonsils and thirteen had poor vision.[3]

The fact that so many of our young men could not meet World War II Army standards is disturbing. The fact that so many defects could be corrected, and that our Army became the finest and the strongest the world has ever known, is encouraging. The hope now is that future generations may be allowed to grow up without developing defects that must be corrected. Prevention costs less in time, money, and health.

[3] Joint Committee on Health Problems in Education of the National Education Association and the American Medical Association. *Health Education*, p. 39. 1948.

THE NEXT HALF-CENTURY

It is always fascinating to try to look ahead and imagine what the world will be like in the future. Will everyone have his own airplane in the year 2000? Will cancer be conquered? What will the human race be doing with atomic energy? Will we reduce food to pills and then breakfast, lunch, and dine on a handful of capsules?

Most of us cannot really answer questions like these. Our answers are wishful thinking or pure fairy tales. But there is one question whose answer lies in large part with the readers of this book. That question is: What kind of men and women will they be?

Another question perhaps comes

| 9 months | 2 years | 5 years | 10 years | 15 years |

He has grown well so far. Will he be as happy and healthy in the year 2000? (From the "Ages and Stages" Series. National Film Board of Canada and McGraw-Hill Text-Films)

before that: Will the readers of this book be alive in the year 2000? Our best answer is found in what are called life-expectancy tables, that is, tables showing average length of life. In 1955, the average length of life of the American people reached a new high of 70 years. Thus, most high-school students of today can look forward to seeing the new century.

What will you be like in the year 2000? That depends in large part on what you do now and in the coming years. You already have almost all the permanent teeth you will ever have. If you care for them, you will probably not have to bother with "store" teeth when you are old. Learning to eat properly will make a difference in the firmness of your muscles and in the energy with which you meet life.

If you avoid communicable diseases and care for yourself when you are ill, you will be less likely to have a damaged heart and kidneys and poor vision and hearing. If you build habits of good disposition and calmness, you will carry these on into middle and old age and be able to sleep better, eat better, and live more comfortably than if you build habits of worrying and feeling irritated. Finding your individual strong points and weak points and dealing with them intelligently will make it possible for you to live longer and to get the most out of life.

No picture of adolescents would be complete without this glimpse into the future. This is the first generation that has been able to look forward and make plans for so many years ahead. This means that it is more important for adolescents today than it has ever been for any other generation to learn how to take care of themselves, so that their added years may be happy and useful ones.

SO WHAT?

Growing up is important for every girl and boy; and

Adolescence, which covers most of the high-school years, is a period of great change; and

Some of the changes can be very disturbing if you do not understand them; and

Future health, both physical and mental, is greatly influenced by what happens during these years;

So, you should understand the growth changes and health problems of this period and what you can do to be healthy and to get all the enjoyment possible out of living.

CHECKING UP

1. How is a 12-year-old different from a 20-year-old?
2. Do all the parts of the body grow at the same rate? Give some examples.
3. What are hormones?
4. When does the adolescent growth spurt usually occur in girls? in boys?
5. What are some of the physical and mental changes that take place during adolescence?
6. What are the chief causes of death among adolescents? Approximately how many adolescent deaths are preventable?
7. What is an epidemic?
8. Why do adolescents have fewer communicable diseases than children or adults?
9. What are the advantages of preventing defects rather than correcting defects?
10. What is life-expectancy? Is life-expectancy longer or shorter now than it was 20 years ago?
11. List several things you can do now that will make for better health when you are older.

THINGS TO DO

1. Discuss: (*a*) What do people expect of adolescents that they do not expect of 10-year-olds? What are adolescents allowed to do that they were not allowed to do when they were younger? (*b*) From your experience, what are some of the problems of being adolescent? How many will disappear in the next 5 years?
2. Find how many pounds and how many inches members of the class have gained in the past year. Is there a difference between the boys and the girls? How many have not yet started their spurt of growth? How many seem in the midst of it? How many are past it?
3. Find how many days' absence are caused by illness in 1 month in your school. What are the causes of absence? How many absences could be prevented?
4. Try writing a description of life in the year 2000. How old will you be then? What kind of person would you like to be? Can you do anything about it now?

CHAPTER 3   You Bet Your Life

Accidents cause about 8600 deaths every year among persons 10 to 19 years of age in the United States. Cancer causes about 1650 deaths; heart disease and rheumatic fever together about 800 deaths; homicide and suicide about 750 deaths; influenza and pneumonia about 560 deaths. Here are five causes of death that take the lives of 12,360 boys and girls each year. Many times this number are left crippled by these accidents and illnesses.

What can be done to control these major killers? You will find some definite suggestions in this chapter and later chapters.

SUDDEN DEATH

The National Safety Council reports that 95,000 persons of all ages lost their lives in accidents during 1956. In this same year, almost 100 times as many were injured as were killed. During 4½ years of World War II, 280,255 Americans were killed in action or died from battle wounds. This was a terrible loss, but during this same period more Americans (355,000) lost their lives as a result of accidents.

This loss does not strike all age groups equally. Accidents are more frequent and more serious among older people than among young people. Perhaps this is not surprising. Older people may not move quickly enough to get out of danger, they do not see and hear as well as younger people, and they do not recover from injuries well.

It may be a surprise to know, however, that more young people between the ages of 15 and 24 are dying from accidents now than died 25 years ago. In 1927, 12,200 young people died as a result of accidents. In 1956, 14,000 died. These young people did not choose to die, but on the other hand many of them did not choose to do the things that would keep them alive.

Accidents are more serious than poliomyelitis. Probably the most dread disease of young persons is poliomyelitis, often called infantile paralysis

18

ACCIDENTS—THE NO. 1 KILLER

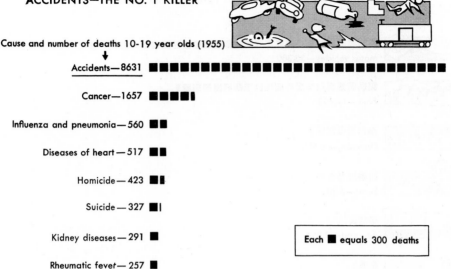

Cause and number of deaths 10-19 year olds (1955)

Accidents—8631 ■■■■■■■■■■■■■■■■■■■■■■■■■■■■■

Cancer—1657 ■■■■■

Influenza and pneumonia—560 ■■

Diseases of heart—517 ■■

Homicide—423 ■■.

Suicide—327 ■|

Kidney diseases—291 ■

Rheumatic fever—257 ■

Each ■ equals 300 deaths

(see Chapter 18). This disease sometimes leaves a boy or girl crippled for life—small wonder that we fear it. Yet accidents cause many times as many deaths and many times as much crippling as poliomyelitis does.

Many of us know people like the girl who was paralyzed from the waist down after the car in which she was riding skidded into a ditch. Another girl has a horrible scar across her face, the result of an automobile accident on the way home from a high-school dance. A fine boy drowned during his senior year in high school. He was an expert swimmer but got a cramp in his leg as he tried to swim to shore from a motorboat with engine trouble. Another boy flew a combat plane all through World War II and came home without a scratch, only to break his neck in a fall in the gymnasium as he tried to dive to a mat from the shoulders

of a friend. He is still living but with a broken back; he cannot move his arms or legs.

The results of such accidents are just as tragic as the worst cases of poliomyelitis. In fact, they are more tragic, because most accidents are unnecessary.

Kinds of accidents. A breakdown of the 93,000 deaths from accidents in 1955 gives some idea of the dangers we all have to meet and of the special safety problems of young people. Deaths from automobile accidents lead all the rest, showing that all of us had better pay a little more attention to how to be a good driver and how to be a live pedestrian. Drowning is second in importance for young people, which shows that you should know how to swim and where and when to swim. Burns, firearms, and falls come next. In almost every case, the real

DEATHS BY ACCIDENTS FOR ALL AGES (1955)

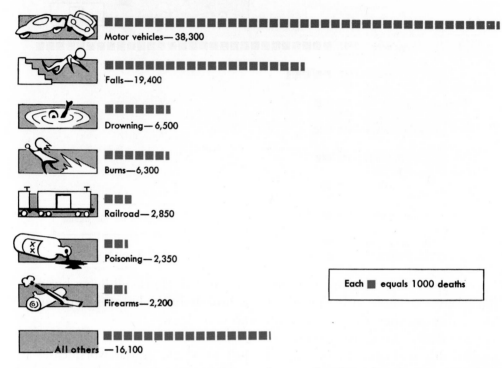

Motor vehicles— 38,300

Falls—19,400

Drowning— 6,500

Burns—6,300

Railroad— 2,850

Poisoning— 2,350

Firearms—2,200

Each ■ equals 1000 deaths

All others —16,100

cause of deaths from these is carelessness.

Among high-school students, 4 times as many boys as girls are killed in accidents. There are doubtless various reasons for this difference. Boys are stronger and do more dangerous things than girls. Perhaps girls are more timid than boys; perhaps they are simply not interested in doing the kinds of things that are most dangerous.

AUTOMOBILE SAFETY

The modern automobile is a superb piece of machinery. It has power, speed, safety devices, and comfort. But this same machine is responsible for one death in this country every 14 minutes and an injury every 23 seconds. Both deaths and injuries are especially high in the 15- to 24-year age group. For this reason, many insurance companies charge higher rates for automobile insurance when persons in this age group drive the car.

If present accident rates continue, one person of every three who is 15 years of age will some time be injured in an automobile accident and more than one of every 100 will be killed. How many injuries and deaths would this mean among your classmates?

Women drivers. Women drivers are involved in fewer accidents than men. It is true that men drive many more

MOST DANGEROUS ACCIDENTS FOR CHILDREN AND YOUNG PEOPLE (1955)

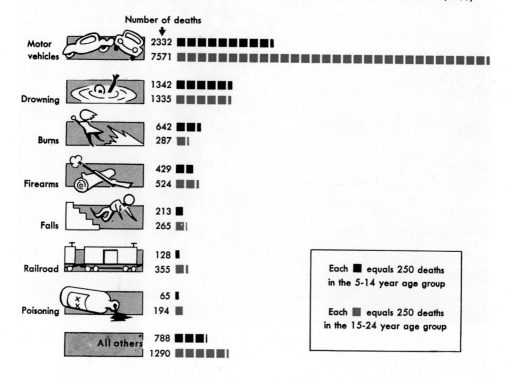

Number of deaths

Motor vehicles	2332	
	7571	
Drowning	1342	
	1335	
Burns	642	
	287	
Firearms	429	
	524	
Falls	213	
	265	
Railroad	128	
	355	
Poisoning	65	
	194	
All others	788	
	1290	

Each ■ equals 250 deaths in the 5-14 year age group

Each ■ equals 250 deaths in the 15-24 year age group

miles than women, but men have just as many, if not more, accidents per miles driven than women.

A study of the accident records of men and women taxicab drivers shows that the women had more accidents, but the accidents in which the men drivers were involved were more serious and more costly. The cost of accidents averaged $5.77 per 1000 miles driven for men, against $2.68 for the women.

Young drivers. Young drivers are involved in more fatal accidents—that is, accidents causing death—than are older people. If we consider the deaths per million miles driven, drivers aged 45 to 50 have the best record,

drivers below the age of 20 have the poorest. In fact, 16-year-old drivers have 9 times and 17- to 20-year-old drivers have 5 times as many accidents as drivers between 45 and 50. Yet young people should be safer drivers than older people, because they can see better, hear better, and act more quickly than older people.

Now that almost everyone drives a car, it is important to learn how to do it correctly. A number of cities and a few states require that courses in driving be offered in all high schools. The value of such courses was shown in a study in Cleveland. Only 3.8 percent of the boys and 0.5 percent of the girls who had had special driver training were involved in accidents

Girls and boys who take driving lessons have fewer accidents than those who do not have lessons. (Courtesy Arsenal Technical High School, Indianapolis)

over a period of 18 months. For the students without such training, the figures were almost twice as great; 6.6 percent of the boys and 0.9 percent of the girls had accidents.

Sometimes beginning drivers are not quite sure they know how to drive and feel they must "prove" that they do know by driving fast, by not letting other cars pass them, by driving close to other cars and throwing the brakes on suddenly, by driving with one hand, by looking away from the road, and by taking chances. As soon as they become expert drivers, they become more sure of themselves. They know the right thing to do at the right time and do not have to "show off" to themselves or to their friends. One of the important results of driving lessons is probably the feeling of self-confidence they give the person who has really learned how to drive and knows that he is a good driver.

In the age group 15 to 24, the drivers and their passengers are most likely to be killed in accidents. Among older people and among persons 5 to 14 years old, it is pedestrians who are more often killed. Drivers should realize that older persons cannot take care of themselves quickly in traffic. Children, of course, should learn not to play in the streets and not to run out from between parked cars. In many cases, however, children forget in the excitement of play, which means that drivers must think for the children as well as for themselves.

Causes of automobile accidents. Driving too fast is the chief cause of accidents. Unsafe driving includes, also, such practices as driving on the wrong side of the road, passing another car on a hill or curve, parking or changing a tire on a highway, cutting in ahead of others, and turning without proper signal. Driving with a windshield that is dirty or is covered with stickers, and facing the sun without eyeshades, are also dangerous.

According to the National Safety Council, about one of every six drivers involved in fatal accidents has been drinking, and about one of every five adult pedestrians killed has been drinking. Alcohol dulls vision and hearing, keeps a person from thinking clearly, and makes him move more slowly (see Chapter 21). Anyone who has been drinking does not belong behind the wheel of an automobile. A driver must be able to see or hear unexpected dangers, decide immediately on the right thing to do, and put on his brakes or steer around the danger without any loss of time.

Sometimes a blowout of a tire or a defect of the car results in an accident. This was particularly true during and soon after World War II when many of the cars on the road should have been in a junk yard. Yet even such cars can be driven with safety if the driver knows his car, has it checked regularly, and adjusts his driving and speed to its age and condition.

Bad weather and poor roads make driving more dangerous. Night driving results in twice as many fatal accidents as does driving in daylight. Pedestrians sometimes cause accidents by playing in the road, walking on the wrong side of the road, or stepping out into traffic.

Prevention of automobile accidents. Care, courtesy, and common sense would prevent most automobile accidents. It is as simple as that.

Care means care of the car so that faulty brakes, wornout tires, dirty windshields, improper lights, or unsafe steering gear will not handicap the driver or take the car out of his control; it means also care of the driver's own physical condition, so that poor vision, fatigue (tiredness), or alcohol do not dull his senses and slow his thinking and acting.

Courtesy applies to yielding the right of way, to passing other cars, to signaling for turns and stops. There is truth to the old jingle:

Here lies the body of Jonathan Gray
He died defending his right-of-way—
He was always right as he sped along
But he's just as dead as tho' he'd been
    wrong.

Common sense means keeping driving speed within safe limits and slowing down on wet or icy highways, on curves, in fog or rain, when it begins to get dark, and in heavy traffic. Trying to save a few minutes in getting somewhere often results in weeks in the hospital or an eternity in the cemetery. Common sense also means no

Driving too fast

Passing on curving road

Overcrowded car

Failure to obey signs

Accidents do not just happen. Point out what is wrong in each of these pictures.

passing on hills and parking off the highway; for pedestrians, it means care in crossing and walking on highways.

These are easy ways to avoid injury, crippling, and death from automobile accidents. Will we follow them and avoid the "Sudden Death," which J. C. Furnas so vividly described?[1]

Telling people that 1,350,000 persons were injured last year in automobile accidents, and 38,000 were killed, never gets to first base in showing a motorist how horribly dangerous motoring is. These are just figures. He does not think of the blood and pain they stand for.

Figures leave out the suffering and horror of savage injury—which means they leave out the point. They need to be brought closer home. Seeing or hearing about a bad smash will make any driver who is not a born fool slow down for a time. But you need to remember that every time you step on the gas pedal, death gets in beside you, hopefully waiting for his chance.

The automobile is dangerous and not to be trusted. Sure, it can make 65 miles an hour feel like nothing at all. But 65 miles an hour is 100 feet a second. Speed like this is sometimes more than brakes and human minds can control. Speed like this can instantly turn a tame plaything into a mad bull elephant.

[1] Adapted from *Reader's Digest*, August, 1935

You bet your life when you play in the street. (Courtesy National Safety Council)

And every time you pass on a blind curve, every time you hit it up on a slippery road, every time you step on it, every time you drive after a drink or two, every time you follow the man ahead too closely, you're gambling a few seconds of time "saved" against blood and suffering and sudden death.

Take a look at yourself. Do you want the man in the white jacket to shake his head over you, tell the boys with the stretcher not to bother, and turn away to somebody else who isn't quite dead yet? Then, take it easy.

You bet your life:

1) When you drive too fast on a slippery highway, in traffic, or in bad weather

2) When you drive without good lights and when your own lights blind other drivers

3) When you pay no attention to stop signs, highway signs, or danger signs

4) When you drive with poor brakes or badly worn tires

5) When you do not signal before you start, pass, stop, or back up

6) When you cut in too soon after passing another car

7) When you pass on curves or hills

8) When you drive after drinking any alcoholic drink

9) When you drive in the wrong lane of the highway

10) When you drive when you are sleepy

11) When you "jump" a traffic

And 2 seconds later his foot slipped! (Courtesy National Safety Council)

light, try to "make it" in front of a train, or take any kind of chance

12) When you let your windshield get dirty or cluttered with stickers

13) When you cannot see in your rear-view mirror what is behind you

14) When you let too many people get in the car or let anyone ride on the running board

15) When you do not keep your mind on your driving, your eyes on the road, and your hands on the steering wheel

16) When you play in the street

17) When you walk on country roads with your back to on-coming cars

18) When you cross a street in the middle of the block or when the traffic light is red

19) When you walk on dark streets or roads without a flashlight in your hand

20) When you step in front of cars in the rain or on a slick road where cars may not be able to stop

HOME SAFETY

Accidents in and around our homes caused 28,000 deaths in 1955. Among young persons 15 to 24 years of age, most of these deaths were caused by fire burns, with firearms second. Burns ranked first among children under 14 and in the age group 25 to 44. Among

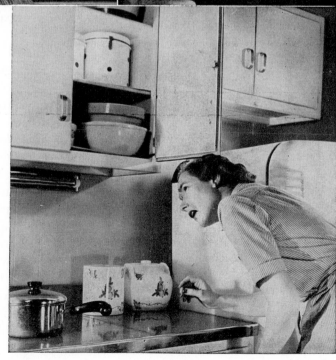

(Top left) Oops! Trouble ahead! (Courtesy American Red Cross) (Top right) Kitchens can be dangerous. Wrap a cloth around your hand. (Courtesy American Red Cross) (Bottom right) Close the cabinet door first. (Courtesy National Safety Council)

Smoking in dreamland

Wondrous weapons

Steeplejack

Waxed floor show

Carelessness is the chief cause of accidents in homes.

older persons, falls caused most of the deaths. Among babies under 1 year, half of the accidental deaths at home were from suffocation by bedclothes and pillows.

In the same year 4,200,000 persons were injured in home accidents. These injuries cost about $850,000,-000 in wages lost and in medical and insurance expenses.

Almost all of these 28,000 deaths and 4,200,000 injuries were due to carelessness. Most home accidents can be avoided by following a few simple rules:

1) Light stairways well; provide handrails for stairways; do not leave toys or other objects on stairs.

2) Keep ice and snow swept off porches and steps.

3) Use stepladders to reach high objects; be sure stepladders and chairs are steady before climbing on them.

4) Guard against slippery floors and loose rugs and toys on the floor.

5) Keep electric cords in good condition; protect electric fans and heaters.

6) Keep knives, garden tools, broken glass, boiling water, open fires, matches, poisons, and medicines out of reach of children.

7) Keep poisons in containers that are plainly marked.

8) Be careful of doors that stand ajar and of swinging doors.

9) Be on the lookout for gas leaks around gas stoves.

10) Be sure cigarettes are completely put out.

11) Do not use gasoline and flammable cleaning fluids indoors.

12) Do not start an automobile in a closed garage (see Chapter 11).

13) Be sure guns are unloaded and out of reach.

14) Arrange bedclothes so that small babies cannot get the bedclothes over their noses.

15) Keep small objects, such as peanuts, that might stick in the windpipe away from babies.

You can list other safety measures that should be taken in your own home against accidents. These measures are simple; they are commonplace. They pay enormous rewards. But remember that safety measures must be taken in advance. It is too late after the accident has occurred.

SAFETY ON THE JOB

To most of us, the years we spend in school seem a long time, at least while we are in the midst of them. Actually, they are only a small part of the years we will spend at some sort of an occupation, or job.

Sooner than a person thinks, school days are over, and interest turns to making a living. Working years may be spent on a farm, in a mine, or in the woods. They may be in a factory, a shop, a store, or an office. Wherever people work, they want their jobs to be healthful and safe as well as pleasant and profitable.

In 1955, some 14,200 persons lost their lives in accidents related to their jobs. Almost 2 million were injured

Top secret

Forgotten flatiron

Treacherous tub

Calamity kitchen

Stairway to doom

Perilous pipes

How many things are wrong in these pictures and those on page 28?

This boy is making sure that flying bits of metal do not injure his eyes. (Courtesy San Francisco Unified School District)

the job could be prevented by the proper upkeep of buildings, tools, and equipment and by the use of goggles, guards, and gloves.

Many accidents occur around machines. The most common unsafe practice is failure to stop the machine before adjusting, repairing, or cleaning it. Power saws are one of the most frequently used machines in industry and one of the most dangerous. The lack or improper use of guards causes a large number of accidents with saws. In the use of grinding wheels, eye protection and proper adjustment of the tool rest are very important.

while at work. Working time lost during 1955 as a result of injuries equals 235 million man-days of working time.

Mining and construction work are the most dangerous occupations. More persons are killed in agriculture than in any other occupation, but this is true because there are more farmers than there are miners and other kinds of workers.

Prevention of occupational accidents. More than eight out of ten occupational accidents are the fault of the person injured or of his fellow-workmen. Prevention of accidents, therefore, depends largely upon the training of workers in safe work habits. About one out of ten accidents on

Farm accidents. Headlines like the following appear every day in the newspapers: "Farm Youth Injured Fatally When Run Over by Combine," "Boy Injured by Tractor," "Man Hurt Seriously in a 20-Foot Fall through Hay Chute." There were 13,000 accidental deaths and 1,100,000 injuries of persons living on farms in 1955.

Farming has become a dangerous occupation. The farmer and the members of his family operate powerful machinery without any special training. They forget that a tractor is top-heavy, that loose clothing or gloves can pull them into cutters or gears in less than a second, that the usually gentle animal may suddenly attack.

The most frequent cause of accidents on farms is falls; the second is machinery. Tractors are the major cause of accidents with machinery; threshing equipment, haying machines, power saws, plows, and corn pickers are also of importance. Train-

Young farmers learn how to operate machines safely. It is the responsibility of the worker to protect himself by using all the care and safeguards possible. (Courtesy International Harvester Co.)

ing in operating these machines is the best way to reduce the number of farm accidents caused by machinery.

Injuries from livestock are the third most common group of accidents on farms. Although many people think that bulls are the most dangerous animals on farms, horses account for most of the accidents from livestock. There are several reasons for this. First, there are more horses on the farm than there are bulls, and the farmer handles them oftener in his daily work. Second, most people treat a bull with respect but are likely to become careless in the handling of horses. The following simple rules

will prevent most of the accidents with farm animals.

1) Never approach an animal without first letting it know that you are near. Talk to it, or sing or whistle to attract its attention.

2) Always be certain that an animal is safely held before trying to do anything that may make it uncomfortable or afraid.

3) Never give a bad-tempered animal the opportunity to make an attack. Provide safe pens for bulls and do not go into a pen with a bull, unless the animal is first tied or has a staff attached to a ring in its nose, so that it can be held at a safe distance.

Safeguard disregarders

Risk rascals

Busy booby trap

Dogs can be controlled by a leash or a muzzle. A farm dog that bites and injures animals can be made into a safe herd dog by pulling its four large tusks, or canine teeth. This operation will make the dog unable to inflict severe injury, and it will not interfere with the dog's eating.

4) Never leave horses unattended or untied. Remember that they are only dumb animals which do not understand well the things they hear or see. Runaway horses still cause too many accidents.

5) Try to be smarter than the animals you handle. Do not take chances with them. Smart people do things the right way; dumb people wish they had.

DROWNING

Swimming, fishing, sailing, canoeing, boating, and other water sports are great fun and healthful recreation. Yet, in deep water, drowning is always possible. During the past 5 years, an average of more than 6000 persons per year have lost their lives by drowning. Most drownings occur during the vacation season. In 1952, the toll was highest among youths 15 to 24 years of age, and the next highest was for children 5 to 14 years old.

Carelessness and foolhardiness are responsible for most of these deaths. Members of the Olympic teams, the best swimmers in the world, are required to follow safety rules in their swimming. The rest of us should be even more careful. To help prevent serious water accidents, the American Red Cross makes the following suggestions:

1) Learn to swim well.

2) Swim out of doors only when the water temperature will not over-chill the body.

3) Select a place for swimming where the depth and current of the water are known. It is safest to swim with a companion or where a lifeguard is present.

4) Know how well you can swim and do not take chances. Even expert swimmers must use good judgment and realize that accidents may occur.

5) Know how long to swim. Get out before becoming chilled or overtired.

6) Do not swim out to a drowning person unless you have special training in lifesaving. Throw out something that will float, such as an oar or a life belt, toward the person in danger.

7) Learn how to handle a boat or canoe correctly.

8) Use only boats that are in good condition and do not overload them.

9) Do not skate on ice over deep water unless the ice is at least 4 inches thick. It is better to wait for solid ice than to be sorry.

SCHOOL SAFETY

For young people of school age, most accidents occur at school or on the way to and from school. Usually, school accidents are not fatal, but many result in serious injury.

Elementary school. Kindergartners and children in the primary grades often fall out of swings and off slides on the playground or fall down when they are running. The best way to prevent these accidents is for teachers and older students to remind children to take turns on play equipment, to

Each ■ equals 5 deaths per 100,000 workers

THE MOST DANGEROUS JOBS (1955)

	Death rate per 100,000 workers	Number killed in 1955
Mining, quarrying, oil and gas wells	104	800
Construction	76	2400
Agriculture	55	3700
Transportation	44	1300
Public utilities	14	200
Manufacturing	13	2100

run only where there is room, and not to push other children.

Many school children are injured by automobiles while going to and from school, but there are fewer of these accidents now than there were several years ago. All states require motorists to slow down when passing schools. Junior traffic officers, in uniforms and with signs and whistles, in many places keep younger children from crossing streets recklessly.

Many children in the upper grades ride to and from school on bicycles.

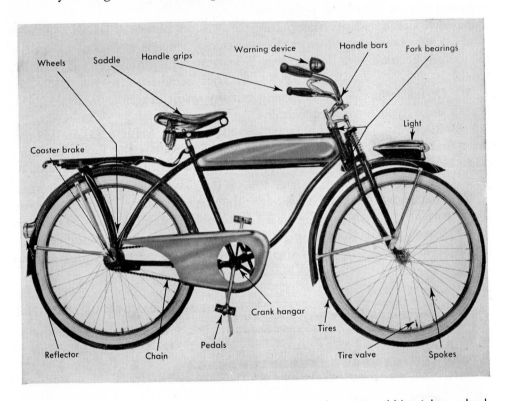

Ride carefully and keep your bicycle in good condition. Eliminate wobble, tighten wheel nuts and oil bearings in wheels. Adjust the saddle to the body and tighten all nuts. Replace worn handle grips and cement them on tightly. Be sure that the warning device works properly. Adjust the handle bars to your body. Tighten and keep the stem well down in the fork. Lubricate the fork bearings. Does your coaster brake brake evenly? Unless you are an expert, have it adjusted by a serviceman. Your light must be visible for 500 feet. Your reflector must be visible for 300 feet. Check the chain for damaged links. Secure a snug fit and clean and lubricate it frequently. Lubricate and tighten the pedal bearings and spindle. Replace worn pedal threads. Keep the crank hangar clean and greased. If it wobbles, have a serviceman make adjustments. Inspect the tire valves often for leaks. Inflate tires to correct air pressure. Remove imbedded metal, glass, cinders, and so forth, from them. Replace broken spokes promptly. (Courtesy Bicycle Institute of America)

He cannot see whether he is falling on a boat, on a floating log, or on another swimmer. Do not horse-play around the water. (Courtesy American Red Cross)

Every year some of them are killed and many more are injured by falling from their bicycles or by collisions with automobiles.

High school. The gymnasium, with locker rooms and showers, is the most dangerous place in high school. Equipment that is not safe, balls and other materials that are left where people can fall over them, and soap dropped on locker-room floors result in hundreds of accidents. Students who do not obey rules while playing and who "horse around" in the gymnasium are equally dangerous.

Other places where accidents often occur in high schools are the laboratories and shops. Machines, chemicals, electricity, and apparatus do not by themselves cause accidents. Students are the "human element" that makes shops and laboratories safe or dangerous. In other words, safety is not an accident.

Sports and athletics. Every sport, in fact every human activity, means some risk. Some sports, however, are much more dangerous than others. Tobogganing is probably the worst. Tobogganing can be fun and safe on smooth, well-cared-for courses. Skiing, too, causes many accidents. Skating, hockey, basketball, and tennis give rise to some accidents. Most of these are the result of improper equipment, lack of skill, poor physical condition, tiredness, carelessness, or taking chances.

Most people think of football as a very dangerous sport. In the eleventh and twelfth grades, one-third of all the injuries reported from schools occur in playing football. This should not be true. If players are well grown, are in good physical condition, are well trained, have proper protective equipment, are taught how to protect themselves against injury, and have proper medical care, football can be

STUDENT ACCIDENTS BY GRADES (1952)

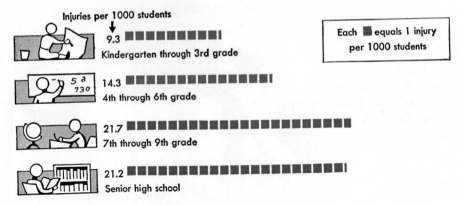

Injuries per 1000 students

9.3 ■■■■■■■■■I
Kindergarten through 3rd grade

Each ■ equals 1 injury
per 1000 students

14.3 ■■■■■■■■■■■■■■I
4th through 6th grade

21.7 ■■■■■■■■■■■■■■■■■■■■■■
7th through 9th grade

21.2 ■■■■■■■■■■■■■■■■■■■■■I
Senior high school

In which grades do most accidents occur? How can they be prevented?

played with very little risk of injury.

Sports are fun and good for people mentally and physically, but when you take up a sport you should get the right equipment, learn how to use it properly, keep yourself in good physical condition, stop before becoming too tired, and use care and good sense when you engage in it.

SAFETY THROUGH THE YEAR

Adding up all the accidents for a year does not give a good picture of *how* they actually occur. For example, accidents in industry are not evenly distributed through the day but reach a peak between 10 and 11 o'clock in the morning and again between 3 and 4 o'clock in the afternoon, although not so many happen in the afternoon as in the morning. Many industries have found that morning and afternoon rest periods keep workers from becoming tired and cut down the number of accidents.

Every weekend brings death and injury. A long weekend with a Friday or Monday holiday means more people killed or injured than on a regular weekend. Most of these injuries and deaths are the result of automobile accidents; drownings and accidents with firearms add to the total at certain times of the year.

It is possible to predict ahead of time about how many accidents will happen. Before a holiday, for example, you may see in the newspapers a statement on how many people will be killed within the next few days. After the holiday, there is a report on how many actually were killed. You know that the holiday, which started as time for fun, was suddenly stopped for that many people, that many families, and that many groups of friends.

If you know more about when and how accidents occur, you will be better able to prevent some of them by being on your guard at these special times and places.

January. New Year's Day means lots of visiting, lots of driving, for some people a good deal of drinking—and lots of accidents. Be on the lookout for drunken drivers, whether you happen to be walking or driving a car.

In January, there are more deaths from poison gases, including carbon monoxide (see Chapter 11), than in any other month. The weather is cold and people are heating their homes with furnaces, gas stoves, electric heaters, and fireplaces. It is a time to be sure that stoves are not overheated and to check electric cords and gas connections. Be careful not to start the car in a closed garage, even on a very cold morning.

February, March, April. Deaths from burns and poison gases remain above the year's average in February, March, and April but are not so numerous as in January. As the weather becomes less cold, the number of such deaths becomes smaller.

In April, the number of deaths from drowning increases. This probably means that people are starting to go on picnics to beaches and rivers and are going swimming in larger numbers. Sunburn and poison oak cause much pain and discomfort when people first start going out into the country in the spring. Automobile deaths are below the year's average in these three months. Easter vacation usually means more people on the highway and more deaths and injuries.

May, June, July, August. In May, there is an upswing in the number of automobile deaths, probably because of the Memorial Day holiday. The weather is usually good in May, June, July, and August; hence, more people are using their automobiles. The result is a steady increase in number of

Practical joker

Show-off

Leg-stretcher

Blockade

Only swimmers trained in lifesaving should attempt this. (Courtesy National Safety Council)

deaths and injuries. Also, during these months, farm machinery is put to its greatest use, and farm accidents are most frequent.

Good weather and vacations mean a large number of deaths from drowning. Learning how to swim, where to swim, and when to swim is a good vacation activity that could save thousands of lives.

In years past, the Fourth of July always meant thousands of deaths and injuries from burns. Now, most cities forbid the shooting of firecrackers and try to encourage people to spend a "safe and sane" Fourth. Every year, however, a few people are killed by fireworks, and others are burned, blinded, or crippled.

These vacation months bring all the pleasures of outdoor life, of picnics and camping trips, but they also bring certain dangers. You should know how to build and care for campfires, so that you avoid burns and also damage to property. You should dress properly for hiking and know how to carry packs, if you want to avoid sunburn, blisters, and strains. A little forethought will prevent many sprained ankles and broken bones. If you hike where there are poisonous snakes, insects, or plants, you should learn what they look like and where to expect to find them. Some people, when they start on a vacation, seem to leave all their common sense behind them; the results are dangerous to themselves and others.

September, October, November. Farm accidents and automobile accidents remain at a high level during September, October, and November. Night comes earlier, and deaths of pedestrians increase as the hours of darkness increase. If you are driving, look out for pedestrians who are crossing at unexpected places, walking on the wrong side of the road, wearing dark clothing, and carrying umbrellas that keep them from seeing your car lights. If you are walking, remember that it is difficult for a driver to see clearly at night, and that it is impossible for him to stop quickly on a muddy or wet road.

Accidents from autumn sports, especially football, reach a peak in these months.

In October and November, there are more deaths from firearms than in any other months. These months are the hunting season. Knowing how to handle a gun and not shooting until you see clearly what you are shooting at are two simple rules that, if followed, would prevent almost all hunting accidents. Wear a red cap and stay on paths or roads if you must be in hunting areas.

Always handle a gun with care and never point a gun, even though it is not loaded, at another person.

December. For many people, December is the happiest month of the year. It is tragic that it is also the time of year when there are most deaths from accidents.

Automobile accidents peak in December. There are several reasons for this. The weather is often bad, and night closes in early. People travel long distances to be with their families at Christmastime. Everyone is excited, many people are tired, and the result is carelessness in driving and in

Labor Day

Christmas Eve

Thanksgiving Day

July 4th

Why do more accidents occur on holidays than on other days? What hazards do the holidays suggested here bring?

crossing streets. Some people start celebrating New Year's several days before the old year ends.

Deaths from burns in December are more numerous than during any other month. Candles on Christmas trees are forbidden in most places, but many fires are caused by poor electric connections in Christmas-tree lights. Check all your Christmas-tree lights, stand your tree in water, light it only while it is green and fresh, put out the lights when there is no one in the room, and take the tree out of the house before it dries.

Deaths from poison gases increase greatly in December. Winter is starting; people shut their houses tightly and use their stoves and furnaces night and day. The high death rate continues through the next few months.

Winter sports, which are in full swing in December, bring their crop of broken bones and accidental deaths.

STAY ALIVE AND WHOLE

The chief purpose of this book is to show you how to be healthier, happier, and more able to do what you want to do. But being healthy, happy, and able means first of all just staying alive and whole. If you want to be able to greet the year 2000 with your friends, you will think about the facts in this chapter and try to see how they relate to you.

SO WHAT?

Accidents are the leading cause of death and of crippling injuries among boys and girls of high-school age; and

Accidents follow us all through life, causing more deaths and more crippling than war does; and

Accidents are a cause of death and injury that we can do something about, each of us individually and all of us together; and

The person with whom to begin on the prevention of accidents is yourself; and

The places to begin are on the highway, in your home, at your school, on your job, and in your community;

So, keep in mind the things you can do about reducing accidents and do them before it is too late.

CHECKING UP

1. What are the chief causes of accidental deaths among young people?

2. Do more boys or more girls die from accidents?
3. How do accidents of men and women drivers compare?
4. Why are people in their forties better drivers than older people? than younger people?
5. What are the characteristics of an expert driver?
6. Give five rules for safe driving that you consider most important.
7. Give the five rules that you consider most important for avoiding home accidents.
8. Give two practices in the use of machines that cause most accidents.
9. Give the three rules you think most important in preventing water accidents.
10. Where do most accidents occur in schools? How may these accidents be avoided?
11. How is it possible to predict ahead of time when accidents will occur and what kinds of accidents will occur?
12. When during the year are deaths from drowning most common? Why?
13. When during the year do the most deaths from automobile accidents occur? Why?
14. When during the year do most deaths from burns and poison gases occur? Why? How could they be avoided?
15. What kinds of accidents should you keep in mind and try to avoid during summer vacations?

THINGS TO DO

School safety

1. How do students in your school come to school? How do younger children in the neighborhood go to school? Make a list of safety rules for those who walk; for those who come by bus; for those who drive automobiles; for those who ride bicycles; for those who roller-skate.
2. Visit the school shop to see what safety measures are used there. Ask a science teacher to explain how accidents are prevented in the laboratory. Ask a physical-education teacher to describe how the gymnasium, the lockers, and the playing fields are kept in a safe condition.
3. Make a plan of the school and the grounds around it. Show on the plan places where accidents may occur. How may they be avoided?

4. Form a school safety council.
5. Form a safety patrol to help with traffic problems in the school and on the grounds.
6. Examine a bicycle equipped with safety devices. Compare it with one that is not so equipped.
7. Make a list of times you have been careless at school in the past week. Why were you careless? Were you tired? sick? angry? excited? paying attention to something else? How can accidents due to carelessness be prevented?
8. Study parking near your school. Could it be improved?

Home safety

9. List the members of your family. Make a chart showing where each one is during the day and what each one is doing. What are some of the safety problems they meet?
10. Where are the dangerous places in your home? How can they be made safe?
11. Write a radio skit or play showing the right and wrong way of doing everyday things, such as getting something from a high shelf, getting rid of used matches, putting away cleaning equipment, handling gardening tools.
12. Make posters illustrating safety rules in the home. Let the class or the school vote on which tells its story best; which is most attractive; which is most unusual.

Occupational safety

13. What jobs or occupations do you and your classmates expect to hold when you leave school? What are the special dangers each of you must be ready for?
14. What occupations are your parents engaged in? Ask them what kinds of accidents occur where they work. How are accidents prevented?
15. Visit a farm to see how machinery is handled and how animals are cared for. What safety rules are followed?
16. Visit a factory or an industrial plant. What dangerous places or activities do you see? Ask someone in charge how accidents are prevented.

Community safety

17. Collect clippings from newspapers telling about accidents. Keep a record of local accidents through the year. When do most occur? How could they have been prevented?

18. Make a list, through one day, of the safe and dangerous habits of pedestrians that you see; of bicycle riders; of automobile drivers. Check against the rules on pages 25–26.

19. Make a map of the neighborhood around your school. Locate places where accidents may occur or have occurred. How may they be avoided?

20. Ask a policeman to talk to your class or to the whole school about some of the safety problems in your town or community. How is the police department helping to make the community safe?

21. Ask a fireman to talk about the fire department's contribution to safety.

22. If there is a safety council in your community, ask a member of it to talk to your class or in an assembly period about what the council is doing and how you can help.

23. Spot traffic accidents on a map.

24. Make graphs showing kinds of accidents in your community; ages of persons injured or killed; numbers occurring in various months and on weekends.

25. Plan slogans and rhymes on traffic safety for each month. Use these in posters, plays, skits, assembly programs, P.-T.A. programs, and community programs.

26. Form a safety patrol to work with the police department in helping school children cross the streets near the school. (The National Safety Council, Chicago, and your own Parent-Teacher Association will give assistance.)

27. Study driving rules of your state and city. Perhaps the police department will assist.

28. List the best drivers you know. What makes them good drivers?

General safety

29. Plan a year's work on safety. For example, September is a good month to consider school safety; October or November may be the time to study safe handling of firearms; December with its Christmas holidays offers a chance to think about home safety; January may be devoted to winter safety; May and June are certainly times to think of water safety, camping, picnics, and vacation activities in general. Elect committees to put up bulletin-board exhibits each month.

CHAPTER 4 What to Do

in Emergencies

A newspaper headline says that a Boy Scout used first aid to save a pal from bleeding to death. Another story tells how a young mother saved the life of her small daughter who had fallen into deep water and almost drowned. She had learned what to do in a first-aid class.

These are stories of lives saved. What they do not tell is about the ones that might have been saved if friends present at the time of the accident had known what to do and had done it quickly.

Preventing accidents should be our number-one aim, as was shown in Chapter 3, but some accidents are bound to happen. And when they happen, knowing what to do and how to do it may mean the difference between life and death for the accident victim; and this victim may be your pal, your brother or sister, or even yourself.

FIRST AID

First aid is just what the words mean, the *first* help that is given to a person who is hurt or becomes ill suddenly. The injury or illness may be serious. In that case a physician (doctor)[1] should be called immediately.

The care that is given before the physician comes may save a life. On the other hand, what is done may be harmful and may even cause death. First aid should reduce the injured person's suffering, keep him from being afraid, and place him in the physician's hands in good condition. Very often the best first aid is to leave the person alone and keep other people away from him.

The term *first aid* is also used for the prompt care of small cuts, bruises, headaches, and all the other conditions we call minor emergencies and ailments. Giving the right kind of care is what keeps many minor emergencies from becoming serious ones.

An emergency is a condition that calls for immediate action. It is not

[1] The word *doctor* has many meanings. *Physician* is a better term for the kind of doctor meant here and all through this book. Chapter 28 tells how a physician is trained.

always possible to tell which are serious emergencies and which are not. There are certain conditions, however, such as severe bleeding, failure to breathe, extensive burns, and broken bones, that should be recognized and cared for at once.

General rules in giving first aid. The following rules always apply to the giving of first aid.

1) Find whether the injured person is bleeding. If so, the bleeding must be stopped immediately. Severe bleeding can cause death in a very few minutes (see pages 45–47).

2) Find whether the person who has been hurt is breathing. If he is not breathing, start artificial respiration at once (see pages 47–49).

3) Do not permit the person to sit up or stand until you know how serious his injury is. Do not move him until you are sure it can be done safely. If the injury appears to be a serious one, bring a physician to the injured person rather than carry him to the physician (see pages 61–63).

4) If there is a deep wound or even a slight break in the skin, there is danger of infection. Be sure that bandages and dressings are *very clean*; sterile dressings (clean gauze with adhesive tape to hold it in place) from a first-aid kit or those bought from a drugstore are safest. Do not touch the wound unless necessary to stop bleeding (see pages 49, 51).

5) In every injury there is some shock, that is, weakness and failure of proper blood flow. Keep the injured person warm; be sure that he is covered and is not being chilled from the ground (see pages 51–52).

6) Do not give liquids to an unconscious person; they may enter the windpipe and strangle him.

7) Keep cool; act quickly but quietly. Speak in a natural voice; do not handle the injured person hurriedly or roughly; try to protect him from being worried; keep bystanders away. *Do not try to do too much.*

CONTROL OF BLEEDING

Bleeding may come from arteries, from veins, or from capillaries. Arteries are the blood vessels that carry blood away from the heart; veins carry the blood back to the heart; capillaries are the tiny blood vessels that connect the arteries to the veins (see Chapter 12).

Blood from veins is dull red in color and flows in a steady stream. Blood from capillaries and very small veins oozes out slowly. Such bleeding is usually not severe and will stop of its own accord as a clot forms in the wound (see Chapter 11). Often simply lifting the injured part will control this bleeding.

Bleeding from arteries is most serious. Blood from arteries is bright red; it comes fast and usually in spurts. If there is bleeding from the arteries:

1) Place a piece of sterile gauze or bandage or a clean handkerchief, towel, or sheet directly over the wound. Press directly on the wound. Tie this dressing in place.

2) Place fingers directly in the

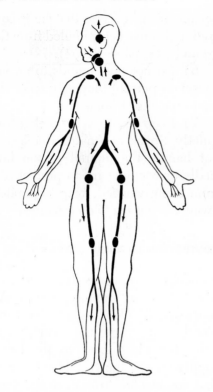

In case of severe bleeding from a wound in the head, neck, shoulder, arm, or leg, find the pressure point between the wound and the heart; press against the bone. This will squeeze flat the artery that lies over the bone and stop the flow of blood to the wound.

wound and the heart where the artery lies against a bone and press with the fingers. The diagram on this page shows the main pressure points for relieving bleeding from arteries in the head, neck, shoulder, arm or hand, leg or foot. Put a dressing on the wound.

4) If bleeding is severe and from an injury below the middle of the upper arm or below the middle of the upper leg and cannot be stopped by other means, apply a tourniquet.

The use of a tourniquet. A tourniquet should be a flat band at least 1 inch wide; it may be a necktie, handkerchief, towel, scarf, or belt. Do not use rope, wire, or sash cord. If possible, a wad of cloth or a folded handkerchief or towel should be placed over the artery. Raise the arm or leg, wrap the tourniquet around it, and tie a half-knot. Then place a short stick, a ruler, a cane, an umbrella, or even a fountain pen on the half-knot and tie a square knot over it. Next, twist the stick rapidly but only tight enough to stop the bleeding. The stick can be held in place by the ends of the tourniquet or by another piece of cloth tied around the arm or leg.

Place the tourniquet close to the wound, on the side toward the heart, but not at the edge of the wound. There should be unbroken skin between the tourniquet and the wound. If the wound is near a joint, obviously the tourniquet should be applied at the nearest point possible above the joint.

Make sure that the tourniquet is applied tightly enough to stop bleed-

wound if bleeding is heavy and you cannot stop it with a dressing. You may need a few trials to get your fingers into the proper position, so that the artery is pressed flat against a bone. Do not mop the blood out of the wound. Wiping away the blood keeps it from clotting and increases the danger of infection. Keep fingers in the wound until bleeding is stopped by pressure above the wound (3) or by a tourniquet (4).

3) Locate a point between the

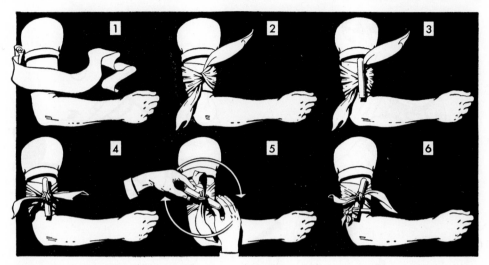

A tourniquet stops bleeding by pressing the walls of the blood vessels together so that no blood can get through.

ing. If it is improperly applied, it may increase bleeding and hasten death. Once a tourniquet is applied, it should not be released, no matter how long it has been in place, except by a physician. Physicians are prepared to control hemorrhage—that is, loss of blood—and replace blood volume adequately.

Write a note telling where the tourniquet has been applied and the time it was applied. Attach this note to the injured person.

A tourniquet should be used only for bleeding that is severe enough to threaten life and that cannot be controlled by other means. Actually, the use of a tourniquet is seldom required. Crushing wounds, or injuries where large arteries are cut, or cases in which an arm or leg is completely or partly cut off are the only instances where the application of a tourniquet may be justified.

BREATHING MUST NOT STOP

When you are sure that the injured person is not bleeding to death, you should find whether or not he is breathing. Watch the chest, the abdomen, and the nose for breathing movements. Or hold your face or hand close to the person's nose and mouth to find whether air is moving through them.

The only way to save the life of a person whose breathing has stopped is to get air into his lungs. This is best done by first putting pressure on the chest and then releasing the pressure. This is called artificial respiration.

Artificial respiration. There is more than one method for giving artificial respiration. The method described here was adopted in 1952 by the Armed Forces, the American Red Cross and other national organizations and agencies with safety pro-

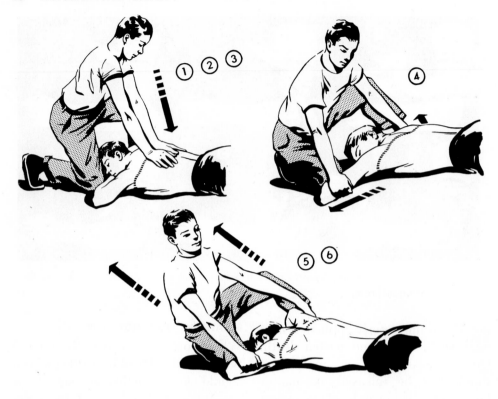

grams. It is called the back pressure-arm lift method. Its purpose is to squeeze air out of the lungs by pressing on the ribs, then to expand the chest by pulling on the arms. When the chest expands, air rushes in to fill the lungs.

1) Lay the person face down, with his head a little lower than his feet if possible; force his mouth open; pull his tongue forward. You may use a handkerchief to pull the tongue forward and to clean out the mouth, so that the air passages will be open. This should be done quickly, so that artificial respiration can be started without delay.

2) Bend the person's elbows so that his two hands are under his head. Put one hand on top of the other. Turn his face to one side and lay his cheek on his hand. Face the person and kneel at his head, on one knee or on both knees, whichever is more comfortable for you.

3) Place your two hands flat on his back with your thumbs touching each other and with your fingers spread apart. Imagine a line around the person's chest just under his arms. Your hands should be just below this line (see diagram on this page).

4) Straighten your arms. With elbows straight, rock forward slowly until your shoulders are above your hands. Let the weight of your body

press down on the person's back as you rock forward. This forces air out of his lungs.

5) Take off the pressure gently. Rock slowly backward and, at the same time, slip your hands down the person's arms until they are just above his elbows.

6) Lift his arms and, at the same time, draw them toward you as you rock backward. Do not bend your elbows. Lift his arms until you feel resistance from his shoulders. Do not pull hard. Lifting his arms expands the person's chest and allows air to rush into the lungs.

7) Lower the arms. Repeat steps 3, 4, 5, 6, and 7 about 12 times per minute.

Artificial respiration should be repeated until breathing begins or until it is certain that the person is dead. Many persons have died because artificial respiration was stopped too soon. It may be 3 or 4 hours before breathing begins. There are instances where breathing has been established after 8 hours.

Sometimes artificial respiration must be carried on so long that more than one person is needed to give it. If someone takes your place, have him time his movements with yours, so that there is no pause when you make the shift.

If a machine for artificial respiration is available, it may be used, but you must carry on the pressure and arm-lifting movements until the machine takes over.

Try to keep the person warm all the time that artificial respiration is being given. Ask someone to loosen the person's clothing and wrap him in coats, blankets, or anything warm that is near at hand. Use hot bricks, pads, heaters, or similar means, but be careful not to burn the injured person. Do not stop the artificial respiration, because getting the person to breathe is more important than keeping him warm.

Keep the person lying down after he starts breathing. You may give stimulants, such as hot tea or coffee or aromatic spirits of ammonia, as soon as he is completely conscious.

After the person starts breathing, watch him closely. If he stops breathing, start artificial respiration again.

WOUNDS MUST BE KEPT CLEAN

If a person has a break in the skin, whether the wound is small or large, there is always danger that tiny harmful organisms—that is, living things—will get into the wound and grow. When this happens, we say that the wound is infected or that there is an infection. The organisms causing the infection are called infectious organisms.

Infectious organisms are of many kinds. People sometimes call them "germs," "microbes," or "bugs," but these are not scientific terms. Bacteria and viruses are correct names for the most common groups of these organisms.

Infectious organisms are so small that they cannot be seen except through a microscope. In fact, viruses are so small they cannot be seen even

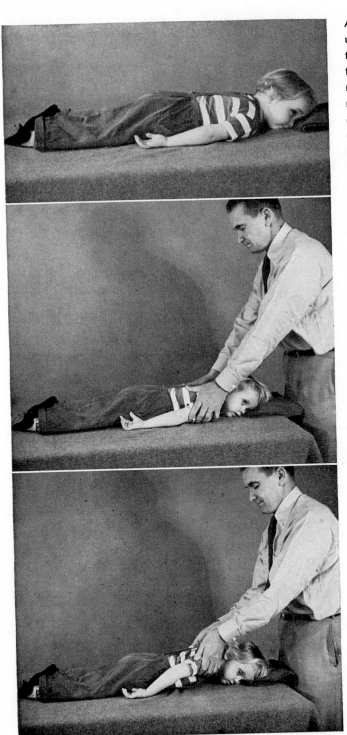

Artificial respiration for use with a small child. If the injured person is less than 4 years old, use a modified form of artificial respiration. (1) Lay the child on his abdomen, arms at his sides, and face turned slightly to one side. If he is on a table, stand at his head; kneel at his head if he is on the floor. In these pictures, padding has been placed under the child's forehead to keep his mouth and nose free. (2) Place your hands beside the child's arms. Press gently with your thumbs on the child's back at a level just below his armpits. Do not press inward with palms of your hands. (3) Slide your hands to his shoulders, with your fingers under his shoulders, and lift his chest enough to take his weight from the floor or table top. Repeat steps 2 and 3, 15 times per minute. (Courtesy American Red Cross)

with the aid of ordinary microscopes. Because of their tiny size, infectious organisms are sometimes called microorganisms. In this book, we are concerned with microorganisms that do harm, but there are other microorganisms that are not harmful.

You can easily understand that your fingers, handkerchief, or almost anything else that has been handled may carry microorganisms, and that some of them may be infectious. Keep your fingers away from wounds, unless a person is bleeding severely and you cannot stop the bleeding in any other way than by putting your fingers into the wound. In this case, stopping loss of blood is even more important than keeping the wound clean.

If a wound becomes infected, the infectious organisms may grow and multiply in the wound. Pus, which occurs in many infections, is composed of dead body cells (see page 72) and infectious organisms that are dead or dying (see Chapter 11). Someone has called pus the "dead from the battle between the body and its enemies, the microorganisms."

Sometimes the infectious organisms get into the blood and spread all over the body (see Chapter 12). They may settle in other parts of the body and destroy cells wherever they settle. This spreading of infection through the body is called blood poisoning.

Bandages and dressings, as well as fingers, may carry infectious organisms. Whenever possible, you should use sterile dressings. These are *very clean* and free from any kind of microorganisms. You can buy sterile dressings at a drugstore or you may find some in a first-aid kit, if one is near at hand.

When sterile dressings cannot be found, use cloths that have been boiled and ironed, such as clean handkerchiefs, sheets, or towels. Heating cloth in an oven hot enough to brown paper lightly or exposing it to sunshine for an hour will kill most infectious organisms and give you a dressing that is safer than cloth that has not been heated or sunned.

SHOCK

A person in shock feels weak, faint, cold, and often nauseated. His face is pale and has an anxious and frightened appearance. His skin is cold and clammy. His breathing is irregular. His pulse is weak and rapid (see Chapter 12).

Shock usually results from injury or from severe burns, but it may be caused by chilling, bleeding, fatigue, hunger, or extreme emotion. Some degree of shock follows all injuries; it may be slight, lasting only a few minutes, or it may last a long time and end in death.

If an injured person is conscious and is not bleeding or vomiting, shock may be prevented if he drinks plenty of water with salt and baking soda mixed in it. This is especially true in case of burns. Mix ½ teaspoonful of baking soda and 1 teaspoonful of salt into each quart of water.

For the treatment of shock, place the patient flat on his back with his

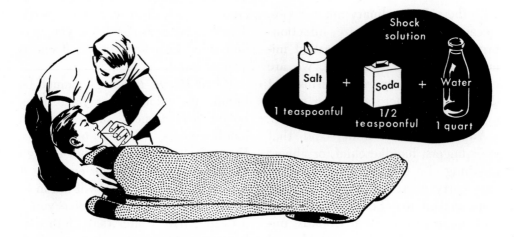

head low. Control bleeding if any is present. Loosen all tight clothing. Do not move the patient more than is necessary.

Keep the patient warm. This is most important in preventing and treating shock. Place coats and blankets over and around the injured person but do not use too many blankets. The injured person should not be made to perspire. He should feel just barely warm. In cold weather, use bottles or canteens filled with hot water, hot stones, or hot bricks. Place these hot objects between the legs, under the armpits, and beside the waist. They should not be placed directly against the bare skin or against very thin clothing, because a burn may result.

Liquids given by mouth are helpful but should never be given to unconscious persons, persons who are bleeding, or persons with skull injuries, apoplexy, sunstroke, or a wound of the abdomen. The best liquids are hot drinks, such as water, coffee, tea, or chocolate.

FRACTURES

A fracture is a break in a bone. A simple fracture is one in which there is no wound extending from the broken bone through the skin. A compound fracture is one in which the broken bone sticks out through the skin or one in which there is a connecting wound from the surface of the skin to the break in the bone. In these cases, there is danger of infection from the outside.

A person with a broken bone usually feels pain at the point of fracture. He usually cannot move the injured part. It may be bent out of shape. There is usually swelling, and later the area becomes discolored, that is, turns red or purple.

A person without special training must be very careful in handling cases of fracture. Usually, the safe thing to do is to persuade the injured person to lie down, keep him warm, and control bleeding if it is present. Send for a physician or for someone who has had special training in first aid, such as a nurse, a policemen, or a fireman.

Sometimes an accident occurs in the mountains or other out-of-the-way place, and an untrained person must take charge. Everyone should know some of the things to do and not to do in such cases. The discussions of skeleton, blood vessels, and nerves in Chapters 6, 12, and 18 give information that will help you remember what is the right thing to do.

Handle all fractures or suspected fractures gently. The ends of a broken bone may be as sharp as knives. Moving the part of the body in which there is a broken bone sometimes pushes the bone to the surface of the skin and results in a compound fracture. Take time to do the right thing.

A person with a fracture of the upper leg, hip, neck, or back, or one who shows signs of shock, should not be moved. Give first-aid treatment to the injured person where he lies. Bring medical help to him rather than take him to the physician.

Splints and slings. Most important in the first-aid treatment of fractures is the use of a splint. A splint holds and protects the injured part. It should be as wide as the arm or leg and long enough to prevent movement of the joints near the fracture. If no ready-made splints are at hand, you can make splints from blankets, pillows, magazines, pieces of tin, mesh wire, bundles of twigs, or any other stiff materials.

The bone should be as straight as possible before a splint is put on. If the bone is not sticking out through

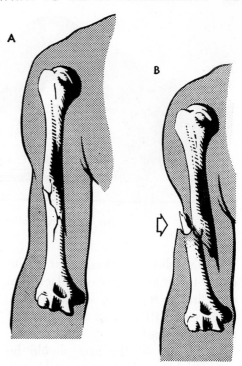

(A) Simple fracture. (B) Compound fracture.

the skin, a gentle, steady pull on hand or foot may be used to straighten a limb. This pull should not be slackened or released until the application of the splint is entirely completed.

Pad the splints with cloth or clothing, especially on the side toward the skin. Bind them securely in place by tying them to the limb at several points above and below the fracture. Do not bind splints too tightly. Examine the splint and the limb at least every half-hour. A bluish color shows that the bandage is too tight.

If a bone is sticking out through the skin, do not push it back. First control the bleeding. Then place a sterile dressing or clean cloth over the wound. Send for aid if at all possible.

An emergency splint with pillow padding.

If it is absolutely necessary for you to move the injured person, place him on a firm stretcher on which he may be carried without any movement of the injured limb.

A fracture of the arm should be supported by a sling after splinting. A triangular bandage makes the best sling. However, arm slings may be made from ordinary bandages or from clothing. In using a coat, fasten the coat sleeve to the front of the coat with safety pins. The injured arm can then be carried in the sleeve for support.

First aid for fractures. Fractures in different parts of the body require different kinds of first-aid treatment.

1) Fracture of the lower arm. Bend the injured person's arm at the elbow, thumb up. Apply one splint to the inner surface, extending it to the tips of the fingers, and another splint to the outer surface, extending it to the wrist. Place the arm in a sling.

2) Fracture of the upper arm. Apply two splints from the shoulder to the elbow, one in front and the other behind. Place the arm in a sling.

3) Fracture of the collarbone. Bend the arm of the injured side to a right angle in front of the body and place it in a sling. Tie the arm snugly to the body.

4) Fracture of the lower leg or ankle. Apply two splints, one on the outside and the other on the inside of the limb, extending from the knee to beyond the foot.

5) Fracture of the thigh, or upper leg. Unless absolutely necessary, a person with a fracture of the thigh should not be moved until a special

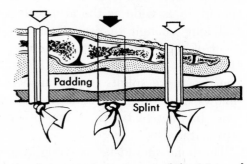

A splint prevents movement of the joint and movement of broken ends (of bones).

splint can be applied by a person who knows how to use it. If the patient must be moved, carry him as gently as possible. Pay special attention to the support of the injured limb.

6) Fracture of the hip or of the pelvis (the bony structure between the hips). A patient with a fracture of the hip or pelvis should be prepared for moving by a physician. If absolutely necessary to move him, a splint should be applied, extending from the armpit to the foot. The splint should be well fastened to the body at several points.

7) Fracture of neck or back. The patient should not under any circumstances be moved except by skilled medical people.

DISLOCATIONS AND SPRAINS

When a bone gets out of place at the point where it joins another bone— that is, at a joint—the condition is called a dislocation. Bones are held together at joints by strong bands called ligaments (see Chapter 6). Muscles are attached to bones by tendons. When the ligaments, tendons, or muscles about a joint are torn or bruised, the condition is called a sprain. In this condition, the pain is usually severe, and swelling rapidly occurs. Shock may be present. Without an x-ray examination, it is often impossible to tell the difference between a sprain or dislocation and a fracture.

The following treatments for sprains and dislocations are recommended.

1) Raise the injured part. If this is an arm, a sling may be used. If it is a leg, have the patient lie down with pillows, coats, or other support under the raised leg.

2) Apply cold compresses (cold wet cloths) to the injury at once to reduce swelling. If the injury is more than 2 hours old, applications of hot water are more valuable.

3) Keep the patient warm. If shock is present, treat it.

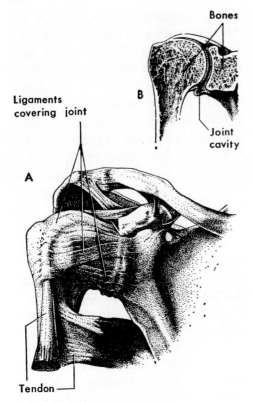

Bones

Ligaments
covering joint

B

A

Joint
cavity

Tendon

(A) Front of right shoulder joint. (B) Cross section of a joint.

4) When in doubt about whether a bone has been broken, treat the case as a fracture and apply splints, especially if the patient must be moved.

5) If a joint has been dislocated, do not attempt to put it back into place.

BURNS

Burns can be caused by heat, sunshine, electricity, and chemicals. In first-aid treatment of burns, the following general rules should be followed: (1) Cut clothing from around the burned part; do not pull it. (2) If blisters are present, do not break or prick them. (3) Treat shock early in all severe burns.

When the skin is reddened but there is no blister, the burn is a first-degree burn. The skin is unbroken and there is little danger from infection. You may use an oily substance, such as petroleum jelly, olive oil, or castor oil, to relieve pain. Cold water or soda in water is soothing if applied immediately.

When the skin is blistered, the burn is a second-degree burn. In a second-degree burn, treat the injury as an open wound. Use material that is known to be clean. Remove loose clothing but do not try to remove material that sticks to the skin. The application of sterile gauze or a clean towel or sheet soaked in a solution of clean warm water, preferably boiled and cooled, containing 3 teaspoonfuls of baking soda to 1 quart of water or 2 tablespoonfuls of epsom salt to 1 pint of boiled water is very good. Keep the dressings moist and warm until further aid is obtained. Never use iodine or oily substances on a second-degree burn. Never apply absorbent cotton to a burned surface. Shock is usually present in second-degree burns and requires immediate attention.

In deep burns, the skin is destroyed. These are called third-degree burns. Third-degree burns are always serious and require medical attention. First-aid treatment consists chiefly of treating shock. If medical attention can be obtained promptly, lay a sterile dressing lightly on the wound. If more than

Steps in making a bandage for the head, for the hand, and for the foot.

30 minutes will pass before help can be obtained, apply one of the dressings suggested for second-degree burns.

Burns caused by chemicals should be washed with large quantities of water, preferably lukewarm, until the chemical is thoroughly removed. All clothing should be cut away with scissors. Apply a petroleum jelly dressing after the chemical is removed and send for a physician. Phenol, or carbolic acid, burns should first be washed with alcohol if it is available.

Eye burns caused by chemicals require careful attention. The best first-aid treatment is to wash the eye thoroughly with large quantities of water and then put in several drops of clean olive oil, mineral oil, or castor oil. A drinking fountain that throws a stream of water is excellent for washing out an eye. The eye should be covered with a sterile dressing until the injured person can get to a physician.

SUNSTROKE (HEAT STROKE) AND HEAT EXHAUSTION

Both sunstroke (heat stroke) and heat exhaustion are caused by extreme heat, but they differ in their symptoms and treatment.

Sunstroke is a dangerous condition caused by direct exposure to sunshine, especially when the air is moist. The same condition is called heat stroke when the cause is excessive indoor heat. The symptoms are headache, dizziness, faintness, and sometimes vomiting; the skin is hot and dry, and the face is flushed; the pulse is rapid and strong. The person usually becomes unconscious; he may have convulsions.

To treat sunstroke, move the person to a shady, cool place if possible and loosen or remove his clothing. Lay him on his back with head and shoulders raised.

Keep his head cool by means of wet cloths, ice bags, or ice. Cool the body by giving cold baths for 20 minutes at a time. Rub his limbs and trunk briskly while he is in the cold water. Cold wet cloths or ice bags may be used. Wrapping the body in a sheet and pouring on cold water every few minutes is effective.

Do not overdo any of these treatments. Stop every few minutes to observe the effects on the patient. If the skin again gets hot, repeat the treatment. Do not give a stimulant. Give cool drinks after consciousness returns.

Heat exhaustion is caused by direct exposure to both the sun's rays and indoor heat, such as high temperature in boiler rooms, foundries, bakeries, and other such places. The first symptoms of heat exhaustion are dizziness, nausea, and staggering. The face is pale, the body is covered with perspiration, and the skin is cold and clammy. Breathing is shallow and the pulse is weak. Fainting may occur.

For treatment, move the patient to cool air, place him in a lying position, and let him drink freely of cool salt water (1 teaspoonful of table salt in 1 pint of water). Call a physician if the patient does not recover promptly.

ELECTRIC SHOCK

If a person receives a severe "shock" from a damaged electric cord or from an electric appliance, turn off the electricity at the nearest switch before touching the injured person. Give artificial respiration if the victim is not breathing.

The rescue of a person from a live electric wire out in the open is always dangerous. The rescuer may himself be electrocuted if he touches the body of the victim. If the switch is near, turn off the current. Otherwise use a dry stick, dry clothing, dry rope, or some other dry material, not metal, to remove the victim from the wire. Start artificial respiration immediately and continue for several hours.

The Red Cross advises that young people do not try to rescue persons from live wires. Call the police or fire department or the electric company.

FREEZING

The symptoms of frostbite are cold in the part affected and finally loss of feeling. The affected part becomes white.

Treat frostbite by rewarming the frozen part rapidly. This may be done by holding the frozen part against another part of the body, by putting it in lukewarm, *not hot*, water, or by wrapping it in a warm blanket. Do not use a hot-water bottle or a heat lamp or place the frozen part close to a hot stove or radiator. Too much heat may increase the damage. Do not rub with bare hands or with snow. As soon as the frostbitten part is rewarmed, the person should begin to move the fingers or toes.

When a person becomes unconscious from cold, carry him into a warm room, cover him well with blankets, and move his arms and legs gently but steadily. If breathing has stopped, give artificial respiration. When consciousness returns, give him hot drinks and let him lie quietly in a warm bed.

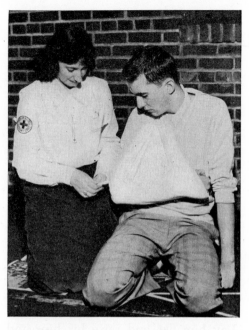

A member of a Junior Red Cross unit is adjusting an arm sling. (Courtesy Arsenal Technical High School, Indianapolis)

POISONING

Two points to be remembered in the emergency treatment of persons who have swallowed poisons are: (1) poisons act more slowly when they are dissolved in large amounts of liquid; (2) the stomach can be cleaned out by causing vomiting.

Get the patient to swallow several glasses of liquid and make him vomit. The following are useful in producing vomiting: (1) lukewarm water, (2) salt water or baking soda water, (3) soapsuds from any type of soap, and (4) 1 tablespoonful of mustard in warm water. Give 4 to 7 glassfuls, preferably lukewarm. Tickling the throat with the finger will then usually cause vomiting.

If the poison taken is known to be acid or lye, do not induce vomiting. For lye, give vinegar or lemon juice; for acids, give baking soda in water or milk of magnesia. In each case, follow up with milk, olive oil, or egg white.

Additional treatments for certain poisons are helpful, but these should be given only upon the advice of a physician.

UNCONSCIOUSNESS

You probably have seen an unconscious person at some time. He appeared to be asleep. Unconsciousness occurs in many illnesses and after many accidents. Sometimes the unconsciousness lasts only a short time and does not seem to be serious. In other cases, the condition is serious and needs medical attention immediately. It is always safe to call a physician. Sometimes it is unsafe not to.

General first-aid treatment. Find whether breathing has stopped and whether there is bleeding. Look for signs of shock, broken bones, poisoning, and sunstroke. Give treatment for these conditions if they exist.

Lay the unconscious person on his back. If his face is red, raise his head and shoulders a little and apply cold cloths or an ice pack to his head. If his face is pale, it means too much blood has flowed away from his head. Lay him flat and raise his hips and legs a little.

Keep the unconscious person warm. Do not move him unless absolutely necessary. Keep everyone around quiet. Do not shake the unconscious person. Do not give him anything to drink until he is awake and you know the cause of the unconsciousness.

Fainting. Fainting, which is a form of unconsciousness, results when, for some reason, too much blood leaves the brain (see Chapter 12). Allow a person who has fainted to lie where he falls if possible. Lower his head and shoulders. Loosen tight clothing. Sprinkling the face with cold water and giving whiffs of ammonia or smelling salts are helpful.

When a person feels faint, he should lie down or bend forward with his head between his knees. This usually will keep him from fainting.

Head injuries. Even mild blows on the head may cause concussion of the brain. This is often what happens when a person is "knocked out" or "stunned." It means that the brain is bruised. More severe blows or falls on the head may cause fracture of the skull and bleeding within the skull.

Persons with head injuries should be handled very gently. When the physician comes, he will have to decide how serious the injury is and what treatment to give.

Apoplexy. Sometimes small blood vessels break in the brain and cause apoplexy, or a stroke (see Chapters 12 and 18). Usually, this occurs in persons who are over 50 years of age. In some cases, muscles are paralyzed on one side of the body.

First-aid treatment is rest and quiet. Apoplexy is a serious condition and needs immediate medical attention.

Convulsions. Convulsions may result from many causes—for example, epilepsy (see Chapter 18), strong emotions, such as great fear or anger, some kinds of poisoning, and various illnesses. In some cases of convulsions, the person's body is stiff; in other cases, the person's arms, legs, trunk, and head jerk wildly.

The first-aid treatment of convulsions consists in loosening the person's clothing, turning his head to one side, placing something between his teeth to keep him from biting his tongue, and protecting him from doing himself injury by threshing about.

Little children sometimes have con-

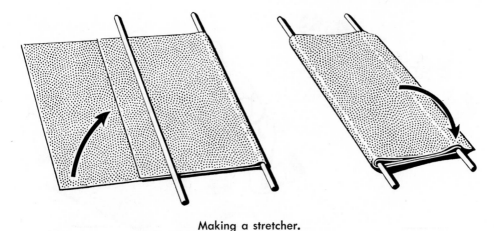

Making a stretcher.

vulsions when they have a fever. When this occurs, a physician should be called, for it may be the beginning of a serious illness.

TRANSPORTATION OF INJURED PERSONS

The first thought of most people who see an injured person is to load him into an automobile and rush him to a hospital or a physician's office. Actually, it is far better in many instances to control bleeding, cover the patient well, make him as comfortable as possible, and wait for an ambulance. A seriously injured person should be taken to a hospital, not to a physician's office.

Transportation by stretcher. When an ambulance cannot be obtained and an injured person must be moved, always use the form of transportation that will do the least harm to the patient. In general, some kind of litter, or stretcher, is the safest form of transportation. If it is impossible to obtain a stretcher, a substitute must be provided.

Many objects, such as camp cots, doors, shutters, benches, boards, ladders—properly padded—may serve as stretchers. An automobile seat may be used to support the body of the injured person if an additional carrier can support the feet. With two long poles, a stretcher can be made by folding a blanket, sheet, or steamer robe over them.

If blankets or sheets are not available, a coat and vest or two coats may be placed over the poles. Turn the sleeves inside out within the coat, button the coat, and stick the poles through the sleeves. If you have a blanket but cannot get poles, place the injured person in the middle of the blanket and roll the edges in from each side. Three or four people on each side can then carry the blanket stretcher by holding the rolled edges.

Care is essential in lifting an injured person onto a stretcher. In most cases, the patient should be flat on his

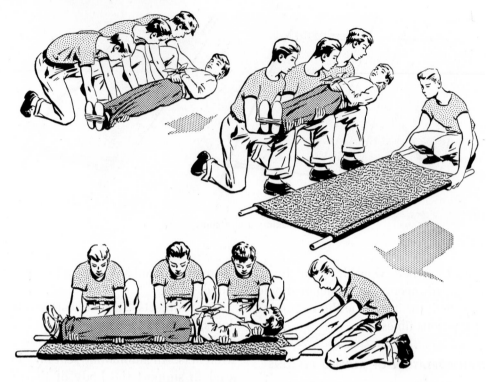

Lifting a person onto a stretcher.

back. Three people should then line up on one side of the patient, usually the uninjured side, and all kneel on the knee nearest the patient's feet. As the carriers slide their hands under the injured person's body, they roll him slightly away from them. They then lift him to their knees. The stretcher should then be placed in front of the carriers so that they can gently lower the patient onto it. If they must carry him a distance to the stretcher, they rise together and carry him carefully against their chests. In carrying a stretcher, one person should stand at each end, and one or two persons on each side.

If a stretcher is not available and an injured person must be moved, the method used depends largely upon the condition of the patient and the number of people available. The pictures on page 63 illustrate the methods of choice when one or two persons find it necessary to move an injured person.

Transportation by automobile. Persons with wounds or fractures of the arms and feet can be transported in sitting position in an automobile, although the driver must drive slowly and carefully, avoiding bumps. Persons with fractures of the skull, thigh, and leg should be transported in a lying position.

When an injured person must lie down, it is difficult to carry him safely in an automobile. In a sedan, a bed can be made of planks, blankets, and pillows placed over the top of the seats on the right side of the car. If a person must be moved very far to a hospital, it is usually better to wait an hour or more for an ambulance than to move him in an automobile.

EVERYDAY EMERGENCIES

You may never have to take care of people who are seriously hurt. Every person, however, has to help himself or someone else in minor emergencies. Be sure to keep the following points in mind.

1) What seems a small injury may turn out to be serious. Be on the lookout for hidden or severe injury.

2) In every injury, there is some shock. Keep the patient warm and quiet for a little while.

3) When the skin is broken even slightly, there is always danger of infection. Keep the wound clean.

Falls and bumps. Everyone falls down once in a while hard enough to "knock the breath" out of him. We should not pay too much attention to ordinary bumps and falls. On the other hand, it is not "sissy" to take time to recover from the shock that always goes along with unexpected jars.

When a little child falls, give him something quiet to do for a few minutes, such as looking at pictures or listening to a story or to music. When

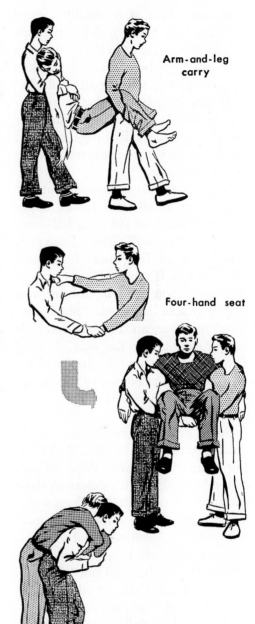

Arm-and-leg carry

Four-hand seat

Pack-strap carry

Here are three different ways to carry an injured person.

a teenager falls, it is usually a good plan for him to sit quietly, perhaps reading or listening to the radio for a little while. If he is severely "shaken up," lying down with a coat or blanket over him is a good idea before returning to work or play. When an older person has a bad fall or jolt, he should lie down, be warmly covered, and be given hot drinks.

When the skin is bruised but not broken by a fall or a bump, apply cold wet cloths or ice for a half-hour or longer. This will often relieve pain and lessen swelling and "black and blue" marks. If a bruise is not treated for several hours, warm, not hot, wet cloths should be used. "Black and blue" marks mean that blood vessels are broken under the skin. It may take days or even weeks for the blood to disappear. A "black eye" is one example of such an injury.

Small cuts and nosebleeds. Allow small cuts to bleed, because the bleeding cleans the wound. Wipe off dirt around the edges with a clean cloth or piece of cotton dipped in clean warm water. Alcohol or some other mild antiseptic (a substance that kills microorganisms or keeps them from growing) may be used but is usually unnecessary. Put on a sterile dressing to keep the wound clean. Strong antiseptics, such as full-strength tincture of iodine, are likely to do more harm than good.

A person with a nosebleed should not try to blow his nose. This removes the clot and causes more bleeding. Hold the nostril closed, with slight pressure. Pressure on one side is usually sufficient. Apply a cold cloth to the nose and face. Sit up but do not move about. Remember, it takes 3 to 6 minutes for blood to clot (see Chapter 11). If bleeding continues, call a physician.

Small wounds. It is difficult to give rules for the care of such everyday happenings as sticking rose thorns into one's finger when gardening, stepping on small pieces of glass when barefoot, running a needle into one's hand when sewing, or getting small splinters deep in the skin. Usually, the object causing the wound can be easily removed or it may come out by itself. A thorn or splinter can be removed with a sterile needle (one that has had the point held for an instant in a flame), unless it is deeply buried, in which case a physician should be asked to remove it.

The danger from small wounds is usually infection. Allow the wound to bleed for a few minutes and then apply a sterile dressing. If infection develops, which may occur in a few hours or a few days, call a physician immediately. Signs of such infection are swelling, pain, redness, and sometimes pus.

If street or garden dirt gets into wounds, tetanus (lockjaw) may result (see Chapter 11). Physicians recommend that children be immunized (be given "shots") against tetanus when they are immunized against diphtheria. If this is done, small wounds are unimportant from the standpoint of tetanus.

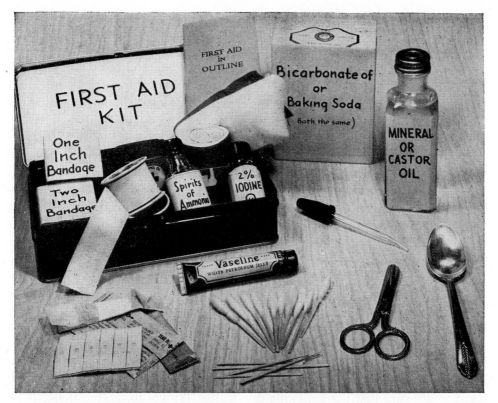

Medicines and instruments for first aid are fairly simple and few but essential. (Courtesy Department of Health, City of New York)

Blisters. If possible, cover a blister and leave it alone. The liquid will be absorbed; that is, it will disappear into the skin. If the blister is on the foot or some other place where the top will probably be rubbed off, wash the area thoroughly with soap and water and then prick the blister on one side with a sterile needle and allow the liquid to escape. Then cover with a sterile dressing (see Chapter 10).

Pimples and boils. Pimples and boils should not be opened except on the advice of a physician. If one breaks, wipe the material that comes out of it, the pus, from the surrounding skin with sterile cotton or gauze. Apply a sterile dressing to an opened boil. If the boil is large enough to need a dressing, a physician should treat it.

Never pick at a pimple, especially one on the nose or around the mouth. Infection spreads more easily from these places than from any other part of the face (see Chapter 10).

Sunburn. Care for sunburn as you would any other first- or second-degree burn (page 56). In many cases of severe sunburn, the person may need treatment for shock.

Stomachaches. Most of what we call "stomachaches" are not pains in the stomach at all. They are due to various causes, and it is important to find the reason for the pain before doing anything about it. In babies, bubbles of gas sometimes are caught in the stomach and intestines and cause stomachache, or colic. Changing the baby's position, patting him on the back, or rubbing his abdomen gently will usually move the bubble.

Sometimes stomachaches in older people are due to the same cause. In this case, loosening the clothing and moving about will usually relieve the pain. Some so-called stomachaches are caused by appendicitis. Appendicitis is one of the leading causes of death in young people. Never give a laxative for a stomachache or put a hot-water bottle on the abdomen, unless you are sure that the appendix is not infected (see Chapter 16).

Earaches. If an earache appears to be caused by cold air, wrap a scarf around the head and sit in a warm place.

Never apply heat directly to the ear. Heat applied to an infection in the ear may rupture—that is, break—the eardrum or may cause the infection to spread into the bone behind the ear, the mastoid (see Chapter 20). Many earaches are due to infection, and a physician should be called immediately to attend them.

Something in the eye. If you get something in your eye, close the eye; often the tears will wash out small objects. Pour clean water over the eye or stand over a drinking fountain where the spray can wash out the eye.

Never rub the eye. It is easy to injure the surface of the eyeball. Usually it is best to let a physician remove even small objects from the eyes (see Chapter 20).

Insect bites. Treat insect bites by applying baking soda and a little water. Try not to scratch them.

Poison oak, poison ivy, poison sumac. If you think you have been near poison oak, poison ivy, or poison sumac, wash yourself immediately with strong soap. If there is much swelling, see a physician (see Chapter 10).

SO WHAT?

Millions of persons are injured in accidents in this country every year; and

Sooner or later every one of us is almost certain to be involved in or present at one of these accidents; and

If the accident happens to be a serious one, knowing what to do may save lives;

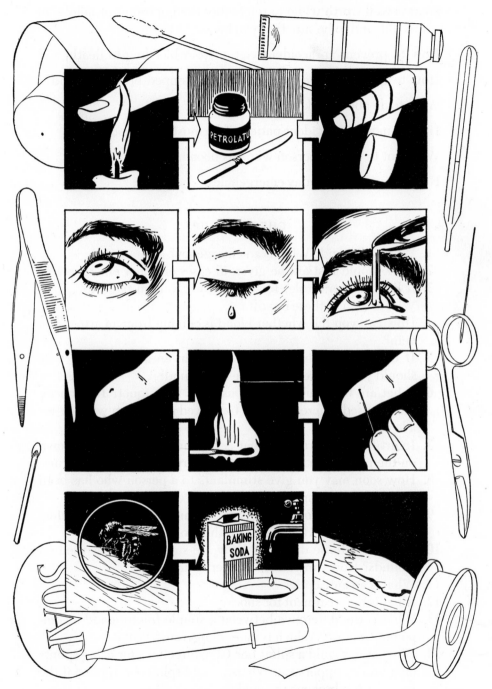

What to do in some minor emergencies.

So, it is well worth while to remember the important principles of first aid, and to be sure that you know

How to prevent an accident victim from bleeding to death; and

How to give help to a person who has stopped breathing; and

What to do about broken bones; and

How to move an accident patient if he must be moved; and

What not to do to a person who has been injured; and

How to care for everyday emergencies.

CHECKING UP

1. What is first aid? What is an emergency?
2. Why should first aid be given in cases of minor emergencies?
3. A list of general rules for first aid is given on page 45. Why is each of these important?
4. How can you tell whether blood is coming from an artery or a vein?
5. If there is bleeding from an artery in an arm or a leg, why should you put pressure above the wound?
6. What are the dangers in the use of a tourniquet? If a tourniquet is used where should it be placed for an arm wound? for a leg wound?
7. In artificial respiration, what is the purpose of pressing down on the patient's back? What is the purpose of lifting his arms?
8. How soon may you give stimulants to a person who has been given artificial respiration?
9. What are infectious organisms? Name two groups of infectious organisms. How large are these organisms?
10. What is a sterile dressing? Why are sterile dressings used on wounds? How can you obtain sterile dressings?
11. What is an antiseptic?
12. What is the treatment for shock?
13. What is the difference between a simple fracture and a compound fracture? Which is more dangerous? Why?
14. How large should a splint be? Give directions for using splints on a broken upper arm. Where should splints be applied if the lower arm is broken? the ankle?
15. What is the difference between a dislocation and a sprain?
16. What is the treatment for dislocations and sprains?

17. What is a first-degree burn? a second-degree burn? a third-degree burn? What is the treatment for each?
18. Why is it dangerous to try to rescue a person from a live electric wire?
19. How can you tell whether a person is suffering from sunstroke or from heat exhaustion? What is the treatment for each?
20. Why should a person with a frostbitten toe or finger not hold the toe or finger close to a hot stove or put it in hot water?
21. Why should a person who has swallowed poison be given a large quantity of liquid? Why should you try to get him to vomit?
22. What happens when a person faints? What is the treatment for fainting? What can be done to prevent fainting?
23. Give some rules for transporting injured persons.
24. Make a list of everyday emergencies and give the treatment for each.
25. What are the general rules to remember in treatment of minor emergencies?

THINGS TO DO

First-aid needs

1. Find where in the school first-aid kits are available. Look in the gym, laboratories, shops, and so forth. What supplies are in each? What supplies are in the school bus?
2. Plan a first-aid kit to be taken on hikes.
3. Plan first-aid supplies that a family should take on weekend trips.
4. Collect first-aid materials that should be in a home. Use these as an exhibit in the school and for a parents' meeting.
5. Find the kinds of accidents that occur in your community. What first aid is useful in each?
6. Collect newspaper clippings about accidents. Discuss the first aid that should be given in each.
7. Take a trip to a firehouse. Ask to see the first-aid equipment. Where else in the community are there supplies for first aid?
8. Examine an ambulance and find what first-aid equipment is carried.

First-aid skills

9. Ask the fire department to demonstrate first aid for suffocation. Ask how firemen treat burns.

10. Plan an assembly program or exhibit of first aid.
11. Ask a second-class Boy Scout to show Scout methods of caring for cuts, bleeding nose, blister, fainting, shock, and drowning.
12. Ask a first-class Boy Scout to tell the first-aid requirements for a first-class Scout.
13. Ask a nurse, a first-aid instructor, or a physical-education instructor to show how to splint an arm or a leg; how to put on a tourniquet.
14. Practice finding pressure points.
15. If you go on trips away from civilization, practice methods of carrying an injured person. (In most cases of severe injury, it is possible to bring a physician to a person who has been injured.)
16. Ask a nurse or a first-aid instructor to show you the important points of bandaging: anchoring the bandage, making a figure 8, putting on a spiral and a spiral reverse, and putting a bandage over a dressing. Practice these on arms, legs, ankles, elbows, and eyes until you can do them correctly and quickly.
17. Find the kinds of accidents that happen to the students in your school. Learn how to care for the injuries. (In some schools, a First-Aid Club can assist the nurse or teacher.)
18. Ask your local Red Cross about classes in first aid. Some students in the class may work for Junior First-Aid certificates (seventh, eighth, and ninth grades), or Standard First-Aid certificates (above ninth grade).

CHAPTER 5　Wonderfully Made

The more you know about yourself, the better chance you have to be healthy, happy, and successful. Scientists all over the world are spending their lives finding out more and more about human beings and other living things, but there is much that is still unknown. We know enough, however, to know that we are truly "wonderfully made."

This chapter may not have many new facts in it for you. Its purpose is to bring together facts you already know and start your thinking about what it means to be alive and about how your body functions and grows.

THE STUFF LIVING THINGS ARE MADE OF

In many museums, there are displays of the substances that make up a human being. In one exhibit case, there will be a life-sized statue of a man. Next to this will be jars and boxes containing a few iron nails, a little copper, some of the yellow gas chlorine, some of the colorless gases oxygen, hydrogen, and nitrogen, a lump of carbon, a few crystals of iodine, and several other substances. These substances are chemical elements.

Scientists have learned that human beings are made up of carbon, oxygen, iron, and other chemical elements— about 35 in all. The greatest scientist in the world, however, cannot put these chemical elements together to make a man. A human being is alive. Copper, iron, and oxygen are not. One of the astonishing things men have learned is that live human beings are made of, that is, composed of, chemical elements which are not alive.

Protoplasm. In human beings and other living things, these chemical elements are combined into living stuff, which is called protoplasm. All living things—human beings, rabbits, rosebushes, flies, the green scum on ponds —are made of protoplasm.

Protoplasm is alive, but almost always when we try to study it we first kill it. Then we have a mass of chemical substances that we can study, but we do not have protoplasm.

Living stuff is always changing. Pro-

71

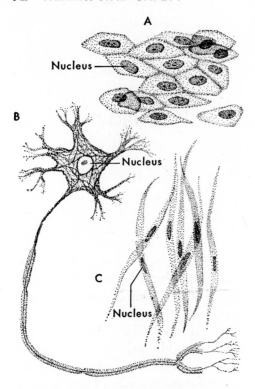

(A) Skin cells. (B) Nerve cells. (C) Smooth muscle cells. Cells carry on various activities, and their shapes are suited to their activities. For example, fat cells are chiefly drops of fat, muscle cells are longer than they are wide and the two ends pull toward each other when a muscle acts, nerve cells are long and slender and carry nervous impulses.

toplasm is always changing, from day to day, and from hour to hour. It is like a river. A river remains a river, yet the water in it is constantly changing. Water comes into the river from the mountains and goes on to the sea. In somewhat the same way, new materials are constantly being taken into protoplasm, and old materials are being thrown out. The materials taken in are food; those thrown out are wastes.

EVERYTHING LIVING IS MADE OF CELLS

Living things are organisms. An organism, whether it is a human being or an oyster, is not just a mass of protoplasm. Instead, the living thing is made up, or composed, of very small parts called cells.

Some organisms, such as bacteria, are single cells. Human beings are made up of trillions of cells. The outside of each cell is a layer of thickened protoplasm, which makes a wall around that cell.

What cells are like. Cells are of different sizes and shapes. They might be compared to the individual bricks, boards, nails, screws, and so forth, that make up a house. Human cells are so small they can be seen only under a microscope.

Near the center of each cell, there is a round body called the nucleus. If the nucleus is removed, the cell dies. Hence, the nucleus is considered the life-center of the cell. Scattered through the nucleus is material called chromatin, so named because it is easily colored by certain dyes.

Growing. When the protoplasm of cells takes in more materials as food than it gets rid of as wastes, the cells grow. When they get large, they divide. During the division, the chromatin arranges itself in short threads called chromosomes. The chromosomes can be seen under a microscope. They are thought to be composed of smaller particles called genes. These chromosomes and genes seem to be important in determining a person's heredity—that is, the ways in which he resembles his parents and grandparents and other ancestors (see page 84).

Every living thing begins life as a single cell. In human beings and in many other living things, this single cell is formed by the union of two cells, an egg cell and a sperm cell, and is known as a fertilized ovum, or egg.

The fertilized egg grows, then divides into daughter cells: first two, then four, then eight, then sixteen, and so on. Gradually, these cells become specialized; that is, some become skin cells, some become muscle cells, others become reproductive cells, bone cells, nerve cells, blood cells, and all the other kinds of cells that make up a human being.

WHAT LIVING THINGS DO

All living things, including human beings, carry on certain activities, or processes. They take in food materials from the outside world, use them, and turn them back to the outside as wastes. They respond to the things around them, that is, to their environment. They reproduce.

These are complicated processes. No machine made by man can perform them. Yet even the smallest living things carry on these activities successfully. No matter how feeble or young, a baby or a fly or a plant is more complex, more mysterious, and capable of more remarkable performances than the most elaborate machine ever invented.

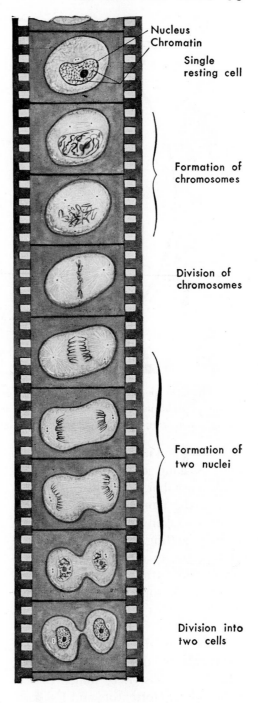

Nucleus
Chromatin

Single
resting cell

Formation of
chromosomes

Division of
chromosomes

Formation of
two nuclei

Division into
two cells

Each new cell has the same number of chromosomes as the parent cell.

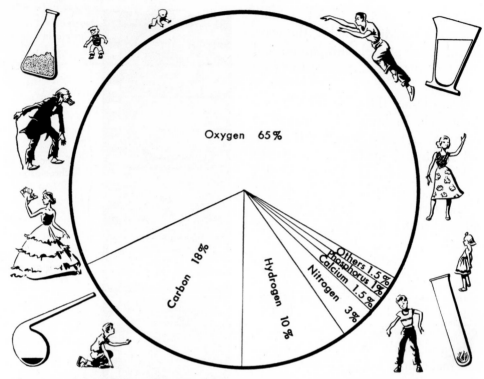

Oxygen 65%

Carbon 18%

Hydrogen 10%

Nitrogen 3%

Calcium 1.5%

Phosphorus 1%

Others 1.5%

The chemical elements in a human body are oxygen, carbon, hydrogen, nitrogen, calcium, phosphorus, and small amounts, or traces, of potassium, sulfur, sodium, chlorine, magnesium, iron, manganese, iodine, fluorine, copper, zinc, silicon, and some others.

Getting and using food. Building up and breaking down protoplasm include a number of processes. Metabolism is the name given to all these processes taken together. Metabolism includes getting food, using it to build protoplasm, tearing down the protoplasm, and getting rid of wastes. Tearing down protoplasm releases energy, which keeps us warm and enables us to move.

What is food? Human beings eat thousands of different things—fish, pancakes, snails, rice, mince pie, to name a few. Hottentots and Eskimos, Chinese and Americans, all eat different foods. What is a food?

For one thing, foods contain the chemical elements needed to build human protoplasm: iron, nitrogen, copper, and all the others. They also contain tiny amounts of substances, called vitamins, that are needed to make the processes of metabolism run smoothly.

Foods supply energy for all the body's activities. This energy comes from the sun. Green plants take up the sun's energy and store it. We get the energy by eating the plants or by eating animals that have eaten plants. Pancakes and snails, mince pie and rice, all supply energy that came originally from the sun.

How much food have you eaten?
Did you ever think how much food
you have already eaten? And how
much more you will eat in the future?

An egg a day, for example, adds up
to more than 30 dozen eggs in a year,
or more than 300 dozen in 10 years.
Two glasses of milk a day add up to
more than 45 gallons of milk in a
year, and 456 gallons in 10 years. And
there are pounds and pounds of meat,
loaves and loaves of bread, bushels
and bushels of vegetables, dozens and
dozens of oranges and apples.

What do you do with all this food?
You have probably eaten a few tons;
yet you weigh only 100 pounds or so.

Suppose you follow some of it, a
cheese sandwich, for example, and see
what happens to it.

Story of a cheese sandwich. Cheese,
bread, butter, and lettuce are good
foods, but they do you no good until
they are digested, that is, changed
into something your cells can use.

This occurs in the long tube called the
digestive tract, which starts with your
mouth. You take bites of the sandwich, chew them, and swallow them.
They are off on their journey to the
stomach and the rest of the digestive
tract that lies below the stomach.

Digestive juices, or fluids, flow out
over the bites of sandwich as they are
pushed along the digestive tract and
change the bread, the butter, and the
cheese into liquids. The liquids are
absorbed; that is, they pass through
the walls of the digestive tract into
the blood. Most of the lettuce in the
sandwich is not digested and is
pushed on out of the body.

The cheese sandwich is now only
drops of digested food carried all over
the body by the blood. This digested
food leaves the blood here and there
through the body and goes into the
lymph, the fluid that surrounds the
cells (see Chapters 11 and 12). Some
is taken by bone cells to build bone;

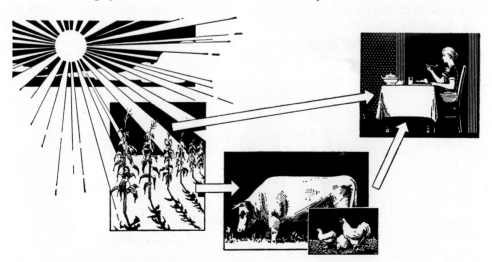

Energy comes from the sun. If all the green plants in the world died, all the human beings
would die too. Can you explain why?

some may be taken by cells in the liver to build liver; some may be taken by cells in the skin to build skin; some may be stored as fat (see Chapter 16).

Now the chemical elements that made the cheese sandwich are part of the protoplasm that makes your body; they are part of *you*. But this is not the end of their story.

In addition to digested food, the blood carries oxygen, which you have breathed in through your nose and lungs. This oxygen combines with chemical substances of the protoplasm and slowly burns, or oxidizes, them. During this oxidation, heat is released. You know that you could have burned the cheese sandwich instead of eating it and gotten a certain amount of heat from it. You get the same amount of heat when you slowly oxidize the protoplasm formed from it. Heat is one form of energy. This heat energy from the cheese sandwich helps to keep you warm. Some becomes the kind of energy that enables you to talk and walk and do all the other things you do.

After oxidation, the chemical elements that were in the cheese sandwich are no longer protoplasm. They are wastes. They are carried by your blood, and you get rid of them through your skin, your lungs, and your kidneys (see Chapter 17).

All the food you eat. What happens to the cheese sandwich is what has been happening to the food you have been eating all your life. Part of it has been built into your body. Most of it, however, has been oxidized and gotten rid of as wastes. This is the reason you do not weigh as much as do the tons of food you have eaten.

As the food was oxidized, it gave you energy to keep warm, to play games, to work, to breathe, and to keep your blood flowing, to digest your food, to talk and yell and sing, to read and write, to laugh and cry.

Systems, organs, tissues, cells. All the work your body does in making use of the cheese sandwich is, of course, done by the individual cells. These cells are arranged in tissues, organs, and systems. Tissues are masses of cells that are alike. Muscle tissue,

What you eat in 1 year.

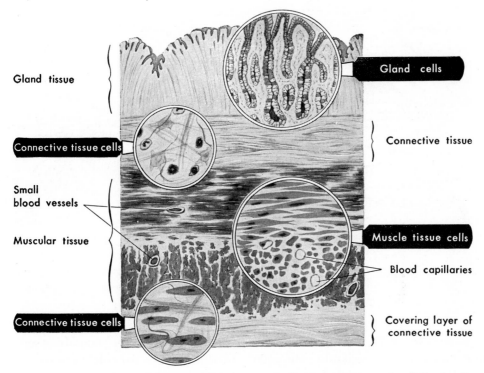

Gland tissue

Connective tissue cells

Small blood vessels

Muscular tissue

Connective tissue cells

Gland cells

Connective tissue

Muscle tissue cells

Blood capillaries

Covering layer of connective tissue

The stomach is made up of many kinds of tissues. The lining consists mostly of gland cells, which secrete hydrochloric acid and digestive juices. Over the lining, is a layer of connective tissue, then a layer of muscle cells and blood vessels, and then an outside covering of connective tissue. The magnified sections in the drawing show the cells in the various tissues of the stomach.

for example, is made up of muscle cells; bone tissue is made up of bone cells.

Organs are made up of tissues. The tongue is an organ made up chiefly of muscle tissue, blood tissue, connective (connecting) tissue, and covering tissue. The stomach is another organ, chiefly muscle tissue, gland tissue, covering tissue, and connective tissue.

Organs in turn make up systems. Each system carries on a series of related activities. The digestive system, for example, is made up of all the or-

gans that have to do with digesting food. The respiratory system is made up of the organs that have to do with breathing.

Using food in the body involves the digestive system, the respiratory system, the systems that carry materials throughout the body, and the systems that get rid of wastes.

Digestive system. The chief part of the digestive system is the digestive tract. This tract, or tube, is about 30 feet long in an adult. It consists of the mouth, esophagus, stomach, small intestine, and large intestine.

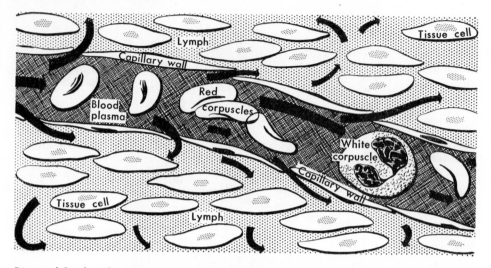

Digested food and oxygen pass out through the walls of the capillaries into the lymph. Lymph lies around all the cells of the body. Everything that goes into or out of cells must pass through the lymph.

Connected with the digestive tract and in its walls are glands (see page 81) that secrete the digestive juices— that is, manufacture and pour them into the mouth, stomach, and small intestine (see Chapter 16). Teeth and tongue also have a share in digestion and are parts of the digestive system.

Systems that carry materials throughout the body. The blood carries digested food, oxygen, and wastes all over the body. Blood flows in a stream through a series of tubes, the blood vessels—arteries, capillaries, and veins. It is pumped through these tubes by the heart. Blood, blood vessels, and heart make up the circulatory system (see Chapter 12).

Some of the liquid part of the blood passes through the walls of the blood vessels with the digested food. This liquid forms the lymph, which surrounds all the body cells. Lymph is carried back into the blood by a series of tubes, the lymph vessels. The lymph and lymph vessels are called the lymphatic system (see Chapter 12).

Heart, blood vessels, and lymph vessels are organs. They are composed chiefly of muscle and connective tissues. Blood is a tissue. Lymph is the liquid around all cells of the body.

Respiratory system. The nose, the lungs, and the passages between them are organs that make up the respiratory system. Through these organs, you breathe in air, which contains oxygen, into the lungs. Through these organs, you also breathe out waste in the form of carbon dioxide.

Getting rid of wastes. The wastes formed in the processes of metabolism are carried by the blood to the skin, the lungs, and the kidneys, where the body gets rid of them. The skin is an organ, the chief part of the covering system; the lungs are part of the respiratory system; the kidneys are parts of the urinary system. All of these act as excretory systems.

Keeping the right temperature. You are constantly producing heat through the processes of metabolism. You are constantly losing heat to the air around you. Your body is remarkably successful in balancing production of heat and loss of heat and keeping itself at just the right temperature. If you are in good health, your temperature will remain approximately the same whether you go to the North Pole or to the Equator.

Normal temperature in the mouth is usually about 98.6 degrees Fahrenheit. Inside the body, the temperature is a few degrees higher than this. It is possible to have a temperature slightly higher or slightly lower than 98.6 degrees and still be healthy. In the morning, a person's temperature may be as much as a degree lower than it will be in the afternoon.

Human cells do their work most efficiently when the body temperature is just right. If the temperature goes up or down, all the processes of metabolism are disturbed. This is the reason a physician always wants a careful record kept of a patient's temperature. This tells him something about whatever is disturbing the metabolism and how the patient is fighting it.

If the temperature rises above 105 degrees, the functions of the body may be seriously interfered with. Body temperatures above 110 degrees are usually fatal.

Low temperatures are also dangerous. They are hard to measure, for chilling is uneven and parts of the body remain warm, while others are cold. A few cases are known of people being apparently "frozen through" and living.

Body temperatures above 99 degrees Fahrenheit are called fever. There is no common name for body temperatures below 98.6 degrees.

Responding to the environment. Taking food, building protoplasm, tearing it down, and getting rid of wastes are the metabolic processes that keep us alive. Just keeping alive, however, would not be very interesting. To know what is going on around us, to enjoy what is happening, to move about, are what most people think of as living.

What happens when you see a friend? You see a friend at the end of the block and call to him. What has happened? Light has been reflected, thrown back, from him and has entered your eyes. Nerves carried messages from your eyes to your brain. From the brain, other nerves carried messages through your spinal cord and out to your "shouting" muscles.

A clinical thermometer is used to measure body temperature. (Courtesy Taylor Instrument Co.)

The light entering the eye was a stimulus; the shouting was a response. Another response was your recognizing him as your friend. Still a third response was feeling happy at seeing him.

Instead of calling to your friend, you may make many other responses, depending on the situation. You may run to him. You may start off in the opposite direction to get the book you want to return to him. If you have something exciting to do, you may jump up and down and tell him to hurry. Your heart beats faster, you breathe more quickly.

In each case, the stimulus is the same—light entering your eyes. The messages are carried over the same nerves to the brain. The brain and spinal cord, however, act like elaborate telephone exchanges. Messages may go out over dozens and hundreds of outgoing nerves. The response you make—whether you run, shout, remember, feel excited, or jump up and down—depends on where the messages go within the brain and spinal cord and which nerves they follow out to other organs of the body. Messages over nerves are called nervous impulses.

You can *choose* some of the responses you will make. For example, you can choose whether you will run to your friend or call to him, whether the nervous impulses will be sent to your "running" muscles or to your "shouting" muscles. You can choose the direction in which you will run. You cannot choose whether you will feel excited or whether you will re-member your friend's name and the good times you have had together.

Sense organs and nervous system. What you do when you see a friend is just one example of how you respond to the environment around you. You hear a clock strike and start for school. You smell a hamburger and onions, and your mouth "waters." You take a bite of a new pudding, like the taste, and ask for more. You feel too warm, start to perspire, and take off your sweater, fan yourself, or go to the refrigerator for a cold drink. You are asked to play the piano and get "stage fright."

Your friend, the clock, the hamburger and onions, the pudding, the warm air, and the audience waiting to hear you play are all in your environment. You learn that they are there through your sense organs—eyes, ears, tongue, nose, and skin. These receive the stimuli from the outside.

Nerves carry nervous impulses from the sense organs first to the brain and spinal cord, then out to muscles and glands. The brain, spinal cord, nerves, and sensitive parts of the sense organs make up the nervous system (see Chapter 18).

You can deliberately control some of the messages sent over the nervous system. This control allows you to choose some of your responses, for example, whether to run or to walk and in which direction. These are voluntary actions. You cannot choose whether your glands will secrete more fluids or whether your heartbeat will be fast or slow. These are involuntary actions. Most of the nervous impulses

Here is a boy making four different responses to the sight of his friend. The stimulus is the same, but he acts differently at different times. How do you respond when you see a friend? Can you trace the nervous impulses from your eyes to the muscles and glands that are set into action?

that result in involuntary actions go out over the autonomic nervous system. You cannot deliberately control impulses over the autonomic nervous system.

How you respond to stimuli. Responding to the environment means doing something about something. You respond to many stimuli by making movements—nodding your head when someone asks you a question, running after a ball, going upstairs to get a coat, moving your eyes, swallowing, breathing fast. Muscles are concerned whenever there is movement.

All the muscles of the body make up the muscular system (see Chapter 6).

When you move your arms, legs, trunk, or head, muscles pull on bones. Bones form the skeletal system. Bones help to hold your body upright as well as take part in movements. They protect your lungs, heart, brain, and other organs (see Chapter 6).

You respond to some stimuli by action of your glands. Glands are groups of cells that manufacture and pour out, or secrete, special fluids or juices. When your mouth "waters" at the smell or thought of food, when you cry at a sad sight or a sad thought, when you perspire in hot weather, it is because your digestive glands, tear glands, and sweat glands are secreting extra amounts of their special fluids, or secretions.

All these glands—the glands in the mouth and along the digestive tract, tear glands, sweat glands—pour out their secretions externally, through tubes, or ducts. For this reason, these are called glands of external secretion.

Other kinds of glands pour out their secretions internally, directly into the blood stream. These are called glands of internal secretion. Another commonly used name for them is endocrine glands. Still another name is ductless glands. The fluids secreted by the endocrine glands are called hormones (see Chapter 22).

Hormones are being produced all the time. Certain stimuli, especially when your emotions are aroused, may cause the endocrine glands to secrete greater amounts of some hormones and smaller amounts of others. The hormones, in turn, have some part in making your heart beat faster, making you breathe more quickly, and making you feel happy and alert or embarrassed and afraid. The endocrine glands are located in the head and trunk. Altogether they make up the endocrine system.

Many of your most complex responses occur within the brain, for example, remembering, choosing what to do, thinking, learning, and being conscious of all the things that are happening. These are ways of re-sponding just as truly as running or talking.

Reproducing. Human beings are mammals; that is, they belong to the group of living things which protect the new organism for some months within the body of the mother. The organs that produce eggs and sperms and provide early care of the young make up the reproductive system. The reproductive systems are different in men and women. As a result, men and women have different shares in reproduction.

The reproductive organs secrete a number of hormones (see Chapter 22). These are chiefly responsible for the differences between men and women in the shape of the body, in voice, in distribution of hair, and in all the other characteristics that we call secondary sexual characteristics. Like other hormones, these hormones also influence a person's metabolism and his emotions.

THE MASTER CONTROL

The cells of a human being are of many different kinds, grouped together in complex organs, tissues, and systems, each able to carry on a different activity. But even if you understand all about these parts, you still will not have a good understanding of how your body functions if you fail to think of the master control.

This master control is centered in the brain and operates through the rest of the nervous system and through the hormones that are poured

Coordination and timing, plus control and good footwork, are necessary in tennis playing. (Courtesy Colby Junior College)

out into the blood stream. It makes it possible for the different parts of the body to function together instead of at cross-purposes. In other words, all the bodily activities are interrelated, or adjusted, one to the other.

When you run, for example, you need more oxygen; involuntarily you breathe faster and your heart beats more rapidly. This is an example of how heart and lungs, in fact, all the organs of the circulatory system and respiratory system adjust themselves quickly to meet the needs of the muscles used in running (see Chapter 7). When you are resting or are asleep, you need less oxygen; your heart beats more slowly and you breathe less rapidly.

When you are hungry and smell good food, your mouth "waters,"

showing that your digestive organs are beginning to function. When the weather is hot, you lose heat by sending more warm blood to your skin and by perspiring. When the weather is cold, you save heat by sending less blood to the skin and more to the inside of the body. Sometimes you shiver when you are cold, which is a way of producing more heat. In other words, each organ and each system of the body carries on its activities in relation to what is happening in other parts of the body.

In emotions, too, you act as a total organism. When you are sad and weep, you are "sad all over," not just with your eyes. When you are angry, it is not just in your mind. Your heart beats faster, you breathe more rapidly, your muscles are tense (drawn tight), but your digestive organs function more slowly than usual. This makes you ready to do something and do it quickly, to use all your energy in action.

Most of these adjustments are involuntary. You do not think of what each cell, organ, and system is doing. In the healthy person, all these work together. The master control makes each person able to act as *one* organism, in spite of the many, many parts that go to make up his body.

GROWING UP AND GROWING OLD

To think of a person as if he were always the same, as if he never began and never changed, would give a poor picture of him. The life of an individual starts when egg and sperm meet and ends with his death. How long an individual lives depends on many things. He may die in an automobile accident or of pneumonia. His life may be shortened because he does not get enough food or the right kind of food. He may die because he puts off getting medical care. Under the best of conditions, human beings would probably live to be around 80 or 90, some more, some less. Actually, so many die in younger years that the average age at death is brought down to about 68 years for white men and 74 years for white women, to about 62 years for nonwhite men and 64 years for nonwhite women. This is the life-expectancy in the United States.

What a child gets from his parents. The egg and sperm contain everything that a child gets from his parents. Nothing is added, nothing is taken away after egg and sperm unite, that is, after fertilization. The environment can influence the way in which certain abilities, or characteristics, will develop—for example, whether a boy will play the piano or the violin or the saxophone. But no environmental influence can make him "musical" if he is not, or change any other of the abilities, or characteristics, that he has inherited from his parents.

Early life. For several months of life, a human being lives inside the body of his mother. He is kept warm, his blood receives food and oxygen from his mother, and his wastes are carried away through her excretory organs. The single cell of which he is composed in the beginning divides and divides. More than a million cell divisions take place in a few weeks as the baby grows.

At first, a baby is so small that it would be almost impossible to see him except with a microscope. Then he grows a head, arms and legs, muscles, bones, nerves—in fact, the beginnings of all his organs. Even though he is not breathing or digesting food and will not until after he is born, he forms all the organs that he will need later for these processes. In these first 9 months of life, the new organism gains in weight about 2 billion times, from $\frac{1}{50,000}$ of an ounce as a single cell to the 7 pounds, more or less, of a newborn baby. This is the fastest he will grow in all his life.

This ability of the fertilized egg to

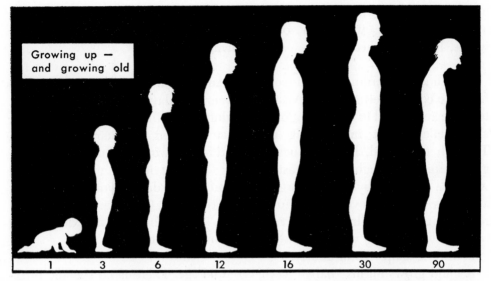

Growing up —
and growing old

| 1 | 3 | 6 | 12 | 16 | 30 | 90 |

Human beings change in size, appearance, the way they think, how much they know, and dozens of other ways as they grow from babies to old people. A person may seem very different at one age from what he was in the past or will be in the future, yet it is important to realize that he is always the same person.

divide and grow is one of the mysteries of life; but equally mysterious is the influence within the organism that controls growth. The eggs of a mouse and of an elephant are approximately the same size; yet the one develops into an animal of several ounces, while the other grows into an animal of several tons.

All through the months before birth, in what is called the prenatal period, the new organism is greatly affected by the health of his mother. What she eats, how much sleep she gets, whether she is sick or well, make a difference in his health and in his development.

Birth means a great change for the baby. Now he must breathe his own oxygen, must eat and digest his own food, must get rid of his own wastes, and must keep himself warm. He is starting on a new kind of life.

Babyhood. A baby develops very fast and learns a vast number of things in a short time. At first, his food consists of milk. By the time he is 2 years old, he has most of his "baby" teeth. At birth, he can get rid of his wastes but cannot control this process. By the age of 2, he can keep dry most of the time. He learns to creep and then to walk and soon gets around surprisingly fast. He can make many sounds, or noises, when he is born, and in the first 2 or 3 years he learns to make these sounds into words and begins to tell people what he wants. If a baby is well and happy while he is doing all this learning, it makes a difference all the rest of his life, not only in his health, but in the way he feels about himself and the world—in other words, his mental health.

Childhood. Learning to eat solid foods, to control getting rid of wastes, to move about, and to talk give a baby an excellent start in growing up. Through childhood, he continues to grow rapidly, though not so fast as when he was a baby. All his organs are growing and developing. Food, rest, exercise, and illness all have a part in determining whether the organs will develop well or poorly.

A child grows all his "baby" teeth, loses them, and gets all his permanent teeth except the last four, the "wisdom teeth." He learns to take care of himself. He goes to school and learns to read, to do arithmetic problems, to name the countries of the world, their capitals and principal products. He also learns how to get along with other people. He begins to understand about the world, about families, about Santa Claus, about time and life.

Adolescence. In the teens, a child enters the period of life called adolescence. Both boys and girls go through a spurt of growth. Certain organs develop irregularly, some faster than others, some more slowly. By the end of the teens, however, the body is pretty well developed, although a slow growth may go on for several years.

Most adolescents stay in school, but their interests spread beyond school and beyond their families. They are becoming independent and are looking forward to being adults and to having their own jobs and their own homes.

Adulthood. Adult life for people in America today lasts for 40 or 50 years. Adults run affairs for themselves, for their children, for their communities, and for the world. Adulthood is a time for "cashing in" on good care and good health during younger years. It is a time, too, for looking ahead to old age, keeping healthy, and developing lasting interests.

Old age. There is no specific birthday when one wakes up and suddenly is "old." Eyes are probably at their best when we are around 10. From then on, we see less and less well. Hearing is at its peak when we are children, but it changes so slowly that we may be 70 or 80 before we wish people would "speak up" and not "mumble their words." Bones become harder and more brittle all through life. Blood vessels are becoming stiff, and it is harder for the heart to pump blood out through the body. Old people cannot walk as far or as fast as younger people. The skin changes. Hair is not so thick. Teeth may be lost. Yet intellectual interests and pleasure in people and their doings may remain at a high level and make the last years of life rich and happy.

GROWTH GONE WILD

Before we leave the subject of growth, we should consider the disease that is the result of "growth gone wild." This disease is cancer. We speak of it as "growth gone wild," because a cancer is a mass of cells that grow and reproduce themselves without limit.

Growth without control. As a human being develops, his arms, legs, feet, hands, ears, eyes, heart, liver, and other organs grow until they reach the proper size and then stop growing. Throughout life, cells become wornout and die, and new cells are formed to take their place. Whenever you suffer a cut or other injury, the cells nearby immediately start to grow and reproduce to repair the damage that has been done. The production of new cells ceases, however, when the wornout or damaged cells have been replaced. What controls this growth is just as much of a mystery as what makes cells grow in the first place.

When the body loses control of cell reproduction, the mass of new cells forms a "growth," or tumor. Tumors are of two kinds: benign and malignant. Benign tumors do the body no harm, except when they are large enough to crowd other tissues and organs. Malignant tumors are called cancers and will destroy tissues and organs and life itself, if not successfully treated.

The way in which a cancer grows and spreads is different from the way a benign tumor behaves. Clumps of cancer cells, which are reproducing wildly, break off from the original growth and get into the blood or lymph. These clumps are carried to every part of the body. Somewhere

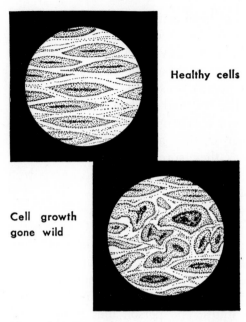

Healthy cells

Cell growth gone wild

These diagrams represent connective tissue. Note that the nuclei of the cancer cells are larger and rounder, and the general pattern of the connective tissue is disorganized.

along the course of their wanderings, some of these cancer cells settle down in other tissues, reproduce, and build new tumors. In time, these tumors become so numerous and so large that the necessary functions of the person's body are interfered with, and the person dies.

If the cancerous growth is discovered early, it can be removed or destroyed before the clumps of cells break off and travel to other tissues and distant parts of the person's body. Such a growth is usually removed by surgery; or it may be destroyed without surgery by treatment with radium or x-rays.

The way cancer acts in the body

has been compared to the way a fast-growing weed invades a healthy lawn. The first tiny weed is so like grass that it may not be noticed. As it grows and spreads, it uses up the nourishment in the soil and chokes the roots of the grass. When such weeds first start to grow, they are easily destroyed, but as they spread they kill everything around them. Much the same is true of cancer.

Importance of cancer. Cancer is the second cause of death in this country. Most of the victims are older people, although cancer occurs in all age groups (see Table 1). In the United States, one person dies from cancer every 20 minutes. During the years of World War II, 2½ times as many Americans died from cancer as died from all causes in all branches of our armed forces in all parts of the world.

Cancer can be reduced. The key to the cancer problem is to correct con-

Table 1. Cancer Deaths in the United States, 1950 *

Age	Number of deaths in every 100,000 persons
Under 10 years	8.6
10–19 years	6.6
20–29 years	12.0
30–39 years	36.4
40–49 years	108.9
50–59 years	268.8
60–69 years	537.4
70–79 years	950.5
Over 80 years	1477.0

* From American Cancer Society.

ditions that may lead to cancer and to discover the growth of cancer cells early. Cancer is a disease for which we need the best treatment as early as possible. In many communities, there are people who promise to cure cancer by pastes, salves, and various "secret" medicines and "rays" from machines. If the person seeking help does not have cancer, he often thinks he is "cured" by these means. If he does have cancer, he may waste so much time on false treatments that cure is finally impossible.

Danger signals. The following are signals that you should go to your physician without delay. In most cases, these symptoms will not mean that you have cancer. If they do, you want to know about it as soon as possible in order to start treatment.

1) A painless lump or thickening, especially in the breast, lip, or tongue

2) Unexplained bleeding or other discharge from any body opening

3) A sore that does not heal, especially about the tongue, mouth, or lips

4) A mole, wart, or birthmark that changes color or starts to grow

5) Repeated "indigestion"

6) Changes in normal bowel habits

7) Continued hoarseness, unexplained cough, or difficulty in swallowing

Guarding against cancer. The first defense against cancer is knowledge. This includes understanding what cancer is and knowing that in its early stages it can be completely removed or destroyed.

We do not know what makes cells go wild and grow into cancer. We do know that continued pressure or irritation often seems to aid the wild cell growth. So it is wise to avoid such irritations.

For example, jagged teeth or rough fillings should be cared for by a dentist, so that they will not scrape the tongue or inner cheek. Moles should be protected from rubbing by clothing (see Chapter 10). Scaly patches on the skin should be treated and protected from irritation by clothes or by shaving. The skin of workers in industry should be protected against long exposure to coal tars, paraffin, arsenic, and other substances that seem to be cancer-producing.

Finally, regular examinations by a physician are important in preventing the development of cancer as well as in preventing other illnesses (see Chapter 26). Most tumors are benign, but all tumors should be checked from time to time to see whether they are benign or malignant. A physician will be on the lookout for irritations that a person has not been aware of and will give advice about further safeguards. Young people should have complete physical examinations at least once a year. After 40 or 50, an examination every 6 months is probably a wise rule. In making these "health examinations," or "periodic checkups," the physician will be on the lookout for any signs of cancer.

Getting more knowledge. For the complete prevention or control of cancer, we need additional information —information that can be provided only by research. During the past few years, funds for cancer research have been provided by the federal government, by many individuals, and by the American Cancer Society. These funds are supporting research work, which we hope will give us the knowledge needed to control this disease. In the meantime, much can be done with the knowledge now available to reduce the deaths from cancer.

SO WHAT?

Your body is not only important but very interesting;

So, be sure you understand

How life begins, and how you grow, and

How the trillions of cells in your body function and depend upon one another, and

How some of these cells may grow wildly to cause cancer, and

What can be done to prevent deaths from cancer.

CHECKING UP

1. What is protoplasm? What is the difference between protoplasm and the chemical elements of which it is composed? Name six of these chemical elements.
2. Which is the most important part of a cell?
3. What is included under the general term *metabolism*?
4. Name the parts of the digestive tract.
5. Is the stomach an organ, or a tissue, or a system? Explain.
6. Is the nose an organ, or a tissue, or a system? Explain.
7. Which systems supply the cells of the body with food?
8. Which systems supply the cells of the body with oxygen?
9. Which systems get rid of wastes?
10. What is the usual temperature in the mouth? How does your body keep at just the right temperature? When is a person said to have a fever?
11. What is the difference between voluntary and involuntary responses? Give examples of each.
12. Which systems do you use when you respond to stimuli?
13. What is the difference between glands of internal secretion and glands of external secretion? What are other names for glands of internal secretion? What do glands of internal secretion secrete?
14. Why is the nervous system called the master control of the body? What illustrations of its acting as the master control are given in this chapter? List two others.
15. What are the stages in the life of a human being? How do we know when one stage stops and another begins?
16. What is a tumor? How is it formed? What are the two kinds of tumors?
17. What are the danger signals of cancer?
18. How can a cancer be removed or destroyed?

THINGS TO DO

Discussion

1. The chemical elements that make up a human being could be bought for a few dollars. How much is a man worth?
2. The Greeks had a saying: "The same man never steps into the same river twice." Can you explain this?

3. Ask an English teacher to tell you what Shakespeare gave as the "seven ages of man." Do these still fit the facts? Try to write the "seven ages of woman."

4. Do other animals, such as dogs, elephants, birds, and fish, go through the same stages of life as human beings? What is the life-expectancy of these animals?

5. Suppose you suddenly had to take a hard examination. What are some of the ways in which you probably would respond?

6. List all the stimuli that are coming to your sense organs at this moment. Are you conscious of all of them? How are you responding to them? What organs are being used?

Laboratory and demonstration

7. Ask a biology teacher to show you microscopic slides of various kinds of cells.

8. Look at an anatomical model of a human being. Find the systems listed in this chapter. How is each one related to all the others?

9. Learn to take a person's temperature. Ask a biology teacher or the school nurse to show you how to "shake down" a clinical thermometer, how long to leave it in the mouth, and how to read it.

10. Get and study pamphlets and films from the local or state office of the American Cancer Society.

CHAPTER 6 The Body's Framework and Power Plant

Inside the body is a framework of bones, which is called the skeleton. The skeleton determines the general size and shape of the body. In fact, from bones of dinosaurs, scientists have been able to learn something of the size, shape, and appearance of these creatures which lived 10 million or more years ago.

Bones take part in movements such as running, pulling, nodding the head, and twisting the body. Bones, however, do not move by themselves. They must be pulled by muscles. Muscles supply the energy for moving.

Muscles are of various kinds. Those that are attached to bones are called skeletal muscles. There are other kinds of muscles in the walls of the blood vessels, digestive tract, and other tubes in the body. The heart is still another kind of muscle. The way you use and control your bones and muscles may help to improve your appearance and help to keep you in good health.

THE SKELETON

The general plan of the skeleton is simple. The skull and backbone form the central part. The skull is composed of flat bones, which make a firm, strong box around the brain. The backbone, or spine, contains the spinal cord.

The backbone is not a single bone but is made up of many small bones called vertebrae. The vertebrae are set one above the other, like beads on a string. Dozens of muscles connect the vertebrae one with another.

Ribs are attached to vertebrae in the back and to the breastbone, or sternum, in the front. Ribs and vertebrae make a cage of bones, the chest. The chest protects the heart and lungs. Muscles attached to these bones make your chest cavity larger when you breathe.

The shoulder bones form anchors for the arms, and the bones of the pelvic girdle form anchors for the

92

The skeleton. Locate on the drawing the skull, vertebrae, ribs, breastbone, hip bones, bones of arm, wrist, and fingers, and bones of leg, ankle, and toes. Find these on yourself. Below are the common and scientific names of some of the important bones.

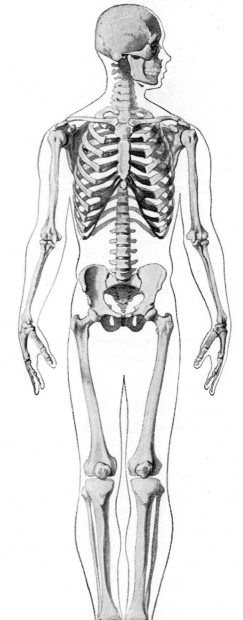

Common name	Scientific name
Skull	Skull
Jawbone	Mandibula
Backbone	Spine
Vertebrae	Vertebrae
Chest	Thorax
Ribs	Ribs
Shoulder bones	Shoulder girdle
Collarbone	Clavicle
Shoulder blade	Scapula
Pelvis	Pelvis
Hip bone	Hip bone
Wristbones	Carpal bones
Long bones of hand	Metacarpal bones, phalanges
Kneecap	Patella
Ankle bones	Tarsal bones
Long bones of foot	Metatarsal bones, phalanges
Breastbone	Sternum
Arm bone	Humerus
Forearm bones	Radius, ulna
Thigh bone	Femur
Leg bones	Tibia, fibula
Tongue bone	Hyoid bone
Braincase	Cranium
Eyesockets	Orbits
Opening for ear	Auditory opening
Mastoid	Mastoid (process)
Base of spine	Sacrum

We make the movements shown above hundreds of times. Each movement appears simple but each one involves many muscles and many bones.

legs. Muscles extending from the shoulder to the long bone of the upper arm make it possible for you to raise, lower, and turn your arm; muscles extending from the hip to the long bone of the thigh make it possible to walk and kick from the hip. Muscles of the trunk, between the shoulders and pelvis, let you bend, straighten up, and twist from side to side.

There are more than 200 bones in the human skeleton. Some are long, some short, some round, some flat.

Bones and cartilage. The bones of a grown person are much harder and stronger than the bones of a tiny baby. A baby's skeleton contains a great deal of cartilage. This is a tough, rubber-like substance, which is sometimes called gristle. Cartilage bends but does not break easily.

As a child grows, most of the cartilage is replaced by bone cells and calcium (lime) salts. The calcium salts make the bones hard and strong. A teenager's bones are not so soft as those of a baby but not so hard as those of an adult.

In an adult, most of the skeleton is bone. Small amounts of cartilage are still found in the ears and in the lower part of the nose. It is also found as pads between the vertebrae and at the ends of bones in the joints.

Bone marrow. One important function of the long bones is the production of blood cells. The blood contains two kinds of cells, or corpuscles, red and white. Marrow inside the bones manufactures all the red corpuscles and some of the white corpuscles of the blood.

The average life of a red blood corpuscle is about 120 days. If new red cells are not formed, a serious condition, anemia, results. If too few white cells are formed, the body becomes an easy prey to infection (see Chapter 11).

One of the effects of atomic radiation is the destruction of the bone marrow. In both Hiroshima and Nagasaki, many persons seemed at first to have escaped injury from the explosion of the atomic bombs but died several weeks later as a result of the effects upon the bone marrow of the atomic radiation to which they had been exposed.

Joints. A joint is formed wherever the ends of two bones are bound together. Around the joint are strong bands of connective tissue, called ligaments.

A few joints, such as those between the bones of the skull, are fixed, but most joints allow some movement. You can swing your lower leg back and forth at the knee but you cannot swing it sideways. The knee is known as a hinge joint. You can swing your leg back and forth and from side to side at the hip. The hip joint is a ball-and-socket joint. Move your arms and fingers and trunk and see whether you

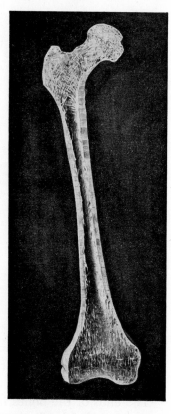

This thigh bone has been split to show the marrow cavity inside.

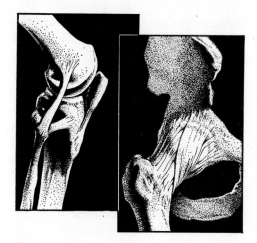

(Below, left) Hinge joint at the knee. (Below, right) Ball-and-socket joint at the hip. Note the ligaments around both joints. What kinds of movements are possible at each of these joints?

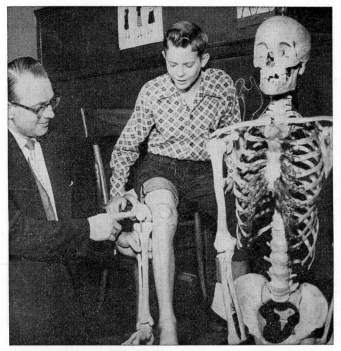

Learning where your own bones are and what sizes and shapes they have is more interesting than simply memorizing the names of bones. (Courtesy Kansas City, Missouri, Public Schools)

can find other hinge joints and ball-and-socket joints.

The ends of the bones in the joints are surrounded by fluid. This fluid allows the bones to move freely at the joints, just as oil allows the moving parts of a machine to move freely. When there is injury to a joint, too much fluid may be produced. This causes swelling. If this happens to the knee, the condition is usually called water on the knee.

Size of the skeleton. Heredity, food, and hormones all influence the growth of the skeleton. In general, tall parents have tall children, and small parents have small children. This is partly due to heredity.

The size of the skeleton is partly controlled by an endocrine gland in the head called the pituitary. Giant-

ism is due to overactivity of this gland in young persons whose bone growth has not been completed. Such persons have been known to reach the height of 9 feet. Underactivity of the pituitary in early life produces dwarfism. The midgets seen in circuses usually have underactive pituitary glands (see Chapter 22).

Most people today have better food than ever before. This is one reason why boys and girls today tend to be taller and heavier than boys and girls in the past. At 14 years of age, boys are 3½ inches and girls 2 inches taller than boys and girls of the same age 50 years ago.

Japanese and Italian children in this country are taller and heavier than children of the same age in their native countries. This is probably due in large part to differences between food here and food in Japan and Italy.

Certain chemical elements, chiefly calcium and phosphorus, and the "sunshine" vitamin (see Chapter 8), vitamin D, are essential for the proper growth and development of bones.

Rickets. Lack of calcium or of vitamin D during infancy results in the disease rickets. In this disease, the bones are soft, weak, and often misshapen. The ends of the long bones and of the ribs may be enlarged. Rickets is the usual cause of bowed legs. Bowing of the legs is not caused by standing or walking at too early an age, as many people think.

Treatment with vitamin D or ultraviolet light in sunshine or from sun lamps results in prompt recovery from rickets, unless the condition has lasted too long. In that case, the bones remain poorly shaped all through life. In girls, poor formation of the pelvis due to rickets may make it difficult for them to have children.

Bones develop rapidly before birth. It is important, therefore, that an expectant mother have plenty of calcium and vitamin D. She must provide not only for her own needs but for those of her baby as well.

ARTHRITIS AND RHEUMATISM

The Greek word for joint is *arthros*; therefore, inflammation of a joint is spoken of as arthritis. Rheumatism is another term commonly used to describe pain in joints, bones, or muscles.

Almost 10 million persons in this

Bowed legs often result from rickets, which occurs when the child has not had enough vitamin D in his diet.

country suffer from rheumatism or arthritis. Some of these people are only slightly uncomfortable; others have much pain and stiffness; some are unable to move.

Kinds of arthritis and rheumatism. In young people, the most frequent type of joint disease is acute rheumatic fever. This is usually preceded by a severe sore throat or scarlet fever. Since the most serious aftereffects of rheumatic fever are upon the heart, rather than upon the joints, the discussion of rheumatic fever is given in Chapter 12.

The causes of the common types of

arthritis which cause so much pain and crippling in older people are not known. Excessive fatigue, chronic infection in tonsils, sinuses, or at the roots of teeth, anxiety, worry, and emotional difficulties are contributing causes in certain cases.

Repeated bending over, lifting, and carrying may cause enough wear and tear on joints to injure them. Overweight may put too much strain on joints. Poor posture also may do damage to joints by continued pulls and pressure in the wrong directions.

Treatment of arthritis. In cases of arthritis caused by infections around the teeth, in the tonsils, and in the sinuses, it may help to remove infected teeth or tonsils or treat infected sinuses early in the illness. After the arthritis has lasted awhile, these procedures are usually not very helpful. Sometimes people have teeth or tonsils removed and sinuses treated but are not cured of arthritis. Aspirin and related drugs have long been used and are still helpful in the treatment of arthritis. They should, however, be taken only under the direction of a physician.

Within the past few years several new drugs, notably cortisone and ACTH, have given relief to some persons crippled by arthritis or rheumatism (see Chapter 22). Unfortunately, this relief generally lasts only as long as the drug is given, and the continued use of these drugs may be dangerous. Other drugs and remedies by the hundreds are advertised and sold for the treatment of arthritis, but most of them are of little if any real value.

Heat from the sun, from various kinds of heat lamps, and from hot water brings great relief to aching joints. Massage and gentle movement of the joints are often helpful. Sleeping on a hard mattress when the arthritis is in the back may help. Well-fitting shoes are important. All these methods of treatment are known as physical therapy (see Chapter 27). They do not cure arthritis but help keep the joints from becoming too painful and stiff.

In some cases, arthritis or rheumatism runs its course and slowly goes away. There is no magic secret for curing it. What can be done is to keep the patient as comfortable as possible during the disease and as free from stiffness as possible afterward. If more people knew this, they would not waste time and money going from one place to another seeking the cure that they never find. And if the money spent in this way could be used in the study of arthritis, we could probably work out a truly helpful program for those who are suffering from the disease.

MUSCLES

You can think of all the cells of your body as little power plants. They take in fuel in the form of food and use oxygen to free energy from this food. This is similar to what happens in an automobile, which takes in gasoline as fuel and uses oxygen to free energy from the gasoline.

Skeletal muscles, tendons, and ligaments. Skeletal muscles are voluntary muscles. The ends of each muscle are attached to bones by tendons. When the muscle contracts, one end remains fixed, while the other end is pulled toward the fixed end. For example, when the broad muscle across the front of the chest contracts, it pulls the arm toward the middle of the body. Locate on the drawing the muscles that raise the eyebrows, close the jaw, move the head, raise the arms, bend the arms and fingers, straighten the arms and fingers, bend the trunk, bend and straighten the legs. Can you find these muscles on yourself?

Some of the energy in your body and in an automobile becomes heat. Your body is warm, just as a running engine is warm, because of the heat produced from the food or fuel.

Some of the energy in your body and in an automobile becomes work energy. In an automobile, energy in the form of work turns the wheels and makes the machine move. In your body, energy takes the form of work in your muscles. Talking, walking, breathing, standing erect, moving your eyes, the beating of your heart— all depend upon your muscles.

Structure of muscles. Every muscle is made up of a bundle of many thousands of individual muscle cells bound together by connective tissue. Muscle cells are long and narrow, thicker in the middle than at the ends. They average $\frac{1}{600}$ of an inch in diameter and $1\frac{1}{4}$ inches in length. Muscle cells can become thicker and shorter, thus

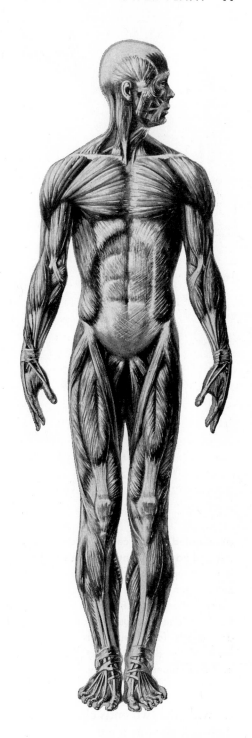

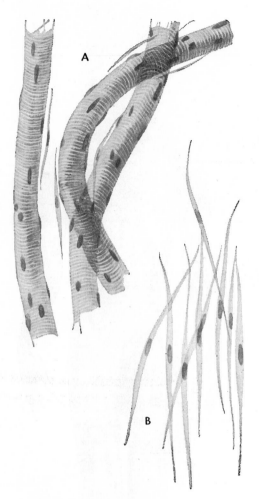

Although a muscle cell is soft, almost jelly-like, it is very strong. When a muscle contracts, it can easily lift 1000 times its own weight. When not contracted, a muscle is said to be relaxed.

Each muscle cell is reached by a nerve. Nervous impulses coming over this nerve cause the muscle cell to contract.

During life, muscles are never completely relaxed, even when a person is asleep. This slight, constant contraction is called tonus. A healthy muscle feels firm because of its tonus. A muscle with poor tonus feels soft and flabby.

Good muscle tonus helps to maintain good posture, good circulation, good digestion, and good elimination of wastes from the digestive tract. Muscle tonus also makes it possible for you to move more quickly than if your muscles were loose and relaxed.

In human beings, there are three kinds of muscles: voluntary, or striated, muscles; involuntary, or smooth, muscles; and cardiac, or heart, muscle.

(A) Striated muscle cells are long and slender and have many nuclei. A skeletal muscle is made up of bundles of striated muscle cells. When a muscle contracts, all the muscle cells shorten. (B) Each smooth muscle cell has only one nucleus. Smooth muscle cells are usually found in sheets and form the walls of the digestive tract, blood vessels, and other tubes in the body.

drawing the two ends closer together. This is known as a contraction.

Voluntary muscles. Voluntary muscles are those that you can deliberately control, for example, the muscles that move your arms and legs. Voluntary muscles are called striated because of the striped, or striated, appearance that they have under a microscope. Skeletal muscles are voluntary muscles. They are attached to bones by bands of connective tissue called tendons.

Skeletal muscles are usually arranged in pairs. For example, the bi-

These boys are using a great many voluntary muscles in this bicycle exercise. Hands, arms, trunk, and legs are all involved. Can you decide which muscles in their legs contract and which are relaxed as they move round and round? (Courtesy San Francisco Unified School District)

ceps muscle on the front of the upper arm is matched by another, the triceps muscle on the back of the upper arm. Both are attached by tendons to the upper arm at one end and to the lower arm at the other. When a boy wants someone to "feel his muscle," he contracts the biceps, and at the same time the triceps relaxes. If both contracted at once, a person could not move his arm up or down.

Muscles that move your fingers are located in the lower arm and are attached by long tendons to the bones of the fingers. When you bend a finger, a muscle on the front of the arm contracts, and at the same time one on the back of the arm relaxes.

These are examples of very simple movements. Actually, most movements are very complex. "Running a scale" on a piano, for example, means that dozens of muscles must contract and relax rapidly and in perfect timing. And each must contract and relax to just the right amount.

Running, or even walking, is almost as complex. Some muscles must relax while others contract. If the muscles on the front and the back of the legs pulled against each other, a person would never get anywhere. Try bending your trunk and moving your head and see whether you can locate the muscles that are contracting and relaxing.

Climbing is good fun for healthy people and exercises most of the muscles in the body.

Another example of muscles acting together is the movement of the eyes. There are three pairs of tiny muscles arranged around the outside of each eyeball. When you turn your eyes up, the muscles on the tops of the eyeballs contract, those below relax. When you turn your eyes to the right, muscles on the right side of each eyeball contract, those on the left relax. If any one muscle is too strong, the eye to which it is attached may turn farther than the other eye. If a muscle is too weak, the eye to which it is attached does not turn as far as the other eye. "Crossed eyes," or cross-eyedness, is one result of this lack of balance among the muscles of the two eyes (see Chapter 20).

Involuntary muscles. Smooth, or involuntary, muscles do not show striations under the microscope, and their actions are not under your deliberate control. They are supplied with nerves from the autonomic nervous system (see Chapter 18).

Smooth muscles are found mostly in the walls of hollow tubes in the body, such as the blood vessels, stomach, intestines, and bladder. Smooth muscles contract slowly but are very strong. If you think of the speed of a snail in contrast with the speed of a mosquito, you will have some idea of the difference between the action of smooth muscles and the action of striated muscles.

Involuntary, or smooth, muscles take part in the basic functions of life about which you do not have to think, for example, circulating the blood and carrying food through the digestive tract. If you take a bite of food, you can decide whether or not to swallow it, just as long as you keep it in your mouth—in other words, just as long as it is held by voluntary muscles. As soon as it gets into the upper part of the esophagus, you have lost deliberate control of it (see Chapter 16). Involuntary muscles push it on to the stomach and intestines, and when it is digested and absorbed, involuntary muscles around the blood vessels push it on with the blood.

Good general health increases muscle tonus of both involuntary and voluntary muscles. Excitement, worry, and fear affect muscle tonus. By maintaining good health and good mental hygiene, you can *indirectly* control the action of involuntary muscles and all the functions of the body with which they are concerned.

A common problem of older people today is high blood pressure. Sometimes this is caused by an increase in tonus of the smooth muscles in the walls of the small arteries (see Chapter 12). This change in tonus may be caused by excitement, worry, changes in hormone secretion, and other factors that we do not fully understand.

Cardiac muscle. Under the microscope, heart, or cardiac, muscle looks very much like voluntary, or striated, muscle. However, it acts like involuntary, or smooth, muscle. In other words, you cannot deliberately decide how fast your heart will beat.

At least two kinds of nerves go to the heart. One kind makes it beat fast; one slows it. When you are working hard, impulses over one set of nerves make your heart beat faster and more strongly. During sleep your heart beats more slowly and less strongly (see Chapter 12).

Emotions, fatigue, and illness have an effect on the rate of the heartbeat. You can control your feelings and avoid overexertion and illness to some extent and, hence, you may partly control the contraction of cardiac muscle.

Muscular action and fatigue. A muscular contraction is very complex. In fact, it is not completely understood. Food, of course, must be provided, for food is our only source of energy. Digested food is brought to muscles by the blood.

When muscles contract, waste products are formed. These are carried away by the blood. If they are not carried away, they act as mild poisons, or toxins, and cause fatigue. If you exercise too long at one time, so many waste products are formed that they cannot be carried away promptly and you become tired, or fatigued. If the muscles around your blood vessels lack tonus, your circulation may be unequal to the job of removing the waste products, and you feel tired after even a little exercise (see Chapter 7).

Sometimes muscles contract strongly and cause pain. These painful contractions are called muscle cramps.

INJURIES TO MUSCLES

Soreness soon after exercise is thought to be due usually to tearing of the thin connective tissue around the muscle cells. The reasonable treatment for this soreness is rest and heat. The rest protects against further injury. The heat brings more blood to the muscles, and the blood helps to heal the injury already there. Massage does more harm than good in such cases.

There is another sort of soreness or stiffness that appears a day or so after exercise. If a person who has not been riding regularly mounts a horse and rides at a trot, his muscles will tell him the next day or the second day after that something is wrong with them. And this soreness will not be limited to the muscles that have been bruised from the saddle but will include also the muscles between the shoulders. This type of soreness is helped most by further exercise of the same sort, by heat, and by massage.

The value of liniment for muscle soreness is chiefly that it provides something to rub on. The liniment probably does not get through the skin and certainly does not reach the muscle, but the rubbing helps the circulation.

With violent exercise there may be serious injury to muscles, such as a pulled muscle or a Charley horse. Both of these conditions occur most often in the legs of untrained athletes.

A pulled muscle usually involves a tear of a muscle covering or even of muscle cells themselves. You may have seen a sprinter in a track meet suddenly check himself and hobble to a stop. He has probably pulled a muscle while running.

The condition Charley horse occurs chiefly among football players. This is an injury and inflammation caused by a strain or bruise. It usually occurs on the front of the thigh and often produces bleeding deep in the muscle. Such an injury should be treated by a physician. Rest is necessary.

Muscle cramps following exercise or during exercise are thought to be caused by a piling up of waste products in the muscle or by a temporary lack of blood supply to the muscle. In long-continued, excessive perspiration, muscle cramps may occur as a result of loss of too much salt from the body. The treatment, again, is massage and heat. Muscle cramps are an all-too-common cause of drowning.

DISEASES OF THE MUSCLES

The muscles are more free from disease than most of the other organs and tissues of the body. Poliomyelitis is commonly thought of as a muscular disease, because it sometimes results in paralyzed, shrunken muscles. Actually, however, the location of this disease is the spinal cord and, sometimes, the brain, where it destroys nerve cells that supply the muscles (see Chapter 18).

In the treatment of poliomyelitis, it is important to keep the muscles in the best possible condition, so that those not paralyzed will be able to do the work of the paralyzed muscles. During the earliest stages, heat is applied to relieve pain and to keep up the circulation of the blood. As soon as the pain is reduced, movements of

(Top) Striated muscle cells. (Center) Cardiac muscle cells. (Bottom left) A thin slice of bone. Note the circular pattern of the cells. (Bottom right) A thin slice of cartilage. All cells magnified many times. (Courtesy General Biological Supply House)

Trichinae curled up in a muscle.

the affected part are started. This type of treatment is now used in practically every hospital in this country.

Trichinosis. One of the few diseases that affect muscles directly is trichinosis. This disease is caused by a tiny worm, about ⅛ inch in length, called the trichina. This worm lives in rats but may infest human beings.[1] Hogs often feed on rats and become infested. Human beings, in turn, become infested from eating pork that has not been cooked long enough to kill the worms.

When infested pork is eaten, the trichinae are set free during digestion. Young worms enter the blood or lymph and are carried throughout the body. Reaching the muscles, they burrow into them and form a shell about themselves. They may remain inactive in this stage for many years.

Usually no effects are noticed immediately after eating infested meat,

---

[1] The term *infected* is used when microscopic organisms live in or on human beings or other animals. The term *infested* is used with reference to worms (such as trichinae), insects, and other organisms that can be seen without a microscope.

but after a period of 10 days to 2 weeks, when the young worms begin to burrow into muscles, muscular pain and weakness, with some fever, usually develop. The disease is sometimes complicated by pneumonia, and death may result. Usually, however, after the early symptoms, which are sometimes not recognized as due to the presence of these worms, the trichinae settle in the muscles and produce few if any symptoms. It is possible, of course, that some of the aches and pains commonly called "muscular rheumatism" are due to trichinae in the muscles.

A study in 114 cities showed that about one person out of every six is infested with trichinae. There is no good treatment for the disease. Government meat inspection does not include inspection for trichinae. However, thorough cooking of all pork and sausage, including hamburger that contains pork, will kill the worms and remove the danger of trichinosis. Fresh pork should be cooked until it becomes white and is no longer red in color in any part of the meat or until all parts of the meat reach a temperature of at least 150 degrees Fahrenheit.

Hernia. When any organ is pushed through the walls around it, the condition is called hernia, or rupture. According to the National Health Survey, some 2 million persons in the United States have hernias.

The most common hernias are those in which a piece of intestine is pushed through the abdominal wall. Two weak spots in this wall are in the groin, that is, where the legs join the trunk. It is here that most hernias occur. Another common location for hernia is at the umbilicus, or navel. Hernias sometimes occur where a wound or an operation has weakened the abdominal wall.

The chief cause of hernia is muscular effort. In the strain of heavy lifting, a piece of intestine may be pushed through one of the weak spots and lie outside the abdominal wall in a pouch of skin and connective tissue.

Keeping the muscles of the abdominal wall strong and in good condition will help protect against hernia.

Young people, especially boys, should not do heavy lifting until they are fully grown and their abdominal muscles are fully developed.

There are two treatments for hernia: a surgical operation to close the enlarged opening, or a truss to hold the intestine in place. A truss usually consists of a flat metal spring, which encircles the body, and a pad, which is placed over the point of the hernia. The force of the spring holds the intestine within the abdomen. A hernia of an infant held in place by a truss may heal, but a truss does not cure the hernia of an adult. Only a surgical operation will cure hernia in adults.

SO WHAT?

The skeleton is the body's framework, and the muscles are its power plant; and

Strength and appearance depend mostly upon eating the right food, upon correct habits of standing and sitting, upon the right kind of exercise, and upon the proper care of injuries;

So, it is important to

Eat food that will provide a strong, well-shaped body; and

Make a habit of exercise and of good posture; and

Take proper care of injuries to bones, joints, and muscles; and

Understand about the common diseases, arthritis and rheumatism, and how to prevent or reduce them.

CHECKING UP

1. Name the important parts of the skeleton. Draw a diagram of the skeleton and label the parts.
2. What is the difference between bone and cartilage? Do you have more bone or more cartilage now than you had when you were a baby?

3. What are corpuscles? Where are they manufactured? What is anemia?
4. How are the joints protected from injury?
5. What is rickets? How can rickets be prevented?
6. What are some of the causes of arthritis and rheumatism?
7. Why does removing infected teeth help the arthritis of some people but does not help others?
8. What is known about treatment of arthritis?
9. How is the work of your muscle cells like the work of an automobile engine?
10. What happens when a muscle contracts? What makes a muscle contract?
11. What is muscle tonus? How is good muscle tonus related to health and attractiveness?
12. Name the three kinds of muscles. How is the action of each kind of muscle controlled?
13. What is the difference between a ligament and a tendon?
14. Why do you feel tired, or fatigued, after exercise?
15. Is massage good for all kinds of muscle soreness? Explain.
16. What is the cause of trichinosis? How can trichinosis be prevented?
17. What is a hernia? What are the treatments for hernia? How can hernia be prevented?

THINGS TO DO

1. Find, on a skeleton or a picture of a skeleton, the bones involved when you kick a ball, sit down, punch a punching bag, pick up a pin, get on a bus, write.
2. Bend arms, legs, fingers, neck, and trunk. Locate the joints that are involved. Notice how smoothly they work. Find the muscles that contract and relax.
3. Get, from the butcher shop, a joint that has not been trimmed too closely. Find the tendons that bind muscles to the bones. Find the ligaments that cover the joints. How do muscles and tendons and ligaments feel? How easy are they to pull or cut? Cut away the ligaments and look at the ends of the bones. Can you find the layer of cartilage? Notice how smooth and moist the inside surfaces of the joint are.
4. Find the tendons on chicken or turkey feet that bend the toes; those that straighten the toes. Compare them with the tendons in your forearms that move your fingers.

5. Look at bones and joints in x-ray pictures. (In some shoe stores you can look at the bones of your feet by fluoroscope.)
6. Find what physicians recommend about food and sunbaths for babies. What relationship have these to the prevention of rickets?
7. Describe a person who is just starting off in the morning for a long hike and the same person coming home at night. How has fatigue affected his muscle tonus? How does this show in his posture? in his facial expression?
8. Ask someone in your public-health department about trichinosis in your community.
9. Watch the cooking of a piece of pork and notice the color when it is thoroughly done.

CHAPTER 7   Keep Physically Fit

and Like It

Every day of your life you have things to do. Some are work, some are play; some are dull, some are fun. But whatever the activity, you do it better and more easily when you are physically and mentally fit.

Fitness means that your body is functioning properly and that you are well balanced and poised. It depends on many things: the condition of your muscles; the foods you eat; the condition of your digestion, circulation, and elimination; your freedom from infections and from damage by tobacco and alcohol; and the exercise, recreation, and rest you get. Emotions of worry and fear injure your health and general fitness, while happiness improves your physical well-being.

EXERCISE

Few things that you do give you so much of a thrill as physical activity.

Combine exercise with sports, with recreation, with the beauty of the out-of-doors, and with good company, and you approach the summit of human pleasure.

For healthy boys and girls, physical exercise is just as much a part of a day's activity as eating and sleeping. When children fail to romp and play, you can be pretty sure that there is something wrong with them.

Rousseau, the famous French philosopher, wrote: "The weaker the body, the more it commands; the stronger it is, the more it obeys." The purpose of exercise is not to develop large muscles or to break athletic records. The greatest value of exercise is that it helps to develop a strong body, and a strong body makes it possible for you to do what you want to do.

Exercise influences almost every process of the body—circulation of the blood, breathing, perspiring, eating, getting rid of wastes, sleeping. If you understand what happens when you exercise, you should be able to decide better what is the proper amount of exercise for you.

Exercise and the circulation. Everyone knows some of the effects of exercise, though he may not be able to explain them. Run around the block or upstairs. Your heart beats faster and more strongly. It may "pound" so hard in your chest that you can count its beats. Or you can count its beats by feeling your pulse. Usually the pulse rate, or number of beats per minute, is found by putting two or three fingers on the wrist just below the base of the thumb (see Chapter 12).

When you exercise, more blood is poured out into your circulation at each heartbeat than is poured out when you are resting. This means greater pressure on the walls of the blood vessels, especially the arteries. In other words, your blood pressure is increased (see Chapter 12).

More rapid heartbeats and increased blood pressure make the blood flow, or circulate, more rapidly during exercise. When a man is at rest, about a gallon of blood is circulated through his heart and blood vessels per minute. In other words, under resting conditions, about two-thirds of the entire blood supply of the body passes through the heart each minute. Under conditions of vigorous exercise, this circulation rate may be 8 or 9 times as great. Instead of traveling at the rate of 55 feet per minute in the

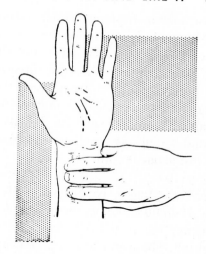

Counting the pulse rate. The pulse tells a great deal about the circulation: how fast the heart is beating, whether it is beating regularly, and whether the beat is strong or weak.

large arteries, the blood travels at the rate of 450 feet per minute there. The same amount of blood does 9 times the work by traveling 9 times as fast.

Warming up. Exercise makes a person usually feel warm and look flushed. This is because the blood vessels in his muscles and underneath his skin are enlarged, or dilated. The blood brings more food and oxygen to the muscles, and more heat is produced. A warm muscle, like a warm engine, does more work.

An athlete usually "warms up" by running a little before going into a game. The running increases muscle tonus and makes him "all ready to go."

Breathing hard after exercise. A person usually "breathes hard" after exercise such as running. Under resting conditions, only about one-fifth of the space in the lungs is used in breathing. During vigorous exercise, breathing is more rapid and nearly all the lung space is used. As a result, about 4 times as much oxygen can be taken in and 4 times as much carbon dioxide lost in one breath.

Exercise makes you perspire. Usually, running makes a person perspire. Perspiration consists chiefly of water and salt. The water dries up, or evaporates, and helps to cool the body. Taking off your sweater and fanning your face are ways of getting more air to your skin and hastening evaporation of perspiration.

The water and salt lost in perspiration must be replaced sooner or later. Many athletes believe that it is unwise to swallow any water at all during strenuous exercise—a notion that accounts for a great deal of gargling and spitting on the football field and basketball floor. It is possible that a man might drink enough to slow his movements, but there is no proof that a few swallows of water do any harm.

If too much salt is lost, muscle cramps may result. For this reason, it is wise to add a little salt to drinking water any time that you perspire a good deal.

When water is lost from the body in perspiration, less water is excreted in urine. In addition to being small in amount, the urine is likely to be highly colored after exercise. There are always colored materials in urine but they are hardly noticed when they are dissolved in a good deal of colorless water (see Chapter 17).

On a warm day, a football player may lose as much as 10 pounds of weight in hard practice or a game, all of which he will regain by the following morning simply by drinking water.

Eating and sleeping after exercise. Exercise makes a person hungry and, in general, being hungry improves digestion. However, it is not advisable to eat immediately after exercising. During digestion, an increased flow of blood is needed in the digestive tract, and this extra supply of blood cannot be brought quickly away from the muscles to the stomach and intestines.

It is just as true that exercise immediately after a meal is not a good idea. An additional supply of blood is needed in the walls of the digestive tract for an hour or two after eating and should not be taken away from there in order to supply the muscles.

Usually, the person who has had some exercise during the day sleeps well. If he exercises too much, however, he may actually be "too tired to sleep." In this case he is likely to lie awake and wonder why his heart beats so fast and why he cannot sleep. In general, exercise of the large muscles used in hiking produces the kind of tiredness that causes sleep.

Effects of regular exercise. If a person exercises day after day, the effects of this repeated exercise are different from the effects of exercising just once in awhile. Each individual mus-

Rope climbing is good exercise for people whose arm and shoulder muscles need strengthening. (Courtesy San Francisco Unified School District)

cle cell increases in size, and the muscles become larger. The larger a muscle, the stronger it is; hence, these exercised muscles can do more work.

The heart becomes larger and stronger and, hence, does not have to beat so fast. The idea that a large heart in an athlete is dangerous is not correct. There was a time when the name "athlete's heart" was given in such cases, and doubtless some perfectly healthy men have been refused life insurance because of this condition. For an athlete, a large and muscular heart is just as much a necessity as is a well-developed system of other muscles.

After a person has exercised regularly for a few weeks, he reaches the point where his pulse rate, breathing rate, and blood pressure change only slightly during exercise. They will increase a little but will return to their usual rates very quickly.

Repeated exercise improves muscle tonus in all the muscles of the body. In the digestive tract, better muscle tonus helps to improve digestion and prevents constipation (see Chapter 16).

Exercise develops coordinations; that is, all the different parts of the body learn to act together, and there are no waste movements (see Chapter 5). Observe a good athlete in any sport and note how few unnecessary movements he makes. The best sprinters, in general, run "straight down the track." To the boxer, quickness and making the right movement at the right time make the difference between winning and losing. Observe an

Folk dancing is fun, especially in the open air. It uses muscles of the arms, legs, and trunk. (Courtesy Boston Public Schools)

expert skater or a good dancer. Every movement is graceful, controlled, and coordinated.

Training. By training, we mean the regular habits of eating, rest, and exercise, which put a person in the best condition to do a job. Usually, we think of training in connection with athletic or, at least, physical jobs. It would be just as reasonable to train for an intellectual job.

In the past, some of the diets given to athletes in training were limited and often foolish. A person in training needs the same kind of good food as any healthy person. He probably needs more food than other persons, because of his heavy muscular work.

Training includes regular periods of sleep and relaxation. Exercise must be regular and increased from day to day as the person's muscles and circulation and his ability to sleep and digest his food show what he is able to do.

The results of proper training are

1) Larger, stronger muscles; ability to work over longer periods of time

2) Better coordination, with fewer unnecessary movements

3) A larger, stronger heart with a slower rate of beat

4) Lower blood pressure during exercise and a quicker return to the usual blood pressure after exercise

5) Good digestion and elimination of wastes

Harmful effects of exercise. When exercise does harm to your body, it is likely to be your heart or blood vessels that are damaged. Most high schools and colleges now require a special physical examination of all students who play on athletic teams. This examination finds the young persons who should be protected from overdoing. A physical examination before going camping or on long trips is a good investment.

In young people with healthy hearts, there is no need to fear injury to the heart from athletics. Fatigue will force a person to stop his activity before his heart can be damaged. However, there is no reason for driving oneself to the limits of endurance. One of the silliest customs in athletics is that a man running a long, hard race should force himself to finish, even though there are eight men ahead of him and the nearest one is a quarter of a mile away.

As people grow older, their hearts and blood vessels change in such a way that violent exercise is not advisable. Serious damage can be done, especially if the person has not been exercising regularly.

How much exercise? A good general rule is that a person should feel better, rather than worse, after exercise. This should be true immediately after exercise and also several hours later. If you feel exhausted, weak, or shaky immediately after, you have exercised too violently or too long. If you cannot sleep that night or feel below par the next day, you have probably done too much and should try a smaller dose of exercise the next time.

POSTURE

The way you hold your body—in short, your posture—is important, not only for your appearance, but also for your health and your self-confidence. Good posture helps you to make a good impression on other people. It is important when you are seeking a job and need to look your best. The expression that a person is "spineless" or

One result of exercise is better coordination. A good ice skater learns not to make unnecessary movements. (Courtesy Colby Junior College)

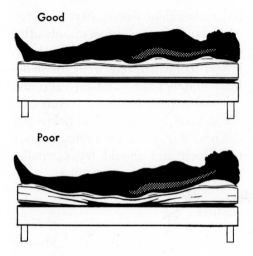

Good

Poor

has "no backbone" suggests a relationship between good posture and courage or self-confidence.

Sleep on a bed that does not sag. Lying down is the most important human posture, since it occupies about a third of the day. A sagging bed allows the muscles and ligaments of the upper side of the body to relax but stretches those on the opposite side and tends to push the abdominal organs out of place. For this reason, sleeping on the stomach almost always results in sway-back.

Many innerspring mattresses and most bedsprings have an undesirable amount of sag, especially with a heavy occupant or two, and many of them bound like a rocking horse when a person moves. The best mattress from the standpoint of posture is one that does not sag, such as a mattress made of felted cotton, hair, or both, or of sponge rubber thick enough for comfort.

Sit correctly. The sitting posture is important because of the large number of hours most people spend sitting and because of the bad effects of poor sitting posture. In the sitting position, the trunk and head should be erect and centered over the pelvis or tilted slightly forward; the hips and knees should be bent at right angles.

A good chair is one that has an opening at the lower back and gives support at the upper back. It is low enough so that the feet can rest flat on the floor and leave an inch or so between the seat and the knee.

Stand tall. For good standing posture, the body should be straight, both from the side and from the back. If you look at a person from the side, a

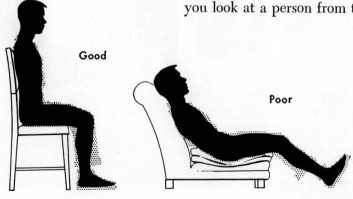

Good

Poor

line dropped from the tip of the ear should pass through the shoulder, the center of the hip, and the middle of the anklebone. The pelvis should be erect, not tilted forward. The feet and knees should point forward, and the ankles should not turn in or out. The chest should be erect, and the abdomen should be flat.

"Throwing back your shoulders" is a poor approach to good posture. "Sucking in your stomach and throwing out your chest" usually results in a stiff, tiring posture, which may be as bad as the posture it is intended to correct.

In good posture, your shoulders should rest comfortably on your chest, your spine should hold you up. You should feel tall, with the top of your head pulling away from the soles of your feet.

Walk smoothly. Correct walking is done with a smooth rhythm; the muscles contract gently and then relax. A person is walking badly when he moves with sudden jerky movements, tense (tight) muscles, and poor balance. Shoes should be comfortable and of the proper shape and fit. High heels and pointed toes prevent good walking. Clothing should be loose and light.

Why poor posture? A person with poor posture is likely to slouch when he is sitting or standing or walking. He bends forward from the hips, his abdomen sags, his chest is flat, his shoulders are bent, and his head is tilted back. Usually his muscle tonus

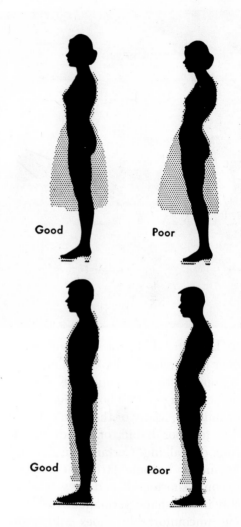

Good Poor

Good Poor

is poor, and he looks as if his muscles were soft, and they probably are.

There is no one cause of poor posture. A person who has stayed up too late too many nights will have poor posture, because he is tired. After an illness, posture is usually poor. Not having enough food or the right kind of food weakens muscles. Worry and discouragement lower muscle tonus and result in poor posture. If a boy or girl feels embarrassed and wants not

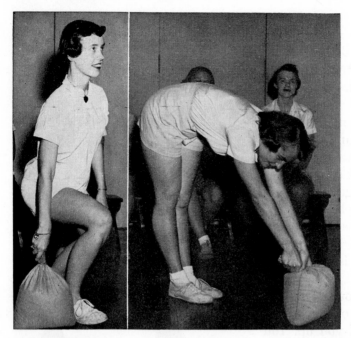

(Left) Correct way and (right) incorrect way to lift a heavy object. (Courtesy Minnesota Health and Tuberculosis Association)

to be noticed, he or she will bend over in an effort to look smaller.

Poor posture is sometimes due to defects in a person's bones, ligaments, or muscles. Many of these defects are due to poor habits of standing, sitting, or walking. Certain muscles and ligaments become stretched, others become shortened; and they tend to stay in this shape permanently. Wearing uncomfortable shoes and tight clothing or using badly designed chairs or desks may force a person to take poor postures for so long that he can no longer take good postures.

Improving posture. The first step in improving posture is to find the cause of the poor posture. Too soft a bed, too high a chair, a desk in poor light, uncomfortable clothes and shoes, can all be corrected. It is foolish to take special posture exercises for 30 minutes a day and sit in the wrong kind of chair for 4 hours a day.

Poor muscle tonus is often due to lack of sleep and exercise, a poor diet, or infections in the teeth or tonsils. One good rule for sleep is to go to bed early enough so that you feel willing to get up in the morning. Exercise should be out of doors if possible. Meals should be regular and should include a variety of foods (see Chapters 8 and 9). Regular visits to the physician and dentist will lead to the early discovery of infections.

It is important that a person have the proper feeling about himself. A tall girl must remind herself that she is more pleasant to look at when she stands up straight than when she stoops over. People pay much more attention to the way a person stands and moves than to his face or his clothes or his size.

Sometimes poor posture is due to defects in the feet, legs, or backbone. An x-ray picture is often necessary to discover these defects. They may need treatment by a physician who is a specialist in this field.

If a person is too tense, he must learn to relax. If his muscles are too relaxed, he needs exercises that will develop strength and muscle tonus.

Sports are a great help in improvement of posture. Swimming should be learned early, because it can be done with little effort, uses the trunk as well as arm and leg muscles, and develops coordination. Ball games, folk dancing, and esthetic dancing have somewhat the same effects. Climbing is good. Rock climbing involves the whole body; rope climbing strengthens arms and shoulders. Rowing is good for shoulder and trunk muscles, and running and bicycling chiefly affect leg muscles. Young people should try to engage in a number of different kinds of sports to get the best all-round development.

Reach for the sky! This is a good exercise to give you the feeling of standing tall. When you are standing in good posture, take a minute to think about how it *feels*. Try to remember the feeling many times during the day when you are walking or standing. (Courtesy Minnesota Health and Tuberculosis Association)

Posture is a 24-hour job. For most people, good posture is possible if they learn how it feels to hold the body correctly and then pay attention to how they sit, stand, and walk. Posture is a 24-hour job. It takes a long time to develop habits of poor posture and just as long to correct those bad habits.

FOOT STRAIN

The feet carry the weight of the body and also protect it from jars. A foot, like a hand, is made up of many bones and joints and can make many kinds of movements. In fact, a person without hands can learn to use his feet for writing, eating, and other complex activities.

The bones of the foot are held together by ligaments, by tendons from the strong muscles in the leg, and by the small muscles in the foot itself. The bones most important for walking and standing are arranged in two arches, which act like springs in the foot. One arch extends from the heel

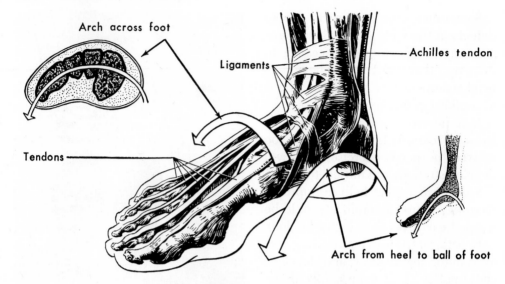

Arch across foot

Ligaments

Achilles tendon

Tendons

Arch from heel to ball of foot

to the ball of the foot; the other extends from side to side across the foot. At each step, the bones in these arches are pressed closer together, then spread apart again. Walking on feet without arches would be like riding in an automobile without springs.

Foot strain makes many people miserable and may cause pain in various parts of the body: in the big-toe joint, in either of the arches, in the calf of the leg, and in the back. It often causes general fatigue, which keeps a person from doing what he would like to do and may result in unhappiness and a "bad disposition."

Arches and flat feet. The shapes of the arches in the feet of different individuals vary; some are high, some are low. A collapsed arch, or flat foot, cannot be judged merely by looking at the foot. There may be strain with arches that appear to be of proper shape, and arches that look flat may give no difficulty.

Weak muscles, tendons, or ligaments tend to let the arches collapse. Standing on the feet for many hours, as policemen, salesgirls, and nurses must do, puts a strain on the feet. Shoes that do not fit are likely to make a person throw his weight on the inside of the foot instead of over the center where the foot is strongest. Turning the toes out also does this. High heels throw the weight forward. This puts too much strain on the arches and often twists the toes out of place. It also shortens the heel cord, or Achilles tendon. Walking barefoot or with low-heeled shoes then becomes uncomfortable.

Standing and walking. In standing, point your feet straight to the front and place them from 2 to 4 inches apart. Standing in this position is less tiring than when the feet are turned out or the ankles are allowed to bend in. As an exercise, "grip the floor" frequently with all your toes. This exercise lifts the long arch between the heel and ball of the foot and places the whole foot in a correct position.

In walking, keep the toes pointed straight ahead. The weight should come first on the heel and last on the ball of the foot. Heels and shoes worn down on the inside or the outside show that the foot is not being used correctly.

Choosing shoes. Shoes should be made so that the inner edge of the sole is straight. When the inner edge of the sole curves toward the outside of the foot, it crowds the toes and forces the big toe to the side. Shoes should be long enough and wide enough for your toes to lie straight and slightly separated. Shoes should be roomy over your toes and should fit snugly around your heel and under the long arch.

Take plenty of time when buying shoes. Try on both shoes of a pair. Shoes may seem to be comfortable when you stand with your weight upon both feet but may be very un-

comfortable when you throw all the weight upon one foot.

Foot exercises help. Exercises that strengthen the muscles of the legs and properly fitting shoes are the best treatments for foot strain.

Arch supports should not be used, unless ordered and fitted by a physician. It is much better, especially in young people, to develop muscles and connective tissue so that they can do the job of supporting the body. Arch supports usually give too much support and, hence, weaken the muscles.

The exercises suggested in the following paragraphs are simple and can be done at home. They will strengthen weakened muscles and arches and will keep healthy feet in good condition.

1) Outward roll. Remove shoes and stockings. Stand with your weight on both feet, with your feet about 6 inches apart. Roll your feet outward so that the weight of the body is supported on the outer edge of your feet. Lift the inner parts of your feet clear of the floor at each roll. Do this exercise twice daily. Work up to 20 to 30 times.

2) Rising on toes, barefoot. Stand with feet parallel, 6 to 8 inches apart. Rise on the balls of your feet, twisting heels inward and trying to grip the floor with your toes. Do this several times slowly, morning and evening. Work up to 20 to 30 times.

3) Walking on toes, barefoot. This exercise is not easy but is wonderful for strengthening the toes. Walk on tiptoe until you find you

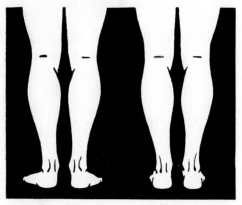

Incorrect   Correct

A good exercise for the toes. (Courtesy *Scholastic Magazines*)

must drop back on your whole foot.

4) Grasping with toes, barefoot. Grasp a large marble or a small solid rubber ball with your toes and take as many steps as possible without dropping it.

5) Ankle bending, barefoot. Sit on a chair, resting your legs on another chair of the same height, with your knees still and your feet and toes stretched out in slightly pigeon-toed position. Bend your ankles and bring your toes toward you as much as possible while you count to 4. You will feel a noticeable pulling of the calf muscles. Work up to 50 times, morning and evening.

6) Lifting arch, barefoot. Stand with feet parallel. Relax your feet and let your ankles bend in. Tighten up to a straight-leg, straight-ankle position.

This will lift your arches from the floor and hold them in the correct position. It may not be easy at first to do this exercise without lifting the inner edges of the feet, but the exercise is so helpful that the ability to do it is worth considerable effort. Work up to 20 to 30 times, morning and evening.

FATIGUE

Take a long hike, stay up late at night, study hard for an examination—the result is fatigue. You say you are tired, you want to rest, or you want to do something different. Sometimes the "let down" after exercise may be pleasant. If exercise is continued too long, fatigue may become actually painful.

Fatigue is caused by waste products, which act as toxins, or mild poisons. These waste products are always produced in muscles when they are contracting but are usually carried away by the blood stream as fast as they are formed. The toxins act first on the brain and make it painful or difficult to continue using the muscles.

Getting tired. Fatigue that is cured rather promptly by rest or by a change of activity is acute fatigue. Children fatigue more easily than adults but recover more quickly. A little child is likely to flop down on the floor for a few minutes in the middle of his play. Soldiers in wartime may become so fatigued that they drop down to rest even in dangerous places.

Extreme fatigue is never good for a person. It may be very bad for older people whose circulation does not carry away the toxins rapidly.

Sometimes infections, such as influenza, tonsillitis, and colds, cause fatigue very like that caused by physical activity. Getting well from the infection usually ends the fatigue.

Tired all the time. Some people are "tired all the time." Rest helps only a little, and they wake up in the morning almost as tired as when they went to bed. This is chronic fatigue and is a sign of general ill health.

Any disease or infection that lasts a long time and pours toxins into the blood may cause chronic fatigue. A diet that does not contain the necessary foods results in fatigue. Eyestrain, constipation, indigestion, painful feet, poor posture, disturbance of endocrine glands, and emotional strain are other common causes of chronic fatigue.

Tired all over. A person is not fatigued just in his muscles. Fatigue is a condition of the whole body. The most striking effects are upon the nervous system. A fatigued person is nervous and upset by small things of no importance. He does not pay attention, makes mistakes, and feels that life is hardly worth living. Child specialists tell us that many behavior problems in children arise from nothing more or less than fatigue. Many poor dispositions in older people have the same cause.

Fatigue causes accidents at home,

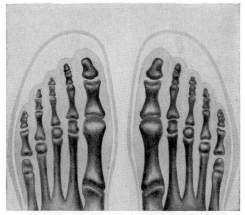
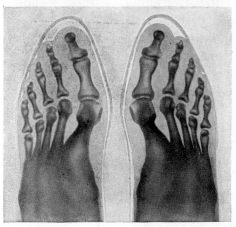

X-ray pictures will show whether shoes fit properly (top). In the bottom picture, the shoes are too narrow. (Courtesy Foot-So-Port Shoe Co.)

at work, and on the highway. A tired person does not judge distance well and does not act quickly. He should stay away from moving machinery and especially from the wheel of a car. It is estimated that more than 4000 deaths, 18,000 permanent injuries, and 400,000 temporary injuries in the United States are caused each year by accidents due to fatigue.

There is good reason to believe that

fatigue makes it possible for some diseases to get started in the body. Many people report that they "take cold" when they are tired. Fatigue also interferes with getting well. The death rate from influenza is highest among those who refuse to "give up," and a person suffering from tuberculosis who tries to build up his health by physical exercise usually is throwing away his chance to recover.

Relief of fatigue. Fatigue is only a danger signal. It means stop, look, and listen and find what is wrong. Usually rest, physical and mental, is what is needed.

The starting point for curing chronic fatigue is to find the cause. Proper shoes and exercise will relieve pain in feet. Good medical care will help in cases of disease and infection. When a person finds jobs hard that once were easy, he should see a physician and find whether the cause is in him and not in the job.

It is advisable for a person to plan his day so that he will not become fatigued. In factories, it has been found that brief rest periods reduce the number of accidents and increase the amount of work done. Recesses at school serve the same purposes, if children use them to get a change of activity. A little food eaten during rest periods is helpful. Changing jobs, that is, going from physical activity to reading or writing and then back again, keeps a person from becoming tired.

Drugs do not help. Some people try to use drugs to "cure" fatigue. They forget that fatigue is a symptom of something wrong somewhere. It is the *cause* of the fatigue that must be cured.

Fatigue has two sides. One is the real effect of the toxins on the nerves and muscles; the other is our being aware of this. Some drugs make people think they feel less tired for a short time but have no effect on the toxins of fatigue. Under the influence of these drugs, a person becomes less aware of his feelings. These drugs are called depressants. Alcohol is one of them. A small amount of alcohol may make a person think he is not tired, simply because he does not feel tired (see Chapter 21).

Other drugs are stimulants. They act on the nervous system to make it send out more and more impulses to action. Coffee has long been used as a stimulant. In some adults, the caffeine in coffee or in tea seems to cause few ill effects. In others, it causes nervousness and sleeplessness. In growing boys and girls, the effects of caffeine are more disturbing than in adults (see Chapter 21).

There are now on the market "pep pills" (benzedrine sulfate tablets). These are more powerful stimulants than caffeine and make some persons nervous and jittery for days. Students sometimes use these while studying and fail their examinations because they cannot think straight after taking this drug. Many automobile accidents have occurred when drivers have taken these pills to keep themselves awake.

Some persons who smoke feel that a cigarette or a cigar gives them relief from fatigue. Scientists offer at least a partial explanation of this. The nicotine from tobacco is absorbed into the blood stream. When it reaches the liver, it causes some of the stored sugar to be released into the blood (see Chapter 8). This sugar gives increased fuel to the muscles. The effect, of course, lasts only a short time.

REST AND SLEEP

From birth until death the body as a whole is never at rest. The heart keeps on beating, breathing goes on, all the muscles are slightly contracted, glands are secreting—all the time.

Yet all tissues and organs have their periods of rest. Even the breathing muscles rest between breaths, and the heart rests between beats. Rest is necessary to rebuild protoplasm and to get rid of the waste-product toxins that pile up during action.

Sleep is the nearest a person ever comes to absolute rest. A person who rests a great deal may get along with less sleep than other people but he must have some sleep. A person without sleep will die. The longest that anyone has been known to live without sleep is not quite 10 days. Sleep can be postponed for awhile but cannot be done away with completely.

How much sleep? A person should sleep enough to feel rested. If he works hard, he needs more sleep than if he rests for part of the day. A person who is excitable needs more sleep than others, because he is usually very active while he is awake. A person in poor health or suffering from chronic fatigue must give his tissues longer periods of rest.

A baby under 1 month of age sleeps from 21 to 23 hours a day. Most children 6 to 8 years old need about 12 hours of sleep. A boy or girl from 13 to 15 requires from 9 to 10 hours. During times of rapid growth, young people need more sleep than when they were younger but growing more slowly. For the average person of middle age, the usual requirement is about 8 hours. With the approach of old age, the sleep requirement again increases.

Sleep well. We keep on responding to stimuli from the outside, such as noises, light, and pressures, even when asleep. For restful sleep, it is best to have quiet and darkness. The bed should be comfortable. A cool but not cold temperature is desirable. Some people insist on opening all the windows, then use a great deal of their energy supporting heavy covers and shivering to keep warm. In mild weather, a window should be open somewhere or some other way should be provided for keeping the air circulating, but there should not be a wind blowing through the bedroom.

It has been supposed that restful sleep is quiet. "Sleeping like a log" suggests a perfect night. Inquisitive scientists, however, have taken pictures and electric recordings of what happens in sleep. They have found that a sound sleeper rarely remains in

These girls are learning that they can work more comfortably if they are in good posture. They feel more confidence in themselves, too. (Courtesy Chicago Public Schools)

one position for more than 10 to 15 minutes at a time. He shifts his arms and legs; he tosses and rolls about all night long.

Sleep is deepest during the second and third hours after going to bed and becomes lighter hour by hour until time for waking. Excitement, worry, and dreams keep the muscles active and, hence, make sleep less restful. A little quiet reading or talk before going to bed makes for better sleep than does excitement and noise. Romping before bedtime is fun but is not good for sleep. Thrilling television and radio programs in the evening hours often make boys and girls too excited to sleep.

Insomnia. Young people usually can sleep if they are physically tired and not too excited. Older people are sometimes troubled with sleeplessness, or insomnia.

The start of insomnia is usually nervousness, worry, or pain. Then the person seems to "get the habit" of staying awake instead of sleeping. Usually he worries about it and becomes so afraid that he is not going to sleep that his fear keeps him awake.

Anyone can learn to relax and so get rest in bed, even though he is not sleeping. Deliberately thinking about relaxing the muscles—eyes, jaws, neck, and so on down to the feet—will let you sink into the bed and rest.

Thinking of something pleasant but not exciting that you have read or done is helpful. "Counting sheep" is a method of shutting out unpleasant thoughts. So is listening to quiet music.

Too much fatigue makes a person restless, but moderate fatigue helps sleep. A leisurely walk may be all that is necessary. A warm bath, not a hot one, and a glass of warm milk at bedtime aid relaxation of muscles. Reading something that leads the thoughts away from the worries of the day may be helpful. For some people, this is poetry; for others, an old story that they know and love; for others, detective stories.

Sleep-producing drugs have been used for years by physicians to control pain. Recently a group of these, the barbiturates, have been used by many people who are trying to cure their own insomnia. If taken regularly, these can be harmful (see Chapters 18 and 21). Our bodies are built to make their own adjustments of activity and rest. Stimulating them through the day with coffee, tobacco, and excitement to overactivity, then putting them to sleep at night with drugs, can lead only to trouble.

YOUR HEALTH INVENTORY

A businessman stops his work once in awhile to take an inventory. This inventory is a checkup, an examination, to find out what stock he has on hand and what things he needs to buy. The inventory tells him where he stands in business and helps him plan what he should do in the future. In many businesses, an inventory is taken once a year. Sometimes checks are made much oftener, every few months or every few weeks, to find whether business is going as planned.

You are near the beginning of a year's work. How about a health inventory?

What is a health inventory? Many people think of a health inventory, or a health examination, as a way of finding something wrong. At your age, this is not the most important purpose of an examination. Adolescents are usually healthy, as is shown in Chapter 2. Your job is to stay healthy, now and in the future. A health examination is a checkup to find how well you are progressing and whether you can do anything that will help you to get along even better. How physically fit are you now? What next?

Making a good health examination requires the work of experts, usually a physician and nurses, laboratory workers, and other helpers for the physician. It is not easy to understand how your body functions. To make the examination demands long training and experience. But anyone can understand something about a health examination, enough to do what is asked of him during the examination and to use the results intelligently.

This is not the place to give a careful description of a health examination. That will be done in Chapter 26, after you have studied the various parts of the body and how they function. Look over Chapter 26 now to get some idea of what you need to know to understand a health examination and keep the main points in mind as you read through the rest of this book.

But you should not wait to have an examination until you understand all about it. You may have had a school health examination at the beginning of the year. Or you may have had a checkup in your physician's office last summer before you started to school. School examinations are useful but they do not take the place of a thorough examination given by a physician in his office. Families and physicians are responsible for getting thorough examinations made. If you have never had one, or if you have not had one within a year, try to have one now. It is a good start for a school year.

What you learn from a health inventory. At your age, it is important to know how your body is growing. Perhaps you are shooting up in height. And what about your weight? Are your bones well developed? Are your muscles, especially your heart, keeping up with your bones? These are some of the questions your health inventory should answer.

Part of the health examination consists of asking about your habits of eating, sleeping, working, sitting, studying, and all the other routine things you do. These are considered in relation to your growth, your posture, and your general well-being. Perhaps you need a few more vitamins in your diet than most people;

perhaps you should wear shoes a little different from those that other people wear; perhaps you should change your study habits.

Every person is different from every other person. There are some general instructions for eating, sleeping, exercising, and so on, but they do not fit everyone. What do *you* need to keep you strong and well?

Almost everyone has minor health problems. A health examination helps to find them and gives some direction on what to do about them. Poor posture, for example, is fairly common, especially among young people who are growing rapidly. Earlier in this chapter, it was pointed out that you must find the cause of poor posture before you can correct it. Perhaps you have some cavities in your teeth; they may be too small to be painful but they need attention. Perhaps you have acne and need help in clearing it up. Perhaps you get tired too easily. Your health examination may tell you why and what you can do about it.

Some health difficulties cannot be completely corrected, but you can learn to live with them if you know about them and take them into account in planning your life. If your vision is not quite as good as other people's, you may need glasses or perhaps you should be extra careful in getting enough light when you study. You should know about any defects in vision before you decide to go into certain vocations, such as aviation or watchmaking. If you have a slight hearing problem, it may not interfere with ordinary living but may help you decide not to be a telephone operator.

Like any other inventory, a health examination looks to the past and then to the future. You learn what progress you are making by looking back to the past. The physician who gives your examination keeps careful records of his findings, so that they can be consulted again and again. He puts into the records what he can find by direct examination and what you and your parents can tell him about your habits, your health in the past, and your family background. Your history of good health or of illnesses and injuries helps him to understand you better now. Your family background tells something about your heredity and your living conditions up to the present.

Use of your health inventory. The person most interested in your health inventory is *you*. You decide what you will do and when, what you will eat, when you will go to sleep, when you will go to the dentist, how long and how hard you will work and play. You need to know your strong points and your weak points, if you are to make these decisions intelligently.

It is also important that parents and teachers know the results of your health inventory. They cannot be fair to you, no matter how much they want to be, unless they know what you are able to do and what you cannot do. This is one reason why many schools give school health examinations. Teachers should know how well their students see and hear before they assign seats or give lessons that require listening or reading or writing. They must know whether students are in good physical condition before telling them to work faster or allowing them to play long and hard.

All the other chapters in this book, and especially Chapter 26, give you information to help you understand your health inventory better. All will help you keep yourself physically and mentally fit.

SO WHAT?

Life looks rosy when we are mentally and physically fit for the things that we want to do; and

Physical fitness means pep, bounce, and energy for work and for fun; and

Exercise, rest, and good posture are necessary to be physically fit; and

Good posture improves appearance, self-confidence, and attractiveness; and

Feet are the foundation of good posture; and

Fatigue contributes to poor posture, to inefficiency, and to poor health;

So, it is worth your while to

Learn sports that combine exercise and fun; and

Make good posture a habit when standing, sitting, lying down or walking; and

Treat your feet properly, with well-fitting shoes and exercises for weak arches; and

Get enough rest to start each day refreshed; and

Get advice from a physician if fatigue hangs on in spite of rest and proper exercise.

CHECKING UP

1. What happens to your circulation when you exercise?
2. Why is it well to add a little salt to your drinking water when you are hot and perspire a good deal?
3. Why should you not exercise immediately before or after eating?
4. How does regular exercise affect the body?
5. What does training include in addition to regular exercise?
6. What is good posture in sleeping? in sitting? in standing? in walking?
7. List common causes of poor posture. How can each be corrected?
8. How many arches are there in the foot? Where are they? What are causes of collapsed arches, or flat feet? Why are arch supports usually a poor way of correcting flat feet?
9. Give rules for choosing shoes.
10. What is the difference between acute fatigue and chronic fatigue?
11. Why is fatigue considered only a danger signal?
12. Do drugs cure fatigue? Explain.
13. How can a person tell whether he is getting enough sleep?
14. What are common causes of poor sleep?
15. Why is it wise to have a health examination regularly?
16. Who should be most interested in the results of your health examination? Why?

THINGS TO DO

1. Run around the building or take some other vigorous exercise. Can you describe the changes that take place in your body and give the reasons for them?

2. Practice counting pulse rates until you are sure you can do it correctly. Taking the pulse for 2 half-minutes is better than for 1 full minute. If your count for the 2 half-minutes is very different, do it again.

3. Work in pairs. Take your partner's pulse when he is sitting quietly. Let him exercise for 2 minutes. Take his pulse again. Let him sit quietly for 2 minutes. Take his pulse again. How much time is required for the pulse to get back to what it was before exercise?

4. Take the pulse of a trained athlete. Let him exercise for 2 minutes. Find how much time is required for his pulse to get back to what it was before exercise.

5. Count the number of breaths your partner takes in 1 minute while sitting quietly. Let him exercise for 2 or 3 minutes. Count the number of breaths he takes in 1 minute. How much time is required for his breathing to get back to what it was before exercising? Do the same for a trained athlete.

6. To find how evaporation of perspiration cools the skin, wet a piece of cotton and place it on the bulb of a thermometer. What happens to the mercury? Try fanning the cotton and see whether this hastens or slows cooling.

7. Ask a physical-education teacher to tell the class about training rules.

8. Keep a record of your outdoor exercise for a week. Do the boys or the girls in your class get more exercise?

9. Study the chairs in your classroom. Can you sit back in the seat with your feet flat on the floor? Is the desk top too high or too low for comfort? Is your posture good while reading or writing?

10. Find whether the chair in which you read and study at home is low enough. Will a footstool or a pile of magazines on the floor make it more comfortable?

11. Stand in your usual posture. Then stand in your best possible posture. What is the difference between the two?

12. Ask a physical-education teacher to tell the class how to improve posture.

13. Wet your feet and stand for a moment on a piece of brown

paper. Can you find from the outline where the arches are?

14. Stand on a piece of paper in your bare feet and trace around your feet. Cut out the outlines. Put your shoes on a piece of paper and cut around them. Put the two together to get some idea whether your shoes are the right size and shape.

15. Examine your shoes. Do they have a straight inner line? Are the heels worn evenly? on the inner side? on the outer side? Are the soles worn evenly? This will tell you how you carry your weight in walking.

16. Watch ten people walking. How many walk with toes in? with toes out? with toes pointing straight ahead? Compare notes with other students in your class.

17. Look at the backs of the feet of ten people walking. In how many are the heels worn on the inner side? on the outer side?

18. Stand against a wall with your feet about 4 inches from the wall. Straighten your back against the wall. Place your head against the wall but do not tilt it. Now walk away trying to hold your back straight, chest up, and chin in.

19. When you go to a movie, watch the way the actresses walk and stand.

20. Find at what hour students in the class go to bed on school nights; on weekends. Find when they get up and how many hours of sleep they have. Keep a record for a week of your sleep. Is there a relationship between how you feel and your sleep?

21. Make a collection of shoes for exhibit: high heeled, buttoned, pointed toes, flats, and so forth; or shoes from different countries (or their pictures): wooden shoes, Indian moccasins, and so forth.

CHAPTER 8   Nutrition and You

"We were half-dead. We did not shift our eyes around to look at things; that took too much effort."[1] A young man named Kenneth Tuttle made these remarks. He and 35 other young men had gone without food to find what happens to a starving person.

Most of us take food for granted. So did these young fellows before they tried doing without it. They will never take it for granted again. They know that when you do not have food, you look and feel old and sick. They know that you dream about food, good solid food, such as meat and bread. They know that you are irritable and quarrel even with your best friends.

Everyone knows that a human being will die if he does not have enough food. What many people do not know is that a human being will die if he does not have the right kind of food.

You do not have to choose between starving to death and not starving to death. You do have to choose whether you will eat the kinds of food that will build good protoplasm and give you pep and energy, or whether you will eat the kinds that build poor tissues and give you only enough energy to creep around.

NUTRITION AND NUTRIENTS

Taking food into your body and using it is nutrition. In almost every chapter in this book, there is some statement about nutrition and what food does for you.

In Chapter 5, for example, the question is asked: What is a food? The answer is that foods are substances that provide energy for the activities of your body, supply materials needed to build protoplasm, and contain substances that make the processes of your metabolism run smoothly. In Chapter 7, you are told several times that you need "good" food or the "proper" food if you are to keep physically fit.

There are thousands of foods in the world. How can you know which

[1] *Minneapolis Tribune*, November 25 and 26, 1946.

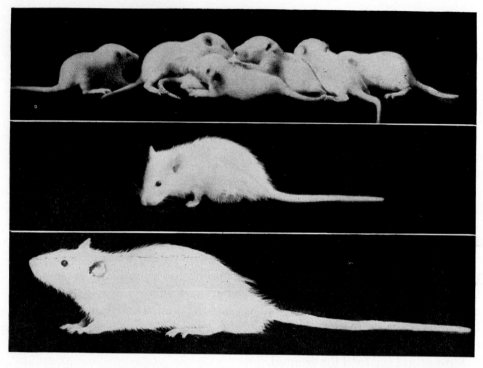

Growth is a measure of good nutrition. Rats are used for nutrition studies because they will eat the same foods that human beings do and quickly show the effect of good and bad diets. A rat grows up 30 times as fast as a child and usually lives less than 3 years. (Top) Two weeks old, each rat weighs 22 grams. Note the soft, fine hair and plump, well-shaped bodies. (Center) Four weeks old, rat weighs 47 grams. Fur and body shape are good. Appears bright and lively. (Bottom) Twelve weeks old, mature rat weighs 193 grams. Weight, posture, shape, fur, eyes—all show signs of good nutrition. (Courtesy Bureau of Human Nutrition and Home Economics, U.S. Department of Agriculture)

are the "good" foods, the ones that give you energy and building materials and regulate your metabolic processes? This chapter and Chapter 9 try to answer these questions for you and show you how to choose foods for breakfast, lunch, dinner, and between-meal snacks.

Nutrients. First of all, you must know something about nutrients. Different foods do different things for you. Sugar, for example, provides energy. Fat, also, provides energy but not so quickly as sugar. Starches provide energy more quickly than fat but not so quickly as sugar. Sugars and starches are called carbohydrates. Carbohydrates and fats are two kinds of nutrients.

In Chapter 6, you learn that calcium and phosphorus are necessary for good bone growth. Calcium and phosphorus are minerals. Minerals are another kind of nutrient. They are needed to build protoplasm.

Chapter 6 also mentions vitamin D. Vitamins are nutrients. Vitamins and some of the minerals help regulate body processes.

Another kind of nutrient is protein. It is necessary for building protoplasm. It also provides energy. Water is also necessary for life but is not called a nutrient.

Good foods, then, are those that give you the nutrients you need, in the proper amounts.

SUPPLYING ENERGY FOR THE BODY

Your body is a human machine. It takes in foods that contain energy, then releases this energy. It releases the energy by oxidizing the protoplasm built from foods (see Chapter 5).

Your body uses energy even when you are asleep. Your heart muscles must keep contracting, your muscles of breathing must act, your glands are always secreting, and heat is always being given off.

When you are awake, you use still more energy, in sitting up, in talking, in walking, in working. In cold weather, you use more energy to keep warm than you do in hot weather. All the energy you use comes from the food you eat.

Basal metabolism. When you are awake but are resting quietly, you are using a little more energy than when you are asleep. This is called your basal use of energy. The amount used

in 1 hour for each pound of body weight is called your basal metabolic rate, or B.M.R. The basal metabolic rate tells something of how well a person is using the food he eats. It is especially valuable in studying the function of the thyroid and other endocrine glands (see Chapters 5, 22, and 26).

Calories. The energy contained in (or provided by) foods is measured in calories. Children need more calories per pound of body weight than adults do, because they are using energy in growing and because they are usually more active than adults.

Boys and girls in their teens need as much food as adults, or more. Sometimes people seem surprised when a boy eats as much as his father. Probably, we should be surprised when a father eats as much as his teenage son.

Tall, slender persons need more calories per pound than short, fat persons. The reason is that they have a larger body surface and give off more heat than do short, fat persons. Boys and men usually need more calories than do girls and women.

Carbohydrates, fats, and proteins supply energy. Carbohydrates, fats, and proteins are the only nutrients that supply energy. Of these, fats contain the most energy, even though they do not release it as quickly as carbohydrates do. For this reason, fatty foods are useful when people need much energy, in winter, for example, or when they work hard.

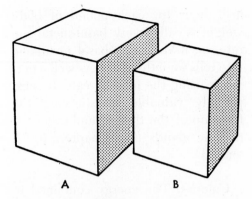

(A) Calories supplied by an ounce of fat.
(B) Calories supplied by an ounce of protein or carbohydrate.

An ounce of fat will supply 270 calories for your body. An ounce of protein or carbohydrate will supply less than half that amount, only 120 calories.

Carbohydrates do not supply as much energy as fats do, but they are more easily used by your body. This is especially true for the sugars. We say that sugar gives "quick" energy.

Table 2. Functions of Nutrients

Nutrients	Functions		
	Furnish energy	Build and repair the body	Regulate body processes
Carbohydrates	x		
Fats	x		
Proteins	x	x	x
Minerals		x	x
Vitamins		x	x
Water			x
Bulk, roughage*			x

* Bulk, or roughage, is not a nutrient but is included in this table because it assists in the digestion of food.

Proteins supply as much energy as the carbohydrates, but they are not as easily used in your body. Important protein foods are meat, eggs, cheese, and fish. Foods that supply proteins are more expensive than carbohydrates, but you must have some protein in your diet to build protoplasm. To supply your needs for energy, it is less expensive to use carbohydrates and fats than to use protein foods.

Carbohydrates come mainly from plants. Foods with a sweet taste contain sugar. All vegetables contain some starch. The best sources of starch are vegetable seeds with little water in them, such as wheat and other cereals, root vegetables like potatoes, and dried peas and beans.

The woody part of cereals, vegetables, and fruits is a carbohydrate called cellulose. Human beings do not digest cellulose, but it is useful because it is bulky and stimulates the muscles in the digestive tract to contract.

Fats come from both plants and animals. Cream, butter, margarine, fat meat, fish oils, and nuts contain fat.

Storing energy. When you take in more food than you need, you store some of it. Between meals, you store extra food chiefly in the liver as a carbohydrate, called glycogen, or animal starch. Over longer periods of time, you store extra food as fat. This fat is chiefly under the skin, in the muscles, and within the great sheets of connective tissue in the abdominal cavity.

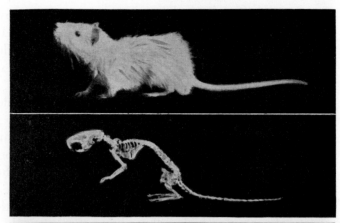

Food makes the difference in these twin rats. (Top) This rat ate only meat, potatoes, bread, and butter. It has poor fur and weighs only 89 grams. Bones show that diet was poor, lacking calcium and vitamins. (Bottom) This rat ate plenty of milk and vegetables, besides meat, potatoes, bread, and butter. It weighs 194 grams. Skeleton shows that diet was good. Bones are strong and well formed. (Courtesy Bureau of Human Nutrition and Home Economics, U.S. Department of Agriculture)

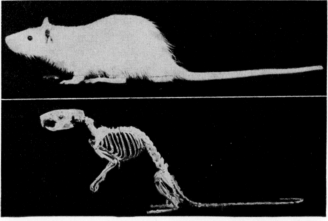

When people talk about certain foods being fattening, they are speaking carelessly. The right amount of food is never fattening. When a person eats too much food, the surplus is stored as fat.

MATERIALS NEEDED FOR GROWTH AND REPAIR

The basic building materials for your body are proteins, minerals, and water. These are needed for growth during your earlier years and for repair throughout life.

Proteins. Proteins are more complicated substances than are carbohydrates and fats. They contain nitrogen, which is necessary for the building of protoplasm (see Chapter 5).

During digestion, proteins are broken down into simpler substances, the amino acids. The body then uses these amino acids to build its own tissues. Put together in certain combinations, the amino acids form muscle tissue. Other combinations of amino acids form brain tissue. Still other combinations form skin, gland, and the other tissues.

Protein foods come from both animals and plants. Animal proteins are found in milk, cheese, eggs, meat, fish, and poultry. These proteins contain all the amino acids needed by your body and are called complete proteins.

Most plant proteins—from grains, nuts, beans, peas, and corn—contain certain amino acids but lack others. These are called incomplete proteins. People who eat only vegetables must be careful to include in their diets a variety of proteins which will provide all the needed amino acids. Vegetarians who use milk and eggs get complete proteins in those foods. Soybeans also provide complete proteins.

Minerals. The tissues of your body need a number of minerals, which must be supplied in the diet. Of these, the ones needed in largest amount are calcium and phosphorus for bones and teeth (see Chapters 6 and 15). A small amount of calcium in the blood helps to clot the blood when there is a cut or much bleeding and keeps the muscles from going into spasms of contraction.

You get most of your calcium and phosphorus from milk, milk products, and leafy vegetables. Meat, molasses, nuts, beans, broccoli, and certain other vegetables are also fairly good sources of calcium.

Iron is needed for the formation of red blood cells (Chapter 11). The foods richest in iron are liver, meat, eggs, green leafy vegetables, beans, molasses, nuts, and whole-wheat bread and cereals. Fluorine is needed for good tooth growth (Chapter 15).

Salts of many kinds are used in making blood, lymph, digestive juices, and other fluids and tissues of the body. These salts are usually provided in sufficient quantities by the meat, fish, vegetables, and common table salt that we eat.

A very small amount of iodine is necessary for the proper functioning of one of the endocrine glands, the thyroid. The total amount of iodine needed in the human body at any time is only about one-tenth of the amount contained in one drop of tincture of iodine. If less than this is available, the thyroid gland enlarges to form a goiter. Too little iodine in children's diets stunts both physical and mental growth (see Chapter 22).

Sea water, sea plants, and sea foods, such as fish, contain a good deal of iodine. In many inland regions, iodine salts have been washed out of the soil. The result is lack of iodine in drinking water and in the plants and animals grown on that soil.

Sea foods and iodized salt are good sources of iodine in the diet. In some communities where the soil is poor in iodine, a small amount of an iodine compound is added to the water supply.

Water. A man can live for a month or longer without food but will die within a few days if he does not have water. About 80 percent of the soft tissues of the body are water. The water in the blood carries food to the tissues and carries wastes away from them. As perspiration, it helps to regulate body temperature. In the diges-

All these foods contain protein. (Courtesy National Dairy Council)

tive juices, water carries the enzymes, which are substances that digest food.

You lose water from your body in urine, in perspiration, and in moist air breathed out of your lungs. How much water a person should drink every day depends on how much he loses and how much he gets in his food. Hot weather and exercise increase perspiration and the need for water.

REGULATING BODY PROCESSES

Some nutrients have their greatest value in regulating the many bodily processes. This is true for certain minerals, such as calcium and iodine, discussed in preceding paragraphs. It is even more true for the vitamins.

Vitamins. The term *vitamin* means something necessary for life. The exact way in which vitamins influence nutrition is not known, but we know some of the harmful effects of not having enough of them.

The letters A, B, C, D, were given as names to the first vitamins discovered. The newer names of vitamins are their chemical names. These are replacing the alphabetical names, but at present many vitamins are called by two or more names.

No one knows how many vitamins there are. Probably some have not yet been discovered. Most foods that contain vitamins A, B, C, and D also contain the other needed vitamins.

Vitamin A. Vitamin A is soluble in fat; that is, it will dissolve in fat. It is found in fish oils (cod-liver oil, halibut-liver oil), egg yolks, liver, butter,

All these foods contain vitamin A. (Courtesy National Dairy Council)

cheese, and cream. In addition, your body can build vitamin A from a substance called carotene. This is the yellow coloring matter, or pigment, in carrots, sweetpotatoes, squash, apricots, and other yellow fruits and vegetables. It is found, too, in green vegetables, such as peppers and peas, although in these the yellow color is covered up by green pigment. In general, the *colorful* foods contain vitamin A, and the deeper their color, the greater their vitamin-A content. Vitamin A is not destroyed by ordinary cooking or canning.

Lack of vitamin A. One of the first effects of deficiency in—that is, lack of—vitamin A is night blindness— that is, difficulty in seeing in dim light. Some accidents at night are probably the result of night blindness of drivers. It is said that many truck-drivers eat raw carrots between meals to improve their vision at night.

High-school and college students often lack vitamin A in their diets.

One study of college students showed evidence of vitamin-A deficiency in one-third of the group. Many of them reported that they had difficulty in finding seats in dimly lighted movie houses, had to cling to their friends, and had to wait a long while before they could find their way alone. They also were made uncomfortable by bright lights. Dryness and roughness of the skin often accompany night blindness.

A more serious effect of vitamin-A deficiency is a disease of the eyes called xerophthalmia. Many cases of this disease occurred among children of Denmark during World War I when Danish farmers were exporting most of their butter and cream to England. When the government limited the amount of butter to be exported and the Danish people, therefore, ate more of it, the children recovered. It is said that the Chinese have used chicken livers and eel fat to cure xerophthalmia. Both of these foods contain vitamin A, although the

Chinese who used them probably did not know this.

Vitamin A has been called the "growth" vitamin and the "anti-infective" vitamin. Neither term is accurate. Vitamin A is essential for growth but so are other vitamins. If an animal does not have enough vitamin A in its diet, it is likely to develop infections of various kinds. Giving the animal more vitamin A will reduce the infections. On the other hand, if its diet already contains enough vitamin A, adding more will not further increase resistance to infection. What has been found out for animals seems to be true for human beings.

It is not known exactly how much vitamin A is needed by the human body. For growing children, the amount of it obtained by daily use of a quart of milk, an egg, green and yellow vegetables, butter, and ½ teaspoonful of cod-liver oil seems adequate. Fortified margarine is vegetable fat to which vitamin A has been added. Most adults require only a pint of milk to meet their vitamin-A needs.

Vitamin B. In 1897, a Dutch physician discovered that by feeding pigeons nothing but rice from which the husks had been removed—that is, polished rice—he could produce beriberi, a disease marked by extreme weakness and paralysis. He found, also, that he could cure the disease by adding whole-grain cereals, milk, and certain fresh fruits and vegetables to this diet of polished rice. The substance in these foods that prevented or cured beriberi was later named vitamin B.

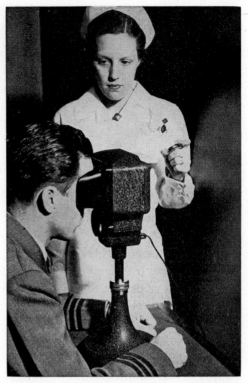

Airplane pilots are tested to find how well they see in dim light. (Courtesy United Air Lines)

Beriberi has been a widespread disease among the people of the Orient who live almost entirely on rice.

It is now known that the substance called vitamin B really includes several vitamins. All of these together are called the vitamin-B complex. Most important of the B group are thiamine (or vitamin B_1), riboflavin (or vitamin B_2 or G), and niacin (or nicotinic acid).

In general, all members of the vitamin-B complex are widely distributed in what are called natural foods. These are foods that have not been refined. A diet containing plenty of whole-grain cereals, lean meat and

All these foods contain vitamin B. (Courtesy National Dairy Council)

liver, milk, and vegetables usually provides enough vitamin B.

Thiamine improves digestion, prevents fatigue, improves the condition of the nerves, and increases muscle tonus. It is often called the "morale" or "pep" vitamin. The diets of most people in this country contain enough thiamine to prevent beriberi. However, many people who are tired and irritable could easily feel better and be healthier and happier if they ate more foods containing thiamine.

Thiamine must be included in the daily diet, since very little is stored in the body. Growing children, adolescents, and athletes need more than other people. The best sources of thiamine are whole-grain cereals, enriched bread, liver, lean meat, yeast, and nuts.

Riboflavin occurs in most foods that contain thiamine. Especially good sources are liver, milk, and lean meat. Lack of this vitamin may cause loss of hair, soreness of the lips and tongue, and cracks at the corner of the mouth.

Niacin was first called the pellagra-preventing, or P-P, vitamin. Pellagra is a disease of people on a very poor diet. In this country, it occurs chiefly among the people who live on a diet of meal (corn meal), meat (salt pork), and molasses.

Some skin rashes and digestive disturbances are due to lack of niacin. So, too, are some cases of loss of appetite, weakness, and failure to grow. Excellent sources of niacin are liver, yeast, and peanut butter.

Enriched bread and flour. When people ground their own flour and cereals, they used the whole grains and obtained from them vitamins and minerals that are lost in the milling of today. The vitamins and minerals are contained in the outer covering and the germ of the grains. These are the parts that are removed from the more refined flours.

In order to restore at least some of the lost nutrients, many millers add thiamine, riboflavin, niacin, and iron to white flour. Breads and other bak-

All these foods contain vitamin C. (Courtesy National Dairy Council)

ery products made from this enriched flour are an important source of these nutrients. However, 100-percent whole-wheat flour and whole-wheat cereals are still to be preferred, because they contain not only all the known but possibly some unknown nutrients present in natural grain.

Vitamin C. Vitamin C, or ascorbic acid, was recognized as necessary for health many years before anyone heard of vitamins. This happened because sailors and others, who were cut off for long periods of time from supplies of fresh food, developed weakness, suffered pain in their legs and joints, had severe bleeding from the gums, and sometimes lost their teeth. This condition was called scurvy. Death sometimes occurred if fresh food was not obtained.

In the year 1600, the crew of a ship sailing from England to India was kept free of scurvy by the use of lemon juice. One hundred fifty years later, the British Navy required that every sailor be given a daily ration of lemon juice. At that time, lemons were called limes. For this reason, British sailors were nicknamed "limeys."

It has since been discovered that vitamin C is contained in most fresh fruits and vegetables. Scurvy rarely occurs in this country. Mild degrees of vitamin-C deficiency, however, are rather common.

Raw citrus fruits (oranges, tangerines, grapefruit, lemons, and limes) are the richest common sources of vitamin C. Tomato juice contains about half as much as does orange juice. Potatoes contain some vitamin C, and some people eat enough of them to supply the body's needs during the winter months. Cabbage is a good source of vitamin C.

Vitamin C is rapidly destroyed by exposure to the air and by heat. Raw vegetables and fruits yield more vitamin C than these same foods do when cooked. Rapidly frozen foods retain most of their vitamin C. Commercial processes of canning have been developed to preserve the vitamin C in tomatoes and tomato juice and in orange, grapefruit, and pineapple juices. These canned products lose their vitamin content with time and should be used within a year of canning.

Ascorbic acid is the chemical name of vitamin C. This is now manufactured in quantity and is sold in various vitamin pills and preparations.

Vitamin D. The body must have vitamin D to build bones and teeth. This vitamin is, therefore, especially important during the years of growth.

A deficiency in vitamin D causes rickets (see Chapter 6). A child with rickets, in addition to having poorly formed bones, is irritable, restless, anemic, and tires easily.

The common foods contain very little vitamin D. The average diet is more likely to be deficient in vitamin D than in any other vitamin. Egg yolk, liver, and fish contain small amounts. The richest natural source is oil from fish livers.

Vitamin D is produced by the action of the ultraviolet light in sunshine on certain oils. For this reason, it is sometimes called the "sunshine" vitamin. These oils are present in your skin and in milk and some other foods. Foods that have been exposed to ultraviolet light are called irradiated foods. They contain vitamin D. Milk ordinarily contains very little vitamin D, but milk that has been irradiated is a good source of this important vitamin. In northern climates, during the months from October to April, cod-liver or halibut-liver oil, a good number of eggs, and vitamin-enriched milk should be included in the diet, particularly of children.

Other vitamins. Vitamin E, vitamin K, vitamin L, and vitamin T are among the other vitamins or vitamin-like substances that have been discovered. Some of these are clearly of importance in human nutrition; the others we know less about. In general, these vitamins occur in so many foods that there is little or no chance of anyone suffering from serious deficiencies in them.

Vitamin pills. Nowadays many vitamins are prepared in the form of pills or liquids and are offered for sale in drugstores, department stores, and grocery stores. These may be prescribed by physicians and are of great value in the treatment of certain conditions.

Most vitamin preparations, however, are purchased directly by the public. Advertisements in magazines, newspapers, and over the radio and television suggest that people should take this or that vitamin preparation for growth, good teeth, and prevention of colds, nervousness, and fatigue. Some are included in cosmetics for the supposed purpose of beautifying the skin. This is especially ridiculous, since vitamins are not absorbed through the skin. People follow these suggestions because they have heard that vitamins are important for health.

Probably most of these vitamin preparations do no harm, although it is possible to take more vitamin A or vitamin D than is good for a person.

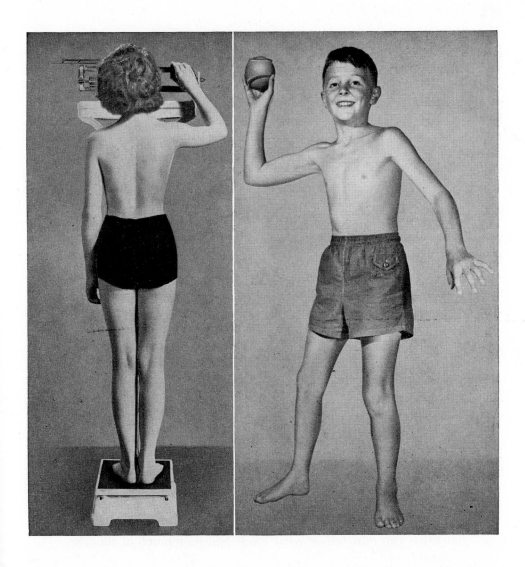

Signs of a well-built body: Proper weight for your height and age. Hair naturally glossy; not dry or brittle. Eyes bright and keen. Skin clear; healthy color. Jaw wide enough for even teeth. Shoulders even; not pushed back. Chest broad; able to expand generously. Nails smooth; not ridged or brittle. Abdomen flat; does not sag or bulge. Spine straight; no side curves. Entire body well proportioned; not too thin; enough fat for symmetry. Legs straight; knees touch without bumping. Muscles smooth and firm; not overdeveloped. Feet well arched; toes well spaced. (Courtesy California Fruit Growers Exchange)

The misfortune is that the American people waste millions of dollars each year upon vitamins that they do not need. Another misfortune is that people depend on vitamin pills and neglect those foods that contain not only the vitamins but other nutrients, some known, some unknown, and all valuable in nutrition.

SIGNS OF GOOD NUTRITION

What are the signs of good nutrition? In young people, steady growth is one sign. It is not important whether you are as tall and heavy as other people. It is important that you gain at your own rate until you have reached your adult height and weight.

Other signs of good nutrition are shown in your appearance. Shining hair, bright eyes, and a clear skin show that you are getting and using the proper food, especially the vitamins and minerals. Muscle tonus, also, depends on nutrition. A person with good nutrition can sit and stand and walk without slumping.

Good nutrition is shown in the way you feel. Sleeping well and awakening refreshed, enjoying life, and facing the world with a smile, feeling full of energy and mentally alert, all these are signs that you are well nourished.

Good nutrition does not solve the problems of living. It does, however, make it easier for us to solve our own problems. In this country, everyone has his own personal problems and, as a nation, we have some of the greatest problems the world has ever known. If everyone could have the right kinds of food, it would be a step in the direction of making all of us stronger, happier, and more able to make the world a better place in which to live.

SO WHAT?

Good nutrition is necessary for proper growth and good health; and

Scientists can now tell us what foods and how much of them we should eat;

So, you should know

Something about the proteins, carbohydrates, fats, vitamins, and minerals of foods; and

What use your body makes of each of these food substances; and

What happens if you do not have enough of them; and

What are the best food sources from which to obtain them; and

Whether it is necessary to spend money for "drugstore" vitamins and other food concentrates.

CHECKING UP

1. What are the three functions that foods serve in your body?
2. List the kinds of nutrients.
3. In terms of nutrients, what are good foods? poor foods?
4. What are calories?
5. Why do children need more calories per pound than their parents do?
6. Which nutrients supply energy?
7. What is cellulose? Why is it important to include some cellulose in your diet?
8. "No food is fattening." "All foods are fattening." What is the basic truth in these two statements?
9. What are complete proteins? incomplete proteins? Why is it difficult for a person who eats only vegetables to get a good diet?
10. Why are milk and eggs a valuable addition to the diet of a vegetarian?
11. Of what value is calcium in the body? iron? fluorine? iodine?
12. Why should you drink more water in hot weather than in cold weather?
13. Do you think there are vitamins we do not yet know about? Give reasons for your answer.
14. Which foods contain large amounts of vitamin A? Why is it important that you have enough vitamin A in your diet? What are some results of not eating enough foods containing vitamin A?
15. Answer the same questions for vitamin B.
16. Answer the same questions for vitamin C.
17. Answer the same questions for vitamin D.
18. What is enriched flour? How does it compare with whole-grain flour?
19. What is fortified margarine?
20. Why is vitamin D called the "sunshine" vitamin?
21. Why is it foolish to take vitamin pills without the advice of a physician? Why do physicians sometimes advise the taking of vitamin pills?
22. List the signs of good nutrition. Do you show all these signs of good nutrition?

THINGS TO DO

1. It is possible to have good nutrition while eating many different kinds of foods. Look up the diet of Eskimos; of Chinese; of natives of India; of Mexicans; of other people in whom you are interested. What foods provide them with protein? with minerals? with vitamins?

2. Find in which countries are the largest numbers of cases of beriberi, scurvy, and pellagra. What relationship do these diseases have to the diets in those countries?

3. Study the diets recommended for dogs and cats by veterinarians and the makers of dog and cat food. If you live in the country, study the diets recommended for chickens and for cattle. Do they provide all the nutrients?

4. Ask a chemistry or biology student to demonstrate tests for starch, sugar, protein, and fat.

5. Look in encyclopedias or books on nutrition for stories of how the vitamins were discovered.

6. Collect labels from bread sold in grocery stores. Find the breads that have been made with enriched flour. Which nutrients have been added?

7. Collect advertisements of vitamin preparations. Which foods contain the same vitamins as those advertised?

8. Find from your health department whether your water supply contains sufficient iodine and fluorine.

9. Read *The Rime of the Ancient Mariner* by Coleridge for the description of scurvy.

CHAPTER 9 What Will You Have to Eat?

Usually, you choose what you will eat, at breakfast, or lunch, or dinner, or for between-meal snacks at recess or after school. Perhaps you eat lunch at the school cafeteria. Should you take two or three salads? Is it all right to eat two or three desserts, or should you not eat any dessert? Should you choose a meat dish, even though it is expensive, or can you take something else that will be just as good? How about a hamburger and a bottle of some sweet drink?

Perhaps you bring your lunch from home. Must you bring sandwiches every day? Is a jelly sandwich as nutritious as a peanut-butter sandwich? Should you use both butter and a sandwich spread? And how many sandwiches should you bring?

What about your breakfast? Should you have toast every morning? Do you need fruit every day? Is there any difference between orange juice and pineapple juice? Is frozen orange juice or canned orange juice as good for you as fresh orange juice?

Chapter 8 tells you what good nutrition is and why it is important to eat foods that contain the right amounts of all the nutrients. But Chapter 8 does not tell you exactly what foods and how much of them you, as an individual, need to keep you in good health. Knowing about nutrients is interesting and gives you some of the basic reasons for trying to eat properly. Even scientists, however, do not figure out exactly which nutrients are in every food they eat at every meal. They have worked out some short cuts that will help you choose good meals for yourself and your family. This chapter answers some of the practical questions that Chapter 8 may have raised in your mind.

HOW MUCH TO EAT

For most growing boys and girls, appetite is a good guide to how much to eat. A few do not eat enough food, usually because they have not developed good eating habits, because they are "nervous" and high-strung, or because they are busy about so many other things that they do not take time to eat. Sometimes girls deliberately do not eat because they are afraid of becoming fat.

A few adolescents eat too much and store the extra food as fat. These may be boys or girls who eat instead of playing or working. They may be individuals whose endocrine glands are not secreting hormones in the right amounts.

Height-weight-age tables. Thousands of people of all ages have been weighed and measured, and the results have been put into charts and tables. These show what *most* people at any age and height weigh and are called height-weight-age tables or charts.

People are built differently and should weigh different amounts. Some people have large, heavy bones; some have small, light bones. Some people have long arms and legs and narrow trunks; some have heavy trunks and short arms and legs. Height-weight-age tables are useful, therefore, in a general way only, that is, as averages. They do not tell exactly what any one person *should* weigh.

The charts on pages 152 and 153 show what most children and adolescents weigh and how tall they are at various ages. For example, boys of 12 usually weigh between 68 and 108 pounds and are between 53 and 64 inches tall. If your height lies toward the upper edge of the height range

for your age, you are "tall for your age." Usually, if a person's height lies toward the upper edge of the height range, his weight will lie toward the upper edge of the weight range, but this is not always the case. If a person has small, light bones, his weight may be down toward the lower edge of the weight range, even though he is tall.

These charts are useful in plotting a person's gain in height and weight from year to year. People in good health usually make steady gains in both height and weight and remain in about the same position on both the height and the weight charts, year after year. Gaining in height without gaining in weight may be a sign of poor nutrition.

Overweight and underweight. People who weigh more than the average, that is, more than most people of the same age and height, are called overweight. Those who weigh less than the average are called underweight.

Up to about the age of 30, people who are slightly overweight are, in general, healthier and have a better chance to live a long time than do those who are of average weight or underweight. After about 35, slightly underweight people are healthier and have a better chance to live longer than those who are overweight or of average weight.

How many calories every day? It takes energy to keep in good health and to grow. This energy is supplied by food. It is measured in calories (see Chapter 8). Table 3 gives the number of calories needed daily by persons of average size at various ages.

An average person who is moderately active uses each day about 17 calories per pound of his body weight. The number of calories used is more than 17 for anyone who does hard manual work and is less than 17 for a person who does sedentary work—that is, who spends a great deal of time in the sitting position. Multiply your weight by 17; the result will approximate your daily requirement.

The number of calories a person needs is influenced by height, weight, age, sex, exercise, work, season, and climate. A boy or girl who is in strenuous athletics may need twice as much energy-producing food as one who ex-

Calories needed per hour for persons weighing about 100 pounds.

ercises very little (see Chapter 7). Averages such as those shown in Table 3 must be adjusted in order to fit any particular individual.

Gaining and losing weight. If a person wishes to gain weight, he should eat food containing more calories than his body is using. Foods containing large amounts of fat and carbohydrates are useful for this purpose

Table 3. Daily Calory Requirements*

Person	Calories
Children up to 12 years	
1–3 years	1200
4–6 years	1600
7–9 years	2000
10–12 years	2500
Children over 12 years	
Girls, 13–15 years	2600
16–20 years	2400
Boys, 13–15 years	3200
16–20 years	3800
Man (weighing about 154 pounds)	
Sedentary	2400
Physically active	3000
With heavy work	4500
Woman (weighing about 123 pounds)	
Sedentary	2000
Moderately active	2400
Very active	3000

*Adapted from Reprint and Circular Series, No. 129, October, 1948. Food and Nutrition Board, National Research Council.

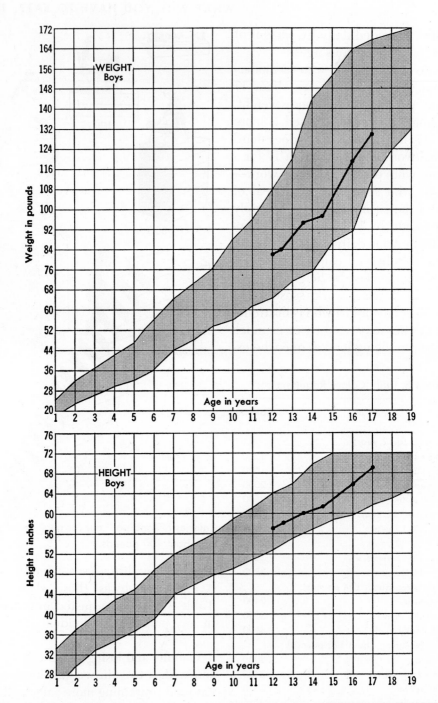

This graph shows how one boy grew in height and weight. He gained steadily and his height and weight were always well within the range where most boys' heights and weights are found. The graph on the next page shows how one girl grew in height and weight.

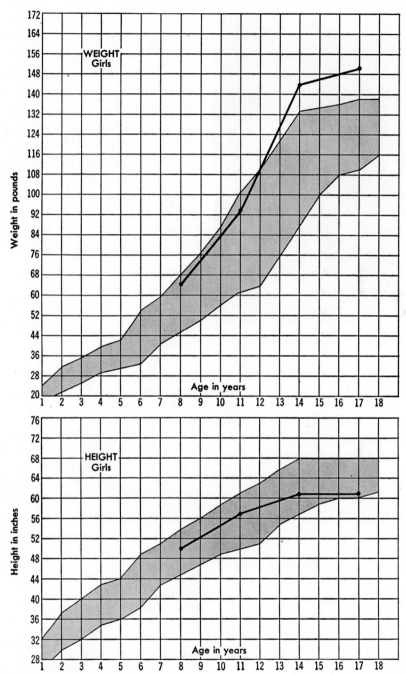

This graph shows how one girl grew in height and weight. At 17 she was among the short 17-year-olds. But her weight was above what is usually found in very heavy 17-year-olds. She may have been heavy because she had heavy bones or because she had too much fat.

Playing baseball demands 300–400 calories per hour for a 100-pound boy. (Courtesy Arsenal Technical High School, Indianapolis)

since average servings of these provide many calories. The person who wishes to gain should eat more butter and cream, more potatoes and gravy, and more bread than other people eat. Taking food and milk at bedtime and, possibly, between meals is helpful in gaining weight.

If a person wishes to slim down a bit, the food he eats must supply fewer calories than his body needs. His body must then use some of its own fat for energy. The simplest way to do this is to cut down on the high-calory foods. Bulky foods, such as leafy vegetables, will provide few calories but will relieve hunger.

In reducing, it is important to get enough foods that contain proteins, vitamins, and minerals. Before start-

ing to reduce, a person should have a thorough physical examination and then follow the advice of his physician. It is not wise to use advertised preparations that claim to reduce weight without dieting. Some are fakes. Some are dangerous, because they interfere with the proper functioning of the body. Some take away the appetite so that the person using them does not get enough of the nutrients he really needs.

Table 4. Calories Needed for Various Activities*

Activity	Calories per pound per hour
Sleeping	0.43
Basal metabolism	0.46
Sitting quietly	0.65
Reading aloud	0.69
Standing relaxed	0.69
Sewing (hand)	0.72
Standing at attention	0.74
Knitting	0.75
Dressing and undressing	0.77
Singing	0.79
Typewriting rapidly	0.91
Dishwashing	0.93
Ironing (5-pound iron)	0.93
Sweeping bare floor (38 strokes per minute)	1.09
Carpentry (heavy)	1.56
Walking moderately fast (3.75 miles per hour)	1.95
Walking downstairs	2.36
Sawing wood	3.12
Swimming (2 miles per hour)	3.25
Running (5.3 miles per hour)	3.70
Walking very fast (5.3 miles per hour)	4.22
Walking upstairs	7.18

* Adapted from Sherman, *The Chemistry of Food and Nutrition*, p. 189. The Macmillan Co., 1946.

THE MUST FOODS

In Chapter 8, there is a discussion of nutrients—proteins, carbohydrates, fats, minerals, and vitamins. The foods you eat, however, are not pure nutrients. Almost all foods contain several nutrients. Milk, for example, which is an excellent source of calcium and phosphorus, also contains protein, carbohydrate, and several vitamins. And meat, which is chiefly a protein food, also contains vitamin B, iron, and other vitamins and minerals. Butter is chiefly a fat, but it is also a good source of vitamin A.

There are so many foods in the world that you would have a hard time memorizing one by one which nutrients each contains. For simplicity, therefore, scientists have classified foods into seven groups, which taken together contain almost all the needed nutrients. Each group gives you several nutrients and is an especially good source of one or two (see Table 5). These are the "must foods," because you must eat them regularly in order to have good health and vigor.

Include something from each of the Basic Seven Food Groups in your diet every day. Several servings are better than one. Be careful never to leave out any group. If these do not supply

Table 5. Nutrients Supplied by the Basic Seven Food Groups *

Food group	Nutrient								
	Food energy	Protein	Calcium	Iron	Vitamin A	Thiamine	Riboflavin	Niacin	Ascorbic acid
1) Green and yellow vegetables			x	x	xx	x	x		x
2) Citrus fruits, tomatoes, raw cabbage					x	x			xx
3) Potatoes, other vegetables, fruits	x			x		x			x
4) Milk and milk products (liquid, dried, evaporated)	x	xx	xx		x	x	xx		
5) Meat, poultry, fish, eggs, dried beans, peas, nuts	x	xx		x		x	x	x	
6) Bread, flour, cereal (whole-grain or enriched)	xx	x		x		x	x	x	
7) Butter and fortified margarine	xx				x				

xx indicates an excellent source; x indicates a good source.
* From Kilander, *Nutrition for Health*, p. 144. McGraw-Hill Book Company, Inc., 1951.

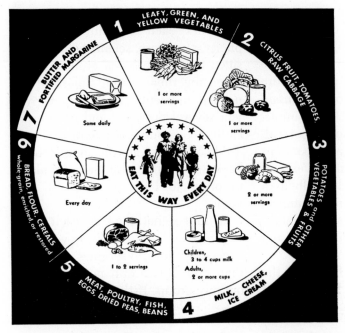

The Basic Seven Food Groups. (Courtesy Bureau of Human Nutrition and Home Economics, U.S. Department of Agriculture)

all the calories you need, eat a wide variety of foods you like.

Meal patterns. Table 6 shows how a day's meals can be planned so as to include foods from all the Basic Seven Food Groups. It shows, too, how the same meal patterns can be used for members of a family who engage in different amounts of work and play. Any family will vary these patterns to suit what the members of the family like. You can easily substitute for one food any other from the same group. For example, instead of spinach or kale for dinner, any green or yellow vegetable from Group 1 could be used.

THREE "SQUARE" MEALS A DAY

Americans usually eat three meals a day—in the morning, in the middle of the day, and in the evening. There is nothing magic or especially healthful about this pattern. In some other countries, people eat four or five meals a day. Some persons in this country have better nutrition when, in addition to the usual three meals, they eat regularly in the middle of the morning, in the middle of the afternoon, and perhaps before going to bed at night.

Breakfast is an important meal. Breakfast usually comes 12 or 14 hours after the last meal of the day before. This makes breakfast an important meal, since your body has been without food for so long. Dashing off to school without breakfast results in your becoming tired and irritable before noon. Or if you go without breakfast, you may become hungry in the middle of the morning,

Table 6. Servings of Food for Different Kinds of Work

Light work	Moderate work	Heavy work
BREAKFAST		
Orange juice, ½ cup (Group 2)	Orange juice, ½ cup (Group 2)	Orange juice, ½ cup (Group 2)
Cereal, 1 oz and ½ cup milk (Groups 6 and 4)	Cereal, 1½ oz and ¾ cup milk (Groups 6 and 4)	Cereal, 1½ oz and ¾ cup milk (Groups 6 and 4)
Egg, 1 (Group 5)	Egg, 1 (Group 5)	Eggs, 2 (Group 5)
Toast, 1 slice and butter or fortified margarine (Groups 6 and 7)	Toast, 2 slices and butter or fortified margarine (Groups 6 and 7)	Toast, 3 slices and butter or fortified margarine (Groups 6 and 7)
Strawberry jam, 1 tbs	Strawberry jam, 2 tbs	Strawberry jam, 3 tbs
Coffee or tea for adults	Coffee or tea for adults	Coffee or tea for adults
Milk, 1 cup for children (Group 4)	Milk, 1 cup for children (Group 4)	Milk, 1 cup for children (Group 4)
LUNCH		
Cheese sandwich, 1 (Groups 4, 6, and 7)	Cream of potato soup, ½ cup (Groups 3 and 4)	Cream of potato soup, 1 cup (Groups 3 and 4)
Carrot and cabbage salad, 1 cup (Groups 1 and 2)	Cheese sandwich, 1 (Groups 4, 6, and 7)	Cheese sandwiches, 2 (Groups 4, 6, and 7)
Fresh or canned peach, 1 (Group 3)	Carrot and cabbage salad, ¾ cup (Groups 1 and 2)	Carrot and cabbage salad, 1 cup (Groups 1 and 2)
Cookie, 1	Fresh or canned peach, 1 (Group 3)	Fresh or canned peach, 1 (Group 3)
	Cookies, 2	Cookies, 3
Milk, 1 cup (Group 4)	Milk, 1 cup (Group 4)	Milk, 1 cup (Group 4)
DINNER		
Meat or nut loaf, 1 serving (Group 5)	Meat or nut loaf, 1 serving (Group 5)	Meat or nut loaf, 1 large serving (Group 5)
Creamed potato or turnips, ½ cup (Groups 3 and 4)	Creamed potato or turnips, ½ cup (Groups 3 and 4)	Creamed potato or turnips, ¾ cup (Groups 3 and 4)
Buttered spinach or kale, ½ cup (Groups 1 and 7)	Buttered spinach or kale, ¾ cup (Groups 1 and 7)	Buttered spinach or kale, ¾ cup (Groups 1 and 7)
Lettuce and tomato salad, 1 serving (Groups 1 and 2)	Lettuce and tomato salad, 1 serving (Groups 1 and 2)	Lettuce and tomato salad, 1 serving (Groups 1 and 2)
Dinner roll, 1 and butter or fortified margarine (Groups 6 and 7)	Dinner rolls, 2 and butter or fortified margarine (Groups 6 and 7)	Dinner rolls, 3 and butter or fortified margarine (Groups 6 and 7)
Pudding with fruit sauce, ½ cup	Pudding with fruit sauce, ¾ cup	Pudding with fruit sauce, ¾ cup
Coffee or tea for adults	Coffee or tea for adults	Coffee or tea for adults
Milk for children, 1 cup (Group 4)	Milk for children, 1 cup (Group 4)	Milk for children, 1 cup (Group 4)

eat a candy bar, and take away your appetite for lunch.

Breakfast should furnish about one-fourth of the day's food. Too little breakfast means that all the needed nutrients must be included in the other meals. This may not be easy to accomplish.

Many people hurry too much to enjoy their breakfasts. Save time for breakfast by laying out your clothes and collecting your books the night before. Even getting up a few minutes earlier is worth while if it gives time to make breakfast more leisurely and more enjoyable.

Lunch. Lunch should provide about one-third of the day's food requirements. It is the meal most often eaten away from home. If you eat at a school cafeteria or at a restaurant, you can usually get soup, salad, and a hot dish. These can be chosen so as to include foods from several of the Basic Seven Food Groups. A hot dish usually aids digestion.

A good lunch packed at home usually contains sandwiches. These should be made with meat, egg, peanut butter, or some other filling that is satisfying and contains protein. To this should be added a raw vegetable, fresh fruit, and milk, to provide vitamins and minerals. Many schools and factories provide a hot dish to add to lunches brought from home.

Dinner. For most people, dinner is the big meal of the day. They have time at this meal to eat in leisure, without rushing off to school or work.

Meat, potatoes, and vegetables, with salad and dessert and some beverage, form the usual pattern for dinner in this country. These foods usually provide between a third and a half of all the needed nutrients for the day.

Between-meal snacks. Eating between meals is a good plan for people who like small meals, who are underweight, or who are exercising strenuously. Also, persons who are trying to reduce sometimes find that several small meals make it easier to keep to a strict diet than two or three large ones. These between-meal snacks should fit into the pattern for the whole day's food supply.

Variety in foods. Some raw food should be included in at least one meal of the day. Raw food lends variety to the meal and makes sure that all the vitamins are not destroyed by cooking. Every meal should have one food that is bulky and filling, one food that requires chewing, and if possible some food or drink that is hot.

There should be some soft foods and some crisp ones. Foods of different colors and flavors add to the attractiveness and interest of a meal. Foods should be served in different ways: sometimes raw, sometimes cooked in various ways. Repeating the same food day after day becomes monotonous.

Buying food. Many families on low incomes have better meals than other families that spend much more money for food. They do this by wise and careful buying. Foods that contain proteins, minerals, and vitamins, come at the head of their shopping lists, even though they cost more in money than do some other foods. These are called protective foods.

Milk is a protective food. No other single food gives so many nutrients at such low cost. So the less money you have to spend for food, the more important milk becomes in the daily diets of yourself and your family.

Fruits and vegetables are also protective foods. These are found in Groups 1, 2, and 3 of the Basic Seven Food Groups. If you must cut down on food costs, buy the fruits and vegetables that are in season and least expensive.

Part of your protein requirement can be satisfied by occasional use of peas and beans, nuts, peanut butter, and whole-grain cereals. These usually cost less than meat and eggs. In low-cost diets, all bread and cereals should be the whole-grain or enriched type.

To get the most value for your money, it is best to plan meals for the whole week and to buy in quantity the foods that will keep. Home-cooked soups, cereals, and desserts cost less than the same foods purchased ready to serve.

DANGERS IN FOODS

Foods sometimes are dangerous. They may contain actual poisons or they may carry organisms that cause diseases.

Poisons in food from sprays. Arsenic, lead, and DDT are used in spraying fruit trees and vegetables in order to destroy insects. These poisons sometimes reach human beings on food and cause serious illness. Thorough washing will remove the poisons from fruits and vegetables.

Botulinus toxin. Bacteria called botulinus organisms sometimes grow in canned food, especially vegetables, and form a powerful poison, or toxin. These bacteria can be killed, and their toxins can be destroyed, by high temperature. For this reason, it is best to use a pressure cooker for canning all vegetables except tomatoes. Vegetables canned by other methods should be reboiled after opening before they are used or even tasted.

Commercially canned foods are less likely to contain botulinus toxin than those canned at home, because they are cooked at higher temperatures. However, the contents of cans that bulge or leak or give off abnormal odors should be thrown away, because they may contain the toxin.

Poisonous mushrooms. Some mushrooms are safe to eat, others are not. Every so often the newspapers carry stories of people who have died from eating mushrooms that they gathered without being certain of the different kinds.

There is no simple rule for telling which mushrooms are poisonous. The best way to be safe is to use only those that are raised for sale or that are gathered by persons who know the kinds of mushrooms that are not poisonous.

Milk can be a dangerous food. Milk is an excellent food for human beings. It is, however, a good food also for many disease-producing organisms. Milk, therefore, can become a very dangerous food.

Diseases spread by milk may come from the cows or from persons who handle the milk. Among the diseases that may come from cows are tuberculosis and undulant fever (brucellosis). Typhoid fever, diphtheria, and scarlet fever may come from persons who handle the milk (see Chapters 24 and 25).

If milk comes from healthy cows and is carefully handled by healthy people, it should be safe to use it raw. However, it is not possible to be sure that raw milk is safe. Therefore, it is wise to use only pasteurized or boiled milk. Pasteurized milk is milk that has been heated to a temperature that will kill the organisms that cause disease.

In most cities and some states, only pasteurized milk can be sold. If it is not possible to buy pasteurized milk, a person can get information on how to pasteurize milk in his home by writing to his state department of health.

Other disease-producing organisms in food. Disease-producing organisms may get into food from rats and mice, from flies, from people who handle the foods, or from containers in which food is placed (see Chapter 25). These organisms can grow in foods that are moist and warm, especially those that contain meat, eggs, and milk. Trichinosis, which is a food-borne disease, is discussed in Chapter 6.

Thorough cooking will kill most of these organisms. Food should be served soon after cooking if possible, before organisms have a chance to grow. If it cannot be eaten immediately, it should be cooled quickly and kept in the refrigerator until used. It should be protected from flies, mice, and other animals.

People who handle food at home or in restaurants should keep their hands and their clothes very clean. Thorough washing of hands before handling food is one of the simplest but most valuable ways of protecting against food infections. Eating utensils, especially forks, spoons, cups, and drinking glasses, should be washed thoroughly in hot water and soap after each use.

COOKING AND STORING FOOD

Most of the foods we eat are cooked. Cooking makes many foods taste, smell, and look better. Certain foods are more easily digested when cooked. Cooking kills most organisms and destroys toxins that cause disease, if any of these happen to be on food.

On the other hand, some of the nutrients may be lost in preparing and cooking foods. Some may be dissolved in the water in which the foods are washed or cooked. Others may be destroyed by heat or by exposure to the air. Minerals are often lost in thick peelings.

Here are a few rules for preparing, cooking, and storing food. If you follow these you will save most of the nutrients in food and will keep food safe.

1) Wash hands before handling food. Wash containers after each use.

2) Keep food covered in the refrigerator or on shelves. Protect it from light, flies, mice, and rats. Store fresh garden foods in a cool moist place.

3) Keep milk cold.

4) Cool leftovers quickly and store in the refrigerator.

5) Wash fruits and vegetables thoroughly and quickly. Keep them cool until ready to cook. Do not soak before cooking. Prepare salads just before serving. Serve fruits and fruit juices as soon after preparing as possible.

6) Cook and serve vegetables in their skins whenever possible. If vegetables and fruits are peeled, make the peelings thin. Cook the green outer leaves of vegetables.

7) Start vegetables cooking in boiling water. Begin the cooking of frozen vegetables while they are still frozen.

8) Cover vegetables tightly when they are cooking. Do not stir.

9) Cook vegetables quickly, until they are tender but not mushy. Use little water. Serve as soon after cooking as possible.

10) Use the liquids in which vegetables are cooked. Add them to sauces, soups, gravies, or vegetable-juice cocktails.

11) Cook meat as soon as possible after it is purchased or taken from a freezing locker. Cook pork thoroughly.

12) Cool milk, meat, or egg dishes quickly after cooking, unless they are served hot. Keep cold. Use soon.

13) Cook eggs slowly. Do not overcook. Overcooking eggs makes them "weep" and makes the protein tough.

FOOD FADS

Food fads come and go. Often the fad of the moment is based in part on some new development in science but does not take account of all the facts. Many fads make money for the people who have something to sell.

Some people rush from one food fad to another. They eat no meat for awhile, drink no water with meals for a few months, eat only chops and pineapple or some such combination for some time, eat protein and carbohydrates at separate meals, then follow one reducing diet after another, and take bottle after bottle of vitamin pills or capsules.

Some food fads are actually harmful, some are expensive, some are merely foolish. Most of them lack some needed nutrients. None of them provide a well-balanced diet.

A GOOD DIET

As scientists have learned more and more about human nutrition, they have come to place more and more emphasis on the kinds of food eaten, not merely on the amount. America is a land of plenty. Very few people die because of lack of food. Few people have serious illnesses because of poor food.

Study after study, however, shows that many Americans are poorly nourished. Because of lack of money, because of ignorance, or because of the wrong food habits, they do not eat enough of the essential nutrients. The result is a host of minor ailments that keep people from being at their best and add up to an overwhelming amount of ill health, lack of vigor, and unhappiness.

Are *you* getting the best that your food dollars can buy?

SO WHAT?

America is a land of plenty, but even in America many people lack vitality, strength, and energy and suffer from ill-health because they fail to eat properly; and

Of these some eat too much, some eat too little, and still more do not eat the right foods; and

It is not healthy to be either too fat or too thin; and

Foods are sometimes contaminated with disease-producing organisms;

So, you should know

What are the "must foods" in your daily diet; and

What your best weight should be and how much food is needed to maintain it; and

How to plan for meals that will be appetizing, nutritionally correct, and economical; and

What diseases are spread by foods and how to avoid them.

CHECKING UP

1. Should people of the same age and height weigh the same? Explain your answer.
2. Find your height and weight on the charts on pages 152 and 153. Are you above average, about average, or below average, in height and weight for your age?
3. Is it better to be average in weight, slightly overweight, or slightly underweight, while you are in your teens? Why? Is it better for middle-aged people to be average in weight, slightly overweight, or slightly underweight? Explain.

4. Why do many boys and girls in their teens need more food than men and women do?

5. Why should butter or fortified margarine be included in a reducing diet?

6. What nutrients should be included in a reducing diet? Why?

7. Why is it unwise to use preparations that are advertised to reduce weight without dieting?

8. What kinds of foods are included in each of the Basic Seven Food Groups?

9. What nutrients are included in each of the Basic Seven Food Groups? Are there important nutrients not included in the Basic Seven?

10. Why is breakfast an important meal?

11. List foods for breakfast from all of the Basic Seven Food Groups; foods for lunch; foods for dinner.

12. Are between-meal snacks good or bad? Explain.

13. Why is it desirable to eat some raw food every day?

14. What are protective foods?

15. Milk has been called the "perfect" food. Which food essentials does it contain? Which food essentials does it lack?

16. Why is it important to wash fruits and vegetables before eating them?

17. What is a toxin? How can botulinus organisms be destroyed? How can botulinus toxin be destroyed?

18. Why is it important to keep cooked, but uneaten, food cold?

19. What is pasteurized milk? Why is it safer than raw milk?

20. When is milk a dangerous food?

21. Give reasons for each of the rules for preparing, cooking, and storing food on page 161.

THINGS TO DO

1. Find what five or six students in the class ate for breakfast. Did these breakfasts include foods from each of the Basic Seven Food Groups? What could be added to each to make it a better breakfast? Suggest lunches, dinners, and between-meal snacks that could be used with these breakfasts to make well-balanced diets for the whole day.

2. Make a list of all the food you eat in one day. Have you included all the Basic Seven Food Groups? Compare your meals with the meal patterns suggested in Table 6.

3. Plan meals for a family, following the meal patterns in Table 6. Find the costs of these meals for a family. Find the prices of different kinds of vegetables and fruits.

4. Make a list of all the foods you know that belong in Group 1 of the Basic Seven Food Groups. Check ones you like and can get at most times of the year. Try to get acquainted with some of those you have never eaten. Do the same for all the other groups in the Basic Seven Food Groups.

5. Make a study of the lunches students eat at your school. How many contain all the Basic Seven Food Groups? Which groups are most often omitted?

6. Ask the manager of the school cafeteria to tell the class how meals are chosen and prepared, and how dishes are washed in the cafeteria.

7. Ask the public-health officer to tell you the rules in your community for washing dishes and examining food-handlers in restaurants. Write to your state department of health to find state regulations.

8. Visit a restaurant or the school cafeteria to see the cooking, serving, and dish washing.

9. Keep a record of your height and weight all through the year. If you fail to gain, try to find the reason.

10. Perhaps you can help the school nurse or the teachers to weigh and measure children in elementary schools.

11. Make a collection of food fads. Which ones omit some of the needed nutrients?

12. Watch children at play or people on the street. See whether you can recognize signs of good and poor nutrition.

13. Find how many calories you need for one day. First, list all the things you do in 24 hours. How much time do you spend on each? Second, multiply the number of hours you spend on each by the number of calories needed (use Table 4). Third, add these together. This gives the number of calories needed by each pound of your body weight. Fourth, multiply the sum by your weight.

CHAPTER 10   Skin Deep

Have you heard someone say: "Beauty is only skin deep"? And have you wondered whether this was true? Of course, everyone likes to look at a boy or girl with good-looking skin, hair, and nails. But real beauty starts far deeper than the skin.

One girl who won a nation-wide beauty contest said that her rules of living include: plenty of sleep; a good diet; lots of exercise, especially swimming; baths every day; and resting her face from make-up when she is at home.

Not many of us can win beauty contests, but anyone can follow rules like these and make the most of his appearance. And while you are thinking about beauty, remember that, in making friends, the expression on your face is more important than your complexion. The most popular boy or girl in the class is not often the most beautiful.

THE SKIN

The skin has been called "the mirror of the body." It grows pink when you are hot, or have a fever, or feel angry or embarrassed. It pales when you are cold, faint, afraid, or tired. It becomes bluish from heart failure and greyish from wasting diseases. It "blooms" with youth and wrinkles with age.

Skin layers. The skin has two main layers: the epidermis, or outer skin, and the dermis, or true skin. The dermis, or true skin, is a network of connective tissue and contains nerves and blood vessels. The sweat glands, the oil glands, and the roots of the hair are in this layer. Smooth (involuntary) muscle cells are found in the dermis. When the skin is suddenly cooled, these muscles contract and cause "goose pimples."

The epidermis has no blood vessels or nerves. The lower cells of the epidermis continually grow, divide, and are pushed to the outer surface of the skin, where they die. Every day millions of these dead cells are rubbed off on your clothing, towels, and whatever else you touch. And every day new cells take their places and give you a fresh new outer covering. Wash-

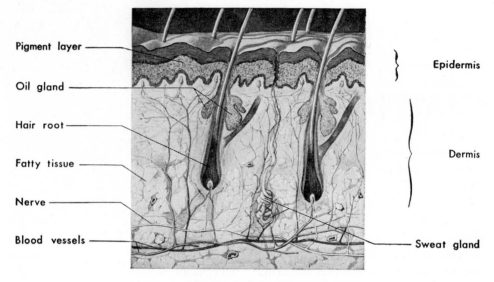

Pigment layer

Oil gland

Hair root

Fatty tissue

Nerve

Blood vessels

Epidermis

Dermis

Sweat gland

Structure of the skin.

ing helps remove the old dead cells and the dirt they have collected.

Skin protects your body. The epidermis is waterproof. It keeps your body from losing fluids and drying up. It also keeps water from getting inside your skin when rain falls on you or when you go swimming or take a bath.

The skin protects your body from disease organisms. Usually an infection cannot get a start unless there is a break in the skin (see Chapter 4). Sometimes, however, an infection begins in a sweat gland or around the root of a hair.

The skin also protects your body from too much light. A brown coloring substance, or pigment, in the skin shuts out most of the ultraviolet rays in sunshine. These are the rays that cause sunburn. Tanning means forming more of the brown protective pig-

ment. Freckles are spots of this brown pigment.

Hair and nails help protect some parts of your body. Hair and nails grow from the skin. The living parts are deep in the skin. The parts we can see and feel are not alive.

Skin helps get rid of wastes. Your skin contains 2 or 3 million sweat glands. A sweat gland is a coiled slender tube starting in the dermis and going up to the surface of the epidermis. Sweat, or perspiration, takes water and a little salt, carbon dioxide, and other wastes from the blood (see Chapter 7). A person loses a pint to a quart of perspiration every day. In hot weather or when you exercise hard, you lose a great deal more.

Skin helps cool or warm your body. Your skin gives off heat to the air around it. When the weather is cold, less blood goes to the skin and less heat is lost, so your body keeps warm. When the weather is hot, more blood goes to the skin, and more heat is lost. The skin is cooled, too, by evaporation of perspiration. After exercise, it is a good idea to put on a coat or sweater. Otherwise, the evaporation of perspiration may make you lose too much heat, and you will become chilled.

Clothing plays an important part in keeping you cool or warm. In cold weather, wool keeps a layer of warm air around the skin. Wool absorbs perspiration when you exercise and lets it evaporate slowly rather than chilling you with quick evaporation. In hot weather, thin, loose clothing helps keep you cool. It allows cool air to circulate close to the skin and it permits perspiration to evaporate quickly.

It may surprise you to know that ventilation is chiefly a matter of keeping the skin comfortable. Good ventilation means that fresh air of the right warmth and dryness is moving about the room and around your skin (see Chapter 23).

Your skin makes you acquainted with things outside. You learn how things feel and whether they are heavy or light, hot or cold, through the nerves in your skin. The skin also contains nerves for pain. This is the reason cuts and burns on the skin hurt more than the same injuries would if they were inside the body.

Beauty treatments. People pay large

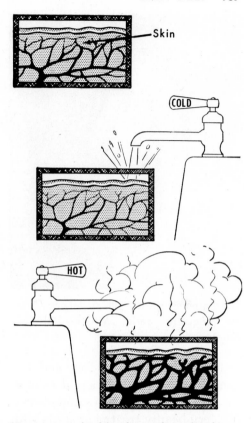

Heat causes the blood vessels in the skin to expand and allows more blood to go to the skin. Cold causes the blood vessels in the skin to become smaller and, thus, reduces the amount of blood that goes to the skin.

sums of money for elaborate beauty treatments when what they need are simple treatments they can get at home. A clear and beautiful skin must have proper food. A diet that contains lots of fruits, vegetables, milk, and eggs provides the right kinds of food. Candy, soda pop, and cigarettes do not provide the right kinds of food.

Exercise and rest are beauty treatments for the skin, because they make for good blood and good circulation. Good red blood does two things for a

Good grooming starts with cleanliness. (From the "Etiquette" Series. McGraw-Hill Text-Films)

beautiful skin. It brings food and oxygen to the cells. It gives a pink color to the skin, especially in lips and cheeks.

Every beauty treatment starts with cleansing the skin. Wash your face at least once every day with warm water and a mild soap. If your skin is oily, wash your face twice a day with soap, and the soap can be fairly strong. Pay special attention to your ears, the corners of your eyes, and the creases beside your nose.

Cleansing the face with cream only is scientifically unsound. Dirt gathers on the face and mixes with oil from the oil glands. Soap and water remove this oily dirt; oils and creams do not. If you have a dry skin, it is well to apply a little oil or cold cream at night after washing your face. This will do no harm to an oily skin and probably not much good. Oils and creams are not good for skins with acne (pimples).

Bathing. We take bathing for granted these days, but it is interesting to know something about people's ideas on the subject in other places and in other times. The early Romans, for example, liked to take baths, and bathing has been popular among the Japanese. In this country, for many years, bathing was thought to bring on tuberculosis, rheumatic fever, and inflammation of the lungs. The first bathtub in the White House was installed by President Millard Fillmore in 1852. Boston actually had a law against taking a bath in a bathtub, and this law was not repealed until 1862.

A bath every day is important for good grooming. People who have little time, or live in crowded homes, can take sponge baths. Most people take shower or tub baths.

Temperature is important in bathing. Hot baths relax sore, stiff (tense) muscles and increase blood flow and muscle tonus. For these reasons, hot baths are stimulating. If a person stays too long in a hot bath, he becomes tired. Steam baths dilate the blood vessels near the surface of the skin and sometimes put too much strain on the heart.

A warm bath is one that is just a little above the temperature of the body. A warm bath relaxes the muscles. It is, also, the best for cleansing the skin.

Cold baths at first drive the blood away from the skin. Most people get warm immediately and feel a "glow all over" after a short cold bath. If a person is cold and shivery after cold baths, he probably should not take them. Most people can at least rub cold water on their faces, arms and legs, and chests after a warm bath and feel more alert and vigorous.

Chapping of the skin occurs in cold weather when the oil glands secrete too little oil. Washing with strong soap removes oil from the skin and makes it easier for it to chap. Oil, cold cream, or glycerin usually prevent chapping.

SKIN DISORDERS

All of us at one time or another have had something wrong with our skins —a boil, a blister, or a rash from poison ivy. Any disorder of the skin is likely to make a person uncomfortable. It may itch and hurt until he can think of nothing else. He may be unhappy because he thinks he looks odd to other people. He may worry because he does not know what to do to cure the ailment.

People used to think that all skin disorders were caused by "impure" blood. The remedy was supposed to be a medicine, especially medicine with a nasty taste.

Actually, there are many causes for skin disorders. Some are rashes that accompany diseases, such as chicken pox, smallpox, measles, scarlet fever, and syphilis. These usually disappear as soon as the disease is cured. Rashes may also result from poor nutrition.

Some skin disorders are caused by

Corns are caused by pressure, usually from shoes that do not fit well.

tiny animals that live in or on the skin, such as body lice or itch mites. Some disorders, such as acne, boils, and impetigo, are infections by bacteria. Some, such as ringworm and athlete's foot, are caused by small plants called fungi. Some, like hives, are caused by allergies. And for some, the causes are not known.

The next eight topics describe the skin disorders that are most common. It is well for you to know something about these, so that you can protect yourself from them and can understand better how to care for the ones you may happen to develop.

Blisters, corns, calluses. Fluid sometimes collects between the layers of the skin to form blisters. The cause is some injury to the skin, usually burning or rubbing. Small blisters need little attention; large ones should be cared for by a physician (see Chapter 4).

Corns and calluses are thickenings of the skin from rubbing or pressure. Poorly fitting shoes or fallen arches may cause calluses on the ball of the foot. Poorly fitting shoes cause corns, usually on the toes. The treatment, of course, is better care of the feet and better fitting shoes (see Chapter 7).

Acne, boils, carbuncles, impetigo. Many young people have trouble with

The skin protects against many injuries and infections. Going barefoot around swimming pools frequently results in infection with the fungus that causes athlete's foot and sometimes results in cuts from stepping on rocks or broken glass. (Courtesy American Red Cross)

pimples, or acne. Usually, acne occurs on the face, the back, and the chest. In these places, the oil glands of the skin sometimes secrete too much oil during adolescence. The oil plugs the openings of the glands and forms whiteheads. If dirt gets into the openings, the whiteheads become blackheads. Bacteria cause the pimples, but whiteheads and blackheads seem to make the skin ready for infection with bacteria. The bacteria usually do not spread from one person to another. It is always desirable, however, to use your own towel.

Caring for simple cases of acne comes down to a few general rules:

1) Avoid greasy foods, pastry, and large amounts of cake, candy, and sweet drinks, especially chocolate.

2) Eat extra amounts of fruits and vegetables to get extra amounts of vitamins.

3) Wash the face carefully once or twice a day with soap and warm water.

4) Soften blackheads and whiteheads by soaking in warm water and remove them by *gentle* pressure. (Be sure your fingers are clean.)

5) Keep your hands off your face.

Acne usually disappears as a person grows older. However, the pimples may leave scars. For this reason, it is wise to have a physician give treatment if following the foregoing rules does not clear the skin within a few weeks.

A boil is an infection of the skin around the root of a hair. Boils may be spread from person to person or from one part of the body to another by fingers, clothing, towels, or anything that carries the disease organisms. Sometimes there are epidemics of boils among members of athletic teams. Clean underclothing and shirts, clean athletic uniforms, trunks, suits, towels, and clean gymnasium mats help to prevent the spread of boils (see Chapter 4).

A carbuncle is a number of boils occurring together. Usually, the person with a carbuncle has a fever and is seriously ill.

A person is more likely to have boils if he has too much sugar in his blood. Persons with boils should eat less sugar and starches. It is wise for them to be examined for diabetes, a disease in which sugar collects in the blood (see Chapter 22).

Impetigo is a common infection of the skin, especially among children. It is caused by disease organisms similar to the ones that cause boils. It occurs most often on the face, hands, forearms, and legs.

Impetigo begins as a red spot, which becomes a blister. The blister breaks and a dry crust forms. The infection is spread easily from person to person by hands, towels, or anything that one person handles and passes on to another. Epidemics of impetigo, especially among young children and athletes, are common. Treatment by a physician usually is needed.

Ringworm and athlete's foot. Ringworm is an infection of the skin caused by a fungus. The ringworm fungus is an organism something like the mold that forms on bread or on other foods that are left in damp places. The ringworm fungus forms sores that tend to heal in the center and spread outward. This gives a ring-like appearance; hence, the name ringworm.

On the face, this fungus sometimes infects the roots of the hair. In this case, it is known as barber's itch. Ringworm infection may also develop in the groin.

On the head, the ringworm fungus causes the hairs to break off and leave small round bald spots. This happens most often among children. The fungus is usually spread by combs and brushes and by caps and hats that have been worn by infected persons.

Powder helps keep feet dry. (From the "Health Education" Series. McGraw-Hill Text-Films)

A common fungus infection of the feet is athlete's foot. It occurs usually in young adults and in people whose feet perspire freely. In mild cases, there is soft whitish skin between the toes, often with cracks. In severe cases, small blisters, raw areas, and scaly patches occur.

The fungus that causes athlete's foot is present everywhere that bare feet have trod. On rugs, cracks in floors, shoes, and clothing, the organisms may remain alive for as long as a year. The infection is usually caught from the floors of locker rooms, bathrooms, showers, and swimming pools where people walk barefoot.

Wash your feet carefully with soap, including between the toes; dry thoroughly. This care makes infection less likely. You should always use your own towel, wash cloth, and bath slippers. After bathing, it is poor practice to dry the feet first and then the groin,

Female body louse magnified about 12 times.

because the fungus may be spread from feet to groin.

If your feet perspire a great deal, you should use a drying powder on them, especially between the toes, in your shoes, and even in your hose. Wash your feet and apply the powder night and morning. Ten-percent boric acid in talcum powder makes a good foot powder.

You should change socks or stockings daily. Socks that can be boiled are best when a person exercises and perspires a great deal. During warm weather, it is well to change shoes every day or two, so that each pair has time to air. Light, roomy shoes with leather soles are best for warm weather. A person should never wear anyone else's shoes or slippers. Doing so is one of the surest ways to get athlete's foot.

People are usually not successful in treating athlete's foot by themselves. Many advertised remedies for athlete's foot are irritating to the skin. It is a common story for the person who goes to a physician with athlete's foot to say: "I've used everything. I've had this stuff between my toes for years; just when I think it's well, it's back again. I've spent a small fortune for remedies, and look at my poor feet."

Scabies and pediculosis. Scabies is a common skin disease, usually called the itch, or the seven-year-itch. If not treated, it lasts indefinitely. When treated with sulfur ointment, it usually disappears rapidly.

Scabies is caused by the itch mite, a spider-like animal so tiny that it can barely be seen with the naked eye. This mite burrows into the skin, usually on the wrists and between the fingers, and lays its eggs. The bite of the itch mite produces a small red spot, which itches intensely, especially at night. It often becomes infected, filled with pus, and covered with a crust.

This disease is most common among people who do not keep their bodies and their clothing clean. It is spread from one person to another by personal contact and by the use of bedding, gloves, or underclothing of an infected person. Epidemics sometimes occur in schools. They are stopped by keeping infected children out of school until they are cured and their clothing and bedding have been cleaned to prevent reinfection.

Pediculosis, often called vagabond's disease, is an infestation by lice (pediculi). Lice are small, flat, wingless insects with short, sharp beaks, and legs ending in claws. The louse feeds by making a hole in the skin and sucking blood through its beak. The area around the hole then begins to itch, becomes inflamed, and often infected with bacteria.

Three kinds of lice infest human beings: the body louse (cootie), the head louse, and the pubic (or crab) louse. Body lice move from skin to clothing. Their eggs (nits) are usually found in the seams of clothing, not on the skin. The eggs of head and pubic lice are found among the hairs.

Lice usually mean uncleanliness. They occur most commonly among the very poor and those living in crowded places. In wartime, lice occur among displaced persons, prisoners, and soldiers who do not have a chance to take baths.

Prevention of pediculosis depends upon personal cleanliness and clean clothes. It is often said that it is no disgrace to get lice, but it is a disgrace to keep them.

Typhus fever is carried by the body louse. It was one of the most important diseases of the world until recent years. Camp fever, jail fever, and ship fever are other names for this disease (see Chapter 25).

Lice are carried from person to person by direct contact or indirectly by clothing, bedding, combs, caps, or insanitary toilet seats. DDT, one of the great developments of World War II, is very effective in destroying lice. For the first time in history, an epidemic of typhus fever was stopped quickly during this war. The epidemic that occurred in Rome was controlled when the American Army treated all persons in the area with DDT powder. A powder containing 10 parts DDT and 90 parts talcum has been used to get rid of head lice among school children.

Dermatitis, eczema, poison ivy, hives. The word *dermatitis* comes from Greek words meaning skin and inflammation of and so means inflammation of the skin. Many substances cause dermatitis in some persons. Among these are soaps, greases and oils, various substances in cosmetics, chemicals handled in some industries, and wool clothing. Preventing dermatitis depends on finding the cause.

Eczema is a general term commonly applied to any wet or scaly inflammation of the skin. It may mean almost anything. Treatment or prevention for any one person depends upon finding its cause. When the cause is known, the condition is usually not called eczema.

Several plants, such as poison ivy, poison oak, and poison sumac, cause inflammation of the skin (dermatitis) in some persons. The inflammation may be merely a few small, red, itchy spots, or there may be blisters over most of the body.

The irritating substance from these plants is an oil or a resin. This may reach the skin by direct contact or through something that has touched the plant, such as clothing, shoes, tennis balls, garden tools, or dogs. The oil or resin may remain on such articles for a long time.

Inflammation of the skin usually develops within 4 to 10 days after exposure. Very tiny amounts of the oil may cause severe reactions. The fact that a person has never been bothered by poison ivy or poison oak or poison sumac does not mean he may not be in the future.

The disease runs a course of one to

several weeks. Treatment of severe cases should be under the direction of a physician. The only sure prevention is to avoid the poisonous plants. Washing the skin immediately after being near the plants with gasoline or alcohol and soap and water may remove the oil and, thus, prevent development of the disease. Eating the leaves of the plant or drinking a "tea" made from them is sometimes suggested as a means of preventing the disease. This is dangerous and should be avoided.

Hives, which physicians call urticaria, consist of small pink and whitish lumps on the skin that look like insect bites. They vary in size, from the size of the head of a large pin to a half-inch or more in diameter. In severe cases, lips, eyelids, hands, and other parts of the body may swell. Itching is usually severe.

Hives are the result of a reaction to some substance to which the body is overly sensitive—that is, allergic (see Chapter 13). Some people are sensitive to dyes or materials in clothing or shoes; some to drugs, like the sulfonamides, penicillin, or even aspirin; some to dusts or materials from animals; and some to foods. Treatment by several new drugs, the antihistamines, gives relief in many cases. Prevention depends upon finding and avoiding whatever causes the hives.

Sunburn and prickly heat. Sunburn and snowburn are the effects of the ultraviolet light of the sun's rays (or of an ultraviolet lamp) upon the skin. Sunburn varies from a mild redness to swelling with blisters (see Chapter 4). In some cases, there is general illness and fever. Many a vacation is ruined for people who try to get a tan in a hurry.

Brown- and black-skinned people do not sunburn. Among members of the white race, blondes sunburn more easily than brunettes, who have more pigment in the skin. In fact, tanning is a natural way of protecting the body from the irritating effects of the sun's rays.

An oily skin offers more protection against sunburn than a dry skin does. Creams and oils help. Some lotions contain special chemicals that shut off the ultraviolet rays from the skin for a short time. A simpler way is not to stay too long in the sunshine until the skin is accustomed to it.

Much tanning causes the skin to dry and wrinkle. Those who wish to avoid looking old before their time should not attempt to bake themselves to a deep brown every summer. If they do, they must expect wrinkles in middle and later life.

Sunlight is irritating, and irritation seems to make the development of cancer easier (see Chapter 5). Skin cancers occur most often on the exposed parts of the body. In fact, one-third of the total are on the nose. Persons who work outdoors develop skin cancers more often than those who work indoors. Persons with fair skins are more likely to develop skin cancer than those with brunette skins. Facts like these indicate that there is a relationship between sunlight and skin cancer.

Wrinkles are to be expected in an old person. Do not encourage them while you are young by overexposing yourself to the sun. (Courtesy Standard Oil Co., N.J.)

Prickly heat is a condition that develops in some persons, especially babies, in hot weather. The skin becomes covered with tiny, red, itchy spots. Small blisters may form. The cause of prickly heat is believed to be too much sweat collecting in the sweat glands. Washing the skin often and putting on alcohol and powder usually give relief.

Herpes, warts, moles. Herpes are inflamed areas of the skin with tiny blisters that tend to run together and dry into crusts. The most common type usually appears on or near the lips and is known as a cold sore or fever blister. Herpes is caused by a virus, but colds, fevers, sunburn, and nervous strain make it easier for the virus to attack the skin. Cold sores are annoying but usually disappear in 2 or 3 weeks. Alum or camphor applied in the early stages may prevent full development of the herpes.

Warts are small, cauliflower-like growths in the upper layers of the skin. They usually grow on the hands. Warts are caused by a virus, an extremely small living thing, too small to be seen even through a microscope. They are not caused, as some say, by handling toads or frogs.

Most warts disappear after a time, even without treatment. Keeping the hands clean seems to help. Warts sometimes occur on the soles of the feet and may become so painful that they must be removed.

If a person wants warts removed, he should go to a physician. You can hear about all kinds of remedies for warts, but most of these do no good and some are dangerous.

Moles are growths in the deeper layers of the skin and contain pigment. Most moles are harmless, but sometimes one develops into a cancer (see Chapter 5). Repeated pressure or rubbing by clothing, shaving, or sometimes an unknown cause may make a mole grow suddenly. Most moles that start to grow and those in locations where they are constantly rubbed or pressed should be removed by a physician.

Birthmarks. A birthmark is a spot on the skin that is present at birth or appears immediately after birth. Some birthmarks are red, usually because of enlarged blood vessels just under the skin. Some are brown, owing to unusual amounts of brown pigment collected in those spots.

Birthmarks are not caused by fright on the part of the mother or by any other prenatal influence of that kind. The mother's influence on her baby is through her nutrition and general health.

Some birthmarks can be removed by a physician. A person should never try to remove one himself. Most birthmarks are small and are not noticed by other people.

GROOMING AIDS

Beauty cannot be bought in a bottle or a jar. Cosmetics may help you to improve your appearance, but they do not take the place of good skin care.

The manufacture of cosmetics has grown to be an important industry in the United States. Our grandmothers used a little rice powder and toilet water. Now a woman's dressing table may contain all kinds of powders, toilet waters, creams, rouges, lipsticks, mascaras, eyebrow pencils, hair dyes, hair curlers, hair stimulants, and nail polishes. Men, too, buy a great many hair oils, hair tonics, and after-shave lotions and creams.

How much do cosmetics cost? The public gets most of its information about cosmetics from the advertising agencies. These agencies have only one purpose—to sell the product they are advertising.

Advertisements are expensive, whether they come over radio or television, in newspapers and magazines, on billboards, or in leaflets left on drugstore counters. Sometimes money is paid to have well-known people let their names be used in advertisements.

Fancy bottles and boxes and elegant shops all add to the cost. The actual cost of any cosmetic is usually very little. Most brands are very much alike. If a person wants to use his money to pay for beautiful bottles he may do so, but he should know what he is buying.

How safe are cosmetics? In the past, cosmetics sometimes contained dangerous substances, which left scars, made people ill, and even caused blindness. The federal Food and Drug Administration now attempts to prevent the sale of these substances. Recently the American Medical Association formed a Council on Cosmetics. Its purpose is to study cosmetics and give its approval to those that are made of harmless materials. There are some commercial companies in the United States that make reports on the materials used in advertised products and on their cost.

Some chemicals in cosmetics are harmless for most people but may be harmful to some people. This is true for some of the new substances about which we do not know too much. Rashes, hives, failure to make red blood cells, and damage to the liver have been reported in persons who are sensitive to such substances.

Face creams, powders, lotions. Ordinary cold cream is the basis for most creams. It adds oil to the skin and so may prevent roughness and chapping. It is especially useful for people whose oil glands do not secrete enough oil. Special creams advertised as "tissue-building creams," or "nourishing creams," or "skin foods" are cold creams with a little something else added. However, tissue building and nourishment are done by food taken into the digestive tract, not by cream on the skin. Any good food is skin food.

The type of cream called vanishing cream is actually a kind of soap. When such a cream is rubbed into the face, it is like leaving soap on the face after washing. Because of this, vanishing creams tend to dry the skin. For people who have an oily skin, this may be all right. Used on a dry skin, vanishing cream will increase the dryness. It may cause scaling and roughness of the skin.

Face powders usually contain talcum, magnesia, French chalk, rice powder, and a little coloring matter. Before the Food and Drug Administration was started, many face pow-

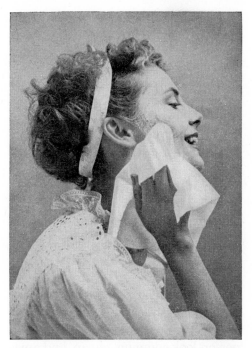

Cold cream may be helpful for persons with dry skin. Using cold cream does not take the place of washing with soap and water. (Courtesy Pond's Extract Co.)

ders contained lead, mercury, or bismuth, all of which are harmful. Some face powders have been made with orris root, to which many people are allergic. At the present time, the better manufacturers do not put any of these into their powders.

In selecting a face powder, a girl should find one whose color and perfume best suit her. The inexpensive varieties in large plain boxes are very much like the expensive ones in decorated boxes. Sometimes girls with little money hope that an expensive powder will work a charm on their complexions, but they should spend their money on good food and build beauty from the inside.

If you know that you are allergic to anything, such as rice, wheat, or orris root, you should choose a powder without this substance in it. If you change the powder you are using, it is well to watch for a little while to see what it does to your skin.

A girl should keep her powder puff clean and never use another person's powder puff. Powder puffs very quickly become full of bacteria. Some of those from your neighbor's face may do harm to your face.

Rouge and lipstick are ordinarily harmless cosmetics. If used skillfully, they may add to a girl's attractiveness. When too much rouge and lipstick are used at any one time or when they are put on inartistically, they make a person look common, cheap, and amateurish. They should, of course, be kept strictly for one's own use, since various disease organisms can easily be passed from one person to another. Good taste demands also that they be applied in private and not in public places. The possible danger in the use of rouge and lipstick is that they may contain certain aniline dyes to which some people may be allergic.

Astringents are sometimes used by older persons whose skins are wrinkling and whose muscles are not firm. They are supposed to "close the pores" and "tone up" sagging tissues. Whatever effect they have wears off very quickly. A little cold water after washing the face will give about the same results by contracting the blood vessels. Astringents usually contain alcohol, which causes a tingling feeling in the skin.

The use of eyebrow and eyelash dyes, eye lotions and creams, in fact anything around the eyes is dangerous. The risk of irritation to the eyes is too great. Sparkling attractive eyes result usually from two things: (1) plenty of sleep, good food, and exercise; (2) being really interested in people and things. Dyes used to darken eyelashes and eyebrows may have carbon (lampblack) or other coloring added to a soap base, which smarts if it gets in the eye, or the colors may be mixed with waxes, which do not smart. These dyes come in solid or semiliquid form, and a brush is sometimes used for their application.

Deodorants. Body odor is caused by fatty acids that are formed from sweat, or perspiration. Body odor is not common in children, but after puberty the sweat glands change and produce the fatty acids, which may become offensive.

Everyone perspires more in hot weather, or when exercising, or when under nervous strain; hence, extra care is needed at these times. People who work close to other persons, such as physicians, dentists, beauty-parlor operators, teachers, and students, should be very sure that they are free of body odor.

The most important remedy for body odor is frequent bathing and frequent changing and cleaning of clothes. A deodorant, that is, something which takes away odors, can be used under the arms.

There are two types of substances

commonly advertised to stop body odor—those that deodorize the perspiration but do not stop its flow, and those that both deodorize and stop the flow of perspiration. The first type depends for its action upon such substances as boric acid, benzoic acid, or zinc stearate. This type may be obtained either in dry or paste form. It is usually harmless to use. The second type usually contains aluminum chloride, tannic acid, zinc sulfate, or aluminum sulfate. Many people use this type of deodorant, usually in liquid form, without harm, but it causes a skin rash or other discomfort in some persons. If this type of preparation is used, it should be used no oftener than is absolutely necessary.

Preparations containing chlorophyll, the green pigment of leaves and plants, have been widely used during the past several years as a deodorant. Spraying into the air or evaporation from wicks are the most common methods of use. Chlorophyll toothpastes, foot and body powders, and tablets or capsules to be taken by mouth are also widely advertised to prevent body odors and are used by many people.

It is difficult to be certain just how effective these chlorophyll preparations are. Some reports are quite enthusiastic; others are doubtful of their value. Time will probably give us the real answer.

Depilatories. A depilatory is a substance that removes hair. The common methods of hair removal are shaving, scraping the skin with pum-

ice stone or emery board, or the use of hair removers. None of these methods removes the hair permanently, because they have no effect on the root of the hair where growing takes place. The only safe method of permanently removing hair is electrolysis. In this method, an electric needle is used to destroy each hair root. Unless this is done by an expert, it may cause scarring. Because each hair must be removed separately, this is an expensive method of hair removal.

Depilatories are of two kinds, chemical and wax. In some individuals, they cause irritation of the skin and may even lead to a skin infection. Some manufacturers of chemical and wax depilatories claim that they remove the hair permanently. Such claims are entirely false.

One safe method for removing hair is use of the safety razor. You can be sure that there is no danger of skin irritation or poisoning from any chemical. Despite a common belief, shaving does not cause the hair to grow out coarser and thicker than it was before. To test this, two scientists had three girls shave the left leg from knee to ankle twice a week for 8 months. After the hair had grown out again, microscopic examination of the hairs of the left leg and of the right leg, which had not been shaved, showed that there was no difference between the hairs on the leg that had been shaved and the hairs on the leg that had not been shaved.

Plucking the hair is a safe method of removing hair but is very time consuming and unpleasant. Plucking the

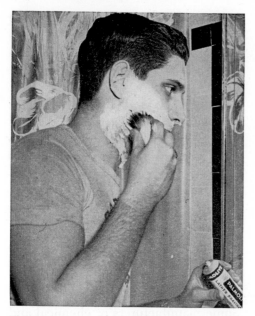

This boy uses a brush. (Courtesy *Scholastic Magazines* and Colgate-Palmolive Co.)

eyebrows is sometimes stylish and seems to be a matter of personal taste. Hair should never be plucked from a mole, because this may cause irritation of the mole.

Shaving. One of the marks of a man as compared to a woman or a boy is the growth of hair on the face. Today, practically every man removes this hair by shaving. In times gone by, beards were common and were considered a mark of distinction and of maturity. In fact many of the bearded generals of our War Between the States were young men in their late 20's or early 30's.

In an adolescent boy, the hair on the face is fine and soft. In a matter of a few years, however, beard hair becomes 2 to 4 times as coarse as scalp hair. Beard hair grows about $\frac{1}{64}$ inch

per day, which is somewhat faster than scalp hair. Shaving does not increase the speed of growth or the development of a stiff beard.

Shaving today is done almost entirely with safety razors or electric razors. Either kind will give a satisfactory shave. The choice between the two is, therefore, a matter of preference. The same can be said of the various types of shaving soaps, creams, and pastes.

The age at which shaving should be started varies for different boys. Delay in the growth of one's beard is no cause for concern. The frequency of shaving should depend upon the speed of growth and the circumstances that make good grooming desirable.

Bay rum, witch hazel, eau de cologne, and other after-shave lotions, as well as various kinds of talcum powders, are widely advertised and extensively used by men. Their appeal lies in the pleasant sensation and odor that follow their use.

THE HAIR

Your hair, like all other structures of the body, gets its nourishment from the blood. If your general health is good, your hair and scalp will be healthy. Cleanliness is one of the most important aids in keeping the hair attractive.

Like the skin of your face and hands, your hair is exposed to smoke and dirt. To keep the scalp and hair clean, your hair should be washed at least once every 2 weeks with a pure mild soap or shampoo preparation.

For some people, a weekly shampoo is necessary. Daily brushing of your hair will prevent accumulation of dirt, and will help to keep your hair attractive.

Dandruff. Extreme dryness, oiliness, dandruff, or falling out of the hair indicate that something is wrong. A physician should be consulted. Certain types of dandruff cause a thick oily scale to appear on the scalp. These types are caused by an infection and should be treated as such by a physician. The more common type of dandruff causes dry scales to appear on the scalp. This type usually results from poor habits of living, such as lack of sleep or nervous strain or sometimes improper diet.

Most of the so-called "dandruff cures" that are advertised are of no more value in curing dandruff than are soap and water.

Hair oils. Hair oils may be helpful to people with dry hair and scalp if the dryness is not caused by disease. The oil need not be expensive. Mineral oil or olive oil, with perfume if desired, is satisfactory.

The common practice among boys of using oils to keep the hair in place sometimes improves their appearance and is not objectionable if the oil is used in small amounts and if the hair is washed often to remove the oil and the dirt that clings to it.

Shining hair is a sign of health and good care. Eating the proper food and brushing the hair and shampooing it make the hair more attractive than

Daily brushing of your hair is important. (Courtesy E. I. du Pont de Nemours Co.)

the use of brilliantine or lacquer. If these preparations are used on special occasions, the hair should be thoroughly brushed or washed afterward to keep it from looking dull and dirty.

Hair dyes. Hair dyes should be avoided. Some seem harmless. Others contain dangerous substances that may cause baldness or severe damage to the skin or eyes or kidneys. The bleaches that remove the color from the hair and enable a brunette to become a blonde at her pleasure are probably not harmful, although they may leave the hair dry and brittle.

Permanent waves. The permanent wave is a method of curling naturally straight hair. Chemicals and, in many cases, heat are applied to change the

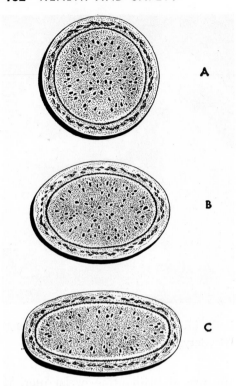

Cross section of (A) very straight hair, (B) wavy hair, (C) very curly hair. Putting a wave in straight hair or straightening curly hair affects the hair for only a short time. It has no effect on the new hair growing from the roots.

shape of the individual hairs. The permanent, if it is done skillfully so as not to damage the scalp or the roots of the hair, probably has no harmful effect on the hair. The heat may make the hair dry, but this effect is usually not lasting.

A process similar to the one used in permanent waving can be used to straighten kinky or curly hair.

Baldness. Hair is thickest in the late teens and becomes thinner as people grow older. Sometimes scalp infec-

tions or poisons from hair dyes cause young people to become bald. Hair may be lost also as a result of severe illness, certain vitamin deficiencies, or other causes. In such cases, the hair usually grows again when the basic difficulty is corrected.

Little is known about the actual cause of baldness in older people. Baldness is far more common in men than in women, probably owing to some influence of the internal secretions of the sex glands. Heredity is one factor; hence, men can usually expect to become bald if their fathers and uncles are bald. In spite of the claims of advertisers and the millions of dollars that are spent on hair tonics and scalp treatments, there is no way known to prevent baldness or to make hair grow on bald spots.

THE NAILS

Good grooming of both boys and girls includes cleaning the fingernails and keeping them smooth and unbroken. A good appearance can be spoiled by fingernails that are dirty or unpleasant looking. Broken nails and sore fingertips interfere with skillful work.

Care of fingernails and toenails. Your nails should be cleaned regularly and the skin, or cuticle, around them should be pushed back with an orangewood stick or some other blunt instrument. Sharp metal instruments may injure the tissues.

Hangnails are torn pieces of cuticle. They should be cut off carefully, not torn. A piece of adhesive tape over the side of the nail gives protection until the skin has grown smooth. Infections sometimes start in torn or bitten skin around the nails.

Nails should be cut when they grow long, never bitten. Fingernails may be rounded but should not be cut down too far at the sides. It is better to cut toenails straight across. This prevents ingrown nails. An ingrown nail curls into the flesh at the edge. This can be uncomfortable and, also, it makes an easy place for an infection to start.

Nail biting. Some people bite their nails without thinking what they are doing. More rest and trying not to get too excited and upset about things is the best treatment. Sometimes a manicure helps a person to remember not to bite his nails.

Nail polish. Nowadays many girls like to use colored polish on their fingernails and sometimes on their toenails. This draws attention to the hands, or feet, and makes it important to give them good care.

Nail polish itself is harmless, unless it contains something to which the wearer is allergic. To look well, polish must be applied evenly. Polish that is half on and half off makes a poor impression.

HOW IMPORTANT IS BEAUTY?

This chapter gives you some important facts about the skin and how to take good care of it. Beauty is not just "skin deep," but care of the skin helps you to make the best of whatever

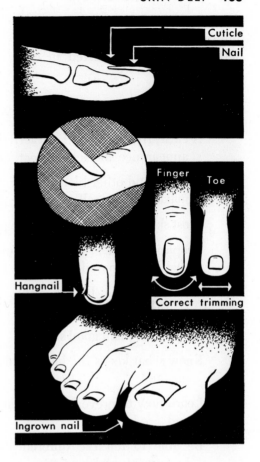

good looks you have. Your appearance is important but only as it adds to your friendships and satisfaction in living.

Great beauty is sometimes a handicap rather than a help. You probably know pretty girls and handsome boys who depend upon their looks to get what they want. There is a temptation for them to become vain and self-conscious, for other people to envy, rather than admire, them.

Usually, the boys and girls with average, or even homely, looks are the ones who become charming and popular. They learn about clothes, exercise, food, and good grooming. They are interested in things outside of themselves. They are interested in other people.

It is a mistake not to pay attention to how you look. It is just as much a mistake to think that your looks are the most important thing about you.

SO WHAT?

A clear, fresh skin, and attractive hair and nails improve a person's appearance and self-respect; and

Pimples and other blemishes of the skin are unsightly and tend to make a person self-conscious; and

Most skin diseases can easily be prevented; and

People waste a great deal of money on advertised preparations that are supposed to improve their appearance; and

Most people can have healthy, attractive skin, hair, and nails by simple, inexpensive means;

So, it is just plain good sense to

Know what keeps the hair, skin, and nails healthy and good-looking; and

Learn how to prevent skin diseases that are unpleasant and ugly; and

Be able to tell the difference between worthless and helpful beauty aids and cosmetics.

CHECKING UP

1. Of what value is your skin?
2. How is the dermis different from the epidermis?
3. There is an old saying "You change your skin every 7 years." What is the "germ of truth" behind this statement?
4. How do infections usually start in the skin?
5. What is good clothing for hot weather? Why?
6. What is good clothing for cold weather? Why?
7. How is good ventilation related to making the skin comfortable?
8. What helps to make your skin beautiful "from the inside"?
9. Should you take hot baths? warm baths? cold baths? What are the values of each? Are there dangers in any of these?
10. How do pimples usually form? How should a person with acne

change his diet? How is careful washing of the face related to acne? Is acne more common among persons with dry skins or oily skins? What should you do about blackheads?

11. What is the cause of boils? How may they be spread?

12. Why is impetigo more common among children than among older people? among athletes than among nonathletes?

13. What is the cause of athlete's foot? How can you keep from getting it?

14. How does keeping yourself and your clothing clean help to prevent skin disorders? Which skin disorders are likely to result from uncleanliness?

15. What does dermatitis mean? List some of the skin disorders that are included under the general term *dermatitis*? If a person says he has infectious dermatitis, what does he mean?

16. What makes the skin tan? What are the advantages of tanning? disadvantages?

17. What are the facts that indicate there may be a relationship between sunlight and cancer?

18. What is the difference between a wart and a mole?

19. On a piece of paper make a table as shown in the example. In the first column, write the names of all the skin disorders listed in this chapter. In the second column, write the cause of each. In the third column, write ways of preventing each. In the fourth column, write how each should be treated. In the fifth column, write any other points you think people should know about each.

Skin disorder	Cause	Prevention	Treatment	Other important points
1) Blisters				
2) Corns				
3)				
4)				

20. What is the difference between cold cream and vanishing cream? What is the usefulness of each? Should you clean your face with soap and water or with cold cream?

21. Make a list of rules for use of cosmetics. Give the reason for each.

22. What are the two kinds of deodorants?

23. How can you remove unwanted hair? Which are the least expensive and safest methods?
24. How is diet related to care of the hair? What does brushing do for the hair?
25. What is dandruff?
26. Can baldness be prevented? Explain your answer.
27. How should you care for your fingernails? your toenails?
28. Is scolding a child the best way to cure him of biting his nails? Explain.

THINGS TO DO

1. To see what evaporation does, wet a piece of cotton and place it on the bulb of a thermometer. Watch the mercury. Why does evaporation of perspiration cool you? Can you explain why a person feels more comfortable in hot dry weather on a desert than in hot moist weather in a tropical jungle?
2. Place a piece of wet cotton on the bulb of a thermometer and fan it. Does the mercury move faster or more slowly? (Fanning blows the layers of wet air away as they form.) Why does an electric fan make a warm, stuffy room more comfortable?
3. Ask the school nurse which skin diseases she finds most often in the schools she visits. How can they be prevented?
4. Ask a physical-education teacher how the physical-education department tries to prevent the spread of athlete's foot in your school.
5. If poison ivy, poison oak, or poison sumac grows in your neighborhood, learn what it looks like.
6. Ask a number of people what they have heard will cure warts. One amusing "cure" is described in *Huckleberry Finn*.
7. Find what people think about the cause of birthmarks.
8. Collect advertisements of cosmetics. What do they claim that the products they are advertising will do? How true are these claims? How much of the advertisements have nothing to do with the cosmetics advertised?
9. Look at the display of cosmetics in a drugstore or a beauty parlor. Which is more important in selling them: the fancy packages or what is in the packages? Ask a druggist to tell about the sale of cosmetics.
10. Arrange an assembly program for the girls of the school. Ask a teacher or a beauty-parlor operator to demonstrate a manicure

and care of the nails; choice of make-up for girls of your age; brushing, shampooing, and arranging the hair.

11. It is fun to make cosmetics. Look in an applied chemistry book or consumer chemistry book for directions for making a suntan oil; a bubble bath; a cold cream. Ask a chemistry teacher to help you.

12. Appoint one member of the class to make a special report on what the Food and Drug Administration does.

13. Arrange a display for boys, showing clothes and shoes for school, for sports, for work, for Sunday, and for various seasons of the year. Stores in the community may be of help in providing exhibits. Ask young men in the community to tell something about grooming and care of clothes.

CHAPTER 11 Your Life Blood

"Red-blooded Americans"—this is what all of us think we are or hope to be. By "red-blooded" we mean strong, healthy, full of life, energy, and courage. All blood is red, of course, but there are different degrees of redness, just as there are different degrees of health and vitality. And there is often a relationship between the condition of the blood and the state of health.

THE BLOOD

The blood is the transportation medium of the body. It is mostly water and moves continuously through the blood vessels. Floating in the blood are millions of tiny cells: the red and the white blood cells, or corpuscles.

Everything that reaches your body's trillions of cells must be carried by the blood—food and oxygen from the outside, medicines you may have taken, and hormones produced within your body. All the waste products from the cells must be carried by the blood to the lungs, kidneys, and skin to be excreted.

Blood and lymph. An adult of average size has 6 to 7 quarts of blood: this amounts to about one-twentieth of the weight of his body. The liquid part of the blood is yellowish in color and is called plasma.

As the blood gives up food materials to the tissues, some of the plasma leaves the blood stream with the food. This fluid surrounds the cells of the body and is called lymph (see Chapter 5). Lymph comes from the blood but is not considered part of the blood.

RED BLOOD CELLS

There are more red blood cells than white cells. The red cells look like thin circular disks, thinner at the center than at the sides. The diameter of one red cell is about 7.5 microns, or 0.0003 of an inch; its thickness is about one-fifth of its diameter. One drop of human blood contains more than 300 million red cells. A cubic millimeter of blood (an amount about the size of the head of a pin) contains about 5 million red cells. In all the blood of any one person, there are some 30 trillion red blood cells. Placed side by side, they would cover almost an acre.

Red cells carry oxygen. The red color of the blood is due to the hemoglobin contained in the red cells. Hemoglobin is rich in iron. It absorbs oxygen from the air in the lungs and becomes bright red in color. As blood is carried to the tissues of the body, some of the oxygen is given off for use by the cells, and the hemoglobin goes back to its original color. This is the bluish-red shade that we see in the blood from our veins.

Red blood cells are formed in the bone marrow and live only about 120 days (see Chapter 6). For this reason, it is necessary that your food contain the iron needed for the manufacture of these cells (see Chapters 8 and 9).

Carbon monoxide poisoning. Certain gases and chemical substances, other than oxygen, are able to combine with hemoglobin. One of these is carbon monoxide, the deadly gas from the exhausts of automobiles and from gas jets. Hemoglobin absorbs carbon monoxide much more easily than it does oxygen. Therefore, if a person breathes air that contains a large amount of carbon monoxide gas, the hemoglobin in his blood cannot carry oxygen, because it is all combined with carbon monoxide. The result is death, owing to the lack of oxygen for the cells of the body. This is really a kind of internal suffocation.

The treatment of carbon monoxide poisoning is to take the victim immediately into fresh air. If breathing has

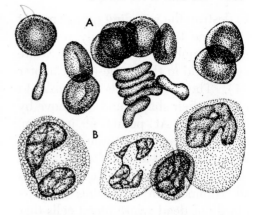

(A) Red blood cells. (B) White blood cells.

ceased, artificial respiration should be started, and pure oxygen should be given by mask if it can be obtained (see Chapter 4).

WHITE BLOOD CELLS

The white blood cells vary in size and in number more than do the red cells. Usually, a person has 5000 to 9000 white cells, as compared with 5 million red cells, per cubic millimeter of blood. Under some conditions, this number will increase many times. Infections are the usual cause of an increase in white cells, although exercise, digestion, and other bodily processes cause a small increase that lasts for a short time.

White cells fight infection. The white blood cells aid your body in defending itself against disease organisms. The white cells are somewhat like a nation's army. When disease organisms invade your body, the white blood cells collect in large numbers at the point of attack and attempt to destroy the invading organisms. At the same time, your body produces large numbers of additional white cells to aid in the battle (see Chapter 24). The white cells are able to change their shapes and can move by themselves. At points of infection, they make their way through the capillary walls and attack the disease organisms in the tissues. The yellow pus so common in infections consists chiefly of dead white blood cells that have been destroyed in this battle.

Knowing how many white blood cells a sick person has will help a physician to discover the cause of the person's illness. The number of white cells is counted under a microscope (see Chapter 26). For example, in appendicitis, the white-cell count frequently increases from the usual 5000–9000 to 15,000–25,000 per cubic millimeter of blood.

Changes in the number of white blood cells during an illness indicate whether the infection is spreading or being brought under control. In fatal infections, the number of white cells often decreases before death, indicating that the battle against the invading harmful organisms has been lost.

Some infections and drugs cause a decrease in number of white cells. In most virus infections, such as influenza and measles, the number of white blood cells tends to decrease rather than to increase. This is true also for a few bacterial infections.

Another serious cause of decrease in the number of white blood cells is the poisonous effect of certain drugs.

Among these are some of the headache remedies and the sulfonamides. The queer part of it is that the poisonous effect occurs only in certain individuals. Such persons are unusually sensitive to the drugs. When such a person takes one of these drugs, he loses so many white blood cells that he has no resistance to infection, and even a sore throat may cause his death. You should not take such drugs unless a physician has prescribed them for you.

DISEASES OF THE BLOOD

The blood goes everywhere in the body. Anything that happens anywhere affects the blood, and the blood has an influence on the whole body.

Anemia. The most common disease of the blood is anemia. Anemia means a lack of hemoglobin. Since hemoglobin carries oxygen, a person with anemia is not getting all the oxygen that his tissues need. There is plenty of oxygen in the air he breathes, but he cannot get enough of it out to his tissues.

This lack of oxygen in the tissues usually results in breathlessness and fatigue after very little exertion. Since hemoglobin supplies the color of the blood, persons with anemia tend to be pale.

What causes anemia? One cause of anemia is loss of blood from a wound or severe bleeding following an accident. Usually, the person is thirsty and drinks a good deal of water. The

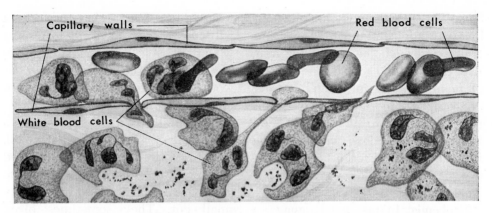

White blood cells moving out of capillary to attack bacteria in area of infection.

blood takes the water rapidly from the digestive tract. It also takes fluids from the tissues. In most cases, the unusual amount of water in the blood stirs up the bone marrow to manufacture blood cells to make up for the ones that were lost. Making hemoglobin for the red blood cells requires iron. This may be given in food or in medicine or both.

Another cause of anemia is failure to form enough hemoglobin. In this case, a person may have plenty of red blood cells, but the cells do not contain enough hemoglobin. Often the reason for this is a diet that lacks iron. The condition is usually found in babies and among the poor.

Pernicious anemia. One type of anemia is known as pernicious anemia, so called because until recent years it was always fatal. In this disease, not enough red blood cells are formed. Individual red cells are large and contain more hemoglobin than normal. The number, however, keeps falling until there are too few to keep the person alive. Iron does no good in this case.

Today, we know that pernicious anemia can be successfully treated. The answer is liver, folic acid, or a new vitamin called B_{12}. These substances contain something that starts the blood factories in the bone marrow working. Treatment with these substances enables people who would have died years ago to live on for many years and enjoy good health.

Watch your hemoglobin. Everyone should have a thorough physical examination every year (see Chapter 26). This yearly checkup should include a test for hemoglobin. The test consists in first taking a drop of blood from the ear or the finger. The redness of the drop will show in general how much hemoglobin is present. Sometimes a chemical test is made to find how much iron is in the blood. Or the physician may find how many red cells are in 1 cubic millimeter of blood.

If your physician finds that you

have too little hemoglobin, he may give you advice about food, rest, exercise, and medicine containing iron, liver extract, folic acid, or vitamin B$_{12}$. Or he may find an infection in tonsils, or teeth, or some other organ that is causing damage to the red cells. Following his directions will keep you from developing a serious case of anemia.

Leukemia. In medical language, a white blood cell is called a leucocyte.[1] In the disease called leukemia, there is a great increase in the number of these cells. There may be 10 to 20 times the usual number.

The cause of leukemia is not known, but it acts like and is considered a cancer of the white cells; that is, the white cells are formed in such numbers that the functions of the body are interfered with (see Chapter 5). This disease usually occurs in young persons and takes more lives per year than better-known diseases, such as scarlet fever, poliomyelitis, and measles.

We do not know how to prevent or to cure this disease. It is possible to slow its progress and thereby prolong life by the use of x-ray or atomic radiation and with certain drugs, including ACTH (see page 373). However, no real cure for leukemia has been discovered.

Hemophilia. When healthy blood is

[1] The word *leucocyte* comes from two Greek words, *leuco* meaning white, and *cyte* meaning cell. *Leukemia* comes from *leuco*, white, and *emia*, blood.

exposed to the air, it clots and forms a jelly-like mass. When a clot forms in a wound, it acts as a seal and stops bleeding. Except for this, a minor cut would lead to death from loss of blood.

Hemophilia is a disease in which the blood clots slowly or not at all. Persons with hemophilia are called bleeders. Such persons are likely to lose a great deal of blood from a very small cut. They sometimes bleed within the body, especially into the joints. A minor operation may be serious in these cases. For this reason, hospitals find out before an operation how long it takes a patient's blood to clot.

Hemophilia is hereditary but in a special way. It occurs almost exclusively in males. However, it is passed on by females. A son does not inherit it from his father; and a man cannot pass it on to his son. A daughter will not show the disease herself but can pass it on to her son.

BLOOD TRANSFUSIONS

A blood transfusion is the transfer of blood from the blood vessels of one person into the blood vessels of another. The person who gives the blood is called a donor.

Blood given in a transfusion does two things. It provides liquid. This means that the person who receives the blood will not have to draw liquid out of his own tissues. The blood also provides red cells. These carry oxygen until the person receiving the blood can make more red cells of his own.

A transfusion is a help in an emergency. It is needed after an injury in which much blood has been lost. In hospitals, transfusions are often given after operations and even to prepare patients for operations.

The blood that comes from the donor is destroyed and excreted from the body of the person who receives it within a few days. By then, it is hoped that the person receiving the blood will have been able to make enough new blood of his own.

Blood types. Sometimes you may see in the newspaper an article asking for blood of a certain type to be given to some child or badly injured person. Human blood seems to fall into four different classes, or types. The types are named A, B, AB, and O. Blood of one type will mix safely with blood of the same type; and some types will mix with two or three other types.

Before a physician transfers blood from one person to another, he must know whether the blood of these persons will mix safely. If the wrong type of blood is injected into a person, the blood cells are destroyed, and the person who receives the blood becomes violently ill and may die.

The same types of blood are found in all races of human beings. So long as blood comes from healthy persons and is of the right type it does not matter whether it comes from a man or a woman, a white person, a Chinese, a Negro, or an Indian.

Rh factor. Recently there has been a great deal of work done on the Rh factor in blood. Some people have the Rh factor in their blood; some do not. Blood containing Rh factor is called Rh positive. Blood that does not contain the Rh factor is called Rh negative. Rh-positive blood should not be given to persons with Rh-negative blood. This may be safely done once, but afterward it would be dangerous, so the best method is to avoid doing it the first time.

The Rh factor may be important also to the health and even the life of a newborn baby, particularly if the father is Rh positive and the mother is Rh negative. It is wise, therefore, when a couple expects to have a baby, to know whether both the father and the mother carry the Rh factor in their blood.

Blood banks. As recently as 1930, sick or injured people often died while waiting for a donor with the right type of blood to be found. About 1936, someone had the wonderful idea of setting up blood banks. Today, in large cities, blood banks are established at central places, usually hospitals. Here, blood of all types is collected from healthy donors and stored under refrigeration, so that it is always ready when someone needs it.

Perhaps a boy on a bicycle has been hurt in a traffic accident. Perhaps a small child has a disease that is destroying his blood. Perhaps a patient has lost large amounts of blood in an operation. Whatever the emergency, the blood bank is ready to meet it. Hospitals are kept constantly supplied. The delivery truck from the

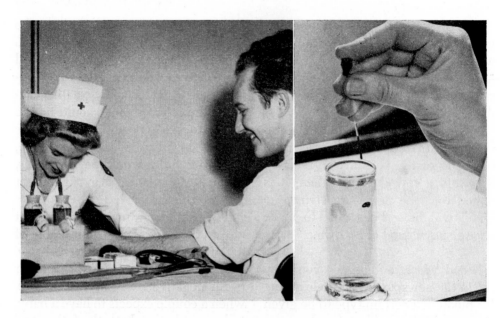

(Top left) Before a person is allowed to donate blood, it is important to find whether it is safe for him to give a pint of blood. Here a nurse takes a little blood from a man who wishes to be a donor. (Top right) The blood is tested to find how much hemoglobin it contains. (Bottom left) It takes from 5 to 7 minutes to give blood after the hemoglobin test is made. (Bottom right) Blood is tested to find the blood type and the Rh factor. (Courtesy American Red Cross)

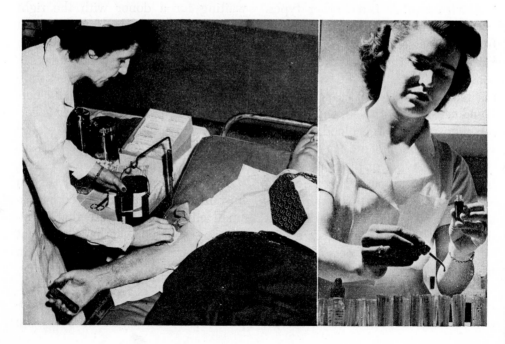

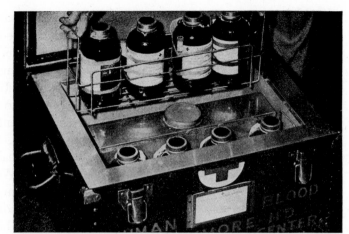

(Top) Typed blood is packed in refrigerated boxes, which keep it at a proper temperature. (Bottom) Having blood of the right type ready for use saves lives. Here a blood transfusion is being given to a badly burned child. (Courtesy American Red Cross)

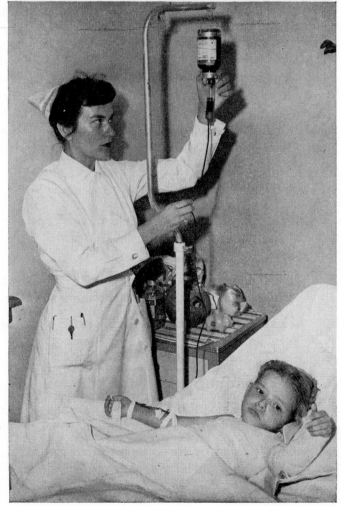

blood bank can reach the place where blood is needed within a few minutes. There is none of the delay that often prevented the saving of a life 15 or 20 years ago.

During wartime a great deal of blood is needed to supply wounded servicemen and women. Refrigerated blood can be taken by air to points immediately behind the front lines and given to injured persons very soon after they are wounded. The American Red Cross collects blood in many places in the United States, types it, and gets it ready to be transported to the places where it is needed.

Blood plasma. Blood in blood banks is whole blood; that is, it contains plasma and blood cells. This cannot be kept more than a few weeks, even under refrigeration. After that, the plasma is separated from the cells and is dried. Dried plasma can be mixed with water and given to accident victims who cannot be reached with whole blood. Used in this way, plasma has proved to be extremely valuable in the prevention and treatment of shock.

A great deal of dried plasma was used during World War II and during the first 2 years of the fighting in Korea when whole blood was not available. Its use, however, has been practically discontinued, and other substances have been developed that serve almost as well as plasma for the treatment of shock.

Plasma, however, is serving another very valuable purpose: from plasma we obtain the gamma globulin used for the prevention of measles and a few other diseases.

SO WHAT?

The blood carries to the cells of the body everything that they need and carries away the wastes that they should get rid of; and

The liquid part of the blood contains digested foods, water, vitamins, minerals, hormones, and other substances; and

Floating in the blood are millions of blood cells, red ones and white ones; and

The red blood cells contain hemoglobin, which makes the blood red and carries oxygen to the cells of the body; and

The white blood cells help the body to fight infections and, like a defending army, increase rapidly when an infection starts; and

Giving blood by transfusion to persons who need it, frequently saves lives and hastens recovery from illness;

So, it is important to

Keep your blood in healthy condition by being certain that your diet contains the proper foods, including plenty of iron to make hemoglobin; and

Know what type your blood is, so that you can safely give or receive transfusions when necessary; and

Keep your body in good condition, so that it can produce the blood cells that are needed for health and to resist disease.

CHECKING UP

1. What are the parts of the blood?
2. What substances are added to the blood in the lungs? What substances are taken from the blood in the lungs? What substances do all of the cells of the body add to the blood? What substances do all the cells of the body take away from the blood? What substances are added to the blood in the digestive tract? What substances are taken away from the blood in the skin? What substances are taken away from the blood in the kidneys? What substances are added to the blood in the bone marrow?
3. How is lymph formed?
4. What is hemoglobin? Which part of the blood contains hemoglobin? What is the function of the hemoglobin?
5. What happens in the blood in case of carbon monoxide poisoning?
6. How many red corpuscles are found in 1 cubic millimeter of blood? How many white corpuscles are found in 1 cubic millimeter of blood?
7. What is the shape of the red corpuscles? of the white corpuscles?
8. What is pus?
9. Why does a physician want to know the number of white blood cells in a patient's blood?
10. Why does a person with anemia get tired easily? Why does a person with anemia look pale?
11. What are the causes of anemia? What is the treatment in each case?
12. Why is leukemia considered a form of cancer?
13. Why is it important to know before an operation whether a patient has hemophilia or not? Do more men or more women have hemophilia?

14. What is Rh-positive blood? Rh-negative blood? Of what importance is it to know whether a person has Rh-positive or Rh-negative blood?
15. What two purposes are served by a blood transfusion? Is a blood transfusion of permanent or temporary value? Explain.
16. Why is it desirable for everyone to know his blood type?
17. Does a blood bank contain whole blood or plasma?
18. In what ways is whole blood more useful than plasma?

THINGS TO DO

1. Ask the biology teacher to show your class blood under a microscope.
2. Next time you cut your finger notice whether your blood clots quickly.
3. Ask the school nurse to show you a test for hemoglobin.
4. Ask the Red Cross about the blood-donor service in your community. Who can give blood? How is the blood collected? How much is needed in your community? What is it used for? How much is sent away?
5. Appoint members of the class to make special reports on hemophilia in the Russian and Spanish royal families; on the Rh factor; on typing blood.

CHAPTER 12 Your Heart and

Circulation

"He has a kind heart." "Have a heart!" "He loved her with all his heart." How many times have you heard statements like these? They sound as if the heart were the organ for kindness, love, and friendship. But physicians and scientists who study the human body think of the heart as a pump. It is an important pump, to be sure, a pump that keeps the blood moving through the blood vessels, but a pump nonetheless.

Your blood circulates through your body; that is, it moves out from your heart through the blood vessels to all parts of your body and then comes back to the heart. There are miles and miles of blood vessels. If all the blood vessels in your body could be stretched out and measured, there would probably be more than 100,000 miles of them.

The blood circulates very rapidly. It takes only 1 or 2 seconds for it to pass through the heart, about 15 sec-onds for it to go from heart to lungs and back to the heart, 10 to 15 seconds to go from heart to brain and back to heart, 20 to 25 seconds to go from heart to toes and back to heart. In other words, the blood can flow completely around your body in about 1 minute. A blood cell can make 2000 or more such trips in a day.

THE HEART

Your heart is a pear-shaped organ made of muscle. It is about the size of your fist. It is hollow and is divided into two parts by a wall of muscle (see Chapter 6). This wall makes the heart a double pump, or rather two pumps that act together.

Each side of the heart, each pump, is divided into an upper part, an auricle, and a lower part, a ventricle. The heart, therefore, contains four parts, or chambers. Blood flows into the auricles from the veins, then down into

199

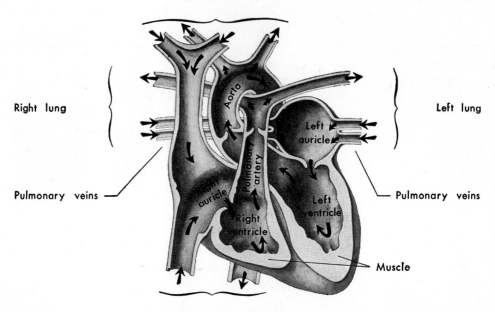

The two auricles receive blood at the same time from veins. Blood passes from the auricles to the ventricles, through valves that prevent flow in the opposite direction. The two ventricles discharge blood at the same time into the main arteries. Valves keep blood from flowing back into the ventricles.

the ventricles. The ventricles pump the blood out of the heart into the arteries.

Valves. There are valves between the auricles and ventricles. There are also valves in the arteries where the arteries leave the heart. The valves open in only one direction. At each heartbeat, the muscles of the heart contract and squeeze out the blood. The valves close during each contraction and do not allow the blood to flow backward. This means that blood flows forward, from veins to auricles to ventricles to arteries.

In certain infections, such as rheu-

matic fever, scarlet fever, tonsillitis, abscessed teeth, and sinus infections, disease organisms get into the blood and may set up infections on the valves of the heart. These infections may damage the valves, so that they do not close tightly. Blood then leaks back through the damaged valves with each heartbeat.

When some of the blood leaks back through a valve with each heartbeat, the heart must work harder to keep the necessary amount of blood circulating. The heart is usually able to do this by increasing the size and strength of its muscle cells. If the damage is very great, or if too much strain is put on the heart by heavy exercise, the heart may not be able to circulate the blood. It may even stop beating.

As the valves of the heart close, they make sounds that are known as heart sounds. If a valve does not close properly, a blowing or swishing noise may occur as the blood leaks back through this defective valve. This noise is called a heart murmur. Sometimes, a similar noise, or murmur, occurs in a normal heart, but in this case it is of little or no importance.

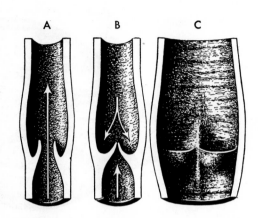

(A) Valve open; blood flowing upward. (B) Valve closed; blood not allowed to flow back. (C) Vein slit open to show valve.

Work of the heart. The amount of work done by the heart is enormous when its size is considered. Under conditions of moderate activity, 5 to 8 quarts of blood are pumped through the heart each minute. In 24 hours, with about 100,000 heartbeats, this amounts to about 2000 gallons, or 10 tons, of blood. The daily work necessary to pump this amount of blood is enough to lift a man to a height of more than 500 feet.

The heart muscles get their rest between beats. The resting, or relaxing, time after each beat is longer than the beat itself. The resting time is called diastole. The beat is called systole. Adding all the diastoles together, the heart rests for about 15 out of the 24 hours each day.

CIRCULATION OF THE BLOOD

The general picture of the circulation is not hard to understand or to remember. Blood leaves the heart in arteries. Arteries have walls that are muscular and elastic. They stretch as the blood is pumped into them under presure with each heartbeat and then press down on the blood between heartbeats to keep it circulating. The large arteries divide again and again into smaller arteries. Finally, the small arteries divide to form capillaries. Capillaries join together to form small veins. These join to form larger veins, which finally empty into the heart.

The right side of the heart, the right pump, pumps blood to the lungs. This blood comes back from the lungs into the left side of the heart.

The left side of the heart, the left pump, pumps blood to the head, the arms, the digestive tract, the walls of the heart itself, the legs—in fact, to all parts of the body except the lungs. This blood then comes back into the right side of the heart.

The pulse. When the heart beats, a wave of blood starts out from the

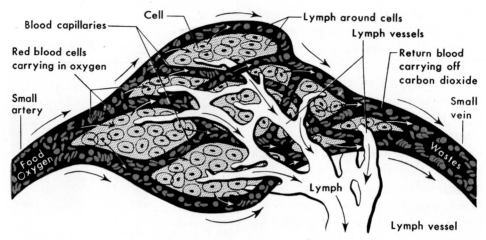

Above (left) an artery divides into capillaries; these (right) unite into a vein. Food and oxygen pass out from the blood, and wastes pass into it, through capillary walls. Fluid from the blood forms lymph and this flows away in lymph vessels.

heart and moves on through the arteries. It is a series of these waves that you feel when you count your pulse. The number of pulse beats in a minute is the pulse rate. This is the same as the heart rate.

The heart of a human infant beats about 130 times per minute. This rate gets slower until the adult rate is reached, usually in the late teens. The rate then averages about 72 beats per minute in men and 80 in women. Athletic training and good physical condition tend to lower the pulse rate (see Chapter 7). It is increased by exercise, excitement, tobacco, alcohol, fever, and various diseases.

One of the first things a physician does in examining a person is to feel the pulse, usually in the wrist. He notes how fast, how strong, and how regular it is.

Circulation through the lungs. The lungs have their own circulation.

Blood from the right auricle goes into the right ventricle, then through the pulmonary arteries to the lungs. In the lungs, the pulmonary arteries divide into capillaries.

In the lung capillaries, the blood

➡

In most cases, blood in the arteries contains more oxygen than does blood in the veins. In the capillaries, oxygen is given off to the surrounding cells and carbon dioxide is received. Blood in the veins then contains less oxygen and more carbon dioxide than does blood in the arteries. In the diagram on page 203, blood vessels carrying blood with large amounts of oxygen in it are shown in red; blood vessels carrying blood with large amounts of carbon dioxide in it are shown in black. Note that the pulmonary arteries are shown in black, the pulmonary veins in red. Can you explain why the blood in these arteries and veins is different from the blood in other arteries and veins?

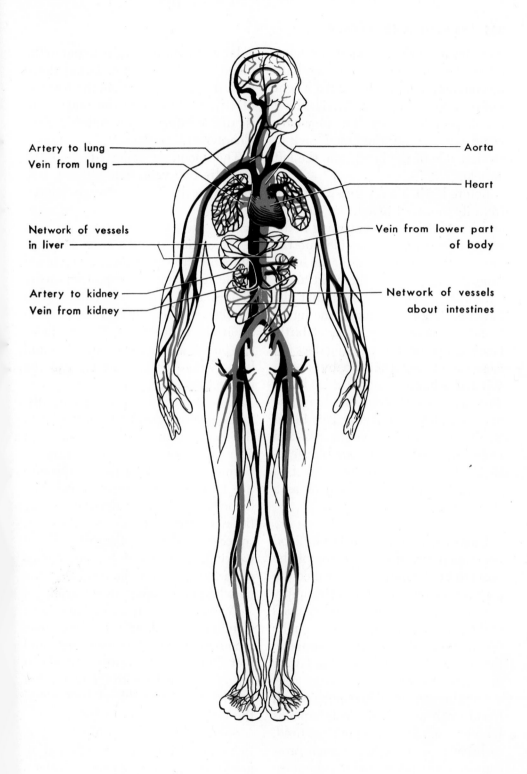

Artery to lung

Vein from lung

Network of vessels
in liver

Artery to kidney

Vein from kidney

Aorta

Heart

Vein from lower part
of body

Network of vessels
about intestines

gives up its carbon dioxide and takes in oxygen. Oxygen combining with hemoglobin makes the blood a bright red color (see Chapter 11). The lung capillaries join to form the pulmonary veins, which carry the blood back to the left side of the heart, into the left auricle.

Before birth, a baby gets its oxygen from its mother's blood, not from its own lungs. There is an opening in the wall between the two sides of the heart, making a short cut for the blood from the right side of the heart to the left. This short cut means that the blood does not go through the lungs. Usually, this opening closes at birth. Once in a while, this opening does not close completely when a baby is born. When this happens, some of his blood does not pass through his lungs, so does not pick up oxygen. This blood is bluish instead of bright red and makes the baby's flesh look bluish instead of the rosy pink we expect to see. Such a baby is spoken of as a "blue baby."

Circulation through the head. Blood is pumped out of the left side of the heart through a large artery called the aorta. Branches from the aorta supply the brain, eyes, teeth, and other parts of the head with blood. A pulse can be felt in these arteries by pressing on the side of the neck below the jaw or in front of the ear.

Fainting occurs when not enough blood reaches the brain. This happens because the person is ill or very tired, or because there is not enough pressure from the heartbeat and the mus-cular walls of the arteries to pump the blood up to the brain. Lying down with the head lower than the feet lets blood run down into the brain. This is the treatment for fainting (see Chapter 4).

The blood is collected from the head by two veins, one on each side of the neck. These are the jugular veins.

Circulation through arms and legs. Branches from the aorta carry blood to the arms, and the aorta itself finally divides into two arteries that go to the legs. We usually feel the pulse in an artery in the wrist, but the pulse can be felt at other places in arms and legs, wherever an artery can be pressed against a bone.

The blood must travel a long distance against gravity to get back to the heart, especially from the legs. The walls of the veins are much thinner than those of the arteries and put little pressure on the blood. The blood keeps moving upward, chiefly because the muscles of the legs squeeze it along as they contract in walking, running, and kicking. Valves at various places in the veins keep the blood from dropping down again.

When you are tired or have been standing or walking for a long time, blood may collect in your legs and feet. On a hike, it is restful to lie down for a few minutes with the feet uphill and let some of the blood drain out of the veins in the legs and feet.

Sometimes, usually in older people, the walls of the veins stretch and allow blood to collect above the valves.

This is the condition known as varicose veins. It can be uncomfortable and may be dangerous if enough blood collects to break the walls of the veins. Many things can be done to relieve varicose veins. Resting with the feet raised is often helpful. Wearing elastic stockings may be advised. Sometimes an operation is necessary.

Circulation in the heart itself. A small artery branches off the aorta and carries blood to supply the heart, or cardiac, muscle itself with food and oxygen. It takes only a few seconds for the blood to pass through the arteries, capillaries, and veins of the heart, but it is easy to see that this is a very important part of the circulation. If the heart muscles do not receive food and oxygen, the heart cannot beat.

Circulation to and from the digestive tract. The circulation to and from the digestive tract is somewhat different from the circulation to other parts of the body. Blood leaving the aorta to go to the digestive tract must go through two sets of capillaries and two sets of veins before returning to the heart.

Blood to the digestive tract supplies the cells there with oxygen and food. At the same time, it picks up from the digestive tract water and the foods that have been digested and absorbed through the walls of the intestines. All this happens in the first set of capillaries.

These capillaries join to form veins that carry blood laden with food to the liver. There, the veins divide again into capillaries. Some of the food from the blood is stored in the liver cells for future use. The capillaries join again to form veins that empty into the large vein carrying blood back to the heart from the lower part of the body.

Circulation through the kidneys. Another branch of the aorta carries blood to the kidneys. Here, the blood passes through capillaries and loses most of its waste products. Extra food that cannot be stored is also taken out of the blood in the kidneys. These substances are collected in the bladder and are gotten rid of in urine (see Chapter 17).

After the blood has passed through the kidneys, it is carried by veins to join the great vein that collects the blood from legs, pelvis, and all the lower parts of the body.

Controlling the circulation. Night and day, all through your life, your heart keeps on beating, and your blood keeps on circulating. Sometimes your heart beats fast, sometimes slowly. Sometimes most of the blood is sent to the digestive tract, sometimes to the muscles. When you are healthy, there is a very neat adjustment between what the various parts of your body need and the amount of blood sent to them (see "The Master Control" in Chapter 5).

Both heart and blood vessels are supplied with nerves. These nerves come chiefly from the autonomic nervous system (see Chapters 5, 6, 18).

CENTRAL HIGH SCHOOL OF COMMERCE

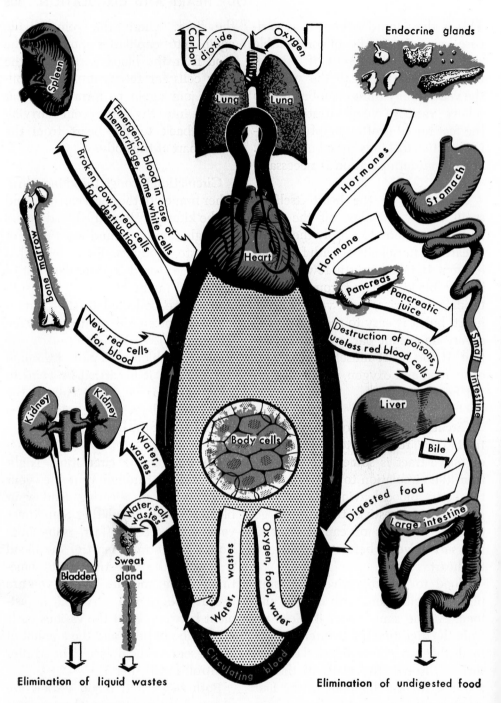

Endocrine glands

Spleen

Carbon dioxide

Oxygen

Lung   Lung

Heart

Emergency blood in case of hemorrhage, some white cells

Broken down red cells for destruction

Bone marrow

New red cells for blood

Hormones

Stomach

Hormone

Pancreas

Pancreatic juice

Destruction of poisons, useless red blood cells

Small intestine

Kidney   Kidney

Water, wastes

Body cells

Liver

Bile

Water, salt, wastes

Sweat gland

Bladder

Water, wastes

Oxygen, food, water

Digested food

Large intestine

Circulating blood

Elimination of liquid wastes

Elimination of undigested food

The tissues of the body take some substances from the blood and give other substances to it.

This means that the impulses are not under your deliberate control. A lack of food or oxygen somewhere in the body, or a piling up of waste materials, starts impulses, which may increase or slow down the rate of the heart without your having to think about it. Other impulses will cause some of the small arteries to contract and shunt the blood to other arteries, or will cause them to dilate, so that more blood goes through them.

As everyone knows, emotions cause many changes in the circulation. You become excited and your heart beats fast. You are embarrassed and the blood vessels in your face and neck dilate, making you blush. This makes you still more embarrassed, and you blush a deeper red than before. Being sad may make your heart beat more slowly. When you are frightened, the blood vessels in your skin may become smaller and make you look pale (see Chapter 5).

BLOOD PRESSURE

When we speak of blood pressure, we really mean arterial pressure, or the pressure in the arteries. The walls of the arteries contain smooth (involuntary) muscles and are elastic; that is, they stretch. There is always enough blood in the arteries to keep them more or less stretched. The stretching of the walls puts pressure on the blood and keeps it flowing into the smaller arteries and capillaries.

When the heart beats, more blood is forced into the arteries. This stretches them still more and puts more pressure on the blood.

The pressure in the arteries at the time of the heartbeat is the systolic pressure. The pressure between beats is the diastolic pressure. Systolic pressure is higher than diastolic. Blood pressure is measured with an instrument known as a sphygmomanometer (see Chapter 26).

Changes in blood pressure. The blood pressure of children is lower than that of adults; it is lower when a person is lying down than when he is standing; it is lower in thin people than in fat people. Blood pressure tends to be low when people are tired or ill, when they do not have enough to eat, or when they have anemia. Low blood pressure means that the blood flows slowly; the tissues may not get enough food and oxygen; hence, the person feels tired and has little interest in doing things. Low blood pressure may cause a person to faint.

Exercise raises the blood pressure (see Chapter 7). So do excitement and fear. The so-called "lie detector" tests are based upon changes in a person's blood pressure and pulse rate. When someone is lying and is afraid he will be found out, his heart is apt to beat faster and his blood pressure is apt to rise.

High blood pressure. Any healthy person's blood pressure changes as he sleeps, gets up, runs, and becomes excited. It is only when the blood pressure stays high that we are disturbed about it. We call this condition high blood pressure, or hypertension.

The dangers from high blood pressure are easy to understand, if you think about the circulation as a whole. (1) The pressure in the arteries may become so high that the heart wears itself out trying to pump more blood out to the aorta. (2) Some of the small arteries may break, letting blood escape into the tissues and clot there. When this occurs in the brain, the parts of the brain affected by the clots do not function well, and this failure is the disease known as apoplexy, or a stroke. Most strokes are not fatal, but if the blood clot is large or is in certain places in the brain, it may cause death. Usually, the clots are absorbed, and the person's brain functions normally again. (3) The blood flow through the kidneys may be reduced by high blood pressure. Waste products then collect in the blood and cause a poisoning, known as uremia (see Chapter 17).

No one knows the cause of high blood pressure. Heredity, overweight, and nervousness are related to it, but we are sure that there are other causes. Keeping in good physical condition with plenty of rest and relaxation, and avoiding worry and overweight usually will help to keep a person's blood pressure from going higher.

RHEUMATIC FEVER

Rheumatic fever, sometimes called inflammatory rheumatism, is a disease that is one of the most serious health problems of young people. It usually occurs first between 5 years and 15 years of age, but other attacks may occur later in the same person. The most serious damage from rheumatic fever is to the heart.

How rheumatic fever spreads. Physicians believe that rheumatic fever is caused by microorganisms very like those that cause scarlet fever, "strep" sore throat, and middle-ear infections. One of these infections often occurs just before an attack of rheumatic fever.

The organisms of rheumatic fever travel from one person to another on fingers, drinking glasses, or any articles that carry them from one person's nose and mouth to the nose and mouth of another person. Many people carry these organisms but do not develop rheumatic fever. These persons are called carriers.

No one knows why some people develop rheumatic fever, while others do not. If one person in a family has the disease, the chances that another person in the family will develop it are 3 times as great as in other families. This may be the result of a family susceptibility. In other words, the tissues of all the members of one family may be alike in not being able to fight off rheumatic fever. Another reason for the spread in families is that members of a family live close together. It is easy for disease organisms to be passed around among them.

Most cases of rheumatic fever occur in the late winter and early spring, so weather may have something to do with its spread. Poor housing, overcrowding, and poor food seem to make people more likely to develop the disease. During World War II, serious outbreaks occurred in some of the Army and Navy camps where young men were living close together.

Effects of rheumatic fever. The first stage of rheumatic fever may be so mild that even a physician may not recognize it. Some of the so-called "growing pains" of children are mild attacks of rheumatic fever. Probably many people have the disease and no one recognizes it. Often, however, the first stage leaves scars on the heart valves, which keep them from closing properly. If the injury is small, it makes no difference in the person's way of living. If the injury is large, the person may have to avoid vigorous exercise all the rest of his life. And there is always the danger of a second attack.

The fight against rheumatic fever consists chiefly in trying not to get other people's disease organisms and in having good medical care. Sore throats and ear infections may make it easier for rheumatic fever to develop.

People who have had rheumatic fever must try to avoid second attacks and must learn what they can and cannot do in the way of physical activity. Studies show that one to five school children in every 100 have rheumatic fever at some time or other, and that more than half of these have some heart damage as a result.

Truly, rheumatic fever is a serious and alarming disease. Fortunately, however, there is a bright side to this picture, since most of the boys and girls who have had rheumatic fever are able to live normal, healthy, and happy lives. If they are under the care of a good physician and follow his advice, they do not have to worry about their hearts.

OTHER TYPES OF HEART DISEASE

You have probably heard that heart disease is now the leading cause of death in the United States. One reason is that people are staying alive longer and are living to be old enough to have heart disease. Some young people do suffer from heart disease, but mostly this is a disorder that occurs in middle and old age.

The term *heart disease* is confusing. It is not a single disease, like measles or smallpox. It includes almost any condition of the heart that weakens it or makes it do its work less well.

Much heart disease is caused by infection. Any infection that gets into the blood has a chance to settle in the heart. Rheumatic fever has already been discussed. Diphtheria, scarlet fever, syphilis, and many other diseases may damage the heart. The way to prevent this kind of heart trouble is to prevent the disease in the first place. However, if one of these diseases occurs, then the patient should have good care during the period when he is weak from illness, until danger of heart damage is over.

In certain cases, the heart damage is the result of chronic infections at the roots of teeth, of tonsils, or of sinuses. Disease organisms may spread

CHANGES IN DEATH RATES FROM CERTAIN DISEASES

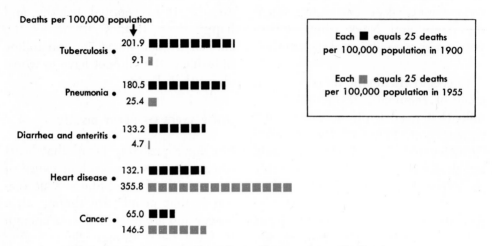

Deaths per 100,000 population

Tuberculosis • 201.9
9.1

Pneumonia • 180.5
25.4

Diarrhea and enteritis • 133.2
4.7

Heart disease • 132.1
355.8

Cancer • 65.0
146.5

Each ■ equals 25 deaths
per 100,000 population in 1900

Each ■ equals 25 deaths
per 100,000 population in 1955

Note the rise in deaths from heart disease as people live longer.

from these foci of infection to the heart and cause heart trouble, just as they may spread to the joints and cause arthritis (see Chapter 6). The best way to prevent heart damage from chronic infections is to care for these infections early, before they become chronic.

Many cases of heart disease in older people seem to be just the result of the wear and tear of living. Hard work, fatigue, worry, and poor food through the years of youth and middle age leave heart tissue unable to do its work properly. High blood pressure increases the work of the heart and may eventually lead to heart failure. The time to begin to guard against these kinds of heart disease is in adolescence.

Sometimes the blood vessels in the heart muscle itself become clogged by small blood clots. As a result, the heart does not receive food and oxy-gen and cannot carry on its work. The largest blood vessels of the heart are the coronary blood vessels. When they are clogged, the condition is called coronary occlusion, or coronary thrombosis (from *thrombus,* a clot). Many deaths from so-called heart failure are deaths from coronary occlusion. If the person can be kept alive for even a few hours, there is a good chance that he will recover.

THE LYMPHATIC SYSTEM

Lymph bathes all the cells of the body. It comes from the blood through the walls of the capillaries and is carried back to the veins by the lymphatic vessels.

Along the lymph vessels are small structures called lymph nodes. These are sometimes called lymph glands, but this is not a good term because they do not secrete lymph. The lymph nodes kill disease organisms that are in the lymphatic vessels. Lymph nodes also manufacture some of the white blood cells (see Chapter 11). Tonsils and adenoids are composed of the same kind of tissue as lymph nodes (see Chapter 13).

When an infection starts anywhere in the body, the nearby lymph nodes swell and become sore. Infection in the leg causes swelling of the nodes in the groin, where the legs are attached to the trunk; infection in the arm causes swelling of the nodes in the armpit; infection at the roots of teeth causes swelling of the nodes under the jaw and the neck. Sometimes, in case of infection, "red streaks" are seen in the arms or legs along the lymph vessels. The red streaks and the soreness show that the lymphatic system is trying to stop the infection.

Tiny lymph vessels collect lymph from all parts of the body. These unite to form larger vessels. Finally the lymph is poured into a vein near the heart. Lymph moves along the lymph vessels chiefly because it is squeezed and pushed by contractions of other muscles—the voluntary muscles such as those used in moving the arms, walking, and breathing, and the involuntary muscles such as those in the digestive tract. Valves in the lymph vessels keep it from flowing backward.

The lymph nodes are found at various points along the lymph vessels. Note the lymph nodes in the armpit, the groin, and the neck. Have you felt swollen lymph nodes below your ear or jaw when you have had a cold?

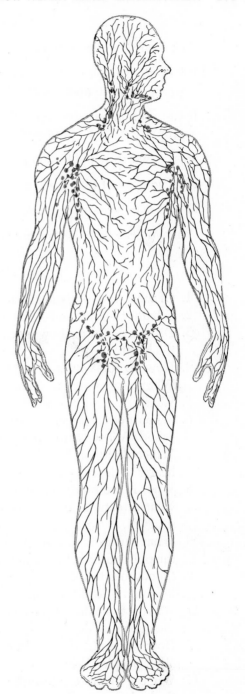

The lymphatic system. The lymph vessels drain toward the heart. They are shown in black. The lymph nodes are shown in red.

SO WHAT?

Your heart is a pump that keeps working all through life; and

It will do its work best if you keep it in good condition and do not worry about it; and

It can do a good job even if damaged, provided that you treat it properly;

So, it is worth while to know

How your heart functions; and

How it may be damaged; and

What you can do to keep it in good condition.

CHECKING UP

1. Of what kind of tissues is the heart composed?
2. What is the function of the heart?
3. Draw a diagram showing the four chambers and the valves of the heart.
4. How do the valves help to keep the blood moving forward? What happens if the valves do not close completely?
5. What is a heart murmur?
6. When does the heart muscle rest? What is the resting time called? What is the contraction, or heartbeat, called?
7. Which kind of blood vessels carries blood away from the heart? to the heart?
8. What is the relationship of capillaries, veins, and arteries? In what direction does the blood flow through these blood vessels?
9. What causes the pulse rate to go up? How does training affect the pulse rate? Where can you feel the pulse?
10. Blood goes to the lungs from which side of the heart? returns to which side of the heart?
11. What is the name of the arteries to the lungs? of the veins from the lungs?
12. How is the blood of a "blue baby" different from the blood of other people? Why?
13. What is the aorta? Branches of the aorta go to which parts of the body?
14. Where are the jugular veins? They bring blood from what part of the body?

15. What keeps the blood moving from the feet back up to the heart?
16. What are varicose veins? How can they be prevented?
17. Trace the blood from the heart to the digestive tract and back to the heart. Where are the two sets of capillaries?
18. How are your emotions related to your circulation? What part of the nervous system is involved?
19. Why is systolic blood pressure higher than diastolic blood pressure?
20. What does a lie detector measure? Do you think that a lie detector really works?
21. What happens when a person has a "stroke"? Are most strokes fatal?
22. What are the dangers of high blood pressure? What are the dangers of low blood pressure?
23. What can you do now that will help to prevent your having high blood pressure when you are older?
24. What is the probable cause of rheumatic fever?
25. Why is the term *heart disease* confusing?
26. What are some of the causes of heart disease? How can they be avoided?
27. When you have a cold, you may find that there are swellings along the sides of your neck. What causes them?

THINGS TO DO

1. Get a sheep heart (or beef heart or pig heart) from the butcher. Find the auricles and ventricles. Look at the valves. Squeeze some water through the heart. Can you see how the valves close? Find the right side of the heart. (The right ventricle is smaller than the left ventricle.) Now find the holes where the veins from the lungs enter the right auricle. Can you find the pulmonary artery? Look at the left side of the heart. Find the veins entering the left auricle. Find the aorta. Find the blood vessels in the walls of the heart.
2. Find the heart, arteries, and veins in a chicken. Ask the biology teacher to show these same things to you in a frog or in some other animal.
3. Put a small goldfish under a microscope and watch the blood circulating in the capillaries in its tail. Notice how small they are. Or put a small tadpole under a microscope and watch the blood flow in its gills or tail.

4. Under a microscope look at the web in a frog's foot. Can you see the blood run in spurts in the arteries? Count the frog's pulse rate. Blood runs slowest in the capillaries, next most slowly in the veins, fastest in the arteries. Find arteries, veins, and capillaries.

5. Find your pulse in front of your ear; at the point of your jaw; in your elbow; in your knee. Review the pressure points (Chapter 4). Can you tell when your heart is resting by feeling your pulse?

6. Ask a doctor or a nurse to show you a stethoscope (an instrument for listening to the heart). See whether you can hear the heartbeat of one of the other students in your class.

7. Roll up a piece of paper. Put one end of the paper tube on someone's chest and your ear at the other end. Can you hear the heartbeat?

8. Ask a doctor or a nurse to show the class how he finds a person's blood pressure.

9. Find from the health department how many cases of rheumatic fever have been reported in your town or county this year.

10. Give a special report on heart disease as a cause of death now and 25 years ago.

11. Give a special report on the work of William Harvey, who discovered the circulation of the blood in 1628.

CHAPTER 13 Sneezes and Sniffles

Noses are important parts of our bodies. They are the first part of the passageway that allows air to get to the lungs. They contain the organs for the sense of smell. They have a great deal to do with making our faces pretty or homely. And, because they stick out from our faces, they are easily bumped.

The size and shape of a person's nose very seldom have anything to do with his getting enough oxygen. A big nose, a pug nose, a pointed nose, a flat nose, can all be useful. Sometimes a nose can be made better looking by an operation. Usually, the best way to treat a nose that is not beautiful is to find a becoming way to do the hair, wear a friendly smile, and forget the nose.

THE INSIDE OF THE NOSE

The air we breathe is often cool, dry, and dusty. The nose warms, moistens, and cleans this air before it reaches the delicate tissues of the lungs.

The two outside openings to the nose are the nostrils. Inside the nose are two large narrow cavities. The wall between these cavities is the nasal septum.

The nasal septum separates the nasal cavities for only 2 or 3 inches. Then the two nasal cavities join and open into the back of the mouth. This space is the pharynx.

Cilia and mucus. If you look at the lining of the nose, the nasal membrane, under a microscope, you see that it is covered with tiny moving threads that look like little hairs. These are called cilia. They move back and forth like stalks of grain when a wind blows over a field.

The cilia are covered with a warm, moist, sticky substance called mucus. This mucus warms the air and adds moisture to it. It also catches dust and microorganisms. The movement of the cilia carries the mucus down to the pharynx. Then it is coughed out or swallowed.

The nose usually secretes about a quart of this mucus every 24 hours. In fact, a new covering is secreted about every 10 minutes. Sometimes a great

215

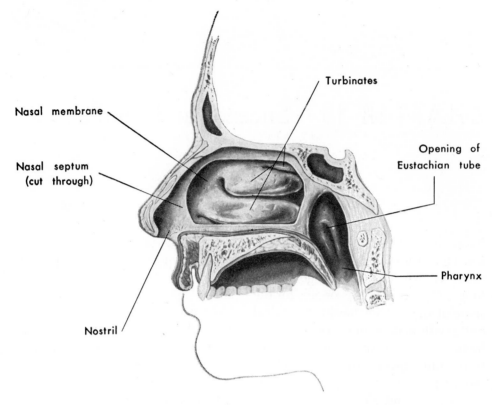

Nasal membrane

Turbinates

Opening of Eustachian tube

Nasal septum (cut through)

Pharynx

Nostril

Air is warmed, moistened, and cleaned as it passes through the nose.

deal more is secreted, and we say that the person has "a running nose."

The mucous covering keeps the delicate tissues under it from being scratched or irritated by dust. It also keeps out disease organisms. Drying up the lining of the nose makes it easier for an infection to start there.

The side walls of the inside of the nose each contains three tiny curved shelves called turbinates. These are made of thin bone, covered with the same nasal membrane as the other parts of the nose. The turbinates provide more surface for the air to travel across than if the walls were smooth. This gives more chance for the air to

be cleaned and warmed and moistened before reaching the lungs.

Openings into the nose. In addition to the nostrils and the pharynx, there are a number of openings into the nose. Two tubes, called tear ducts, from the eyes empty into the nasal cavities; eight small openings, four on each side, lead from the nasal cavities to sinuses, or cavities in nearby bones; and two tubes, the Eustachian tubes, lead out from the pharynx to the ears.

A STUFFED-UP NOSE

The mucous membrane that lines the

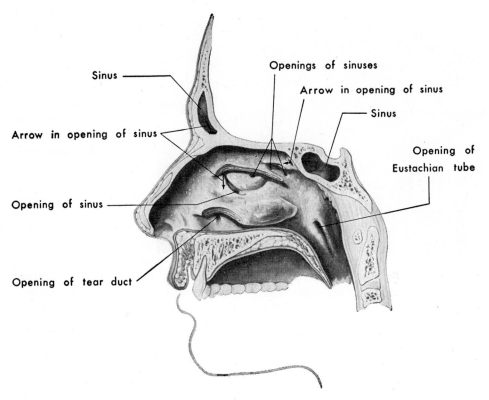

Sinus

Openings of sinuses

Arrow in opening of sinus

Sinus

Arrow in opening of sinus

Opening of
Eustachian tube

Opening of sinus

Opening of tear duct

Openings into the nose. Note the arrows showing passageways into sinuses.

nose can swell or shrink very rapidly. If the air is too cold or too hot or contains irritating gases, the lining swells and lets less air through. When you lie on the right side of your body, the right side of your nose may close. Then when you turn to the left, the right side may open and the left side may close. This is the effect of gravity —that is, the pull of the earth.

When you have a cold or some other infection in the nose, the mucous membranes swell. The infection may develop rapidly and last only a few days; such an infection is called an acute infection. Or the infection may last for a few weeks or months; in this case, it is called a chronic infection. Allergies, as well as colds and other infections, may cause swelling of the nasal mucous membranes.

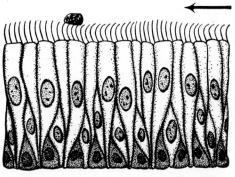

Note the small particle being pushed along by the cilia as they move back and forth.

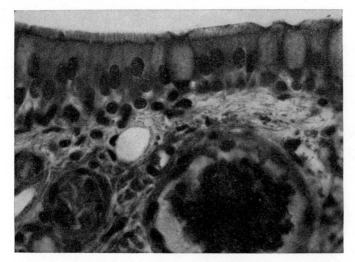

A section of the nasal membrane, which has been magnified many times. Note the cilia. (Courtesy General Biological Supply House)

When a person's nose is so stuffy that it is uncomfortable, sometimes exercise or a hot bath will cause it to open. It opens because blood is drawn off to the muscles and the skin, and less blood is left in the lining of the nose.

Breathing through the mouth. Sometimes after running we cannot get enough air through our noses, so we take in great gulps of air through our mouths. Air that is taken in through the mouth is not warmed or moistened or cleaned before reaching the lungs.

If this happens only once in awhile, it is not important. If the nose stays obstructed, however, cold, dry, and dirty air may cause irritation in the lungs. Breathing through the mouth all the time sometimes makes the lower part of the face grow out of shape. A person who breathes through his mouth should try to find the cause of the obstruction and do something about it.

Blowing the nose. Everyone thinks he knows how to blow his nose, so that it seems silly even to mention it. But there is a right way and a wrong way to blow your nose.

Holding the nose tightly and blowing hard is the wrong way. The pressure within the nose may blow infection up into the sinuses and cause sinus infection. It may force infection into the Eustachian tubes and lead to ear infection and earache. Or it may cause infection and swelling of the tear ducts, so that tears spill over the face all the time, instead of draining down through the nose.

Instead of squeezing the nose shut, blow with both nostrils open. Whatever is closing the nose should come out easily. Many times, what a person is trying to blow out is a swollen mucous membrane that is a part of the nose and cannot be moved.

Nose sprays and drops. Having the nose closed is so annoying that people will try almost anything to relieve

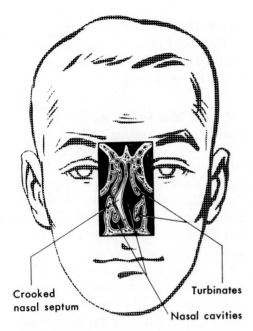

Crooked
nasal septum

Turbinates

Nasal cavities

medicine. Then more gentle treatment can be used. And there is a better chance to find what the real cause of the obstruction is.

Crooked nasal septum. The septum between the two nasal cavities is partly bone and partly cartilage. It is usually fairly straight. Sometimes it grows crooked or is bent by a hard blow on the nose. It may be so badly bent that air cannot pass through the nose, and moisture from eyes, sinuses, and nasal membrane cannot drain out. Usually the crooked part of the septum can be removed by a small operation.

Nasal polyps. In some persons, obstruction to breathing is caused by small growths from the mucous membrane of the nose. These are called polyps. They grow when the mucous membrane of the nose is continuously irritated. The usual cause of the irritation is chronic sinus infection plus the fact that the person's membrane is more sensitive—that is, more easily irritated by infection than is usual. The polyps can be easily removed, but they will almost certainly grow again unless the sinus infection is cured and the membrane becomes less sensitive.

it. They use sprays, drops, jellies, and inhalers, usually without the advice of a physician. Most of these contain drugs that shrink the mucous membrane and squeeze it dry, much as you would squeeze water out of a sponge. As soon as the effect of the drug wears off, the mucous membrane swells more than ever. After a few days, or perhaps weeks, of this kind of treatment, the little muscles around the blood vessels in the membrane become too tired to contract. The person then uses more and more or stronger and stronger medicine.

The widespread use of these nose medicines makes good business for the companies that make and sell them, but it is bad business for the person who uses them. Most physicians advise people who are always dosing their noses to stop everything and wait until the nasal membrane has recovered from the effects of the

SENSE OF SMELL

When we smell a perfume, an onion, a good dinner, or a skunk, we really smell the vapors, or gases, given off by each. The gases reach nerve endings in the nasal cavities and start im-

Noses are of many shapes and sizes.

pulses that travel to the brain over special nerves. The nervous impulses must reach the brain before we really know that we are smelling anything.

An odor can be very strong at first, but we soon become used to it and no longer notice it. This is the reason that a room may smell stuffy to a person coming into it, when a person sitting in the room does not notice it. It is the reason, also, that a person may not notice the odor of his own perspiration or his own "bad breath." Another reason that a person does not notice the odor of his own breath is that the air he breathes out passes along the lower part of the nasal cavities, and the nerve endings for the sense of smell are in the upper part.

A person does not smell things well when he has a cold, because the nerve endings are covered with too much mucus. Usually, too, the membrane is swollen and does not allow air to reach the upper parts of the nasal cavities.

Taste and smell are closely related. In fact, we often think that we are tasting food when we are really smell-ing it. This is the reason that a person with a cold often complains that all foods taste alike and that nothing tastes the way he likes it.

THE NOSE AND MOUTH AS PATHWAYS FOR DISEASE

Most of the microorganisms that cause diseases in people enter the body through the nose or mouth. Some reach the nose and mouth on hands; some on droplets of moisture from coughs or sneezes; some on air and dust. Among the diseases that we get in this way are influenza, whooping cough, and diphtheria, which are discussed in Chapter 24; pneumonia, measles, scarlet fever, and tuberculosis, which are discussed in Chapter 25; poliomyelitis, which is discussed in Chapter 18; and the common cold.

COLDS

Of the foregoing diseases, there is none that causes so much trouble and misery and costs so much money as the common cold. The nation's bill for the common cold is probably between 2 and 3 billion dollars every year. Part of this large bill is for days lost from work; part is for medicine and for physician's and hospital bills for the treatment of the cold itself or of the other infections that frequently follow colds. This does not take account of all the days of school and all the good times lost by people with colds.

People use the word *cold* very loosely for a wide variety of conditions of the head and chest, such as

Spray from the nose and mouth is thrown many feet by sneezing and coughing and even by talking. If another person is near, he will almost certainly receive some of the moisture, and any microorganisms it may contain, in his nose and mouth. (Courtesy Dr. M. W. Jennison, Syracuse University)

allergies, sinus infections, influenza, or anything that causes a stuffed-up nose. They do not bother to get a diagnosis of what ails them, that is, a careful study to find whether they have a cold, an allergy, or some other condition with the same symptoms.

Most people, however, have a general idea of what is meant by a real cold in the head, or coryza. A person usually sneezes, has a watery discharge from the nose, is chilly, and cannot breathe easily, because the membrane lining his nose is swollen. After 2 or 3 days, the discharge becomes thicker and yellowish.

What causes a cold? Many colds seem to be caused by a virus. These colds are communicable from one person to another. An epidemic of colds occurs during September in most parts of the United States. This is about the time when schools open. People who have not seen one another for several weeks or months come back together in school, and the cold virus has a good chance to spread. People in isolated villages, even in the arctic regions, do not have colds, unless other people bring the virus in from the outside.

Interesting experiments have been

made with people and the virus that can cause colds. Scientists have learned how to grow the virus in laboratories and have found that one drop of liquid containing the virus is enough to give a man a cold in the head, or coryza.

Secondary infections. Colds are usually mild and last only 4 or 5 days, unless the person develops a secondary infection. A secondary infection is caused by an infectious organism different from the one that caused the cold. The cold simply makes it easier for the other organism to grow on the nasal membrane. Once started, the secondary infection may spread and cause sinusitis, infection of the ear and of the mastoid bone behind the ear, tonsillitis, bronchitis, or pneumonia.

Treatment of colds. There is no other subject upon which one gets so much free and worthless advice as upon the treatment of colds. It is not necessary to look for it. Newspapers, magazines, and radio and television are full of it. Friends are always willing to suggest their pet remedies.

It is often said that if you treat a cold you can cure it in 14 days and if you do nothing about it you will be well in 2 weeks. An acute cold without secondary infection should not last this long. If it does, you can suspect an infection of the sinuses.

Rest and keep warm. Rest in bed is advisable in the early stages of a cold. Its value lies in increasing one's general good health and resistance to infection, in keeping warm, and in protecting others from infection.

Hot baths, of hot water, hot air, or steam, are often used for the treatment of colds. They dilate the blood vessels of the skin and increase the flow of blood through them. As a result, the nasal discharge and stuffiness are reduced for a little while. If the body gets chilled after the hot bath, the cold may become worse than before.

Large quantities of water, lemonade, or orange juice are often used in the treatment of colds, but we are not sure that they are of any value.

Medicines for colds. Medicines advertised for treatment of colds usually make one feel better for a little while but do not cure the cold. Aspirin and other drugs of the same kind reduce the fever, if there is any. Nose drops and sprays have the same undesirable effects in treating a cold that they do in treating any nose stuffiness (see page 219).

Certain drugs prepared from opium are helpful in the treatment of colds. These, of course, must be ordered by a physician. Recently some of the sulfonamides and antibiotic drugs, such as penicillin, have been used for colds. They probably have no value except for the secondary infections that sometimes follow colds. Furthermore, these drugs must be used with great care. One reason is that some persons are made very ill by them. Another is that if these drugs are used for minor infections, such as colds, they sometimes cannot be used later for the treatment of more severe infections.

Avoiding colds. The virus causing the cold is only half the story. The other half is the person himself and his ability to resist the virus. Some people take cold much more easily than others. In some school groups, one-fourth of the students have three-fourths of the colds. These are the ones who have one cold after another. Other students never seem to have a cold. Some people have many colds one year and none the next.

We do not know all the reasons why some people catch cold and others do not, but we have pretty good ideas about some of these reasons. Many people think colds are caused by chilling. In fact, this is probably the reason for the name *cold*. It is true that chilling or sitting in drafts makes many people sneeze and blow their noses. If they can get warm immediately, especially if they can draw the blood away from the nasal membrane to the skin by a bath or by getting close to a fire, they stop sneezing and shivering.

Keeping warm and dry is important. Children especially should have warm clothing and shoes that will keep their feet dry. Wet clothing and shoes should be changed as soon as possible. Schools and homes should be warm and free from drafts but not overheated. Air that is neither too dry nor too moist seems to keep the nasal membrane in best condition.

Many persons seem to take colds easily when they are tired. Chilling and fatigue lower their ability to fight the cold virus. It has been found in many schools that large numbers of colds occur after holidays when students have stayed up late at night, gone on trips, and tried to do too many things. This is just one more reason for getting enough sleep and rest; no one wants his good time spoiled by a cold.

Vitamins and special diets are widely advertised for the prevention of colds. People on poor diets probably have more colds than people on good diets, simply because they may be in poor general health. If a person's diet is already a good one, more vitamins or special diets do not prevent colds.

A chronic infection in the sinuses or nose or tonsils is almost sure to lead to many colds. A crooked nasal septum does not allow mucus and the microorganisms in it to drain out of the nose and, hence, may lead to colds.

Antiseptics. Sprays, nose drops, gargles, and mouth washes are widely advertised for the treatment and prevention of colds. Many of these contain an antiseptic, that is, something that will kill microorganisms. The antiseptic is supposed to kill the microorganisms in the nose or mouth before they can multiply and cause the cold.

This sounds well but a little thought shows that it is not good reasoning. First of all, the lining of the nose is very delicate, and any antiseptic strong enough to kill the cold virus will injure the nasal membrane. Second, the antiseptic can reach only a small part of the membrane, and for only a few seconds, before it is drained off by the mucus. In fact, instead of preventing colds, these sprays and drops may interfere with the action of the cilia, and change the mucous secretions in the nose, so that they cannot protect the membrane from infection as well as before.

Cold vaccines. Many scientists have tried to develop vaccines for colds. These vaccines are made by killing some of the microorganisms usually found in the nose and throat during colds and placing them in some substance that can be injected into a human being or can be taken by mouth. These killed microorganisms, of course, cannot give a person a cold or any other disease. The hope is that the vaccine will make a person build up his own resistance to live microorganisms.

In experiments, the vaccine is given to one group of persons, in pills, in sprays for the nose, or by injections. This group is called the experimental group. Another group of persons is given pills, sprays, or injections that do not contain the vaccine. This is called the control group. No one in the experiment knows whether he is in the experimental group or in the control group, whether he is receiving the vaccine or not. A careful record is kept of the colds in each group.

All these experiments show about the same results. The persons who receive the vaccines have just as many colds as those who do not receive the vaccines. But, surprisingly, both groups usually report fewer colds than they remember they had during the previous year. There are many possible explanations for this. Perhaps the persons in the experiment are not around many people who have colds and take better care of themselves. Perhaps they do not remember exactly how many colds they have had.

What to do about colds. So, although almost everyone has colds now and then, and many, many people have made careful studies of colds, still we have more questions about them than we have real information. On the other hand, most people could do much more about avoiding colds than they do. Some simple rules are

1) Keep at a distance from a person with a cold.

2) Wash your hands before meals.

3) Keep your hands away from your nose and mouth; keep pencils and other things out of your mouth.

4) Be sure that dishes and silverware are washed carefully with soap and are rinsed with boiling water.

5) Use individual drinking glasses even within the family, at the table, in the kitchen, and in the bathroom.

6) Never take bites of other people's food.

7) Avoid chilling, drafts, and excessive fatigue.

If you follow these rules, you will keep most microorganisms from reaching your nose and throat. People live so close together now that it is impossible to stay completely away from those with colds. It is important to keep in as good condition as possible so that you can fight off the cold virus. And if you have more than two or three colds a year, you should try to find the reason.

Do not forget to protect other people from your colds. Stay at home and away from friends and family. Cover your nose and mouth when sneezing or coughing. Do not talk "in another person's face." Use paper tissues as handkerchiefs and destroy them or keep your handkerchiefs away from other people. Use your own dishes and silverware and have them washed separately. Wash your hands frequently.

SINUSES AND SINUS INFECTION

The sinuses are cavities in the bones of the face and the skull. It is important to remember their connection with the nasal cavities.

The lining of the nose, the nasal membrane, extends up into the sinuses. Any infection in the nose can easily travel into the sinuses and cause sinus infection, or sinusitis.

Blowing the nose too hard or using nose sprays sometimes forces infection into the sinuses. Diving or swimming with the nose under water may do the same thing. Some people develop sinusitis more easily than others, no matter what they do.

Acute sinusitis, like all other acute diseases, lasts only a short time. The linings of the sinuses fight the infection by secreting large amounts of mucus. This mucus has to drain down into the nose and pharynx. The person with sinusitis usually has to cough and clear his nose and throat often. Usually, he has a headache and a fever, feels tired, and "aches all over."

Acute sinusitis sometimes becomes chronic, that is, it does not clear up. It may cause little or no pain. The infection, however, may get into the blood and cause damage in the heart, kidneys, joints, brain, or other parts of the body.

Heat and rest are often all that is needed to treat a sinus infection. If it does not clear up quickly, the safe thing is to consult a physician. Self-treatment, with nose drops, sprays, or inhalers, usually just makes matters worse. They spread the infection that they are supposed to cure.

NASAL ALLERGIES

The most common cause of repeated sneezing, sniffling, and nasal obstruction is allergy. This condition is not easy to understand or to diagnose. In fact, no one knows the real cause of allergies.

All of us every day touch and swallow and breathe in such things as pollens of plants, tiny bits of feather, house dust, wool, cosmetics, many kinds of food, and hair from horses, dogs, and cats. To most of us, they do no harm. But, for some people, these same things make the nasal membrane swell, so that air cannot pass easily through the nose. Or they may cause headaches, upset stomach, hives (see Chapter 10), or asthma (see Chapter 14). We say that people who react in these ways are sensitive to these substances, that they are allergic to them, or have an allergy for them.

Allergies often occur in several people in the same family, so heredity seems to have something to do with them. Allergies may come and go or change from one substance to another. Emotions are related to allergies in some people, perhaps because emotions change the circulation and the condition of the mucous membrane. Hot and cold weather affect allergies, perhaps for the same reason.

Many persons have allergies who do not know it. They may think they have chronic sinus infections. A person who thinks he has many colds or "a cold most of the time" may, instead, have an allergy to something around him.

Treatment of allergies. The first step in treatment of an allergy is to find the cause. Physicians can often do this by making "skin tests." Small amounts of pollen, dust, feathers, wool, and other things to which many people are allergic are put into the skin. Swelling and redness of the skin where one substance has been used show allergy to that substance. When a person knows the cause of his allergy, he can sometimes avoid it. For example, he can stop sleeping on a feather pillow, or keep away from horses, or stop wearing woolen clothes.

Sometimes allergies can be treated by giving the person first a very small dose of the substance to which he is allergic, then larger and larger doses. He seems to build up some kind of resistance to, or tolerance for, the substance.

Many drugs have been used in the treatment of allergies, but none has been completely successful. Within the last few years, however, a new group of drugs, the antihistamines, have been developed, which promise more success. The use of these drugs is based on the belief that an allergic person has free in his tissues more than the usual amount of a substance called histamine. The drugs are expected to act against this surplus histamine.

There are several kinds of antihistamines. Some people are made ill or sleepy by one kind but can safely take another kind. What relieves the symptoms of one person's allergy may be quite useless for another person.

For this reason, it is important to consult a physician before taking any antihistamine. He can help find the kind that a person can take safely and successfully, if at all. He can also adjust the dose to the individual.

Many antihistamines can be purchased at drugstores without a physician's prescription. Some of these may be dangerous to certain individuals. In many cases, those sold freely are weak enough to do no harm and very little good.

Sneezing, a stuffed-up nose, and running eyes are symptoms of a cold. They are also symptoms of hay fever and some other allergies. If these

Wrong way

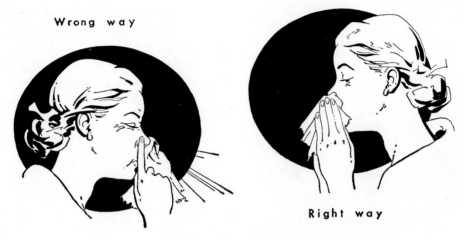

Right way

How do you blow your nose?

symptoms are due to an allergy, such as hay fever, antihistamines usually are useful in making the person feel better. If the symptoms are due to an infection, the antihistamines cannot be expected to have much effect.

Hay fever. The sneezing and sniffling called hay fever is usually not caused by hay and is not a fever. Hay fever is an allergy, usually caused by pollens of trees, grasses, or other plants. It is more properly called allergic rhinitis.

Some people think that goldenrod is a chief cause of hay fever, but this is not true. Goldenrod pollens are too large to be blown about by the wind; so are the pollens of most common flowers.

On the other hand, pollens of grasses, trees, and many other plants are carried by the wind and bring misery to hundreds of thousands of persons every year. During the season when one kind of pollen is being formed, it is not uncommon to find 1500 to 2000 pollen grains in 1 cubic foot of air.

Most cases of spring hay fever, sometimes called rose cold, are due to grass pollens. The attacks of hay fever that occur in the late summer or early fall are usually due to the pollens of ragweed, wormwood, Russian thistle, or pigweed. Some cities have laws that all ragweed in vacant lots must be destroyed by the owners. Some health departments report every day in summer and fall how many grains of ragweed pollen they are finding in 1 cubic foot of air. The first heavy frost kills the plants that form the pollen.

Hay fever tests. When a person has hay fever and does not know the cause, a physician will often make a "skin test," using pollens from plants that are forming pollen at the time that the person has symptoms. Usually, a person will be allergic to more

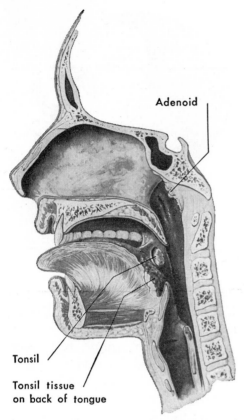

Adenoid

Tonsil

Tonsil tissue
on back of tongue

Location of tonsils and adenoids.

than one kind of pollen, so he is tested with all the pollens that develop at the time he has the hay fever.

Prevention of hay fever. When a person knows what causes his hay fever the simplest way to prevent it is to live where the pollen to which he is sensitive, or allergic, does not exist. Or he may be able to take his vacation at the time that pollen troublesome to him occurs. If this is not possible, he may be able to spend most of the day during the hay fever season in filtered air (see Chapter 23). Air-conditioning, however, is not always an answer to the problem. Some peo-

ple sneeze and sniffle in air-conditioned rooms, because of the chilling of the skin.

Another method of preventing hay fever is to give small injections of the pollen to which a person is allergic. This helps only when it is known to which pollens, and all of the pollens, a person is allergic.

ADENOIDS AND TONSILS

In the throat, there are three pairs of tonsils. One pair is located far back on the tongue, another pair in the side walls of the throat, and the third pair behind the nose in the pharynx. The pair in the side walls of the throat are commonly called tonsils. The pair in the pharynx are called adenoids, especially when they are enlarged. The third pair has no common name.

Tonsils and adenoids are made up of the same kind of tissue as lymph nodes. They guard against infections that enter the body through the nose and throat.

Enlarged tonsils and adenoids. In childhood, tonsils and adenoids are naturally large but they become smaller in later life. They usually need not be removed just because they are enlarged. Adenoids may, however, become so large that they block the air passages and cause a person to breathe through his mouth. Enlarged adenoids may, also, plug up the Eustachian tubes. This plugging makes it harder for children to hear well and makes it easier for infections to develop in the nose and in the ears.

Infected tonsils and adenoids. Many microorganisms that enter the body through the nose and mouth are caught and killed by the tonsils and adenoids. At times, however, these organs themselves become overloaded with infection. They may even pour infection into the rest of the body, interfere with growth, and cause infection of organs like the heart. When this occurs, the infected tonsils and adenoids should be removed.

Tonsillitis. Acute infection of the tonsils, called tonsillitis, is a frequent illness among children and young adults. It is usually caused by a streptococcus, one of the same kind of microorganisms that causes rheumatic fever.

A person with tonsillitis has a sore throat and usually a headache and fever. He may feel chilly and ache in his back and arms and legs. His tonsils look red and swollen and sometimes have white spots on them.

Usually, tonsillitis lasts only a few days, but the infection may spread to the sinuses, ear, and the mastoid, which is the bone behind the ear (see Chapter 20).

The organisms that cause tonsillitis are spread from person to person by hands, drinking glasses, cups, spoons, or little drops of moisture that a person throws out when he coughs or sneezes or even talks. Keeping away from persons with sore throats, keeping hands away from your mouth, and using your own drinking glass and silver are the best ways of preventing tonsillitis.

SO WHAT?

Your nose air-conditions the air you breathe; and

Tonsils and adenoids help destroy disease-producing organisms that enter through your nose and mouth; and

More diseases get into the body through the nose and mouth than in any other way; and

The common cold and related respiratory diseases cause more loss of time from school and from work than all other diseases together; and

Other conditions of the nose, such as hay fever, are responsible for a great deal of misery; and

People waste a lot of money and frequently do themselves more harm than good trying to treat these conditions;

So, be sure that you understand about colds and other disturbances of the nose and throat and what you can do to prevent and cure them.

CHECKING UP

1. What happens to air as it passes through the nose?
2. What are cilia? Of what value are they?
3. What is a "running nose"?
4. How many openings are there into the nose? To what does each opening lead?
5. If your nose is stuffed-up, why may a hot bath make you feel better?
6. What are common causes of mouth-breathing? Why is it better to breathe through the nose than through the mouth?
7. What is the wrong way to blow the nose? the right way? Explain.
8. Why is it unwise to use drugs to shrink the mucous membranes, except on a physician's advice?
9. Can anything be done about a crooked nasal septum?
10. What are nasal polyps?
11. You have heard "Even your best friend won't tell you about B.O. (body odor) and bad breath." Why cannot a person know for himself that he has B.O. or a bad breath?
12. What is the cause of the common cold (coryza)? What relationship does getting chilled have to catching a cold?
13. Why do some persons have more colds than others?
14. Why are preparations containing antiseptics probably useless in preventing colds?
15. What is a cold vaccine? Can it give you a cold? Explain.
16. Describe an experiment to find whether cold vaccines do any good. Of what value is a control group in such an experiment?
17. List rules for preventing colds. Give reasons for each.
18. What is the difference between a chronic infection and an acute infection?
19. When a person has a sinus infection, should he immediately start to use sprays, nose drops, or inhalations? Why or why not?
20. What is an allergy? What are some of the causes of allergies?
21. Persons with hay fever and colds often have the same symptoms. Is hay fever the same as a cold? Explain.
22. Do the antihistamines stop the cause of an allergy or merely relieve the symptoms?
23. What are tonsils and adenoids?
24. Are enlarged tonsils and adenoids always infected? Should enlarged tonsils and adenoids be removed? Explain.

THINGS TO DO

1. Look at a model of a nose. Find the nasal septum. Find the openings of the sinuses; of the Eustachian tubes; of the tear ducts.
2. Find how dishes and silver are washed in the school lunch-room. Ask the public-health department to tell you the regulations about dish washing in restaurants.
3. Visit a kitchen in the school or in a community restaurant and see the dish washing. Is soap used? How hot is the water? Is a dish-washing machine used? How does it work?
4. Washing hands before meals at school is sometimes hard to arrange. Is hot water provided in your school? Is soap provided? Find how many students wash their hands before lunch. If most of them do not, find out why. Can something be done to make it easier?
5. Keep a record for a month of the absences in your class. How many were due to colds? Are there more colds on Mondays? on Wednesdays? on Fridays? Ask the school nurse or the principal how many absences are caused by colds in the whole school.
6. Collect advertisements of cold "cures." Ask a number of people how they try to prevent or to cure colds.
7. Plan a school campaign to make students and teachers think a little more about keeping colds from spreading. Place slogans in the halls. Write jingles and short plays on what to do and what not to do when you have a cold. (Someone once wrote a lively article on "Ten Ways to Get a Cold.")
8. If you know people who have hay fever or other nasal allergies, ask them what are the causes.
9. Ask your public-health department whether hay fever is common in your community and what causes it. If ragweed grows in your community, learn what it looks like. What can you do to help get rid of it?
10. Use a mirror and see whether you can locate your own tonsils.

CHAPTER 14   The Breath of Life

For thousands of years, human beings have known that they must breathe to live. A man can live for weeks without food, and for several days without water, but for only a few minutes without air. People used to think that breathing cooled the blood. They also believed that a man's spirit was in some way connected with his breath. It is only in recent years that we have learned the real reason why we need air.

The body is a machine that releases energy from food. It does this by combining oxygen with the food or with the protoplasm made from food. This is the process of oxidation. It is very like what happens when wood or coal or gasoline burns. Burning, or oxidation, goes on in our bodies without producing a flame, but it does give off heat.

We live our lives surrounded by air, about one-fifth of which is oxygen. We cannot take in this oxygen through our skins. We must breathe it into our lungs before we can use it. Our lungs are the only place where air and blood are brought so close together that the oxygen can be taken up, that is, absorbed, by the blood.

HOW AIR REACHES THE LUNGS

Chapter 13 explains how air is warmed and moistened and cleaned in the nasal cavities before it goes down the passageway to the lungs.

From the nose, the air first passes back into the pharynx and then downward through the larynx, or voice box, into the trachea, or windpipe. You can feel your larynx in the upper part of your neck. Its walls are composed of cartilage, which moves up and down when you swallow. It is sometimes called the "Adam's apple."

The trachea extends down into the upper part of the chest and divides into two bronchi. Each bronchus divides and subdivides into smaller tubes, ending in tiny air sacs called alveoli. The smallest air tubes and the alveoli make up the lungs. In the alveoli, oxygen from the air is absorbed into the blood. In the alveoli, also, carbon dioxide is given off from the blood into the air.

232

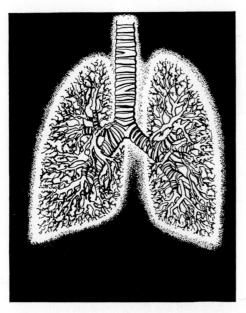 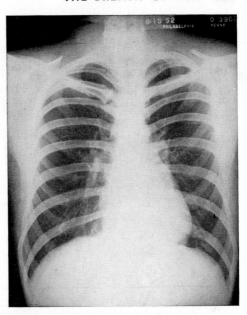

(Left) The lungs, showing the trachea (center), the bronchi branching from the trachea, and the thousands of tiny alveoli. (Right) X-ray of a healthy chest.

This air passageway looks something like a tree turned upside down. The trachea is the "trunk," the bronchi are the "limbs," and the alveoli of the lungs are the "leaves."

Keeping the air lines open. It is important that this "pipe line" for air be held open at all times. In the head, the face bones keep it open. The larynx, trachea, and bronchi are protected from collapsing by heavy rings of cartilage.

All the upper parts of the air passages are lined with membranes, which produce mucus and are covered with cilia. The mucus catches some of the dust and microorganisms in the air. The beating of the cilia pushes the mucus and substances caught in it toward the pharynx, where they can be swallowed or coughed out. In the nasal cavities, the cilia beat downward toward the pharynx. In the trachea and bronchi, the cilia beat upward toward the pharynx. Studies show that at least three-fourths of the bacteria in air are destroyed and removed before the air reaches the lungs.

THE LUNGS

The two lungs hang in two cavities in the chest, or thorax, one on the right, one on the left. Each lung almost fills the chest cavity on its side. The thousands of tiny air sacs, the alveoli, make the lungs feel something like sponges.

The surfaces of the lungs and the inside of the chest cavities are covered by a membrane called the pleura. The

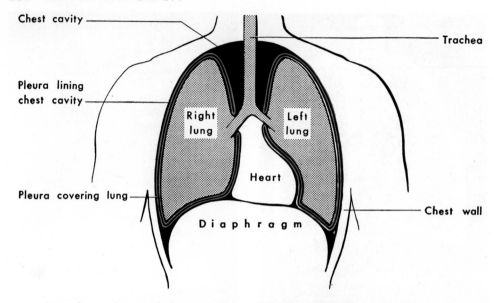

Chest cavity ——————

Trachea

Pleura lining
chest cavity ——

Right
lung

Left
lung

Heart

Pleura covering lung ——

Chest wall

D i a p h r a g m

Note the two layers of pleura, one over the lung and one lining the chest wall.

pleura is smooth and moist and allows the lungs and chest walls to move easily when you breathe. Sometimes infection or injury makes the pleura rough. When this occurs, the membranes on the lungs may become sticky. This condition is known as pleurisy and usually causes pain in breathing.

Each lung is attached to the walls of its chest cavity at only one place. This is on the side toward the middle of the body where the bronchus and pulmonary blood vessels enter the lung. The rest of the lung hangs free in its chest cavity.

The chest cavities are completely enclosed and are airtight. The outside walls of the cavities are the ribs and the muscles between the ribs. The bottoms of both cavities are formed by the diaphragm, which is a large

sheet of muscle that separates the abdominal cavity from the chest. The cavities are separated from each other by a middle wall composed chiefly of the heart and blood vessels and projections from the vertebrae in the back. At the top, the chest cavities become smaller, like rounded cones.

BREATHING AND RESPIRATION

We often use the terms *breathing* and *respiration* as if they meant the same thing. However, they refer to two different bodily functions.

Breathing is a means of getting air in and out of the lungs. This is only the first step in getting oxygen into the blood and to the cells all over the body and getting carbon dioxide and water away from the cells. Air breathed out contains more carbon

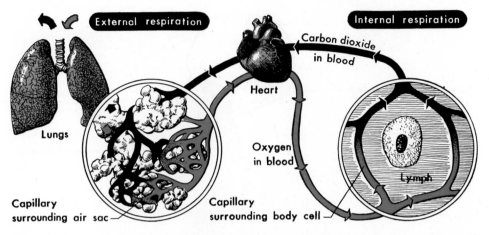

External respiration

Internal respiration

Carbon dioxide
in blood

Heart

Lungs

Oxygen
in blood

Lymph

Capillary
surrounding air sac

Capillary
surrounding body cell

This is a very schematic diagram to help you understand external respiration and internal respiration.

dioxide and more moisture than air breathed in.

Respiration includes the use of oxygen by the cells. We sometimes speak of external respiration as the exchange of oxygen and carbon dioxide in the lungs, and internal respiration as the exchange of oxygen and carbon dioxide between the blood and the cells.

How do we breathe? Breathing has two parts: breathing in, inhaling, or inspiration; and breathing out, exhaling, or expiration. Your chest expands, or grows larger, in inspiration. It grows smaller during expiration.

Many people think that in inspiration the chest expands because air is forced into the lungs. This is just the opposite of what is true. In inspiration, the chest expands, and air is sucked into the lungs. You can see how this happens if you press the air out of a rubber bulb and then put the open end of the bulb in water. As the

bulb expands, it sucks in the water.

Expanding your chest is brought about by contracting the diaphragm and the muscles between the ribs. The diaphragm when at rest, or relaxed, is shaped like a dome that is pushed up into the chest. When it contracts, it flattens and makes the chest cavities larger from top to bottom. Contracting the muscles between the ribs moves the ribs up and out. This makes the chest cavities larger from front to back and from side to side. The lungs become larger as the chest cavities become larger.

During expiration, the diaphragm and muscles between the ribs relax. The diaphragm goes back to its dome shape and the ribs drop down into their relaxed position. The chest cavities are now smaller and air is pressed out of the lungs.

In artificial respiration (see Chapter 4), air is forced out of the lungs by pressing on the chest wall. When this

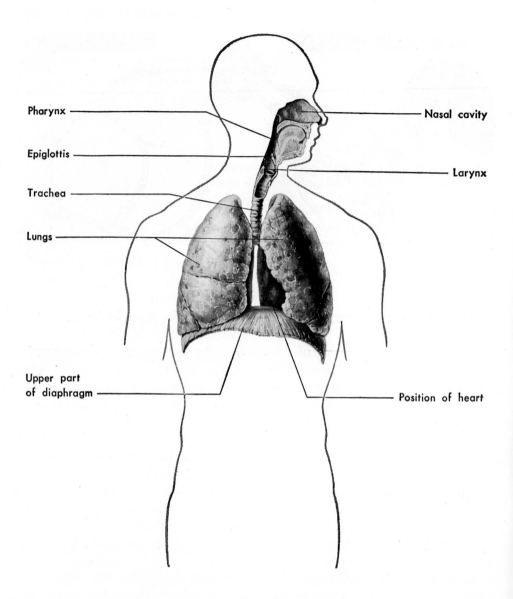

Pharynx

Epiglottis

Trachea

Lungs

Upper part
of diaphragm

Nasal cavity

Larynx

Position of heart

The air passages. Air passes from the nose down through the pharynx, larynx, and trachea, to the lungs. The epiglottis closes when you swallow and keeps food from going down into the trachea and lungs.

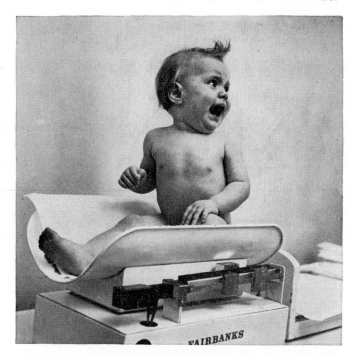

You continually vary your pattern of breathing. Happiness, excitement, fatigue, odors, dust in the air, and dozens of other stimuli affect the way you inhale and exhale. Crying, for example, causes a number of rapid adjustments in your breathing. (Courtesy Standard Oil Co., N.J.)

pressure is released, the chest expands, and air is sucked into the lungs. Pulling up on the arms aids this expansion.

You have more lung space than you need. You have much more lung space than you usually need. In quiet breathing, an adult breathes about a pint of air in and out with each breath. This is only about one-fourth of what his lungs will hold. It is only when you run or do strenuous work that you take deep gulps of air and really fill your lungs.

In breathing, some people have the habit of keeping their diaphragms still and using only the upper part of their lungs. Other people use their diaphragms for most of their breathing. It is a good idea for healthy people to use all the muscles of breathing and

keep fresh air going to all parts of the lungs. Tight clothing, poor posture, or incorrect habits of breathing can keep a person from getting full use of his lungs. It is probably easier, also, for disease organisms to grow in parts of the lungs that are not used.

Having more lung space than you need is very important in some injuries and in some diseases. If one of the chest cavities is opened to the outside air, as in a bullet wound, the lung on that side collapses, and in breathing, little or no air is sucked into it. Fortunately, as long as one lung is in good working order, a person can get along quite well.

In some people with tuberculosis, physicians collapse one lung by forcing air into the pleural cavity around the lung. This is called pneumothorax, meaning air in the thorax. The col-

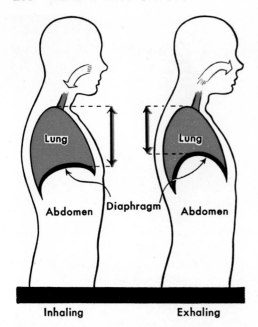

Inhaling   Exhaling

What makes the lungs change in size from front to back? from top to bottom?

oxide finally stimulates the respiratory center so much that strong nerve impulses are sent out to the muscles of breathing, and the person takes a breath whether he wants to or not. Then he will breathe quickly for a while, until the carbon dioxide in the blood is reduced to the usual amount.

On the other hand, if you breathe deeply and rapidly for a minute or two, the carbon dioxide in your blood becomes less and less, and the respiratory center sends out only weak impulses to the muscles of breathing. The result is that breathing is slowed down until the carbon dioxide in the blood builds up to the usual amount.

CHANGES IN BREATHING

An adult inhales and exhales 15 to 20 times per minute when he is resting. Children breathe more rapidly. Exercise makes a person breathe more quickly. So do some diseases. In other illnesses, the rate of breathing may slow down. This is the reason that nurses and physicians keep a record of how fast their patients are breathing.

There are many variations in the way a person breathes, in addition to breathing fast or slow. Talking, for example, involves a continuous series of adjustments in breathing. When you are happy you laugh, that is, you inhale deeply and exhale in a series of short breaths. When you are sad, you cry. Yawning is a deep inspiration with the mouth wide open. It may mean that you are sleepy or tired or bored. Sometimes you may yawn

lapsed lung cannot be expanded in breathing and has a better chance to heal. In time, however, the air in the pleural cavity is absorbed by the tissues, and the lung begins to function again. In other patients with tuberculosis, part of a lung or even a whole lung may be removed, and the person may live a long and useful life (see Chapter 25).

Controlling your breathing. Breathing is regulated chiefly by a nerve center in the brain called the respiratory center. This nerve center is influenced by the amount of carbon dioxide in the blood. You can change your rate of breathing if you wish to but only for a little while. If a person holds his breath, more and more carbon dioxide piles up in the blood. This carbon di-

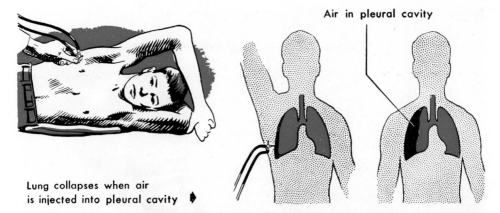

Air in pleural cavity

Lung collapses when air
is injected into pleural cavity ◗

Pneumothorax. Usually, there is no space between the layer of pleura that covers the lungs and the layer that lines the chest wall. The two layers can be separated, however, and the space between them is called the pleural cavity. When air enters this pleural cavity, the lung collapses. This drawing shows how air is injected into the pleural cavity and what happens to the lung.

simply because you see someone else yawn.

Getting dust or bits of food into the trachea makes you cough and sneeze and blow them out. Breathing a strong gas may make you "catch your breath," in other words, stop breathing for a little while. A sudden shock may do the same thing. Hiccoughing is caused by a series of spasms of the diaphragm. Most hiccoughs can be controlled by holding your breath, sipping some water, or deliberately breathing slowly and regularly.

All these breathing adjustments are very delicate. They are responses to many kinds of stimuli—to smoke, dust, and gas in the air you breathe, to the amount of oxygen and carbon dioxide in the blood and in the muscles, to the way you feel. You have only a little control over these changes in breathing, yet breathing adjustments are a successful part of your be-

havior. Your ability to breathe to suit your needs and feelings is an example of how your body works as a total organism, of that "master control" discussed in Chapter 5.

THE AIR WE BREATHE

Air is a mixture of gases: nitrogen (about 78 percent), oxygen (about 21 percent), carbon dioxide (about 0.4 percent), and traces of other gases. Air also contains more or less moisture.

The nitrogen in the air is not used by the body. It is the oxygen that is important for respiration. At high altitudes, air pressure is reduced, and a given amount of air contains only about two-thirds as much oxygen as at sea level. Therefore, people who exercise on mountains, such as Pike's Peak, breathe more quickly, and their hearts beat more rapidly.

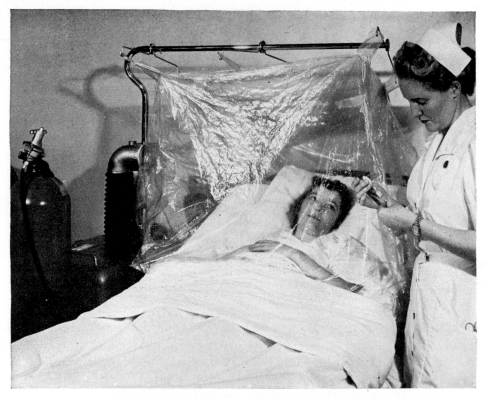

Sometimes a seriously ill person is not able to get enough oxygen under ordinary conditions. Pure oxygen that has been stored in a cylinder can be pumped directly to the sick person through a "tent." (Courtesy Dow Chemical Co.)

Persons who live at high altitudes become adjusted to the lower percentage of oxygen in the air. Part of the adjustment a person makes to mountain air is an increase in the number of his red blood corpuscles, so that more oxygen can be absorbed and carried by his blood stream. This adjustment takes several weeks to accomplish.

The carbon dioxide in the air is important for breathing. It is an interesting fact that when people are suffocating we do not give them pure oxygen but a mixture of oxygen and carbon dioxide. The carbon dioxide gets into the blood and acts on the respiratory center to make a person start breathing.

Gases of many kinds are always being poured out into air from factories, automobiles, and stoves. (See Chapter 23; also see the discussion of carbon monoxide poisoning in Chapter 11.)

Pollens and other substances that cause asthma and hay fever. Pollens in the air are discussed in connection with hay fever (Chapter 13). Asthma is another allergy, which may be

The pollen from ragweed brings suffering to many millions of people each summer. People who are allergic to ragweed should learn to recognize it and try to avoid it. Many cities make some effort to destroy ragweed on a city-wide scale. (Courtesy Department of Health, City of New York)

caused in some people by the same pollens that cause hay fever. In asthma, the muscles in the walls of the bronchi contract so that the bronchi are made smaller and less oxygen can go through them to the lungs. This makes it hard for a person to breathe and gives his breathing a wheezing sound.

While the most common cause of asthma is pollens, other substances in the air sometimes cause it. Wherever there are horses, dogs, cats, cattle, and other animals, tiny particles of their dandruff and hair are always being shaken out into the air. The same thing is true for duck or chicken feathers. Some people react to these particles and have attacks of asthma when near a horse, when in the same room with a dog or a cat, or when using pillows stuffed with chicken or duck feathers. Some people develop asthma if they breathe house dust. Foods, also, are sometimes the cause of asthma.

Physicians can give drugs that will relieve an attack of asthma for a time. We need to learn more about asthma and about allergies in general. Until we know more, the best treatment for a person with asthma is to carry on

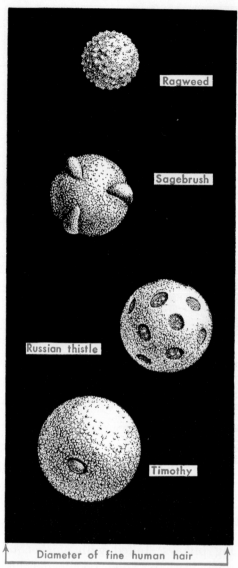

Ragweed

Sagebrush

Russian thistle

Timothy

Diameter of fine human hair

The size of some pollen grains compared with a fine human hair. It is easy to see that many pollen grains can be spread for miles by the wind.

the detective work necessary to find the cause and then avoid it as much as possible.

Disease organisms in the air. Many common diseases are caused by bacteria and viruses that live in the nose and throat and lungs and are sprayed out into the air when we breathe and talk and cough. The common cold is one of these diseases (see Chapter 13). Measles, whooping cough, chicken pox, mumps, scarlet fever, and diphtheria are others. Some of these diseases are discussed in Chapters 24 and 25. A number of different kinds of organisms cause sore throats and sinus infections. Tuberculosis is a very serious disease caused by organisms that usually live in human lungs and go from one person to another in the moisture breathed and coughed out. This is discussed in Chapter 25. There are other diseases, too, like smallpox, that are often spread in material from the nose and throat. And there are still others, like poliomyelitis, about whose spread we are not sure, but which may be spread in this way.

One reason why it is so hard to prevent these diseases is that it is not possible to keep the organisms from one person's nose and throat from getting into the air and to keep other people from breathing them in. You can, of course, stay away from people who are coughing and sneezing. You can keep out of crowds during epidemics. And you can keep as healthy as possible (see Chapter 7), so that your defenses are in good condition.

Furthermore, if you are thoughtful of others and are a good citizen, you will try to keep your microorganisms from reaching other people. Staying home when you are ill, not coughing and talking in other people's faces or on their food, sneezing and coughing into a handkerchief, using your own dishes and silver, washing dishes and silver properly—all of these are com- mon-sense ways of stopping the spread of diseases. These habits of living are also good manners, signs of respect for yourself and your compan- ions.

SO WHAT?

The cells of your body must have oxygen; and

They get this oxygen from the air that you breathe; and

Air frequently contains dust, gases, and microorganisms that may be harmful;

So, try to remember

What healthful air is; and

How to avoid breathing air that may cause you trouble.

CHECKING UP

1. How is oxidation in your body like burning wood in a stove? How are these two processes unlike?
2. How are the air passages in your body kept from collapsing?
3. Why do the lungs feel spongy? What are the air sacs in the lungs called?
4. What is the difference between breathing and respiration?
5. When the diaphragm and the muscles between the ribs con- tract, is the chest made larger or smaller? Is this called inspira- tion or expiration?
6. What is pneumothorax? Can a person with pneumothorax get enough air to breathe?
7. Explain what happens when you hold your breath. Can you hold your breath for a long time?
8. Why is a mixture of oxygen and carbon dioxide given to a person who is suffocating?
9. What happens when you hiccough? when you yawn? when you catch your breath?
10. Air at high altitudes contains less oxygen than air at lower levels. What adjustments does your body make when you stay in the mountains for a few weeks?

11. What are some of the substances that cause asthma? How does asthma differ from hay fever? What is the best treatment for asthma?

12. Why is it hard to stop the spread of diseases that are spread by discharges from the nose and throat? List some of these diseases.

THINGS TO DO

1. Get lungs of a sheep or pig from the butcher shop. Find the trachea and bronchi. Put a glass tube into the trachea and see whether you can blow up the lungs. Notice the tiny air sacs.

2. Ask the biology teacher to show you a model of a chest and lungs or a dissection of a small animal. Find the ribs and the muscles between the ribs, the diaphragm, and the wall between the two chest cavities. Can you see the pleura?

3. Experiment with your own breathing: How slowly can you breathe? how fast? What happens to your ribs when you take a breath? Hold your ribs quiet and use your diaphragm in breathing. Hold your diaphragm quiet and use your ribs in breathing.

CHAPTER 15 Attractive Teeth

Good teeth are important for good health and good looks. They help make your smile attractive when you are young and make you look distinguished when you are older. They add to your self-respect and improve your chances of making friends and getting the kind of job you want.

Physicians and dentists see person after person with decayed, broken, and missing teeth and what we sometimes call "filthy" mouths. It is hard to think when one is young that he or she could ever have such a mouth. Yet this is just what can happen if teeth are not cared for in childhood and early adult life. No one wants to have to buy "store teeth" when he is 30 or 40. Yet every study made of teenagers shows an unbelievable number of their teeth already decayed or missing.

WHAT TEETH DO FOR US

Teeth tear apart and break up solid food, so that the digestive juices can more easily act upon it. The first of these digestive juices is the saliva in the mouth. Chewing should be con-tinued until the food is finely divided and thoroughly mixed with saliva.

Some years ago, an American by the name of Horace Fletcher insisted that many ills resulted from the poor chewing of food. He thought people should chew their food until all solid food becomes liquid and until all the taste is gone. This was known as "Fletcherizing" one's food.

Fletcher undoubtedly claimed too much for his idea. He did, however, make people more interested in chewing their food thoroughly. He made them aware of the fact that much so-called "indigestion" is caused by "bolting" one's food before it is well chewed.

HOW TEETH DEVELOP

A tooth consists of three parts: a crown, which is what can be seen above the gum; a neck, which is the narrow part surrounded by the gum; and a root or roots, which are buried in the jawbone.

The inside of the tooth is chiefly dentin, or ivory. On the crown of the tooth, this dentin is covered by a layer

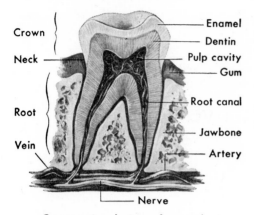

Crown
Neck
Root
Vein

Enamel
Dentin
Pulp cavity
Gum
Root canal
Jawbone
Artery

Nerve

Cross-sectional view of a tooth.

of hard enamel. In the center of the tooth is a small space. This contains a nerve, blood vessels, and lymph vessels. This material is called pulp. The root canals extend from the pulp to the tip of the roots, where the nerves and blood and lymph vessels enter the tooth.

Each person has two sets of teeth: a first set, called primary, "baby," or deciduous teeth; and a second, or permanent, set. The first, or primary, set includes 20 teeth, 10 in the upper jaw and 10 in the lower jaw; the permanent set is made up of 32 teeth, 16 in each jaw.

Teeth start forming before birth. Teeth start forming in the jaw months and even years before they erupt, or appear above the gum where they can be seen. When a baby is born, he has all his "baby" teeth, and some of his permanent teeth, already formed in his jaws.

Care of the teeth, then, starts early in prenatal life, months before birth. Dental care at that time consists chiefly of making sure that the mother eats the kinds of food that build teeth.

Anything that disturbs the work of the cells while teeth are being formed may lead to poor tooth formation. A poor diet will do this. So will infectious diseases—that is, diseases caused by infectious organisms. This is especially true for diseases in which there is a rash. Years later, dentists can often tell that a person has had chicken pox or measles by the defects in the enamel formed at the time of the illness.

Usually, the first primary teeth are the central incisors, the two teeth in the center of the front of each jaw. They erupt during the sixth or seventh month after birth in most babies. The lateral incisors, the teeth at the sides of the central incisors, appear usually between the seventh and ninth months. Then come the first molars, usually between the twelfth and fourteenth months; the cuspids, or eyeteeth, about the eighteenth month; and the second molars, between the twentieth and twenty-fourth months. There is a great deal of difference among babies in the ages at which their teeth erupt.

Take care of primary teeth. In many families, there is much excitement when a baby's teeth appear and then they seem to be forgotten. A baby should be taken to the dentist at least by the time he has all his primary teeth. At the same time, he should begin brushing his teeth, or having them brushed for him.

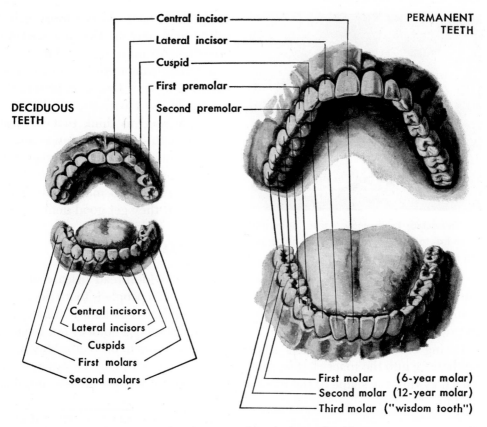

DECILUOUS TEETH

PERMANENT TEETH

Central incisor
Lateral incisor
Cuspid
First premolar
Second premolar

Central incisors
Lateral incisors
Cuspids
First molars
Second molars

First molar (6-year molar)
Second molar (12-year molar)
Third molar ("wisdom tooth")

Each person has two sets of teeth during his lifetime.

Parents know that the primary teeth will be lost and sometimes think that it is a waste of time to take care of them. This is a mistake. Taking care of primary teeth is important in the development of good permanent teeth. All the time a baby has his primary teeth his permanent teeth are forming under them. Infection at the roots of the primary teeth may affect the permanent teeth.

The 6-year molars. The sixth year of life is an important one in the development of a child's teeth. At this age, the permanent teeth begin to erupt. The first permanent teeth, often called the 6-year molars, come in back of the primary teeth. There are four 6-year molars, one on each side of each jaw.

The 6-year molars are very useful for chewing and grinding food. Under good conditions, a person should keep them all his life. Yet they are the teeth most often lost. In one city, it was found that one junior-high school student in every three had lost at least one of the 6-year molars. Often parents think that these are primary teeth and let them decay. Adolescents sometimes do not understand how im-

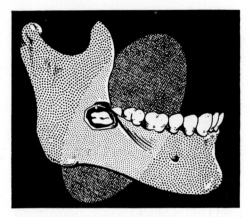

An impacted tooth may cause pain and often has to be removed, since it is not growing straight in the jaw.

portant these teeth are and postpone going to the dentist until it is too late to save the 6-year molars.

Losing the 6-year molars lets other teeth move into the spaces left vacant. This may ruin the shape of the mouth for life.

The "toothless" age. Starting at about the age of 6, a person loses all his primary teeth and replaces them with permanent teeth. We sometimes call 7 and 8 the "toothless" age. If we had "x-ray eyes" we could see that it is really a very "toothy" age. The jaws are crowded with permanent teeth all ready to erupt.

The 12-year molars and "wisdom" teeth. Around 12 years of age the second molars, sometimes called the 12-year molars, erupt behind the 6-year molars. The third, and last, molars, or "wisdom" teeth, come in usually after the age of 17. Some people do not appear to have wisdom teeth, either be-

cause these teeth do not form or because they stay in the jaw without erupting. An impacted wisdom tooth is one that cannot erupt, because it is crowded against the roots of the 12-year molar next to it.

People used to think that the last step in tooth development was losing their permanent teeth. Dentists tell us now that most people can keep their own teeth no matter how long they live if they get good dental care.

DENTAL CARIES

The most widespread disease among the American people is tooth decay, or dental caries. It is almost impossible to find an adult who does not have at least one filling in his teeth. Most people have a great many fillings or have lost many teeth that were not properly filled.

We do not understand all that happens in dental caries. Acids are formed in the mouth by the action of bacteria on carbohydrates, especially sugar, left on and around the teeth. The acids are capable of dissolving enamel and dentin and causing cavities.

Three conditions seem necessary for dental caries to develop: bacteria in the mouth; material in which bacteria can live and produce acids; teeth that are not able to resist decay. Scientists have been trying for years to learn how to change these conditions so that decay cannot develop.

Diet. For teeth to form satisfactorily, the diet must contain the materials used in building teeth. Calcium and phosphorus are the two minerals found in largest amounts in bones and teeth. Milk, green vegetables, and fish foods are good sources of calcium and phosphorus. During the years when the teeth and bones are growing, a person needs every day the amount of calcium contained in about a quart of milk. After his teeth are formed, he probably needs the calcium from 1 pint of milk a day (see Chapters 8 and 9).

The body must have vitamin D before it can make use of the calcium and phosphorus. Extra amounts of vitamin D are usually given to babies in cod-liver oil, vitamin-D milk, or some other vitamin-D preparations. Older people may need these during the winter when there is little sunshine.

Sometimes special foods or vitamins are advertised to prevent caries, but there is no proof that they do. A well-rounded diet, containing milk, orange juice, vegetables, and, for children, extra vitamin D, contains the materials for building teeth. But even with a good diet some people develop caries.

Lemon juice sometimes has been advertised for the prevention of colds and the treatment of rheumatism and constipation. As a result, some people make a habit of sucking lemons or of taking lemon juice in a little water every day. The acid in the lemon juice seems to make it easier for dental caries to develop.

This does not mean that lemons should be left out of the diet. They are an excellent source of vitamin C (ascorbic acid). Taking undiluted

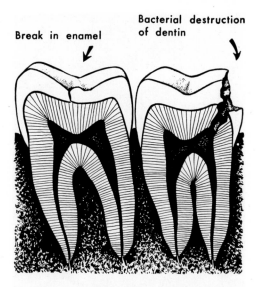

Break in enamel

Bacterial destruction of dentin

Dental caries starts with a break in the enamel. Filling this small cavity takes little time, costs little money, and does not hurt.

lemon juice, however, is not good for the teeth.

People who take little or no candy, cake, and sweet drinks have fewer cavities, on the average, than those who use these edibles often. The sugar and starches allow more bacteria to live in the mouth and form acids. Cleaning the mouth after eating or drinking gets some of the sugar out but not all. Milk, fruit juice, fruit, and peanuts are better between-meal snacks than candy and bottled sweet drinks.

Fluorine. Within the last few years, it has been found that teeth which decay do not have as much fluorine, one of the chemical elements, in them as those which do not decay. This fluorine must come from food or water.

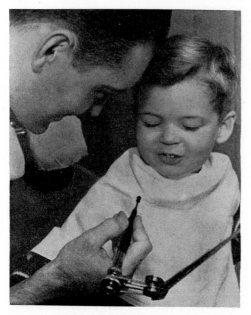

This small boy is having his deciduous teeth cared for and, at the same time, is learning not to be afraid of the dentist. (Courtesy American Dental Association)

Studies were made of the drinking water in communities where there was much dental caries and in those where there was little dental caries. One part of fluorine in a million parts of drinking water evidently resulted in preventing caries in many people. More than this amount resulted in teeth that resisted caries, but it also caused the teeth to become chalky in appearance and easily stained with brown from food and drink.

Fluorine, in the form of sodium fluoride, is now being used in two ways in the fight against caries. It is being added to the water supplies of some communities. The amount added is equal to the amount found naturally in the water in communities where people's teeth resist caries but

are not made brown. It will take a number of years, long enough for children to grow up, before we know exactly how much protection against caries has been given by fluorine. Already, however, it seems that children who use this water have only about half the number of cavities that children have who do not use water with fluorine added.

Many dentists are putting sodium fluoride directly on the surface of children's teeth. First, the teeth are dried very thoroughly and the sodium fluoride is put on carefully. This is done every 3 years during the time when teeth are erupting. This, too, seems to reduce the number of cavities by almost one-half the number there would otherwise be.

Some attempt has been made to put sodium fluoride into chewing gum and toothpastes. This has not been very successful in reducing decay, but we need more studies of its value.

Cleanliness. Everyone has heard: "A clean tooth never decays." If we could keep our teeth so clean that no bacteria were left on them, this statement might be true. But such extreme cleanliness is impossible.

Brushing the teeth and rinsing the mouth after getting up in the morning, after every meal, and before going to bed is a good practice, because it gets rid of particles of food and of mucus from the nose and throat. Five times a day may seem a good many times to brush the teeth, but the results are probably worth the effort. People who are regularly away from home, at school or work, usually have lockers or desks where they can keep a toothbrush for use after lunch.

Your toothbrush should be small enough to reach all parts of your mouth easily. The bristles should be short and firm. The tufts of bristles should be widely separated and should form a flat brushing surface. There are many kinds of good brushes, some costing very little.

Cold water should be used in brushing the teeth, for hot water softens the bristles of the brush. After a brush has been used, it should be washed and placed where it will dry. It is well to have more than one brush, so that each one can dry thoroughly before being used again.

A good way to brush your teeth and massage your gums is to hold the brush with the bristles slanting downward on the upper jaw and upward on the lower jaw. Use a gentle stroke, downward on the upper gums and upward on the lower gums, so that you push the gums *over* the necks of the teeth, not away from them. Turn the brush gently and work the bristles between the teeth as well as over the surfaces.

Some dentists think that people should not use dental floss, because the gums can be damaged by rough use of the floss. Certainly, "sawing" back and forth on dental floss with such force that it injures the gums between the teeth does more harm than good. When dental floss is used as a dentist advises, it cleans the sides of the teeth that cannot be reached by a brush.

Well-formed, clean teeth help make your smile attractive. (Courtesy *Scholastic Magazines* and Modern Plastics Competition)

Toothpastes and powders. The American people spend some $80 million a year on dentifrices, that is, on toothpastes, powders, and liquids. The sale of these is promoted through "high-powered" advertising. In fact, one year's advertising of dentifrices is reported to cost $16 million.

The chief value of dentifrices is that they are pleasant to use and encourage people to brush their teeth. As an inexpensive dentifrice, soda, salt, or precipitated chalk with or without flavoring, is considered quite satisfactory.

Efforts are continually being made to put into dentifrices materials that will destroy bacteria. Actually, a dentifrice stays in the mouth such a short time that it can have little effect on bacteria. To kill bacteria, it would have to be so strong that it would injure the gums and the lining of the mouth.

Quite recently, great interest has developed in so-called "ammoniated" and "chlorophyll" dentifrices. The ammoniated dentifrices are said to act against the acids formed in the mouth from sugars and starches and reduce the number of acid-forming bacteria. It has not yet been shown for certain that any kinds of tooth powders and toothpastes reduce dental decay.

Dental repair. The one thing we are sure about in the control of dental caries is that a small cavity tends to become a large one. Filling a small cavity saves time, money, and pain, and may save a tooth. This is one reason why it is important to take babies to the dentist. Filling small cavities does not hurt, and children can grow up without being afraid of the dentist or his office.

A tooth does not begin to ache until the decay is close to the pulp. Then pressure, heat and cold, or sweet things reach the nerve. To wait until this happens usually means that the nerve dies and the tooth must be pulled.

After the nerve dies, the tooth is known as a dead tooth. Infections grow more easily at the roots of dead teeth than of live ones. Some dentists think that dead teeth should not be left in the mouth. X-rays should be made regularly of dead teeth that do stay in the mouth in order to find beginning infections. With the nerve gone, there is no way for the person to feel pain from beginning infections.

And they may do a great deal of damage before they are discovered.

"Visit your dentist twice a year"—everyone has heard this again and again. It is good advice for many people. A better rule is "Go to the dentist often enough so that he finds only small cavities." This may mean going every 3 months.

Other conditions affecting dental caries. Some people eat what seems to be an adequate diet, brush their teeth, go to the dentist regularly, and still have many cavities. Some people never take care of their teeth and have no cavities.

Heredity is undoubtedly part of the answer. Hormones from endocrine glands may be another. And there may be parts of the puzzle that we have not yet found. However, we know enough now to enable most of us to save most of our teeth, if we will just use the knowledge.

MALOCCLUSION

Irregular teeth or poorly formed jaws make it impossible for the teeth to fit together and chew well. The result is malocclusion, meaning poor bite.

Preventing malocclusion. In a survey in one city, it was found that almost 10 percent of the children in school needed treatment for malocclusion. All the treatments put together would cost about $3 million. Could some of this have been prevented?

Taking care of the primary teeth

and of the 6-year molars is the best way to prevent malocclusion. This means filling cavities and replacing lost primary teeth or putting in retainers, which keep the spaces open until the permanent teeth can grow in. Safety habits that keep children from knocking out their teeth by falling, running into things, being hit by balls or bats, biting nuts, or hitting their teeth on drinking fountains are all important in protecting teeth.

Pressure on teeth and jaws can change their shape. Thumb-sucking is a common way of applying pressure that may deform a baby's or young child's jaws.

Sleeping on the face or with one hand pressed against the cheek, pushing the tongue against the teeth, leaning the head on one hand, mouth-breathing, all are forms of pressure that should be avoided.

Treatment of malocclusion. The treatment of malocclusion is known as orthodontia. The dentists who give this treatment are called orthodontists. Usually, orthodontia includes putting "bands" on the teeth, which gently but firmly push the teeth into place or pull on the jaws so that the bones grow as they should. This takes months and, sometimes, years and often causes strain and discomfort.

Every case of malocclusion is different from every other. Sometimes treatment is best given when a child is young before his permanent teeth have come in. In other cases, it is better to wait until some of the permanent teeth have erupted. An or-

thodontist studies each case and tries to give each child the kind of treatment he needs at the time he needs it.

Results of malocclusion. If the teeth do not meet, food cannot be well chewed. It is as simple as that. Malocclusion sometimes causes mouth-breathing. It may interfere with speech. In addition, a jaw that is too small or teeth that stick out often make a person unhappy, self-conscious, afraid that he looks odd. These effects on personality and self-respect are some of the best reasons for trying to prevent and treat malocclusion.

ROOT INFECTIONS

Bacteria sometimes reach the roots of a tooth by traveling down the pulp and along the root canal. Here, they may form root abscesses. Occasionally, abscesses form around the roots of healthy teeth.

When an abscess works its way to the surface, it forms a "gum boil." Many people do not know that gum boils mean infections that should be cared for.

Often poisons from the abscesses and even the bacteria themselves are taken into the blood and lymph and are circulated through the body. Abscesses at the roots of some of the teeth on the upper jaw may extend directly into one of the sinuses, producing a serious sinus infection (see Chapter 13).

The development of a root abscess on a healthy tooth usually causes pain.

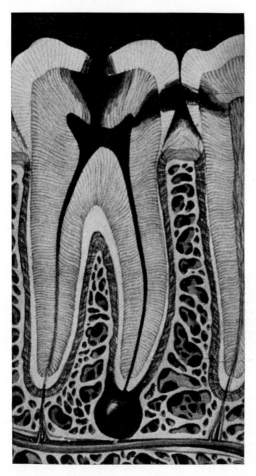

An abscess on the root of a tooth. (Courtesy American Dental Association)

However, abscesses may develop on the roots of dead teeth without any warning.

Removing the tooth and allowing the abscess to drain is the best treatment. Getting rid of the bacteria on the roots of the teeth does not cure the infection that may have spread to other parts of the body. It does prevent the spreading of more toxins—that is, poisons—and bacteria from the teeth.

PYORRHEA AND GINGIVITIS

Healthy gums are firm and pink or light red. Unhealthy gums become bright red or purplish, soft and swollen, and bleed easily. This inflammation of the gums is called gingivitis. Pyorrhea means an infection of the gums, usually accompanied by pus.

There are several causes of gingivitis. Too little vitamin C (ascorbic acid) in the diet may result in sore, bleeding gums. Anyone with these symptoms should make sure that he is eating enough foods containing vitamin C, such as oranges, tomatoes, and cabbage.

Sometimes gums are injured and inflamed by toothbrushes or dental floss. Sometimes a layer of tartar forms on the teeth, especially near the necks where it is not brushed away. Tartar is something like lime. Chewing or brushing may rub the soft gum against the tartar and injure the gum. A dentist's cleaning of teeth includes scraping off the tartar. This helps to prevent gingivitis.

If pyorrhea develops, it should be treated by a dentist. Home treatments with mouth washes, toothpastes, or powders do little good.

Biting and chewing help keep the gums in healthy condition by improving the circulation. Missing teeth, poor fillings, and malocclusion prevent the proper use of the teeth in chewing. Coarse food, which gives something really to bite on, is good for the gums.

Trench mouth is a severe form of gingivitis. It is caused by microorganisms, which may be passed from person to person on food, drinking glasses, and eating tools that are not properly washed. If trench mouth develops, it should be treated by a physician or a dentist.

HALITOSIS

Advertisements nowadays make people aware of the dangers of halitosis, or unpleasant breath. No one wants other people to avoid him or talk about him behind his back. We usually cannot smell our own breaths, because the nerves of smell are located in the upper part of our noses (see Chapter 13). The result of this advertising is a lot of worry and the purchase of mouth washes, which can have only a temporary effect.

Some disagreeable odors are caused by decayed teeth or decaying food between the teeth. Anyone who goes regularly to the dentist and keeps his teeth clean need not worry about halitosis from this cause.

Infections in the nose, tonsils, and sinuses sometimes cause unpleasant odors. Good medical care will remove these.

Some odors are breathed out from the lungs. These come from substances in the blood, usually fats. Diets with little fat in them usually reduce these odors or do away with them entirely.

WHAT A GOOD DENTIST DOES FOR YOU

Good dentistry takes time and skill. Cavities must be carefully cleaned,

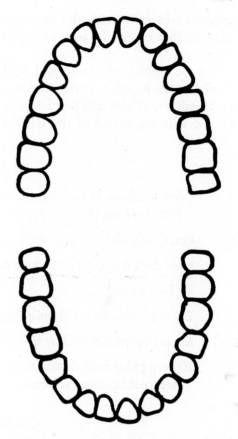

Chart for permanent teeth. Your dentist keeps your dental record on such a chart. Refer to Exercise 12 on page 258.

so that no decay is left to spread down into the pulp. Fillings must be carefully fitted, so that they do not become loose or allow decay to start around their edges. Teeth must be carefully cleaned and examined, so that cavities are found while they are small. Malocclusion must be treated at the right time, and the treatments must be continued until the teeth and jaws are as near the normal shape as it is possible to get them. X-rays must be taken and studied to find root abscesses and small cavities on the sides of teeth that cannot be seen with the naked eye.

A good dentist can do a great deal to make you happier, better looking, and healthier if you will just let him. People who are afraid of the dentist are behaving very foolishly. True, he may hurt you a little. But if you wait 6 months, a year, or 2 years, he is certain to hurt you even more. And the cost also will be a great deal more. Regular care helps you keep your own teeth now and all the rest of your life.

SO WHAT?

Good teeth are of importance, not only for health and for comfort, but also for a pleasing appearance; and

Practically all teeth that are lost could be saved; and

Most dental decay can be prevented;

So, be sure to

Eat the foods that will build healthy teeth; and

Keep your mouth and teeth clean; and

Have regular dental care, so that if decay begins it can be stopped before it becomes serious.

CHECKING UP

1. Why should you chew your food thoroughly?
2. What are the parts of a tooth? Draw a diagram of a tooth and label the parts.
3. When do teeth begin to form? When should care of the teeth begin? When do teeth begin to erupt?
4. When should a baby make his first trip to the dentist? Why?
5. Why should you give special care to the 6-year molars?
6. What is an impacted tooth?
7. You know that diet is important in the formation of teeth and in the prevention of caries. Which foods should be included in the diet? Which foods should be used in only small amounts? Which foods make good between-meal snacks?
8. What facts lead us to think that fluorine is important in the prevention of caries? What two methods seem most successful in supplying the needed fluorine?
9. Describe a good toothbrush. How often should you brush your teeth? Why? How should you brush your teeth?

10. Is it true that "a clean tooth never decays"? Explain.
11. What are the values of toothpastes and powders?
12. Why is it important to have cavities filled while they are small? How often should you go to the dentist?
13. What is malocclusion? What is an orthodontist?
14. List causes of malocclusion. How can malocclusion be prevented?
15. Why are root abscesses dangerous?
16. Why is care of the gums important? How can you care for your gums?
17. How can halitosis usually be prevented?
18. Why is it foolish to be afraid to go to a dentist?

THINGS TO DO

1. Make a collection of teeth—animal teeth and human teeth. Which are biting teeth? Which are chewing teeth? Find the crown, neck, and roots. If possible, examine a tooth with a cavity in it. Can you see the dentin and pulp?
2. Ask the biology teacher to show you the teeth in a skull.
3. Count the number of times you chew a bite of apple or a bit of meat before swallowing it. Try "Fletcherizing" a bite.
4. If any members of the class have baby brothers and sisters, keep records of when their teeth erupt.
5. If you have your own "baby book," find when your own teeth started to come in.
6. How many members of your class have their second molars? Do any of you have your wisdom teeth?
7. Do you know any adult whose wisdom teeth never erupted? Do you know any adult who still has some primary teeth?
8. Borrow tooth x-rays from a dentist, or ask the school nurse to borrow some. Try to get some of children, showing primary teeth with permanent teeth already formed in the jaw. Try to get some showing root abscesses and dead teeth.
9. Sometimes a dentist will lend casts or models of teeth. He may show you or your teacher how to make casts and models of your own teeth.
10. Discuss how you could answer arguments of people who think it is silly to take 3- and 4-year-olds to the dentist.
11. Refer to Chapter 8 to find which foods contain calcium, phosphorus, vitamin D, and vitamin C. Did you have some of these yesterday? How much?

12. Make a chart of your own teeth. Mark the teeth where there are fillings. Look at your teeth in a mirror. Can you find any cavities? Mark these on the chart. If you have not been to a dentist in the past few weeks and you find what seem to be cavities, make an appointment to have your teeth examined.

13. Ask a member of the class to look up the experiments with fluorine and make a report to the class.

14. Show the proper way to use a toothbrush; to use dental floss.

15. Answer the following questions. Give your answers to your teacher or the school nurse and let her total them for the class. Get answers to the same questions from other classes in your own school and in the elementary school.

    a) Do you have a toothbrush?

    b) Did you brush your teeth this morning?

    c) Do you usually brush your teeth when you get up? after breakfast? after lunch? after dinner? before going to bed?

    d) Have you ever been to a dentist?

    e) Have you been to a dentist within the last 6 months?

    f) Did you eat any candy yesterday?

    g) Did you have any bottled sweet drink yesterday?

    Talk over the answers to the questions and see what you need to do to improve the care of your teeth.

16. Look at some toothpastes and powders under a microscope. Write to the American Dental Association, 222 East Superior Street, Chicago, Illinois, for information about some of the new dentifrices.

17. Collect advertisements of dentifrices. What do they claim?

18. If someone in the class has bands on his teeth, ask him to tell the class what his dentist or orthodontist is trying to do.

19. Ask the school nurse to get figures for you on the amount of dental caries and malocclusion in your town or city.

20. Ask parents and nurses and doctors how to keep children from sucking their thumbs. Which do you think are the best ways? Why?

21. Visit a dentist's office or a dental clinic. Ask the dentist to explain how he uses some of his tools and his x-ray machine.

22. If your school does not have movies and slides relating to teeth, write to your state department of education or your state department of health for a list of ones you can obtain. Show these at an assembly for a number of classes.

CHAPTER 16   Digestion

The food we take into our mouths is not ready to be used by our cells. Digestion is the process of making it ready for use. A bit of beefsteak, for example, tastes good and is good for you, but it would make you very ill if you took it straight into your blood. It must be changed into a different form before you can use it.

Beefsteak is chiefly protein. Digestion breaks it down into amino acids (see Chapters 5 and 8). Your cells can use amino acids to build the various kinds of protoplasm that make up your body. The cells cannot use the meat itself.

Digestion changes proteins to amino acids. It changes carbohydrates to simple sugars, and fats to fatty acids and glycerin. All these products of digestion can be absorbed through the walls of the digestive tract into the blood.

It is somewhat as though you had some houses that other people had built, out of which you could build a house of your own. First, you would tear down the old houses into piles of boards, nails, doors, plumbing fixtures, shingles, and windows. Then,

you would put these together again to make the house you wanted.

Food is like the old houses. It has been made by plants and animals. Before you can use it to make your own "house," your own body, you tear it apart into sugars, amino acids, minerals, fatty acids, and glycerin. Out of these, you make your protoplasm.

HOW THE DIGESTIVE TRACT FUNCTIONS

Most pictures and models of the digestive tract make it look very complicated. It is easier to understand if you know its general plan.

First of all, the digestive tract is a tube. It starts at the mouth in the head, goes down through the chest and abdominal cavity, and ends with the opening from the large intestine, the anus. From mouth to anus is only 3 or 4 feet, but the digestive tube is about 30 feet long. This means that it is twisted and curled back and forth in the abdomen, so that it fits into what seems a small space.

The walls of the digestive tube contain rings of smooth muscle. Waves of contraction, called peristaltic

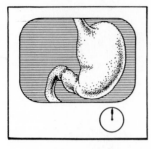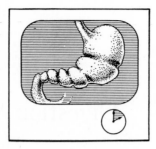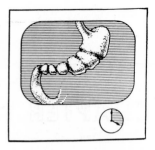

Waves of peristalsis mix the food and push it on down the digestive tract. (Left) Stomach full. (Center) 2 hours later. (Right) 4 hours after the meal.

waves, or peristalsis, pass down the tube every few minutes. The muscles at the top of the tube contract and make the tube smaller. Then the next muscles contract, and the next. Good muscle tonus makes them ready to act and aids peristalsis (see Chapter 6).

Peristalsis pushes the food along the digestive tract. Whatever is not used accumulates in the large intestine and finally is pushed out as wastes, or feces.

Along the walls of the digestive tract are glands. These glands make digestive juices. The digestive juices contain enzymes, which are chemicals that act upon the food as it is pushed along. They change it into simpler substances—amino acids, simple sugars, fatty acids, and glycerin— that can be absorbed through the walls of the digestive tract.

PARTS OF THE DIGESTIVE TRACT

The digestive tract is all one tube, but it can be thought of in six parts: mouth, pharynx, esophagus, stomach, small intestine, and large intestine. Most of the digestive tract—part of the esophagus, the stomach, and intestines—is located below the diaphragm in the abdominal cavity.

The mouth contains the teeth, the tongue, and the outlets of the salivary glands. The teeth break up the food. The tongue pushes the food about. It also contains taste buds, the organs of taste.

The salivary glands secrete the digestive juice called saliva. This contains an enzyme that changes starch to sugar. You can test for this change by chewing a piece of bread or cracker and noticing its taste. After a few seconds, the saliva changes some of the starch to sugar, and you get a sweet taste.

The pharynx is back of the mouth. Its walls contain much lymph tissue, chiefly in the tonsils and adenoids. The openings of the Eustachian tubes, which lead to the middle ears, are on the side walls of the pharynx (see Chapter 13).

The larynx opens from the front part of the lower end of the pharynx. A lid of connective tissue, the epiglottis, closes over the larynx when you swallow. This means that you cannot breathe and swallow at the same time. Sometimes the epiglottis does not close quickly enough and a little food "goes down the wrong way." The result is violent coughing and sneezing until the food is blown out.

Pushing food out of the mouth into the pharynx is within your control; that is, it is voluntary (see Chapter 6). From this point on, the movements of the digestive tract are not under your control; that is, they are involuntary. Producing digestive juices in the digestive tract is involuntary. This is true even for the salivary glands in the mouth.

The esophagus is a narrow tube. It lies behind the trachea and connects the pharynx with the stomach. When you take too big a swallow of water, you can feel the walls of your esophagus stretch as the water goes slowly down to the stomach.

Stomach. The stomach is a baglike part of the digestive tract. A 10-year-old's stomach holds something less than a quart. Through the teens the size of the stomach increases as the size of the body increases. A man's stomach holds 1½ quarts to 2 quarts. A woman's stomach is somewhat smaller. The stomach serves chiefly as a temporary storage place for food. This makes its size important on Thanksgiving and Christmas.

People often speak of the stomach as if it were the most important organ of the digestive tract. Actually, it is possible for a person to have his stomach removed and to live a comfortable and healthful life.

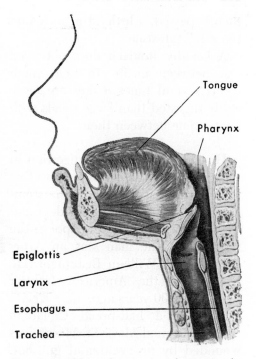

How is food kept from going down into the trachea and lungs?

The food is mixed in the stomach by the peristaltic action of the muscles in its walls. Glands in the walls produce gastric juice. This contains the enzymes pepsin and rennin. Pepsin changes proteins to simpler forms. Rennin curdles milk. The stomach glands also produce an acid. Sometimes, people complain of having an "acid stomach." They forget that a healthy stomach is always acid.

Food stays in the stomach for 3 or 4 hours. Fatty foods stay longer than other food.

Very little if any food is taken into the blood from the stomach, although alcohol and certain drugs and poisons are absorbed from it. The food is mixed and partly digested and then is passed, a little at a time, into the small intestine.

A healthy stomach does not need rest between meals. In fact, small meals several times a day are more easily digested than large meals with longer time between them.

How we learned about digestion in the stomach. The story of how we first learned about digestion in the stomach is an exciting one of accident and the right man in the right spot at the right time. The man was an Army surgeon, Dr. William Beaumont. He worked on the American frontier more than 100 years ago.

In 1822 a half-breed Canadian boatman named Alexis St. Martin was wounded by an accidental gunshot. Part of the front wall of his stomach was torn away. Dr. Beaumont stitched the edges of the stomach to the skin. Much to his surprise St. Martin lived.

Dr. Beaumont was a man of scientific curiosity. He watched the movements of St. Martin's stomach through the hole in the wall of the abdomen. He could see the drops of gastric juice as they oozed from the glands in the walls of the stomach. If he placed food directly into the stomach through the opening, more gastric juice formed. It formed, also, when St. Martin took food into his mouth and even when he thought about food.

Here was a chance to find what gastric juice does to food. Dr. Beaumont tied pieces of food on silk strings and placed them in the stomach. He pulled them out from time to

time to see what had happened to the food.

He found that gastric juice acted upon meat. Nothing seemed to happen to a piece of meat during the first hour. After 2 hours, the surface of the meat was soft. An hour later, the meat was half gone, and 2 hours later when he pulled out the string the meat had completely disappeared.

Dr. Beaumont hired St. Martin as a servant, so that he could continue these studies on him. It was not easy. Dr. Beaumont was moved from place to place by the Army. And sometimes St. Martin disappeared for weeks or months. However, Dr. Beaumont kept on working and studying digestion whenever his patient came back to him. All the work on digestion in the years since then has been built on what he learned.

Small intestine. The small intestine is 20 feet to 25 feet long. It is about $1\frac{1}{2}$ inches wide when it is filled. Bile from the liver and pancreatic juice from the pancreas empty into the upper part of the small intestine. There are other glands in the walls of the small intestine itself that secrete digestive juices.

Bile from the liver helps in the digestion of fat. Enzymes in the pancreatic juice and the digestive juices from the intestinal glands finish the digestion of all the foods—fats, starches, and proteins.

The upper part of the small intestine may be said to be the most important part of the digestive tract. Digestion is finished there. Digested

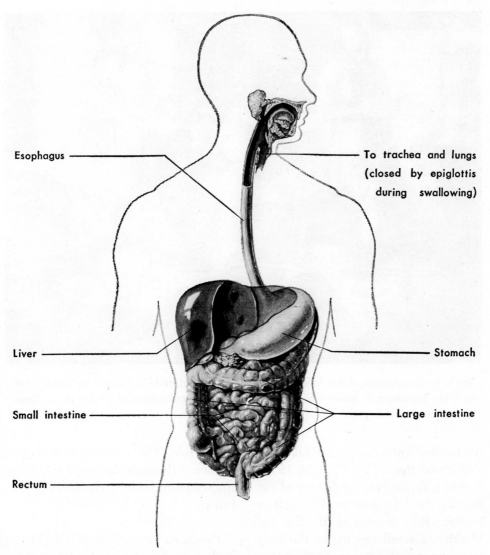

Esophagus

To trachea and lungs
(closed by epiglottis
during swallowing)

Liver

Stomach

Small intestine

Large intestine

Rectum

The digestive tract is a continuous tube. Digestive glands are located at various places along this tube. Locate these glands and name the digestive fluids which come from each gland. The walls of the tube contain smooth muscles. Try to trace a wave of peristalsis through the digestive tract. Do not mark in this book.

food is also absorbed into the blood stream there. The parts of food that are not digested and absorbed in the small intestine become waste material, which is to be pushed on down into the large intestine.

Liver. The liver is a large organ weighing about 3 pounds. It is located in the right side of the upper part of the abdomen. All the blood from the small intestine passes through the liver. Some foods that are

This is a reproduction of the famous painting "Beaumont and St. Martin" by Dean Cornwell. Dr. Beaumont is shown making one of his routine collections of gastric juice. (Courtesy Wyeth, Philadelphia)

not needed immediately are taken out and stored there (see Chapter 12).

Bile is formed in the liver and carried by the bile duct to the small intestine. Bile is stored in the gall bladder, a small sac under the liver. Sometimes, bile forms hard masses known as gall stones. Usually, these must be removed by an operation.

If the bile duct is closed by an infection or by gall stones, bile may be absorbed into the blood and give a yellow color to the skin. This condition is known as jaundice.

Red blood cells are always being destroyed in the liver. Part of the hemoglobin gives a dark green color to the bile. This coloring matter goes on down through the small and large intestines and makes the feces appear brown.

Pancreas. The pancreas is a gland 3 inches or 4 inches long, lying along the lower side of the stomach. It produces two kinds of secretions. The pancreatic juice is an external secretion poured into the small intestine through a duct, or tube. A hormone called insulin is an internal secretion. It is poured directly into the blood stream.

Insulin is produced by masses of cells scattered through the pancreas,

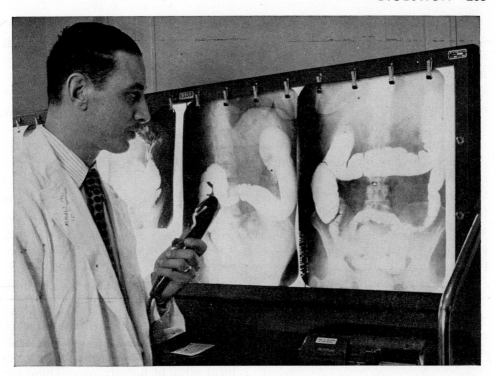

Here a physician is studying x-ray pictures of the digestive tract in order to make a diagnosis. (Courtesy Department of Health, City of New York)

known as the Islands of Langerhans. Insulin influences the oxidation of sugar in the tissues of the body. Too little insulin is the cause of the disease called diabetes (see Chapter 22).

Large intestine. The large intestine is the lower part of the digestive tract. It is 5 feet or 6 feet long. Near its beginning is attached the well-known vermiform (meaning wormlike) appendix.

Peristalsis along the large intestine is slow; hence, it takes 12 hours to 20 hours for material to pass through it. During this time, most of the water in the contents of the intestine is absorbed into the blood.

Quantities of bacteria live in the large intestine, although there are few in other parts of the digestive tract. Most of these bacteria are harmless. Certain bacteria produce gas by acting on the wastes from beans and other vegetable proteins.

The waste material in the large intestine consists of food material that was not digested and masses of bacteria and dead cells from the lining of the intestine. These wastes, or feces, are gotten rid of, or eliminated, about once in 24 hours in a bowel movement.

Diarrhea. When the feces are watery and bowel movements occur more often than usual, the condition is known as diarrhea. Peristaltic movements have pushed the wastes so fast that water has not been absorbed from them. The result is that a large mass gathers in the lower part of the large intestine, the rectum.

Nervous upsets sometimes cause diarrhea. In some persons, too much raw fruit, vegetables, and bran make the muscles contract too much and too often. Infections may irritate the walls of the intestines and cause rapid peristalsis. Irritating substances in the food may do the same.

Diarrhea itself is only a symptom, a condition resulting from some other cause. Usually, it is the cause of diarrhea that is important rather than the diarrhea itself.

Constipation. Most people have a bowel movement once a day, often after breakfast. Some people have a bowel movement only once in 2 days or 3 days, while others have two or three in one day. There is no rule as to what constipation, or failure of normal bowel movement, is. What one person thinks of as constipation may be quite normal for another. If you are in good health and your bowel movements are fairly regular, you probably need not feel concerned about having constipation.

If constipation does exist, it may be the result of one of several conditions. One of these is an inflammation, such as appendicitis, in the abdomen; another is a blocking of the intestine. In either condition, a laxative, something to make the bowels move, is

dangerous. Another cause of constipation is that one's foods contain too little roughage and bulk to stimulate peristalsis. Still another cause of constipation is overactive muscles that stay contracted and do not allow waves of peristalsis to pass down the intestine. What is needed in this case is a chance for the muscles to rest and relax.

In some cases an enema is used as a treatment for constipation. An enema is usually warm water containing a little salt. It is put directly into the rectum and stretches the rectal walls until they contract and force out both the enema and the wastes.

Sometimes blood vessels in the lower part of the large intestine enlarge and blood collects in them to form piles, or hemorrhoids. These are very like the varicose veins described in Chapter 12. Hemorrhoids often occur in cases of constipation when the muscles of the large intestine and of the blood vessels are not contracting strongly enough to push the blood along. Curing the constipation may cure the hemorrhoids. In other cases, they may need medical or surgical treatment by a physician.

The laxative habit. Laxatives act in different ways, but the result is to stimulate the muscles of the digestive tract to contract. There are times when a person may need a laxative. More often the person does not need a laxative.

Sometimes, parents give laxatives to a baby whenever he is cross or does not have a bowel movement exactly when they think he should. Some- times, they think laxatives are neces- sary, "to clean out the system." A healthy baby on a good diet does not need laxatives. Such drugs should not be given to a child except on a physi- cian's orders.

It is easy to build the habit of tak- ing laxatives. Soon larger and larger doses are needed to produce a bowel movement, or the person moves on to stronger and stronger laxatives. The muscles of the intestines become fa- tigued and sometimes are actually in- jured.

Regular bowel movements. For most persons, regular bowel move- ments are possible without the aid of laxatives. You should

1) Eat enough fruit and vegeta- bles, so that the muscles have some- thing to act upon.

2) Drink enough water. Some- times a glass of warm water taken at the same time each day will start a wave of peristalsis strong enough to bring about a bowel movement.

3) Take some regular exercise ev- ery day. Be sure the muscles of the abdomen are exercised.

4) Form the habit of going to the toilet at the same time each day. Do not postpone bowel movements.

5) Learn to relax. Keep from be- ing excited and upset, especially at meal time.

GOOD DIGESTION AND INDIGESTION

Good digestion means that peristalsis goes on smoothly and that all the di- gestive juices are poured out in the right amounts. We cannot control either of these actions directly. The smooth muscles and the glands are supplied with nerves from the auto- nomic (involuntary) nervous system (see Chapters 6 and 18). Impulses over these nerves are not under our conscious control.

Yet we can do a good deal to in- fluence digestion. Suppose you want to keep a person from digesting his food. Scaring him thoroughly would probably do it. Making him angry, scolding him, making him very un- happy, would have the same effect.

Emotions influence digestion. In strong emotions, impulses sent over the autonomic nerves interfere with peristalsis and with secretions from the glands. Has your mouth ever be- come "dry" when you were afraid or embarrassed? A "dry" mouth means that the salivary glands are not pro- ducing saliva. At the same time, the stomach may be a "dry" stomach and the intestines "dry" intestines, be- cause other digestive glands are not secreting well. This is not a time to eat a large meal.

In India long ago, persons sus- pected of a crime were sometimes given dry rice to chew. After a time, they were told to spit it out. If it was still dry, it was taken as proof that the person was guilty, that his fear had prevented the secretion of saliva.

On the other hand, the smell, the taste, the sight, and even the thought of food can make your mouth "wa- ter." Think of a lemon; your salivary

Pleasant company and attractive surroundings during meals are valuable aids to good digestion. (Courtesy National Dairy Council)

glands start secreting. So do the other digestive glands. The muscles of the digestive tract contract (see Chapter 6). This sometimes makes the stomach and intestines "rumble."

Eating habits. Scolding and fighting and worry are bad for the digestion. The surroundings at meal times should be pleasant. Adults probably like more quiet at their meals than young people do, but too much noise is bad at any age. Dishes, walls, and tables should be clean. Eating should be slow. Resting a short time before dinner often helps digestion.

Should you drink water with your meals? *Yes,* and *No.* Yes, if you take swallows of water between swallows of food. This really gives the enzymes a better chance to act. But water used to help swallow or "wash down," large bites interferes with digestion. Ice water tends to slow digestion.

Actually, the eating habits of most people are abominable. We rush through our breakfasts without taking time to chew our food. We eat lunch and dinner in a mad scramble. We turn on the radio and try to talk over it. We overeat and undereat and do not choose the foods that we need (see Chapters 8 and 9).

The result is often nervous indigestion. The cause of nervous indigestion is not in the digestive tract but in the nervous system.

Indigestion. When a person says he has indigestion, he may mean anything from a loss of appetite, a bad taste in his mouth, gas in his abdomen, or cramps, to vomiting and diarrhea. Sometimes the cause is emotional strain. Sometimes the cause is appendicitis, gall stones, stomach ulcers, or cancer of the stomach or intestines. In any case, the person should find the cause of his symptoms and do something about it.

Vomiting. At times irritating mate-

Friendly people, appetizing food, orderliness, flowers, and time to eat and talk, all contribute to good digestion.

rials get into the stomach. Then the stomach may get rid of its contents by vomiting. Usually, before vomiting, a person feels nauseated, that is, he is "sick to his stomach" and thinks he is going to vomit. He is faint and weak, he perspires, his mouth fills with saliva and he yawns.

Vomiting itself is produced by reverse peristalsis in the stomach and esophagus. At the same time, the abdominal and chest muscles contract strongly.

The center for control of vomiting is not in the stomach but in the brain. There are many places in the body from which nervous impulses can travel to this vomiting center. Hence, many different stimuli may result in vomiting.

Irritation in the stomach, for example, may start impulses over nerves leading to the vomiting center. When a person has swallowed a poison, we can usually make him vomit it out of his stomach by giving

him mustard and warm water. Tickling his throat will also start impulses to the vomiting center (see Chapter 4). Irritations in the abdomen may act in the same way. This is the reason that appendicitis often produces vomiting. Gall bladder disease, injuries to the abdomen, typhoid fever, and other intestinal diseases may do the same.

Other illnesses that do not seem at first to be related to the digestive tract also may cause vomiting. Some of these are pneumonia, scarlet fever, poliomyelitis, and some kinds of heart disease.

In children, the vomiting center is more easily stimulated to action than in adults. This does not mean that we should pay no attention to vomiting in children. Vomiting always means some disturbance. Sometimes this is a symptom of a dangerous illness.

One interesting thing about vomiting is that we can sometimes "think ourselves" into it. Unpleasant sights and sounds and sometimes unpleasant thoughts can stimulate the vomiting center.

Car sickness, air sickness, sea sickness. Large numbers of people become nauseated whenever they travel by car, by ship, or by airplane. Impulses to the vomiting center in these cases come partly from the eyes and partly from the parts of the ear that have to do with balancing the body (see Chapter 20). Shutting the eyes and lying down make one feel less ill.

Some new drugs are now being used for the various kinds of motion sickness. One of these, Dramamine, was tried first as a treatment for hay fever. One patient found that it did nothing for his hay fever but it did cure his car sickness. Other people have used it in airplanes, trains, and ships. Many of them report that they travel much more happily after taking Dramamine.

ULCERS IN THE STOMACH AND INTESTINE

An ulcer is a kind of sore. We do not know what causes ulcers in the stomach and small intestine. The acid in the gastric juice may help produce them. It certainly slows their healing. Feeling nervous and worried is related in some people to the development of ulcers. The reason may be that the gastric glands secrete more acid when a person is nervous.

Discomfort or pain in the stomach is the most common symptom of ulcer. The treatment starts with eating food that is not irritating. Physicians can give simple remedies that reduce the amount of acid in the stomach. In many cases, the ulcers heal completely.

Some people seem to feel that the only reason a person develops an ulcer is because he worries. They call it psychosomatic and insist that the cause must all be "in his mind."

Worry can influence circulation of blood and secretion of acid by the stomach glands. It is probably never the only cause of ulcers. And when ulcers are formed, no matter what the cause, they are real and should be treated by a physician. Keeping calm and unworried is an important part of the treatment but certainly not all of it.

APPENDICITIS

Almost everyone knows that a person should not use a hot-water bag or take a laxative for a "stomachache" when the cause is not known. We have been told again and again that heat or a laxative may make an infected appendix break. The infection then spreads through the abdominal cavity and causes inflammation of its lining, or peritonitis.

Yet appendicitis is the twelfth cause of death in the 15-to-24 age group in the United States. More than 2500 people of all ages die every year from appendicitis. Practically every one of these deaths is preventable.

A study in one city showed that only one appendicitis patient in 62 died among those who took no laxative. One in 19 died among those who

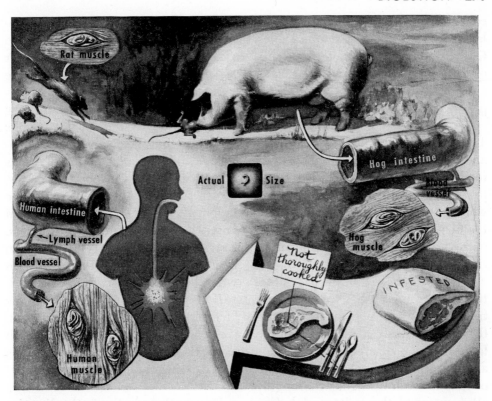

Trichinae are often found in the muscles of rats. Hogs sometimes eat rats and become infested with trichinae. The worms go out from the hog's intestine into the blood and finally reach the hog's muscles. If pork from one of these hogs is not well cooked, live trichinae may get into the digestive tract of a human being. From the intestine they may go into the blood and then locate in muscles (see Chapter 6).

took one dose of a laxative. One in 9 died among those who took more than one dose.

The first symptom of appendicitis is usually pain. This may be sudden and severe, or it may be only mild discomfort. Later, there may be nausea, vomiting, constipation, fever, and soreness over the appendix. However, there may be none of these symptoms. There may be diarrhea instead of constipation.

A physician who suspects appendicitis usually makes a blood count (see Chapter 11). An unusual number of white blood cells tells him that there is infection some place, probably in the appendix.

An early operation is the great lifesaver in appendicitis. If an operation is performed within 24 hours of the beginning of the attack, fewer than 1 percent of the patients die. If the operation is delayed for 4 days or 5 days, about 12 percent die.

You should call a physician when you have a "stomachache," especially if you vomit and have diarrhea or constipation. You should not take a laxative. These are simple rules. Obeying them would save thousands of lives every year.

INTESTINAL INFECTIONS AND INFESTATIONS

The digestive tract is warm, moist, and dark. It is well supplied with food. This makes it an excellent place for bacteria and viruses and even worms to live. These organisms or their eggs get out of the digestive tract with the feces from the large intestine.

This means that intestinal infections and infestations of all sorts travel from one person to another through the waste materials from the large intestine. If a person is careless about putting his fingers in his mouth, or fails to wash his hands thoroughly after going to the toilet and before eating, he may pass on any intestinal infection he has to the water, milk, or food of other persons. He may also reinfect himself.

In towns, human waste is taken care of by the public-sewage system. In the country, where outdoor toilets are used, these must be carefully screened from flies and kept clean. It is very important, as you can see, that an outdoor toilet should not be placed so that its drainage contaminates a well or stream. In parts of the world where the weather is never cold enough to freeze the ground, worms from the digestive tract can live in the ground for months or years.

Flies are attracted to filth and carry it on their feet to our food. They can be kept out of our houses by screening. The best way to control flies is to clean up the manure piles and other accumulations in which fly eggs are laid and hatched.

Food can be protected from being contaminated by flies or by people. Groceries and meat markets are generally careful to keep out flies. Persons who handle food, such as clerks, cooks, and waitresses, should be taught how to keep their hands clean and, thus, protect their customers. Animals sold for meat should be in good health and free from infection when butchered.

If everyone remembered these few facts and acted according to them, we would not need to learn much about the different kinds of organisms that can live in our digestive tracts.

Worms that can live in the digestive tract. Ascaris, hookworms, tapeworms, and pinworms are so frequently found in the digestive tracts of human beings that it is worth knowing something about them.[1] Many of these leave a person's digestive tract after a time without his having taken any treatment, or even knowing that he was infested. If this does not happen, it is fairly easy for a physician to give an infested person something to rid him of the worms. The more important problem is keeping people from becoming infested and keeping a person who has been cured from becoming infested again.

[1] Trichinae are worms that are taken into the digestive tract with food, but they do not stay there (see Chapter 6).

The ascaris is about the size and shape of a large earthworm. It may live in the digestive tract for years without causing the person to be ill. The eggs leave the digestive tract in bowel discharges. When human waste is used to fertilize the soil, it is possible for the eggs of ascaris to be carried on fresh vegetables. Washing the vegetables thoroughly will remove the eggs.

Hookworms are 1/4 inch to 1/2 inch long. The adult worms attach themselves by small hooks to the wall of the human small intestine. They get their food from the blood of the person in whose intestines they are living. People with hookworms are often called lazy; actually, they are really ill. This is because hookworms produce anemia (see Chapter 11). Children are stunted in growth by hookworm infestation. Adults lose weight and strength.

Hookworm eggs leave the body in the wastes from the large intestine. They will live where the ground is warm. There, the eggs hatch into tiny forms called larvae. These larvae can bore through the pores of the skin and enter the blood. Going barefoot gives them a chance to bore through the skin of the feet, usually between the toes where the skin is thin and tender.

Once inside the body, the hookworm larvae take a long pathway to reach the small intestine. They are carried by the blood from the feet to the heart and on to the lungs. They are too large to pass through the capillaries of the lungs. They bore through the walls of the air sacs, the

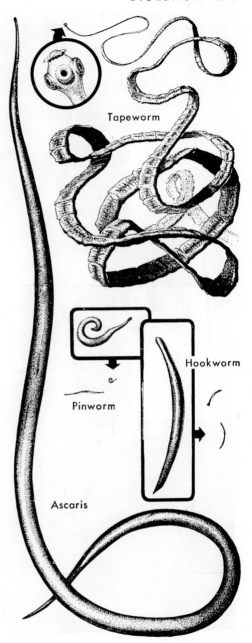

Tapeworm

Hookworm

Pinworm

Ascaris

These are worms which may live in the digestive tracts of human beings. An ascaris is about the size shown in the drawing. Tapeworms may be much larger, up to 30 feet in length. The pinworm and hookworm are shown in actual size and also enlarged.

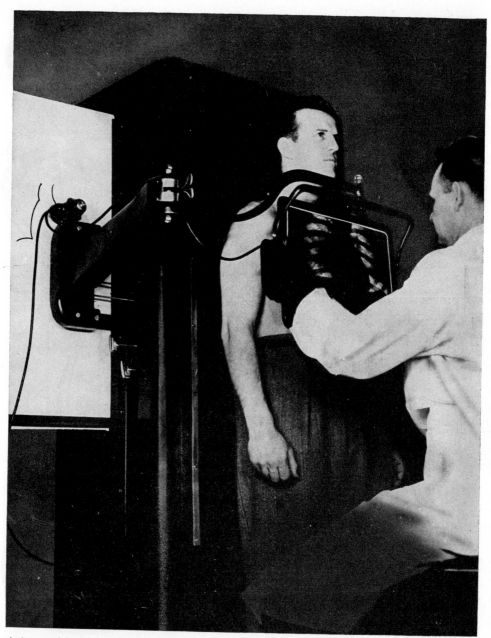

It is possible by use of the fluoroscope to find the size and shape of the stomach and intestines and to see whether anything is interfering with peristalsis. In the photograph a physician is looking at a man's heart and making an outline of it on the paper at the left. To make his digestive tract throw a shadow on the screen as the heart does, the patient drinks a barium solution. (Courtesy Picher X-Ray Corp.)

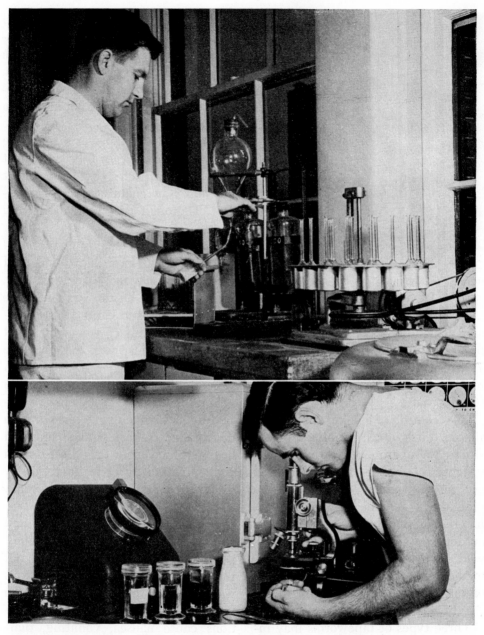

Many dairies test their milk daily to make sure of its purity and food values. In the upper photograph a man is making chemical tests of measured amounts of milk. Below he is making a microscopic examination to find what kinds of microorganisms may be in the milk. If harmful organisms are found, the company will search for the source of infection and remove it. (Courtesy Borden Co.)

Government inspection of meat protects against certain infections but not all. (Courtesy U.S. Department of Agriculture)

alveoli, and pass up through the bronchi and trachea to the pharynx. Then they are swallowed and finally reach the intestines, where they may stay for years.

The control of hookworm is very simple. First of all, people in places where there are hookworms in the soil must wear shoes, so that they will not pick up the larvae already in the ground. Eggs can be kept from reaching the ground by the use of clean outdoor privies. And finally, persons who have the disease can be given medical treatment that will rid them of the worms already in their digestive tracts.

Three types of tapeworms may infest human beings: the beef tapeworm; the pork tapeworm; and the fish tapeworm. A tapeworm may reach a length of 6 feet to 30 feet. It is made up of a head and a series of segments, arranged in a row behind the head. The head becomes attached to the wall of the human small intestine by hooks, or suckers. The fish tapeworm causes a serious anemia. The others may make a person uncomfortable but they do not make him ill.

Larvae of the tapeworm may live in muscles of meat or fish. Even beef and pork inspected by government officials may contain tapeworm larvae. Thorough cooking will destroy them.

Pinworms are smaller than hookworms. They look like pieces of thread ¼ inch to ½ an inch long. They live in the human large intestine near the anus and cause severe itching. The itching is worse at night when the worms move out onto the skin.

Scratching may allow the worms to get on the hands. Or they may be carried by flies, which have picked them up from feces. Washing the hands and keeping food and drink safe from contamination by dirty hands or by flies prevents the spread of pinworms.

Infection with bacteria and viruses. Most cases of so-called "ptomaine" poisoning and food poisoning are not true poisonings. They are infections with bacteria or viruses that are in food and drink. Most of these infections cause nausea, vomiting, diarrhea, and a little fever.

These infections may last a few days. In adults, they are usually not serious. In young children, they are often very serious.

The organisms that cause these infections are usually carried on meat or meat products. Sometimes, meat comes from infected animals. Sometimes, flies or fingers carry the organisms to the meat. Particularly dangerous is meat that has been cooked and handled and served some time later without being thoroughly recooked.

There are a few more serious diseases whose chief action is on the intestines. These are typhoid fever, paratyphoid fever, cholera, and dysentery. They are discussed in Chapter 25. The organisms that cause these diseases leave the body in urine and feces. Prevention depends upon keeping the organisms away from food or drink or anything that goes into a person's mouth.

SO WHAT?

The digestive system is a wonderful chemical laboratory; and

Health depends to a large extent upon how well this laboratory does its work; and

Many of the things people do to improve digestion, do more harm than good;

So, you should know

How the digestive tract functions; and

What to do and what not to do to keep it functioning properly; and

What foods and what habits may interfere with digestion; and

How to avoid the disease-producing organisms that sometimes get into the digestive tract.

CHECKING UP

1. Digestion changes the food that you eat into simpler substances. Why is this necessary? What are these simpler substances?
2. What is peristalsis? How does peristalsis aid digestion?
3. What are enzymes? Of what use are they in digestion?
4. What happens to food in the mouth?
5. What happens to food in the stomach?
6. What did Dr. Beaumont learn from his study of St. Martin?
7. What is considered the most important part of the digestive tract? Why?
8. Why is the skin of a person with jaundice yellow?

Title

9. What two kinds of secretions are produced by the pancreas? What purposes do they serve?
10. What is meant by the statement that "diarrhea is only a symptom"?
11. What are some of the causes of constipation? Why is it unwise to make a habit of taking laxatives? What are desirable ways of preventing constipation?
12. How do emotions influence digestion? Describe a school mealtime situation that would make for good digestion; one that would make for poor digestion.
13. What is meant by motion sickness?
14. How may worry help cause stomach ulcers?
15. How can many deaths from appendicitis be prevented?
16. How are intestinal infections spread from one person to another? How can this spread be stopped?
17. Why does wearing shoes prevent the spread of hookworm?
18. What is usually the cause of "ptomaine" poisoning?

THINGS TO DO

1. Look at a model of a human being. Find the parts of the digestive tract.
2. Look at the digestive tract in a small animal, such as a frog. a rat, a rabbit, or a chicken. The digestive tracts in these animals are somewhat different from those in a human being, but you can see the esophagus, stomach, intestines, liver, and, in some of them, the gall bladder and pancreas.
3. Let a slug or a snail move over a glass plate. Look at it from underneath. The waves of contraction in its foot (the part on which it moves) are very like peristaltic waves.
4. Perhaps you can look at some x-rays of the stomach and intestines. Ask a nurse or a physician to tell you how x-rays of the digestive tract are made.
5. Chew a cracker and notice the change in taste.
6. Ask a chemistry student or a biology student to show you tests for starch and sugar. Test a piece of cracker for starch and sugar. Put some saliva in a test tube; add a little cracker; keep it warm (at body temperature, around 98.6 degrees Fahrenheit) for 20 minutes or 30 minutes. Now test for sugar. What is the enzyme in the saliva doing to the starch in the cracker?
7. The biology teacher may help you plan experiments with gastric and pancreatic digestion.

8. Rennin can be obtained from a grocery or drugstore. Add a little to milk. Keep it at body temperature. What happens to the milk? This makes it easier to digest in the stomach.
9. Collect advertisements of laxatives. What do they claim? Are their claims correct?
10. Do you know people who become car sick or air sick? What do they do about it? Have any of them used Dramamine or any other new drug? Be on the lookout for articles in newspapers or magazines about these drugs.
11. Find how many deaths from appendicitis occur in your community or your state each year. (Ask the local health department or write to the state health department.)
12. It is fun to do some experiments with taste and smell. Blindfold a student; have him hold his nose. Now put a piece of apple on his tongue; a piece of onion; a piece of potato. Can he tell which is which? Dissolve some sugar in water. Use a camel's-hair brush and put drops of the sugar solution on the tip of the tongue; the sides of the tongue; the back of the tongue. Do the same with water containing salt. Where do you taste sugar and salt best?
13. Think of some foods—for example, soup, milk, potato, lemon. Which makes your salivary glands secrete the most saliva? Smell some foods. Does smelling or thinking about food cause more saliva to flow? Hold your nose. How does looking at foods affect your salivary glands? Do some of these experiments before lunch when you are hungry. Do them again after lunch. What difference does being hungry make?
14. Make a study of your school lunchroom. Does it look attractive? Is it too noisy? Does it smell pleasant? Does it need improvement? Can you do something about it?
15. Ask your teacher to make a record during a study period of all the things he sees in students' mouths. Can you break the habit of putting things in your mouth? Talk it over. Then ask your teacher to make the same kind of a record another day.
16. Find whether there is any hookworm disease in your community. If there is, ask the public-health department what should be done about it. Find what you can do to help prevent its spread.
17. Ask one of the members of the class to give a special report on meat inspection by the government.

CHAPTER 17　Getting Rid of
Body Wastes

Everyone knows about the clinkers and the ashes that have to be removed from furnaces and fireplaces. These are waste products. They are parts of the fuel that would not burn.

Other waste products go up the chimney—moisture, carbon dioxide, carbon monoxide, and other gases. These come from the fuel that was actually burned or oxidized.

WASTES IN THE BODY

There are the same two kinds of wastes in the human body. Food that is not digested is pushed down into the large intestine and got rid of as feces (see Chapter 16).

The other kind of wastes comes from the breakdown of foods and of the protoplasm in the cells. These wastes are the result of metabolism, that is, the building up and tearing down of protoplasm (see Chapter 5). They are chiefly water, carbon dioxide, salts, and compounds that con-

tain nitrogen. These last are called nitrogenous wastes.

Excretory organs. All the wastes from the cells are picked up by the blood and carried to the excretory organs, which remove, or excrete, them (see Chapters 5 and 11). If the wastes were not removed, they would pile up in the blood and poison the body. Death would result in a very short time. The chief excretory organs are the lungs, the skin, and the kidneys.

The lungs excrete carbon dioxide and some water (see Chapter 14). The skin excretes water and some salts as perspiration (see Chapters 7 and 10). The nitrogenous wastes, some salts, and water are excreted through the kidneys and the other organs in what is called the urinary system.

THE URINARY SYSTEM

The urinary system consists of two kidneys, one on each side in the ab-

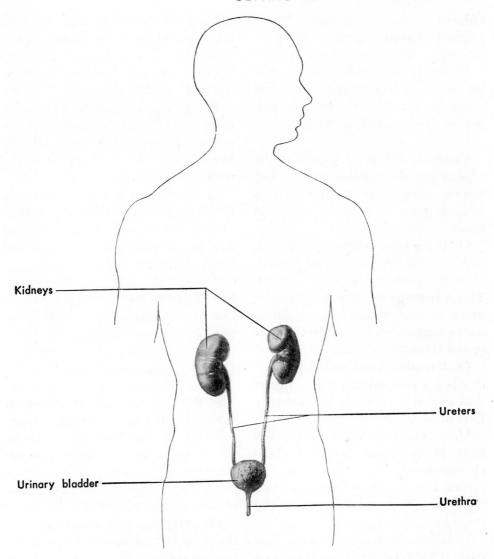

The urinary system.

dominal cavity, two ureters, the bladder, and the urethra. The kidneys remove water and wastes from the blood. The ureters carry this liquid, which we call urine, from the kidneys to the bladder. The ureters are small tubes, each about as large as a lead pencil. The bladder is a hollow sac

that stores the urine. The urethra is a tube that carries urine from the bladder to the outside.

The kidneys are located in the back of the abdomen, near the small of the back. Large arteries and veins carry blood to and from the kidneys. All of a person's blood travels through his kidneys every few minutes. Waste products pass through the walls of the capillaries into the ureters.

We have more kidney tissue than we need. In fact, a person can get along quite well with only one kidney, or even part of one kidney.

Urine. Urine is being formed all the time, a few drops every minute. The healthy adult, on an average, excretes from 1 quart to 2 quarts every 24 hours.

Drinking large amounts of liquids increases the amount of urine formed. It is also increased in cold weather. This is because we do not perspire as much in cold weather as we do in warm, and more water must be excreted through the kidneys.

On the other hand, in hot weather or when a person has a fever, a good deal of water is lost in perspiration. Less urine is then excreted.

Many kinds of wastes leave the body in the urine. Some of these change its appearance and odor. Everyone knows how quickly after eating asparagus the odor appears in the urine.

Usually, urine is a yellow color. The color is light yellow when there is a good deal of water in the urine, dark when there is less water.

Colored materials are sometimes used to test how well the kidneys are working. Harmless dyes are eaten or injected under the skin, and the time it takes for these dyes to color the urine is measured.

Sugar in urine. In a healthy person, there is always a little sugar circulating in the blood. If the amount in the blood increases, some will be taken out by the kidneys and removed from the body in the urine.

Eating a large amount of candy or other sweets and starches will increase the amount of sugar in the blood. Sugar will then appear in the urine.

In the disease known as diabetes, the body loses its ability to oxidize (burn) sugar (see Chapters 16 and 22). Sugar collects in the blood and some is excreted in the urine.

Sugar in the urine may be a symptom of diabetes or it may simply mean that the person has been eating too much sugar and starch.

URINARY DISTURBANCES

The work of the urinary system is closely related to the health and metabolism of the body as a whole. When parts of the body are not functioning properly, there may be some disturbance in the functioning of the urinary system. On the other hand, anything that interferes with the excretion of wastes through the urinary system will disturb the health of the whole body.

Damage to the kidneys. Bacteria and viruses may be carried to the kidneys by the blood. Certain ones may settle there and cause an infection. Tuberculosis organisms, for example, may cause tuberculosis of the kidneys.

Other infections may spread from

When a person exercises vigorously, a great deal of water is excreted through the skin in perspiration. (Courtesy Arsenal Technical High School, Indianapolis)

the tonsils, sinuses, roots of the teeth, or other parts of the body. At times, the toxins (poisons) made by bacteria or viruses in other parts of the body will be carried to the kidneys and damage them. Sometimes infection may travel up though the urethra, bladder, and ureters to the kidneys.

Poisons that get into the blood stream, such as alcohol and lead, may injure the cells in the kidneys. Sometimes, too, drugs such as the sulfonamides can cause serious damage to the kidneys if they are not properly used. This is one of the reasons why such drugs should be used only when a physician orders them and tells the person exactly how much to take and how often to take it.

Nephritis. The infections mentioned in the preceding section may cause nephritis, which means inflammation of the kidneys. Another cause of nephritis is high blood pressure, which interferes with the circulation of blood through the kidneys. You learned some of the results of high blood pressure in the chapter on circulation (see Chapter 12).

The kidneys may be damaged slowly over a long period of time. The condition that results is called Bright's disease after the physician who first described it. Another name is chronic nephritis. Neither of these names tells us much about what is wrong with the kidneys.

Whatever the cause, nephritis interferes with the excretion of urine. This means that wastes pile up in the blood, which may result in the serious illness called uremia (see Chapter 12).

Kidney stones. Once in awhile salts in the urine form hard balls, or kidney stones. These are somewhat like gall stones (see Chapter 16).

If kidney stones start down toward the bladder, they stretch the ureters and cause severe pain. Usually, stones must be removed by an operation.

Most kinds of kidney disease do not cause pain. Many people think that a backache in the lower part of the back comes from the kidneys. In almost every case, the backache has some other cause. Kidney "medicines" and kidney "pills" should be taken only when a physician orders them after he has made a careful examination and found exactly what is wrong.

Bladder disturbances. Infections may reach the bladder, usually from the outside. They happen more often in children than in adults, and more often in women than in men. Usually, they clear up quickly with proper treatment.

"Stones" may form in the bladder, too. They can usually be removed by a minor operation.

Controlling elimination of urine. When the bladder is partly full, the pressure of its contents starts nervous impulses that cause it to empty. A person can keep the bladder from emptying by contracting the muscles in the walls of the urethra. In babies, the nerves that control these muscles are not developed enough to make it possible for the babies to contract these muscles at will. Usually, control is possible after a child is 18 to 30 months old. Babies cannot be expected to learn to keep dry until they are able to control these muscles.

Control is easier in the daytime than at night. Not keeping dry at night is called enuresis. This is quite common in preschool children. In school children and adults, enuresis sometimes occurs, usually as the result of strain, excitement, or illness. When this happens, a physician should be consulted. Scolding or making fun of the unfortunate person makes matters worse.

EXAMINATION OF THE URINE

It is easy to see that finding what is being excreted in the urine will tell a good deal about what is happening in the body. From the earliest times, physicians, and even the medicine men in primitive tribes, have examined the urine of their patients. They noted the color, the odor, the cloudiness, and how much was eliminated in a certain length of time, usually 24 hours.

Physicians still make these simple examinations. In addition, they use chemical tests and microscopic examinations to give more exact information. Examination of the urine is called urinalysis (see Chapter 26).

A dark color in the urine may be caused by perspiring a good deal or by

Making a urinalysis. (Courtesy Michael Reese Hospital, Chicago)

failing to drink enough water. A reddish color may result from food the person has eaten. These are not important. But if the color is caused by bleeding in the kidney or in other parts of the urinary system, the condition may be serious. Physicians use a microscopic examination to find whether red blood cells have gotten into the urine and, thus, whether bleeding has occurred or not.

Cloudiness may be caused by harmless salts, or it may be caused by an infection. Chemical tests will give information on which salts are present. Microscopic examination for white blood cells and for bacteria will help in discovering whether the cloudiness is caused by infection.

Kidney diseases may cause less urine or more urine to be excreted. In diabetes, the amount of urine is increased. Chemical tests for sugar in the urine are a useful check in this disease.

TAKING CARE OF THE URINARY SYSTEM

There is little that a person needs to do or that he can do about the health of the urinary system. Some persons think that it is important to drink a certain amount of water each day to "flush out" the kidneys. This sounds more reasonable than it really is. You need to take enough water to make up for the water lost through the lungs, the skin, and the kidneys. This will be more on hot days, less on cold days. It will also depend on how much milk, soup, orange juice, and other liquids you take.

It is true that a person can forget to drink water or can form a habit of taking very little. Drinking water several times during the day is probably a good habit to form. When the body really needs water, however, a person becomes thirsty. This means that usually we get as much water as we need.

Special kinds of water have never been proved to be of any real value for the kidneys.

Some people think that meat is bad for the kidneys. If this were true, all Eskimos would have kidney disease, because their diet consists almost entirely of meat. Actually, there is no evidence that they have more kidney disease than people like the Chinese who eat very little meat.

Infections any place in the body make the work of the kidneys more difficult. The best thing you can do for your urinary system is to keep in as good general health as possible. Beyond that, it needs no special care.

SO WHAT?

Your body not only must have food for growth and energy, but it also must be able to get rid of the waste products, which act as poisons if they accumulate; and

The organs that help you to get rid of waste products are the kidneys, the intestines, the lungs, and the skin; and

Fortunately, these function very well if you just let them do their jobs in their own way;

So, you will do best if you

Understand how the body gets rid of its wastes, and then

Stop thinking or worrying about it, and taking this or that to try to improve excretion and elimination.

CHECKING UP

1. What two kinds of wastes are formed in the body?
2. List the metabolic wastes.
3. Where are the various metabolic wastes excreted?
4. What are the parts of the urinary system? Draw a diagram of the urinary system and label the parts.

5. What is the relationship between amount of perspiration and formation of urine?
6. How much water should you drink?
7. Under what conditions does extra sugar appear in the urine?
8. How may infections reach the kidneys?
9. Why are babies not able to control elimination of urine? What is enuresis?
10. What is a urinalysis? What information does a physician gain from a urinalysis?

THINGS TO DO

1. Examine a sheep's kidney or a pig's kidney from the butcher shop. Find the ureter. Can you find the little tubes that form the ureter?
2. On a model, find kidneys, ureters, bladder, and urethra.
3. Give a special report on how we learned to control diabetes.
4. Review the test for sugar (Chapter 8). This test is very important in discovering cases of diabetes.
5. There is an interesting discussion of enuresis in *Baby and Child Care* by Spock (Pocket Book Edition). Members of the class who have baby brothers or sisters, or who sometimes "baby sit" might read this.

CHAPTER 18   Brain and Nerves

"Oh, she's a brain!" "He's certainly the brains of the class." "Wish I had a brain like that!" What we mean, of course, is that he or she always knows the right answers. But what do "brains" really have to do with knowing things? Does a "brainy" person have a bigger brain than the rest of us have? Or does he put his brain to better use?

You jump when the door slams; you burst into tears for no reason; you get angry and want to fight when someone bumps into you. It is "just nerves," you say. But what are nerves, and why do they make you act that way?

Actually the brain and the rest of the nervous system may well be called the master control system of the body (see Chapter 5). It is through the nervous system that you find out what is going on in the world around you. It is through the nervous system that you are able to run, to talk, to play the piano, and to do all the other things that make life interesting. Impulses traveling over your nerves keep you breathing, keep your heart beating,

keep your stomach and intestines pushing the food along. And it is through your nervous system that you learn your lessons, decide what you will do today and tomorrow, dream your dreams, and think all your wise and foolish thoughts. Knowing something about this very important system should help you to manage your life better.

STRUCTURE OF THE NERVOUS SYSTEM

Like all the other systems of the body, the general plan of the nervous system is simple (see page 296). Long slender nerve cells carry impulses from the skin, eyes, ears, and other sense organs to the brain and spinal cord. Other nerve cells carry impulses from the brain and spinal cord to muscles and glands. Brain and spinal cord make up the central nervous system. (This is a good time to read again the section in Chapter 5 on how we respond to things about us.)

Nerve cells. Each nerve cell consists of a cell body and threadlike projec-

288

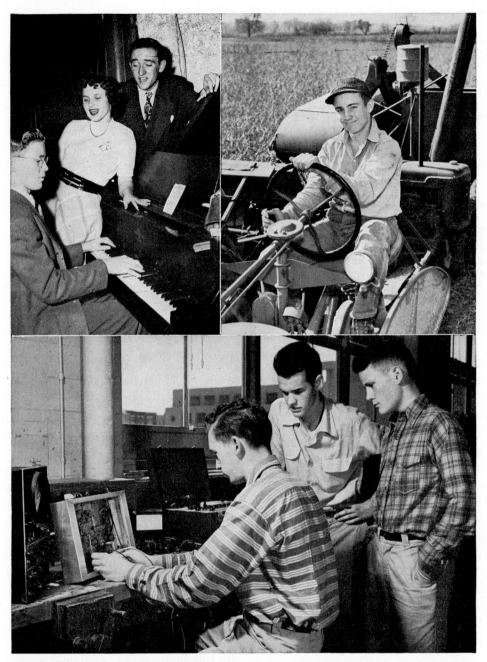

It takes skill to run a complex machine, to play a piano and sing, and to work with electronic equipment. Your nervous system makes it possible for you to learn these skills. (Courtesy International Harvester Co., top left; New York *Herald Tribune*, Staff Photographer, top right; San Francisco Unified School District, bottom)

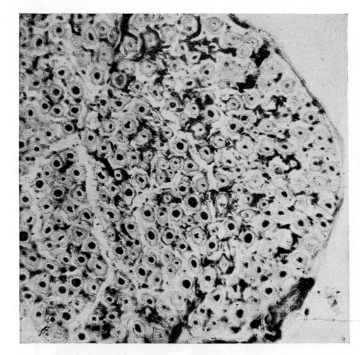

Cross section of a nerve. Note the many nerve fibers that make up the nerve. (Courtesy General Biological Supply House)

tions from the cell body. The nucleus is in the cell body (see page 293). Most of the cell bodies are located in or near the brain and spinal cord.

The projections from the cell body are called nerve fibers. Nervous impulses pass from one nerve cell to another over the ends of the nerve fibers, that is, over the nerve endings. Impulses can travel in only one direction from one nerve cell to another, never backward.

If a nerve fiber is cut or injured, it can grow again, though slowly. If the cell body is killed, the whole cell will die and no new one will grow to take its place.

Autonomic nervous system. Outside the brain and spinal cord, there are masses of nerve cells, or ganglia, located within the head, chest, and ab-

domen. These ganglia belong to the autonomic nervous system (see Chapter 6 and page 297).

Nerve fibers from these ganglia carry impulses to the organs that are not under voluntary control. For example, impulses going out over the autonomic system make the heart beat faster or more slowly, make the glands secrete, and start waves of peristalsis in the digestive tract.

Nerves. Nerve fibers can be seen only under a microscope. These are bound together in bundles, which we call nerves. The large nerves look like white strings. Nerve fibers are like single telephone wires, while nerves are like telephone cables, which contain many wires. Most nerves contain both afferent and efferent fibers (see the next two sections).

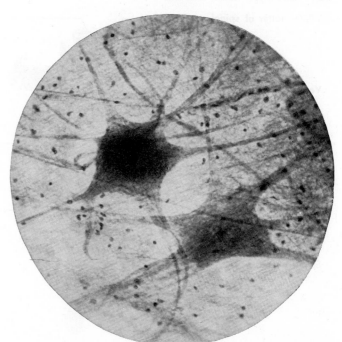

Photograph of two nerve cell bodies magnified many times. The nucleus of a nerve cell is in the cell body. If the nucleus is injured, the nerve cell dies. (Courtesy General Biological Supply House)

Nerves reach all the tissues and organs of the body. Some are very short. Others, like those to and from the toes, are several feet in length.

Afferent nerve fibers. Some nerve fibers carry impulses *toward* the central nervous system from the sense organs. These are afferent nerve fibers. When the nervous impulses that they carry reach the brain, you become conscious of them as light, color, heat, cold, pressure, pain, taste, or other sensations.

If these afferent fibers are cut or blocked, impulses cannot reach the brain, and sensation is lost. Physicians and dentists make use of this fact when they use local or spinal anesthesia (loss of sensation). They block the passage of impulses over nerves by injecting certain drugs around them.

For example, if a dentist has to pull one of your teeth, he probably injects a few drops of the drug Novocain inside the tissues of your mouth, toward the back of your jaw. He waits 10 or 15 minutes. Then he pulls your tooth without your feeling any pain. This is possible because the drug has stopped the passage of impulses over the nerve from the jaw. If you notice which part of the mouth feels numb, you can get an idea of the area served by this nerve. When the effect of the drug wears off, you usually have a little pain for a while from the nerve endings that were temporarily damaged by the operation.

In spinal anesthesia, the surgeon injects a drug around the spinal cord. This blocks the passage of impulses to the brain. The patient may be conscious and know what is going on, but

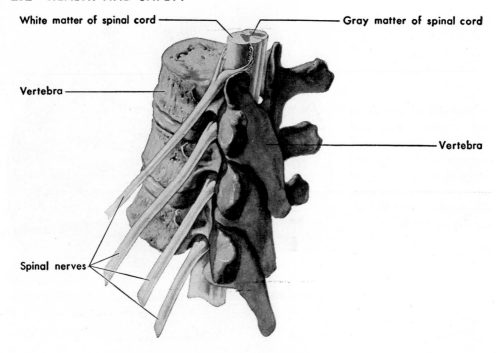

White matter of spinal cord ——————— Gray matter of spinal cord

Vertebra ——————

—— Vertebra

Spinal nerves

A section of the spinal cord.

he will not feel pain below the point at which the drug has been injected.

Efferent nerve fibers. Efferent nerve fibers carry impulses *away* from the central nervous system. Efferent nerve fibers go to muscles and glands. Impulses over these nerve fibers cause the muscles to contract or to relax and the glands to secrete or to stop secreting.

Cutting or blocking one of these nerves leads to crippling or paralysis of the muscles or glands involved. If a nerve is cut, as occurs in some accidents, the person cannot use the muscles supplied by this nerve, because impulses cannot get over it to the muscles.

Association nerve cells. Within the brain and spinal cord are many nerve cells with short fibers called association nerve cells. Once a nerve impulse gets into the central nervous system, many pathways are open to it over these nerve cells.

You can think of many examples of this. For instance, there is a loud noise. The nervous impulse comes into your brain over the afferent nerve fiber from the ear. It goes to the hearing center in your brain, and you know that you have heard a noise.

But the nervous impulse started by this noise may go over many other pathways, also. You may send impulses down your spinal cord to your legs and walk toward the noise. Or

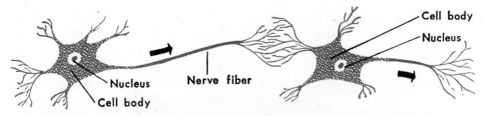

Nervous impulses travel in only one direction.

you may go away from it. You may walk, you may run, you may scream, you may faint, you may be angry, you may be sad, your heart may beat fast, you may gasp, you may turn on the light, you may listen a moment and pay no more attention, or you may do several of these things and many others—all because there are so many association nerve cells in your central nervous system.

You can choose whether you will walk or run, whether you will go in one direction or another. You cannot choose whether your heart will beat fast or slowly, or whether you will breathe more quickly. This is because nervous impulses to your heart and breathing muscles go out over your autonomic system.

Spinal cord and brain. The spinal cord is enclosed within the backbone. It goes from the top of the neck almost to the end of the backbone; hence, it is 1½ feet or more long. It is made up of cell bodies, association nerve cells, and bundles of nerve fibers that carry impulses to and from the brain.

The brain is the largest collection of nerve cells in the body. It is located within the skull, which gives it excellent protection from injury. The top

layers of the brain are mostly cell bodies. These are gray, hence, the name gray matter for this part of the brain. Under these layers is the white matter of the brain. This is made up of nerve fibers, which have a white covering.

Nerve centers in the brain. The brain is so complex that we do not understand very much about how it functions. We know that certain groups of cell bodies in the brain seem to control actions of various kinds. Others are related to sensations. These groups of cell bodies are called nerve centers.

For example, there are centers for vision, hearing, touch, pain, smell, and other sensations. If the vision center is injured, the person cannot see, even though his eyes are in good working order. If the taste center is injured, the person cannot taste. It is an interesting fact that right-handed persons use the speech center on the left side of the brain, while left-handed persons use the speech center on the right side.

Seeing and hearing with the brain. People usually think they "see" with their eyes and "hear" with their ears. Really, they see and hear with their

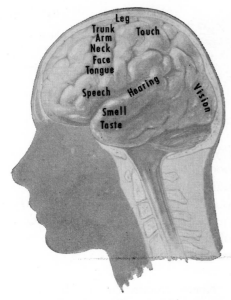

Location of the brain centers for sensations and movements.

brains. The eye is necessary for sight, because light starts impulses in the eye that go to the brain. Without the brain, however, or without the center for vision in the brain, you would never know what these impulses mean. You would never "see."

The same thing is true for all your other senses. Sound waves set up impulses in nerve endings in the ear. These impulses go to the hearing center in the brain, and then you have the sensation of sound.

Centers for movement. There are nerve centers in other parts of the brain that control movements of the various parts of the body. You think about moving an arm or a leg; the impulses go out from the arm center or the leg center in your brain to the muscles you wish to contract.

As the nerve fibers pass up and down the spinal cord, most of them cross over to the opposite side from that on which they started. For this reason, if the arm center on the right side of the brain is injured, the arm on the left side of the body will be paralyzed.

There are nerve centers in the brain that control breathing, the beating of the heart, digestion, circulation, and other activities necessary for life. If these nerve centers are destroyed, the person dies.

Thinking. Sensations and movement are important, but the human brain controls other activities. The human brain contains millions of nerve cells not possessed by other animals. These make it possible for a human being to think, to reason, and to understand.

We do not know how these mental processes occur. We do not know how consciousness and will power are related to them. We do know that many nerves and many nerve pathways are involved. Having a "good mind" depends in some way upon having a "good brain."

REFLEXES AND HABITS

If a person unexpectedly touches a hot object, he instantly jerks away. This happens before he feels any pain. Such an action is spoken of as reflex. Blinking the eye when an insect flies near it is another example of a reflex act. Breathing fast when one runs and needs more oxygen is also a reflex.

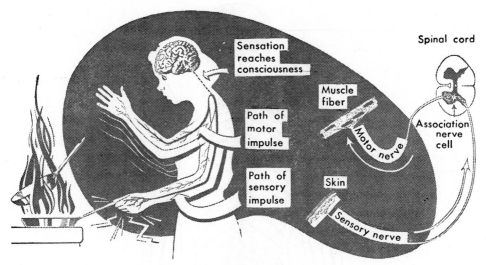

The path of a reflex.

Reflexes are, for the most part, protective. They also save time. You do not have to learn them. You do not have to think about them. The nervous impulses travel over pathways already set up in your nervous system.

The path of a reflex. In the case of touching a hot object, this is what happens: (1) Heat acts as a stimulus and sets up a nervous impulse over afferent (sensory) nerve fibers from the skin. (2a) When the impulse enters the spinal cord, it crosses over association nerve cells and fibers to efferent (motor) nerve cells. This starts an impulse out to muscles, which contract and jerk the hand away. (2b) At the same time, an impulse goes up through the spinal cord to the brain. Here, it reaches the heat and pain centers, and the person knows that he has burned his hand.[1]

[1] 2a and 2b occur at the same time.

(3) Another nervous impulse goes up to the brain from the muscles that have contracted, and the person then knows that he has pulled his hand away. All this takes place in much less time than it takes to read about it.

Habits. There are other actions that we do not have to think about, because we have done them so many times. When nervous impulses have traveled over the same pathway a number of times, they tend to follow the same pathway again. We call these actions habits.

Learning to ride a bicycle is an example of forming a habit. At first, a person thinks of every move: how to get on the bicycle, when to push with the right foot, when to push with the left foot, how much of a push to give each time, where to place his hands on the handle bars, how to turn this way and that, how to stop, how to get off, how to dodge other people, how

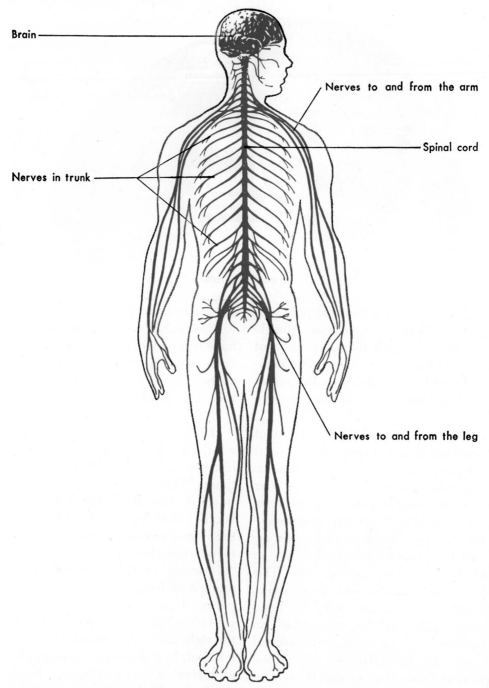

Brain

Nerves to and from the arm

Spinal cord

Nerves in trunk

Nerves to and from the leg

Central nervous system. Impulses are carried inward over nerves from sense organs to the central nervous system and outward over nerves from the central nervous system to muscles and glands. Every part of the body is reached by nerves.

to cross a street, and so on, through dozens of separate actions. After a while the person does not have to think about his bicycle at all. He can plan his day while riding to school, he can talk to other people, he can think about what he did yesterday and what he will do tonight after school, he can review his history lesson.

Habits are like reflexes in that they do not demand constant attention.

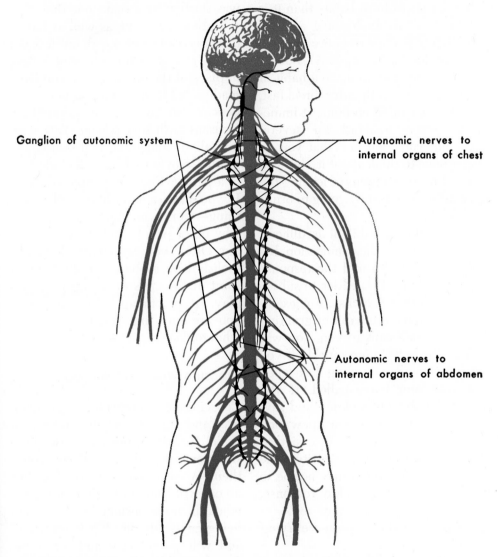

Ganglion of autonomic system

Autonomic nerves to internal organs of chest

Autonomic nerves to internal organs of abdomen

Autonomic nervous system. Nervous impulses go out over the autonomic nerves to such organs as the heart, stomach, and others in the digestive tract. These nervous impulses are not under our deliberate control.

They are different from reflexes in that they must be learned. This gives us some choice as to what habits we will develop. We can deliberately set ourselves to learn habits that we think are worth while and to change ones that we do not like.

It is easier to form habits than it is to change them. In forming a habit, you learn to make a response to a certain stimulus (see Chapter 5). For example, if you wish to make a habit of brushing your teeth after breakfast, you put your mind on doing it immediately after breakfast for several days, and you soon find that you no longer have to think about it, that you respond to the stimulus of leaving the table after breakfast by going to brush your teeth.

In changing a habit, it is difficult merely to break the connection between the stimulus and the response and do nothing. It is easier to substitute some other response. For example, if you have the habit of grunting when someone calls to you, you will change the habit more quickly if you put your mind on saying *Yes* when you hear your name called. If you have the habit of thinking, and saying, "I don't like it," when a new food is presented to you, it is easier to change the habit if you substitute the idea, "I'll try a little; it may not be so bad," for the undesirable response. You are then putting a new response in the place of the one you are trying to avoid.

Habits of feeling. It is important to remember that there are habits of feeling as well as habits of doing. A big dog knocks a baby over and frightens him. Next time the baby sees a dog, it is easy for the impulses to travel the same pathway. The result is that he is afraid of dogs. A person develops fear of snakes, because he was startled by a snake one time.

Habits of feeling, as well as habits of doing, can be changed, but it is not easy. Try to develop a pleasant feeling in place of the unhappy one you have made a habit of. If you do not like a person, try to associate something pleasant with that person. Talk with him about something that you enjoy, go to a movie with him, include him in a party with other people you like. If you have a foolish fear of something—worms or bugs—try to see why other people find them interesting. Often, you can change habits of foolish fears, such as fear of talking in front of the class or taking part in a play, by practicing beforehand until you are sure that you know exactly what to do.

CHOOSING WHAT YOU WILL DO

Consciousness, understanding, memory, and thought depend upon the brain. Human beings can understand situations and do something about them. A cat enjoys a warm fire, but no cat will bring in kindling for a fire when the fire is burning low. A human being enjoys the fire but looks ahead and will go get coal and wood before the fire dies down.

Human beings, because of their superior brains, have many choices

In our democratic society, every person has the privilege of choosing what he wants to do. It is important that you learn to use your mind to its full capacity and make decisions that are good both for yourself and for others. (Courtesy Lakewood, Ohio, High School)

concerning what they will do. If a lower animal is frightened, it can either run away or fight. If a human being is frightened, he can think about what is frightening him. He may decide to run away; he may decide to fight; he may decide that this is nothing to be frightened about and pay no attention to it.

Being able to choose what you will do has its dangerous side. You can do the wrong thing as well as the right. It is not easy perhaps to see the relationship between what you are learning in this book and what you

learn in social studies and history, but there is a very important connection. We live in a democratic society. This means that every person is free to choose how he will take care of himself and what he will do.

Human beings can make the right choices for themselves and for other people, because they have the kind of brain that makes right choices possible. They can also make the wrong kind of choices. The first thing for you to do is to decide whether you want to do the right thing. Being able to make that decision is the finest part of

Unreasonable fears can make you miserable (see pages 298 and 314).

being human. Then you must learn as much as you can, so that you will know the right thing to do. And you must keep healthy, so that you will be strong enough to do what you decide you want to do.

DISTURBANCES OF THE NERVOUS SYSTEM

The organs of the nervous system are better protected than most of the other organs. They are closely connected, however, with all the other organs by nerves and by the blood stream. Anything that happens, anywhere in the body, is likely to influence the nervous system in one way or another. And anything that influences the nervous system affects all the rest of the body.

Oxygen and food. If there is not enough oxygen in the blood, the nerve cells are the first to suffer. Nervous impulses are carried more slowly; the person becomes slow and drowsy. If oxygen is cut off too long, the nerve cells die and breathing stops. (See the discussion of carbon monoxide poisoning in Chapter 11.)

There is no such thing as a "brain food," but nerve cells are quickly affected by any kind of poor diet. Enough thiamine (vitamin B_1) seems especially important. If the body is deprived of thiamine for some time, muscles may become paralyzed, because nervous impulses cannot be carried to them. The higher centers of the brain, those concerned with thinking and reasoning, may become affected. The person becomes irritable, and mental illness may result. (See the discussion of beriberi in Chapter 8.)

Iodine is another nutrient necessary for good brain development and use. Without iodine, the thyroid gland cannot develop properly, and this in turn affects the brain.

Toxins, poisons, and drugs. Any substance that gets into the blood stream soon reaches the nervous system. The toxins from infections often disturb the nerve center in the brain that regulates the body's temperature (see Chapter 5). This disturbance usually produces fever.

Alcohol, tobacco, and many drugs produce their effects by acting on the brain cells (see Chapter 21). When a person becomes tired and waste products collect in his blood, it is the nervous system that is most affected.

Pain. Severe pain sends a flood of

impulses to the brain. The sensations of pain may be so strong that the person cannot think about anything else and cannot use good sense in what he does and says.

Sometimes impulses flood into the brain from many parts of the body at the same time and cause overactivity. This may happen when a person is badly sunburned. The same thing may occur when itching continues for a long time. Tickling, also, may send so many impulses into the central nervous system that the person cannot control his actions. He may laugh and cry and throw his body about until he is exhausted.

At times the flood of impulses causing overactivity starts in the brain itself. A memory may be so strong that it stimulates nerve cells to action and interferes with breathing, heartbeat, peristalsis, and other bodily activities.

Infections of the nervous system. Infections may reach the central nervous system through the blood stream, through the nose or ears, or through wounds.

Once in a while tuberculosis organisms from the blood stream settle in the central nervous system. This form of tuberculosis always caused death until recent years when a new drug called streptomycin has been saving the lives of many of the people who suffer from the disease.

Syphilis organisms may be carried in the blood stream and settle in the brain or spinal cord. Syphilis in the brain produces a kind of insanity called paresis. In the spinal cord, it

Try not to worry about situations over which you have no control (see pages 304 and 315).

destroys nervous tissue. As a result, the person has difficulty in using his arms and legs (see Chapter 25).

These symptoms may not develop until years after the first infection with syphilis. Treatment in this late stage will stop the disease. It will not make the damaged tissues grow again.

Tuberculosis and syphilis are diseases that may attack almost any other organ of the body as well as the nervous system. Poliomyelitis, or infantile paralysis, chiefly affects the nervous system.

Poliomyelitis. Poliomyelitis, which is frequently called infantile paralysis, is caused by a virus. We are not certain just how this virus enters the body. It is known that infection can occur by way of the mouth, and this appears to be the most common means of infection. The virus leaves the body chiefly in the feces, but it is also found in discharges from the nose and throat.

The illness that follows infection by this virus is usually not severe enough to be recognized as poliomyelitis. Such mild infection, which is as common as measles, can be diagnosed at the time only by a test for the presence of the virus.

The recognizable disease, which develops in a small percentage of the persons affected, results from infection of the spinal cord, the brain, or both. The virus attacks nerve cells that control various muscles of the body, the result of which is paralysis. Some nerve cells are damaged only temporarily; others, beyond repair. The extent of paralysis depends on the number of nerve cells attacked. When death occurs, it is usually because of damage to nerve cells that control the muscles of breathing.

Epidemics of poliomyelitis seem to occur during warm weather and stop when cold weather starts. More children than adults are affected. Although there is much that we do not know about the spread of poliomyelitis, there are precautions we can take, particularly for young children, during epidemics.

Avoid crowds. Do not become too fatigued from play, overwork, or late hours. Avoid crowded bathing beaches and swimming in lakes and streams that might have sewage in them. Do not have tonsils removed or vaccinations performed when poliomyelitis is present in the community.

All the rules for keeping hands clean, protecting food and garbage from flies, and using your own handkerchief and eating utensils are especially important during epidemics of poliomyelitis.

Much research work has been done in the hope of providing immunity to poliomyelitis. For years only disappointment resulted, but recently several different vaccines have been developed, some of which have been or are being tested on groups of children.

During 1955 among approximately 5,000,000 school children who had had the "Salk vaccine" 5.7 per 100,000 got the paralytic type of the disease. The corresponding rate among approximately 5,000,000 unvaccinated classmates was 26.7 per 100,000. This suggests that this vaccine is 75 to 80 percent effective in preventing paralytic poliomyelitis.

How long the protection produced by this vaccine will last has not yet been determined. Since it consists of killed virus, it may not give as good protection as some of the other new vaccines which consist of live poliomyelitis viruses, but viruses that are so weak that they do not produce disease. In spite of these questions, however, it appears certain that one or more of these vaccines will provide us with a safe and effective means of preventing this dread disease.

If the disease does occur it is important that it be treated early. To accomplish this a child with headache, nausea, upset stomach, muscle soreness or stiffness, or an unexplained fever should see a physician. This is very important in helping to prevent crippling. If the physician orders hospital care, his advice should be followed promptly.

Meningitis. Infections of the membranes covering the brain and spinal cord are called meningitis. These infections, which are always serious, may be caused by many different bacteria and viruses. One type of meningitis, sometimes called "brain fever," is highly communicable. This is caused by a microorganism that is spread through discharges from the nose and throat. Fortunately, some of the new drugs are effective against this infection, which used to kill a large number of those who caught it. Other types of meningitis are caused by microorganisms that are carried to the brain by the blood from infections in other parts of the body or are spread to the central nervous system from infections in the nose, ears, and sinuses.

Encephalitis. An inflammation of the brain is known as encephalitis. Since persons with this disease appear drowsy, the condition is sometimes called "sleeping sickness." Fortunately, it does not occur frequently. Its most common cause is a virus that is probably spread by a mosquito. In Africa, there is another type of "sleeping sickness" that is spread by the bite of the tsetse fly and is always fatal.

Injuries and pressure. The brain and spinal cord are covered by thick bone. This protects them from all except very serious injuries from the outside. Sometimes high blood pressure

causes a blood vessel inside the brain to break. Bleeding occurs, and the blood forms a clot, which causes pressure on the nerve cells around the break. People commonly call this apoplexy or a stroke (see Chapter 12).

If the bleeding occurs near a nerve center that controls a movement, there will be paralysis of the muscles controlled by that center. Bleeding near the centers that control breathing or heartbeat may cause death. Usually, the blood is absorbed slowly into nearby capillaries, and the paralysis disappears in a few days or weeks.

Epilepsy. Most people think of epilepsy as a convulsion. This is true of very severe cases. Most cases are mild. The person loses consciousness for only a few seconds. He may only blink, roll his eyes, and wave his hands about.

Epilepsy is caused by a disorder of the central nervous system. In some cases, it is caused by pressure on the brain. In most cases, the cause is not known. It occurs in some families more than in others. Highly intelligent persons are just as subject to it as others. Napoleon is said to have had it, and Julius Caesar had "the falling sickness." It sometimes occurs in young people.

Between attacks, the person with epilepsy looks, acts, and feels like other people. One distressing feature of the disease is that attacks may occur at any time: on the street, in the classroom, at a dance or party, or when a person is quietly at home. The attacks can be so embarrassing that the person does not want to go out or to be with people.

Anyone with epilepsy should be under the care of a physician, even though the case is mild. Drugs will usually help him to ward off attacks. Friends can do a great deal to make life happier for such a person by welcoming him in their play and work, protecting him when he has an attack, and not letting other people stare at him or talk about him.

Headaches. Almost everyone has headaches at times. A headache is not a disease but a symptom of something wrong somewhere in the body. There are dozens of causes for headaches— eyestrain, fever, fatigue, sinus infection, indigestion, alcohol, nervousness, worry, or even sometimes a wish for attention and sympathy.

One special kind of headache is known as migraine, or "sick headache." It usually comes at more or less regular intervals, every few weeks or every few months. In addition to having a severe headache, the person is likely to be nauseated and to vomit. He usually has to go to bed until the attack is over. Migraine headaches tend to run in families and sometimes seem to be due to an allergy. In most cases, however, the cause is a mystery.

Headache medicines. American people use tons of drugs every year for headache. Most of these drugs do little harm, but some may cause serious illness and even death. Many people take aspirin every time they have a headache, but even aspirin is not safe for all persons to use as a remedy.

All headache medicines have one undesirable effect on the person who takes them. By relieving the headache, these drugs make him forget that there is something really wrong with him, else he would not have needed the medicine. These headache remedies block pain impulses over the nerves, so that a person does not feel the headache. In the meantime, the real cause may be growing worse and worse.

The way to cure headaches caused by eyestrain is to do something about the eyestrain. The way to cure headaches caused by indigestion is to improve digestion. The way to cure headaches resulting from fatigue is to rest.

Nervous breakdown. We often say that a person is having a nervous breakdown when he seems to have lost control of his feelings and his behavior. Usually, such a person is unhappy, and nothing anyone can say or do makes him feel better. He cannot think about anything except his own problems and his own unhappiness. He is tense and cannot relax even in sleep. Some people become excited and talk a great deal. Others do not even answer when spoken to. Sometimes, appetite and digestion are disturbed.

There are many causes for such symptoms. Tuberculosis, anemia, and other illnesses may make life too hard for a person. Sometimes, a person is too tired to do what he knows he must do. Sometimes, people have more

POLIOMYELITIS

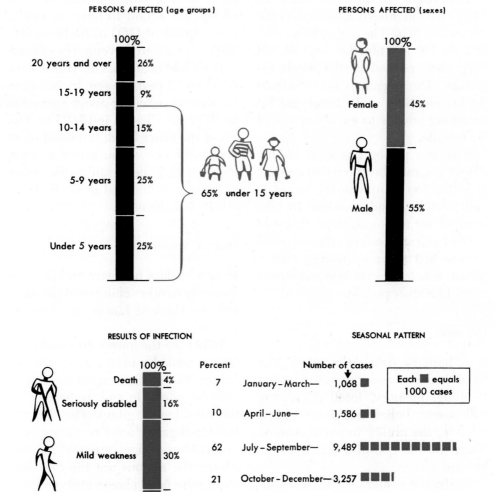

PERSONS AFFECTED (age groups)

100%
20 years and over — 26%
15-19 years — 9%
10-14 years — 15%
5-9 years — 25%
Under 5 years — 25%

65% under 15 years

PERSONS AFFECTED (sexes)

100%
Female — 45%
Male — 55%

RESULTS OF INFECTION

100%
Death — 4%
Seriously disabled — 16%
Mild weakness — 30%
Complete recovery — 50%

SEASONAL PATTERN

Percent		Number of cases	
7	January – March—	1,068	
10	April – June—	1,586	
62	July – September—	9,489	
21	October – December—	3,257	
100	Total—	15,400	

Each ■ equals 1000 cases

Based on data from the National Foundation for Infantile Paralysis. The seasonal pattern is for the year 1956.

worry and strain than they can carry.

The result is that impulses no longer flow in orderly fashion over the nervous system. The higher brain centers do not act together and do not keep their control of the whole organism. The person is overwhelmed by his emotions and cannot use his reasoning powers to see a way out of his trouble.

If such a person has some hidden illness, it should be found and treated. If he has too many worries, he needs understanding and someone to take some of his responsibilities. Being in good health and feeling safe and cared for are first steps in making such a person able to face the ups and downs of life like other people.

THE MIND

It is hard to define the mind. The mind includes consciousness, understanding, memory, intellect, reason, will power, belief, imagination, personality, the ability to make choices. These are the qualities that make us human.

The nerve centers for these qualities seem to be in the front part of the brain, but just where they are and just how they work we do not know. Sometimes an injury to the brain does not seem to do anything to a person's mind. Sometimes an injury will make a person forgetful and unable to reason correctly. It may make a friendly person moody and quarrelsome.

Scientists have worked out tests so that we can compare the intelligence of people of different ages. If a child

of 10, for example, does as well on these tests as most children 10 years of age, he is said to have an intelligence quotient (IQ) of 10/10, or 100. This is considered average or normal.

If a child of 10 does as well as most children 15 years of age, he is said to be above average or above normal in intelligence. His IQ is 15/10, or 150.

On the other hand, if a child of 10 does only as well on a test as most children of 7, he is said to be below average or subnormal in intelligence. His IQ is 7/10, or 70.

MENTAL RETARDATION

If a child does not learn and develop mentally as other children of the same age, we think of him as mentally retarded.

Idiots are the lowest group of mentally retarded persons. They are like babies in intelligence, though they may be adults in age. Imbeciles are the next lowest group. They stay at the intelligence level of young children. Above them are the morons. Above the morons are the dull normals, who have almost average intelligence.

Mentally retarded people cost the community a great deal. Idiots and imbeciles can do little work and must be taken care of. Morons can do many kinds of work, but they are not able to do work that requires a high degree of intelligence or technical skills. They do not know how to spend their money wisely or how to plan for themselves. Dull normals get along quite well in ordinary living.

Causes of mental retardation. Mental retardation may occur as the result of an injury to the brain. Lack of iodine in the diet (Chapter 8), or syphilis, or other diseases may keep the brain from developing and produce mental retardation. Some cases, however, are hereditary.

If both parents are mentally retarded, the children are almost certain to be mentally retarded. If one parent is mentally retarded and the other is of average intelligence, probably some of the children will be mentally retarded. If both parents are of average intelligence, probably none of the children will be mentally retarded.

Caring for the mentally retarded. There is no treatment for mental retardation. It is important to find what a person is able to do and then help him to do it. This is true for everyone: the mentally retarded, the average, and the genius. A mentally retarded person can be happy and often useful if he is given care and understanding.

MAKING THE BEST OF OUR MINDS

Each person inherits certain kinds of brain cells from his parents, grandparents, great grandparents, and so on. These are what you have to work with. You cannot add to them or make them different. You can, however, learn to use them to full capacity, which few people ever do.

Your brain is part of your body and works best when the rest of your body is healthy. A person does not do his best thinking and studying when he is sick, or tired, or hungry. Sometimes the best way to begin a piece of work is to take a short rest and get something to eat.

Having a high IQ does not mean that a person will get good marks and make a success of his life. Will power, drive, wanting to succeed, a calm disposition, doing things on time, and getting along well with other people are important. They help a person to make use of his intelligence.

Two boys. Everyone knows people like M.C. and J.F. The first was a boy with an IQ of about 100, just average. No one expected him to get more than passing marks. But M.C. was husky, never in a hurry, never upset about things. He handed in his homework assignments on time. He never stopped studying a lesson until he knew it. His friends could always depend on him.

One teacher said of him: "That boy has only a four-cylinder brain but he clicks on all four." M.C. knew he had to work hard for what he got, but he thought it was worth it. He was graduated with honors and went on to make a good record at college and in his work.

J.F. had an IQ of 160, far above the IQ that most of us have. He could learn things easily, so he put off studying. He went to class unprepared. Some days he recited brilliantly, some days he failed. He did everything in a slapdash fashion. In spite of his high IQ, he had not developed the other characteristics needed for success. He knew that he was not doing well and often felt unhappy about himself but never enough to make him do better.

J.F. received passing marks and was graduated but in the lower part of the class. He never became a leader at school or in business. Of the two, M.C. had more of what it takes to make a really good mind than J.F.

SO WHAT?

Your nervous system makes it possible for you to think, to learn, to remember, to do interesting things, and to be happy and successful in life; and

This same nervous system keeps your heart beating, keeps you breathing, and controls your temperature and your digestive and excretory processes; and

It is this system that makes you different from the lower animals; and

For these reasons the nervous system is frequently called the master control system of the body;

So, it is interesting and important to understand

What this system is and how it functions; and

What you can do to keep it functioning properly.

CHECKING UP

1. Why is the nervous system called the master control system of the body?
2. What makes up the nervous system? What is the central nervous system?
3. Draw a nerve cell and label the parts. Which is most important? Why?
4. Why do nervous impulses travel in only one direction?
5. If a nerve is cut, will it grow again? Explain.
6. If impulses over an afferent nerve are blocked, what is the result? If impulses over an efferent nerve are blocked, what is the result?
7. What does it mean to say that you "see" with your brain? that you "taste" with your brain?
8. If you had only a few association nerve cells, what difference would it make in what you could do if you heard or saw something unusual?

9. How are habits and reflexes alike? How do they differ? Trace a nervous impulse over a reflex pathway.
10. What are some examples of habits of feeling? How do they develop? Can they be changed? How?
11. How do the brains of human beings differ from those of lower animals? In what ways is this an advantage? What special problems and responsibilities result from this difference?
12. Do human beings have a choice of how they will act? Give some examples. (Include some examples not given in this chapter.) What will help you to make the right, instead of the wrong, choices?
13. How do food and oxygen influence the nervous system?
14. How may infections reach the central nervous system?
15. What precautions should you take during an epidemic of poliomyelitis?
16. What is a "missed case" of poliomyelitis? How do missed cases make it difficult to control the disease?
17. How does a stroke cause paralysis of an arm, a leg, or some other organ?
18. How should other persons treat a person with epilepsy?
19. What are common causes of headache? Should you take medicine to relieve a headache? Explain your answer.
20. What is meant by a nervous breakdown?
21. What are the various groups of mentally retarded? How should the mentally retarded be cared for?
22. Can a person be happy and successful if he has a high IQ? an average IQ? a low IQ? What other characteristics are important?

THINGS TO DO

1. Look at a sheep brain or a calf brain from the butcher shop. Find the "gray" matter; the "white" matter. Look for the places where nerves have been attached.
2. Look at models of the brain, spinal cord, and nerves.
3. Examine the skull and backbone of a skeleton. Look inside the skull to get an idea of the size and shape of the brain. Trace the spinal cord down through the openings in the vertebrae. If you cannot see a human skeleton, you may find dried skulls and vertebrae of animals out in the fields or in a museum.

4. Study a few reflexes. (*a*) Let one person shut his eyes for 2 minutes, then open them. Watch the pupils grow smaller. Is this a protective reflex? Can you trace the pathway of the nerve impulse? (*b*) Smell a lemon. Your salivary glands secrete saliva and make the mouth "water." Is this a useful reflex? Trace the pathway of the nervous impulse. (*c*) Sit on a table or high stool and let your legs hang free from the knees. Have someone strike just below the knee with the side of the hand. This reflex is known as the knee jerk. (*d*) Draw your fingers down the sole of a baby's foot and watch the toes. (*e*) Ask a doctor or a nurse to tell you of other reflexes.

5. Study some of your habits. Watch yourself get dressed, for example. What habits have you formed? What are your habits of standing? On which arm do you carry your books? Watch everything you do on the way to school. What habits have you formed? Make an estimate of how much time habits save you every day.

6. Practice forming a habit. First, decide what habit you will form and when and where you will practice it. Then, never let slip a chance to practice. How long does it take you to form the habit?

7. Practice changing a habit. How long does it take? Is it easier to make a new habit or to change an old one?

8. Make a list of the foolish fears of members of the class. How did they start? Can you change them? (One way is to attach something pleasant to whatever causes the fear.) Do the same for the fears of some children that you know.

9. Ask a druggist to tell about some of the headache medicines he sells.

10. Name two or three people you admire or that you think have successful lives. Then make a list of the characteristics that you admire in them. Can you develop some of these characteristics?

CHAPTER 19 Mental Health and Personality

What do you value most in life? Is it brains, money, strong muscles, being popular? Or is it happiness, success, friendships, peace of mind? There is no question about your preferring the four last named values. The only question is, how can you gain them?

The most important things in life depend upon mental attitudes and emotional reactions—in short, upon mental health—more than upon anything else. A person may think that, if he only had the other person's good looks or money or social position, he would be happy. But he would find that these things alone do not bring happiness.

Everyone has seen people who did not get what they wanted. A school team loses a game. A girl is not invited to a party. A boy does not have money enough to take a trip with the other fellows. One person meets problems like these with a smile and "Better luck next time." Another person puts the blame on someone else, says "It isn't fair," "What's the use of trying!"

What is the difference between them? Why do some people act one way and other people act another way? Part of the difference is due to heredity: to the intelligence and nervous system that a person inherits from his ancestors. But most of the difference is due to habits developed during infancy and childhood.

Some people build habits of facing problems calmly and making the best of whatever comes along. Others develop habits of temper tantrums, daydreaming, or even becoming ill to avoid unpleasant situations.

Each person can make some choices as to what habits he will make and what habits he will change. This means that you can do a great deal to make yourself the kind of person you want to be.

GOOD, FAIR, AND POOR MENTAL HEALTH

Everyone knows that being healthy is more than just not being sick. A person with diphtheria is sick. He needs someone to take care of him. He needs

Anger (see page 315).

to stay in bed. He usually can be cured if he receives proper care.

Many people who are not sick in bed are not really healthy. They need help from other people in learning what to do to improve their health, but mostly they must do things for themselves: for example, rest more, choose better food, take better care of their eyes. Often small changes in their daily living will make great changes in their health.

In the field of mental health, also, there are various degrees of health. A person may be in good mental health, fair mental health, or poor mental health. People in poor mental health are usually mentally ill or mentally disordered. They need care and, in some cases, can be cured. People in fair mental health can do a great deal to help themselves. They may need advice about what to do, but they must improve their own ways of thinking and feeling. People in good

mental health can safeguard their mental health, just as they can safeguard their good health in general.

MENTAL ILLNESSES OR DISORDERS

Patients with severe mental disorders do not act or feel as other people do. They may forget their names, or their friends, or where they live. They may be wildly excited or very depressed. They do not use their reasoning ability well.

Such persons are said to be insane, or to have a psychosis. There are many kinds of insanities, or psychoses. (*Insanity* is the legal term for a severe mental disorder. *Psychosis* is the medical term for the same condition.)

People sometimes confuse insanity with mental retardation. The two are not at all alike. Mental retardation is the condition in which intelligence does not develop as it does in most people (see Chapter 18). Insanity refers to a disordered mind. It may occur in very intelligent people, in average persons, or even in the mentally retarded.

Physicians who specialize in the treatment of mental illnesses are called psychiatrists. As with other illnesses, the sooner a mentally disordered patient can be taken to a physician, the better are the chances of his cure. It is unreasonable to be afraid or ashamed to admit that a person is mentally ill and is receiving treatment.

Persons with less severe mental disorders often think or act like other people in most things but not in all.

They may be afraid of something that does not exist, and this fear may color everything they do or say. They may not be able to see or hear or move, yet their eyes and ears and muscles are perfectly healthy.

These people, and many of those with psychoses, are usually considered mentally healthy by other people. Their friends and relatives call them "odd" but do not recognize for months or years that they are really mentally disordered. It would save worry and time if they could be discovered in the early stages of their illness and given treatment.

Causes of mental disorders. When a person behaves badly or oddly, there is somewhere an explanation why he behaves as he does. In other words, the law of cause and effect applies to human behavior, just as to other natural occurrences. Because human behavior is so complex, it may not always be possible to find the reason people behave as they do.

Many people think that all mental illnesses are inherited. This idea is false. Its effects are unfortunate, since it makes people believe that mental illness cannot be prevented or cured. Heredity undoubtedly plays a part, but it is not the most important cause of mental illness.

Sometimes, psychoses or other mental illnesses are caused by injury to nerve centers in the brain. Brain tissue may be destroyed by a wound or by a fall on the head. Diseases, such as syphilis and meningitis, or toxins from infections in other parts of the body also may damage brain cells (see Chapter 18).

Alcohol and other drugs may reach the brain through the blood stream and keep the nerve centers from functioning properly. Tumors or blood clots in the brain may interfere with thinking. Blood vessels and nerve tis-

Daydreaming (see page 319).

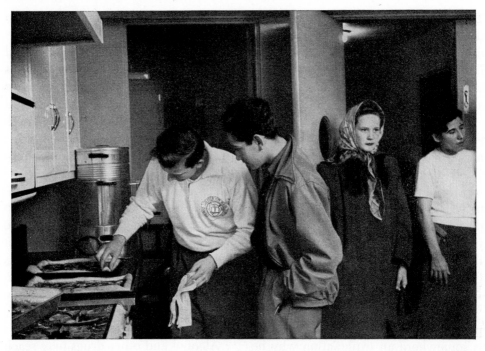

Try not to be uneasy around other people. You can develop the ability to be part of every group in which you find yourself. (Courtesy Standard Oil Co., N.J.)

sue sometimes undergo changes in old age that result in a kind of mental disorder.

Some mental disorders are related to poor functioning of the endocrine glands or to lack of certain vitamins (see Chapter 18). Other causes of mental illness are unhealthy mental and emotional habits.

EMOTIONS AFFECT THE WHOLE BODY

Strong emotions, such as fear and anger, have an effect on the whole body. Impulses race out over the autonomic nervous system. Adrenalin from the adrenal glands is poured into the blood stream. The heart beats faster, breathing is more rapid, and muscle tonus increases—in other words, the body gets ready to act. When people are frightened or angry, they sometimes do things like lifting heavy weights or running long distances that at other times would be impossible.

Fear. Fear may be useful. Fear of accidents makes us cautious drivers; fear of being burned keeps us away from fires; fear of serious illness sends us to a physician; fear of hurting someone's feelings makes us think before talking.

Strong fears, however, interfere with thinking. Many children are so afraid of the dark, of ghosts, of strangers, or of large animals that they cry and scream and make themselves sick.

Young people are sometimes so afraid of being laughed at or of being different from other people that they say and do things that they are sorry for later.

Most fears are habits built on experiences of childhood. Finding why you are afraid is the first step in doing something about the fear. Talking about your fears to an understanding person sometimes makes the fears disappear.

Anger and temper tantrums. Most babies scream or have temper tantrums when they cannot get what they want. This is almost the only way babies can react at such times. As they grow older, most of them learn quieter ways of meeting problems. Parents help by keeping calm themselves when the baby is angry and by showing him other things to do and think about.

Some people develop such a strong habit of temper tantrums that all their lives they scream and throw things when they do not get what they wish, or, as we usually say, when they cannot "have their own way." They may make themselves so unpleasant that other people let them have what they want. At the same time, people around a person in a tantrum lose respect for him. This is much more important than whatever is gained by the bad temper.

Anger, like fear, leads to greater secretion of adrenalin. Like fear, also, it interferes with thinking. A boy who is "fighting mad" is usually not at his best in playing a game, or studying, or

doing anything else where intelligence is needed. We say that a person "loses his head" in such cases. It is a fact that the most important parts of his brain, those that make him able to control himself, are no longer functioning.

It is important to know that getting angry easily is a bad habit that can be changed. Looking ahead is important, too. For example, a girl may know that her younger brother's teasing will make her angry. She can plan what she will do and say. She can, perhaps, think of something to get his attention away from her. Perhaps, she can arrange an excuse for leaving the room before she gets "mad."

Worry. Sometimes a person worries so much about his problems that he has no time or energy left to do anything about them. A hard examination may be coming up tomorrow. The thing to do, of course, is to study for it, learn all that you can, then get a good night's sleep.

The "worrier" thinks how bad the examination is going to be, remembers that he went to the movies last week instead of studying, thinks of all the questions he does not know the answers to, tells his family how hard this course is, calls up his friends and tells them about this "awful" examination, looks at his books but cannot study because he cannot keep his mind on anything. Finally, he goes to bed but does not sleep. He turns and tosses and has dreams of failing and having to leave school.

Every human being meets some

Feeling inferior.

problems that he cannot solve. Worry does not help; it really interferes with doing the best possible. Sometimes, a person has to act immediately, before he knows the best thing to do. It is hard not to go back over the situation again and again and think: "If I had only done that," "If I had just said that."

Worry about mistakes you have made, about situations you cannot control, about things in the future, does no good. Yet such worry is difficult to avoid. Exercise out of doors will sometimes take your mind off a problem that is causing worry. Doing something you like very much— playing, reading, working at a hobby— often makes it easier to come back later and see things in their true relationship. Talking things over with a friend or an older person whom you respect is often a help.

Feeling inferior. Everyone feels humble at times and thinks that other people are better than he. Such feel-ings come to everyone and need not be disturbing. No one can excel in everything. Most people never do anything quite as well as they would like to.

A.C. was not as pretty as her sister. She did not talk as much and did not make friends as easily. Her brothers and sisters called her "homely" and laughed at her for being "tongue-tied." All her life she had heard people refer to her as "that plain little thing."

The result was that she thought that no one could like her and became afraid to try to do anything. She felt before she started that she could not do as well as her sister. She developed what is commonly called an inferiority complex.

Feeling that one is not as good as other people and that there is no use trying is no way to meet life. Every human being has some worth. A.C., for example, learned to play tennis well and won respect for her playing and for being a "good sport."

Feeling superior. It is just as natural to feel superior in some situations as it is to feel inferior in others. When a person leads his class or wins a race or sings well, he knows that he has done something that most people cannot do as well.

At the same time, it is important to remember that other people do well at other things. The person with a superiority complex forgets this. He thinks that what other people do and have cannot be as good as what he does and has. Such a person is not popular. In addition, his feeling of being better than other people is not a healthy state of mind, because it does not fit the facts.

Many people who seem to feel superior are really trying to hide a feeling of being inferior. A big boy may be a bully on the playground and, thus, try to make up for not feeling important in the classroom or among other boys of his own size. A girl who is a show-off or who boasts of how much money her father makes may be feeling that other girls and boys do not like her. She may be trying to prove to herself, as well as to them, that she really is important.

Mental conflicts. Everyone is disturbed at times at the difference between what he wants to do or be and what he thinks he should do or be. J.L. thought she hated her baby brother, yet she was ashamed of the feeling. She hid her feelings and did not admit them even to herself. She said, and believed, that she loved her brother. Yet her relationship with him was upsetting, because of the layers of feeling underneath. She sometimes kissed him when she wanted to hit him, then felt that she must be "bad" to have such thoughts.

Such mixtures of feelings are called mental conflicts. They sometimes lead to behavior that does not seem related to the cause. For example, J.L. broke things—her toys, her mother's dishes, her grandmother's glasses. Some way or other, breaking things was tied up in her feelings with hitting her brother.

Feeling superior.

Another example is the case of a boy 9½ years old who stole things from his home and from stores in the neighborhood. He was scolded, he was whipped, he was kept home from the movies, all without success. Finally, he was taken to a psychiatrist for study. The psychiatrist made friends with him and finally got the story from him.

An older boy had taught him to steal and at the same time had taught him some "bad" words. The words bothered him. He tried hard to forget them and he never repeated them. The more he tried to forget the words, the more restless and unhappy he became. So he turned to stealing, which he had learned from the same older boy, to relieve his feelings.

Getting a mental conflict out into the open helps a person to get rid of it. J.L. was helped to understand that she did not have to feel guilty about being annoyed with her brother at

One way to keep in good mental health is to have a hobby. (Courtesy General Electric Co.)

times. When that was off her mind, she discovered that he really was very "cute" and she became fond of him.

Just admitting to the psychiatrist that he wanted to say the "bad" words helped the boy reach the point where he no longer wanted to say them. He did not feel guilty and ashamed and he no longer felt he had to steal.

WHEN WE CANNOT HAVE WHAT WE WANT

No one can have what he wants all the time. We must learn to accept disappointment, and to meet unpleasant situations, and to adjust ourselves to what we can have. And, since we live in a world with other people, we sometimes must adjust our desires to their desires and rights.

Some people become ill, run away, or spend their time in daydreams whenever they find that they cannot have what they want. They may seem to avoid unpleasant problems and situations for awhile, but they miss a lot of life and often get themselves into worse difficulties than the ones they started with.

Illness. Children learn by experience that when they are ill they become the center of attention. They are waited upon by the whole family. No one expects them to do anything for themselves; no one blames them for not doing their schoolwork or helping at home.

E.B. was a charming young lady of 14. She was always the "life of the party." She had many friends and was always happy and gay. Then, gradually her disposition changed. She seemed unhappy and was cross and hard to get along with. She spent many hours in bed. Again and again, she was so ill she could not go to school.

The physicians who examined her found nothing wrong with her, but she continued to get worse. Finally, she was studied at a large hospital, and one of the physicians talked with E.B. about herself.

E.B. told the physician that this was her first year in high school and that she was failing in her work for the first time in her life. This had worried her. She began to feel that she was "dumb" and that her teachers "had it in" for her. Further, she feared that if she failed this year in school, her younger brother would catch up with her. What would her family and friends think if that happened?

E.B. was given a number of tests, which showed that she was a very bright girl but had not learned to read properly. She had been bright enough to pass her first eight grades just by listening in class. In high school, the work was harder. Each student was expected to work more independently, and E.B. could not keep up.

Once her problem was discovered, E.B. was given special lessons. She wanted to be graduated from high school and go to college, so she worked hard. Reading became easier for her, and E.B. became her old self again.

E.B. had found herself in a situation that made her unhappy. She did not consciously make believe she was ill. She was really ill, though the cause was mental and not a virus or a bacterium. She could not face the idea of failure at school, and illness gave her a good excuse for staying home from school without being blamed.

During World War II, many young men were discharged from the Army and Navy because they developed headaches, severe pain in various parts of their bodies, digestive upsets, and other symptoms of illness, even though no cause for the illness could be found. Perhaps, some of them had learned at school or at home the habit of getting out of things by becoming ill.

Daydreaming. Most persons daydream at times. Out of such dreams, inventions, great ideas, poetry, and social movements often rise and grow. Imagining things as they could be rests the mind and gives strength and courage to tackle problems.

Daydreams become unhealthy when they take the place of action. It becomes easier to be successful in a make-believe world than in the real world.

D.H. was a very brilliant boy who was promoted into the seventh grade when he was only 9 years old. All the boys in the seventh grade were bigger and older. They teased D.H., "rough-housed" him, made him cry, and then laughed at him. They said he was too little to play their games and told him to go play with the girls.

D.H. was unhappy and lonesome. At first he hung around the edge of the field where the other boys played. Then he began going off by himself, reading a book, or just imagining himself in another school where he had lots of friends and could win all the games and be elected to all the school offices.

A teacher became afraid that D.H. would develop the habit of getting pleasure only out of dreams, not out of doing things. She got his mother interested in letting him learn to swim and to do other things where size was not important.

Most daydreamers are not mentally ill. They can help themselves to turn their dreams into reality. They can find interesting things to do and friends to do them with.

Running away. Daydreaming is one form of escaping from problems.

Running away.

thought about it. He was unhappy and bitter again, felt that he was being cheated because he did not have his own mother and father.

So he ran away. He came home, then ran away again. He was so disturbed that he forgot the love and care his foster parents had given him. He did not stop to think that running away from his foster home would not bring back the home of his early childhood.

Some people all their lives simply "disappear" when anything difficult occurs. This does not solve their problems, of course. Most of their difficulties are within themselves, and no one can run away from himself.

TOWARD BETTER MENTAL HEALTH

Discussions of mental health always seem confusing. When discussion is too simple, it gives a false idea of the facts. When it is complex, people get lost trying to follow all the details.

Are there any practical guides toward better mental health? The remaining topics in this chapter are suggestions. Some relate to you as an individual, some are concerned with your relationships with other people, while others deal with your reactions to work and life in general. Each one has to do with something that you can do yourself.

Keep in good general health. Being rested, well fed, and well will not make you mentally healthy. But good general health will make it easier for you to keep your temper in hard situa-

Sometimes, people try to escape by really running away when they meet a situation they do not like and cannot change.

G.W. began to fail at school and to run away from home when he was 15. Before that he had done good schoolwork, was liked by everyone, and was a willing helper for his father on the farm. Why the change?

It went back to a day when he was rummaging through his father's desk. He found his adoption papers. G.W. knew that he was an adopted son, but he had not thought about it for years. Now, he suddenly remembered how angry and bitter he had been when his own home was broken by the death of his parents.

He did not tell anyone that he was disturbed, but he thought and

tions, to meet disappointment with courage and good nature, and to live happily with your friends and family.

Accept and believe in yourself. Many adolescents are really just getting acquainted with themselves and with other people and worry about the ways in which they are different. It is normal to be different—some people are taller than others, some have pug noses, some do not do arithmetic as well as others. These individual differences are not anything to be unhappy about; some of them disappear as the years go by; others last all through life.

Everyone has strong points and everyone has weak points. If you cannot sing and entertain your friends, it is foolish to feel sick and unhappy about it. Perhaps you can learn to cook so well that other people enjoy coming to your home or going on picnics with you.

Set your mind to make the best of yourself without fussing too much about what you do not have and cannot do. Beethoven was deaf. Milton was blind. Robert Louis Stevenson had tuberculosis, and Franklin Roosevelt was a cripple. Each made a place for himself by cultivating his strong points, not mourning over his weak ones.

Develop some interests and hobbies of your own. Having a hobby, something interesting to do and knowing how to do it, is a help in furthering mental health. A hobby gives pleasure and a feeling of security. You know

This adolescent does not want advice.

that if things get too difficult, you can work at your hobby for a while and get a new outlook on life. Then, you can go back to your problems and be better able to solve them.

In addition, a person with a hobby —whether it is reading, games, collecting, handwork, music, or any of thousands of others—is a more interesting person. Other people enjoy knowing him.

Develop poise. Everyone admires the person who never becomes em-

Indecision; mental conflict (see page 317).

This boy feels at ease speaking to a group. He is self-assured and poised. (Courtesy Standard Oil Co., N.J.)

barrassed or upset. He seems to know what to do, to be sure of himself without being conceited. We say that he has poise, or is poised.

A very simple start toward self-assurance and poise is to learn what is expected of people in the ordinary situations of life—for example, how to introduce girls to boys, how to make or second a motion in a committee meeting, how to serve refreshments. Knowing exactly what to do and how to do it in ordinary situations makes it easier to "keep your head" and to do the right thing in more complicated situations that come up unexpectedly. As far as possible, take every chance for work or play that comes to you and learn how to feel assured in many kinds of situations.

Poise also depends in part on your feeling about your appearance. You can keep yourself looking your best, your hair combed and clean, your fingernails clean, your shoes and clothes neat. Then, you can feel at ease about your appearance (see Chapter 10).

Appreciate differences among people. It would be a dull world indeed if every person were just like everyone else. Cultivate your own personality so that you have something of your own to contribute to other people. Look for the interesting characteristics in other people that are different from yours.

Sometimes people make fun of a boy because he does not dress or speak or look like other boys. Yet he may be a fine person with a sense of humor and lots of interesting ideas. If you do not make friends of many

Do you know how to introduce your friends to your family? (From the "Etiquette" Series. McGraw-Hill Text-Films)

kinds of people, you may miss lasting friendships and fail to learn exciting and interesting things.

Change from dependence to independence. Good parents make home a place where children can feel loved and secure. This satisfies one of the fundamental needs of human beings. But as children grow older, they need to do things for themselves.

Often when boys and girls are in their teens, they begin feeling that they want to make decisions for themselves, choose their own friends, go places without their families. Even when parents know that this is going to happen, they are sometimes surprised at its coming so suddenly. They want to go on protecting their children from the problems of life.

The ideal is for young people to take responsibility gradually. They can ask advice and can continue to feel secure in their parents' love and care. When children prove that they can use good judgment, parents are usually ready to let them make more and more decisions for themselves.

Children always remain children to their parents, and parents always remain parents to their children, but in addition they can develop a new relationship as adults. As one mother said of her daughter: "She used to be only my child; now she is my friend, too."

Find an understanding friend. It is

Illness (see page 318).

helpful to talk out your problems with someone who will help you to understand them. Young people need someone older and wiser than themselves to whom they can go, perhaps a parent, a religious worker, a teacher, or a counselor. All our lives we need such friendship, from husband, wife, or close companion. It is most important, of course, that this friend be worthy of a person's confidence and respect.

Develop friendships with both boys and girls. In the early teens and even before, girls are likely to spend most of their time with girls, and boys with boys. They form girls' clubs and boys' gangs and avoid association with the opposite sex. Often they become shy and awkward in a mixed group.

During adolescence there is increasing interest in persons of the opposite sex. This is the time for making many friendships and for doing things in mixed groups. Games, folk dancing, committee work, dramatics, singing, and picnics are more fun when boys and girls join forces. Doing things together in groups and forming friendships with a number of boys or girls are the best preparation for the pairing off and choosing mates which come a few years later.

Sometimes boys or girls in a new place feel lonesome and do not know how to meet other young people. Common hobbies bring people together. Schools, churches, and communities usually have clubs or groups that anyone can join.

Set goals for yourself. Select goals that challenge the best in you and then try hard to reach them. Find things to do that are worth working for, then try to do them. Some people drop a job when it is half-done or half-learned, and wonder why they are bored. We find our greatest satisfaction in doing something better than we had thought possible.

You may reach some of your goals in a few days or a few weeks, making a dress or learning to swim, for example. You may take years to reach other goals, such as making a good record in high school or organizing a collection of stamps or rocks. Other goals, such as being a good worker or a good friend, you will work toward all your life. Working toward worthwhile goals, whatever they are, gives purpose to your life and makes you a more dependable person.

Do one thing at a time. The efficient person is one who works when he works and plays when he plays. B.J. goes to the movies but worries all the

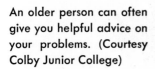
An older person can often give you helpful advice on your problems. (Courtesy Colby Junior College)

time about the studying she is not doing. This does not get the studying done, it keeps B.J. from enjoying the movies, and it does not make her good company.

C.T. has a study period for his mathematics. He starts a problem, thinks of the baseball game after school, works a little more, then makes a list of the baseball players and the positions they may play. At the end of the period, his studying is not done, and the baseball game is still hours away.

A day should have in it time for work, time for play, time for rest and sleep, time for meals, and time for such personal routines as combing hair and brushing teeth. The wise person goes through his day with zest for what he is doing at the time. Plan for the future but do not try to live through the future before it arrives.

Find a lifework. Decide on a way of earning a living that calls for the best in you and gives a sense of doing something worth while. There are thousands of different kinds of work to do in this country, all of them necessary, all of them interesting to people who look at them from the right point of view.

A good example of different points of view about work is in the story of a traveler and three workmen. The traveler asked each workman what he was doing. One replied, "I am earning $8 a day." The second said, "I am laying brick." The third replied, "I am helping to build a cathedral." The person who does not see what his work means to the world is losing something from his life.

Carry your share. There are many things to be done if home, school, camp, and the community are to run smoothly. The shirker loses in two ways. No one likes the person who lets other people carry all the responsibility and do all the work. And the

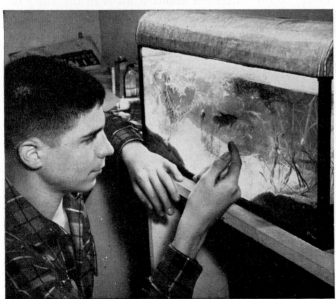

There are hundreds of interesting hobbies. Some call for cooperation with other people. Other hobbies give you a chance to be independent and do things by yourself. (Top, courtesy Arsenal Technical High School, Indianapolis. Bottom, from the "Adolescent Development" Series. McGraw-Hill Text-Films)

Make friends with boys and girls. (From the "Adolescent Development" Series. McGraw-Hill Text-Films)

person himself loses the real satisfaction that would come from doing his share.

Expect life to have its ups and downs. All through this chapter, there are suggestions on how to feel and act when trouble comes. Some people call life the "school of hard knocks." This is one way of looking at it. But it does not fit all the facts. Neither does seeing only the easy things of life fit all the facts.

You will not be happy all the time. You will make mistakes. You will not always get what you want.

Some people seem to forget when they have troubles that there is anything else in the world. Some people, when they are happy, forget that they

ever had troubles or that other people may be in trouble now. These are the people who are so shocked when trouble comes that they lose their sense of balance and act in some of the ways described earlier.

Making mistakes and wishing that you had not is human. Knowing that you make mistakes helps you to understand other people better. It makes you easier to live with.

You make some of your troubles for yourself. Others come because you are living in a world with other people, and sometimes their rights and wishes clash with yours. Some troubles arise because you want something it is not possible for you to have.

Think of the people you most respect. They are not the ones who have had the easiest lives. They have been able to learn from their mistakes and troubles and to build stronger personalities because of them.

You probably do not learn from your troubles when you are in the middle of them. All you can do then is to remember that you have been happy in the past and to believe that you will be happy again in the future. After your troubles are past, you can see how much you have learned from them. You understand yourself, the world, and other people better. You are closer to becoming the ideal person you admire and would like to become.

Human beings have brains that make it possible to remember the past and to look forward to the future. They also can make some choices of what they remember and look for-

ward to. The person with good mental health is the one who sees life as it really is, with the good and the bad in it, but always the good overbalancing the bad in the long view.

Tranquilizing drugs. A group of new drugs, knows as tranquilizers, are being used for the treatment of persons with certain nervous and mental disturbances. Some of these drugs quiet seriously disturbed patients so that they can be more satisfactorily treated and cared for in the hospital or in the home. Others help persons who tend to be nervous and high strung to live at a more even tempo. These drugs, however, do not cure mental illnesses and all of them are potentially harmful. They should be used, therefore, only under the direction of a physician.

SO WHAT?

Mental health is exceedingly important for happiness and success; and

Everyone at times experiences some of the symptoms of poor mental health, such as fears, anger, temper tantrums, feelings of inferiority, mental conflicts, undue worry, excessive daydreaming, or illness without any physical cause; and

These conditions, if recognized and corrected early, are of little or no importance; but if allowed to progress, they may lead to chronic illness, unhappiness, and even to insanity (psychoses);

So, a sensible person will

Learn the causes and the symptoms of poor mental health; and

Cultivate habits that make for good mental health, such as accepting himself as he is, developing hobbies, interests, poise, and friendships, doing one thing at a time, setting worth-while goals in life, carrying one's share, and accepting the ups and downs which occur in everyone's life.

CHECKING UP

1. What is the difference between mental illness and mental retardation? between insanity and psychosis? What is a psychiatrist?
2. Can mental illness be prevented or cured? Explain.
3. How do fears and temper tantrums develop? Why are strong fears and anger undesirable ways of responding to a situation? What can be done about them?
4. How can you avoid being a "worrier"?
5. Why is feeling inferior or superior to other persons not good mental hygiene? Does this mean that you should not know you do some things better or less well than others do?
6. What is a mental conflict?
7. Some persons use illness, daydreaming, and running away as ways of getting out of difficulties. Are these ways usually successful? Explain.
8. How are habits related to good or poor mental health?
9. The term *psychosomatic* was discussed briefly in Chapter 1. What illustrations of psychosomatic relationships are given in this chapter?
10. How is good general health related to mental health?
11. How does believing in yourself differ from feeling inferior or superior?
12. How does a hobby contribute to mental health?
13. Why should you cultivate your strong points?
14. How can you develop poise?
15. What problems do parents and their children often meet when the children reach their teens? How can these be solved?
16. Why is adolescence an especially important period for developing independence?
17. Of what value are friendships with older persons? with boys and girls?
18. How can you work toward goals and, at the same time, put your mind on one thing at a time?
19. What can you learn from meeting trouble? What are some of the troubles people of your age often meet?
20. What are some good study habits suggested in this chapter?
21. Why is it advisable to have friends of many kinds, of different ages, and of both sexes?
22. Does a person with good mental health ever make mistakes? Explain.

THINGS TO DO

Look over the suggestions for better mental health in this chapter and discuss ways of using them in everyday living. Here are some examples of what you might do.

Feeling comfortable and well poised

1. Make a list of situations that occur at school in which you feel embarrassed, for example, reciting in class, going alone to a party or to a club meeting, explaining to a teacher why you do not have your homework ready. What are desirable ways of acting in such situations? What are undesirable ways of acting?
2. Before a school party, discuss how to introduce parents to teachers, boys to girls, friends to parents. Write some skits showing the correct way and the incorrect ways of making introductions.
3. Ask the home economics teacher to show you correct ways of setting a table and serving refreshments to large and small groups.
4. Make a list of other social situations in which knowing how to do things correctly will save you embarrassment. Find what to do from teachers, parents, or books on etiquette.
5. Learn how to conduct meetings. Use a good book on parliamentary procedure, such as *Sturgis Standard Code of Parliamentary Procedure,* for a reference.
6. Review Chapter 10 on skin and grooming. Make a week's schedule that will keep you well groomed all the time: set aside one day for giving your hair a shampoo, another for manicuring your nails, another for putting your clothes in order, and so forth.
7. Review Chapter 4 on what to do in case of illness and accident and think about the advantages of knowing what to do, keeping your head, and doing the right thing in emergencies.
8. List some annoying situations that you have handled well. What did you do? Can you do the same thing when other situations come up?
9. List the times you felt unhappy or uncomfortable when you were a new student in school. Could someone have helped you to feel better about yourself or the situation? Make some plans for helping new students next term so that they will not feel unhappy.

10. Discuss ways you can be tactful in refusing to do things you think you should not do—for example, going to a movie you do not approve of, smoking, staying out late at night.

Worries and fears

11. List situations that make you worry—for example, getting ready for an examination, being nominated for an office and not being sure of being elected, wanting to be on the honor roll, wanting to be invited to a party. What are desirable ways of acting and feeling? undesirable ways?
12. Make a list of times various members of the class have felt inferior. Why did they feel inferior? How could they have helped themselves to feel more at ease?
13. Make lists of your fears and the things that make you angry. How can you control these strong emotions? How can you keep from showing your fear or your anger?
14. Ask parents who have young children what their children are afraid of. Do they know how these fears started? Can you think of ways of helping the children feel less afraid?

Relationships with parents and with people of your own age

15. List the problems that parents and young people of your age sometimes disagree on. Separate these into three groups: (*a*) questions that parents should settle for their children; (*b*) questions that children should be allowed to settle for themselves; (*c*) questions that call for family discussion and agreement. Discuss these with your family.
16. Ask three parents and three students to conduct a panel discussion on what parents would like to expect of their children and what children would like to expect of their parents.
17. Discuss ways for a lonely person to make friends with boys and girls in your school and community. Ask the girls what kinds of boys they like and what they like boys to talk about. Ask the boys what kinds of girls they like and what they like girls to talk about.

Hobbies

18. Make a bulletin-board display of the special interests and hobbies of the members of your class; of the teachers in your school.
19. Arrange a Hobby Show for the school.

20. Ask someone with an interesting hobby to discuss it with the class.
21. Get suggestions from all the class for a list of hobbies. Check the three or four you would be most interested in. How can you start learning about them?
22. What courses in the school open up interests that may become hobbies through life?

Work

23. Make a study of your study habits. Do you settle to work promptly? Have you a place where you can be quiet? Do you have a regular time for study? Do you plan your work? Do you keep at it until the job you have set yourself is done?
24. Choose five occupations that you think might interest you when you leave school—for example, nursing, working in a service station, engineering, teaching, working in a beauty parlor. Look up information about each of these. Talk with people who are already doing each kind of work. Visit places where these kinds of work are being done. Write a description of what it means to be in each of these jobs. What are the qualities that seem important to make a success in each?
25. List your strong points and your weak points and compare them with the qualities needed for success in each of the occupations in Ex. 24. Talk over your list with counselors, teachers, parents, and other people who know you.
26. Ask your counselors to let you take some vocational aptitude tests.
27. Think of other ways of discovering the kinds of jobs you will fit into best. Take time to decide what you are going to do when you leave school, but remember it should be something you enjoy and for which you have the needed qualities.

Making the best of life

28. Read biographies of men and women who have lived successful lives. Look especially for the ways they reacted to hardships and easy times.
29. Think about some of the people in your community whom everyone knows and admires. How have they met problems?

CHAPTER 20 Seeing and Hearing

Almost everything we learn about the world we learn through our eyes and ears. Stop and ask yourself how many things you have seen since you got up this morning and how many sounds you have heard.

Think what the world would seem like if you could not see. You would not know how your friends and family look. You would not know that flowers and pictures are colored. You would not know the words in books. Or suppose you could not hear. You would not know how voices sound, or music, or water running, or bells ringing.

Eyes pick up light waves and change them into nervous impulses. Ears pick up sound waves and change them into nervous impulses. The nervous impulses travel over afferent nerves to the centers in the brain. There, you become conscious of them as sights and sounds. (If you need to review the nervous system, look in Chapter 18.)

Sights and sounds give great pleasure. They are important in learning. It seems foolish, indeed, to treat eyes and ears carelessly or ignorantly.

THE EYE

The human eye is shaped like a round ball, about an inch in diameter. It is well protected by the bones of the head. The eyelid keeps dust and insects from the front part of the eye, which is covered by a transparent membrane called the cornea (see page 334). A steady stream of tears keeps the cornea clean and moist.

The human eye functions very much like a camera. Light comes in at a small opening behind the cornea, the pupil. The pupil looks black because there is no light behind it, just as a doorway into a dark room looks black.

The iris is the colored band around the pupil. In bright light, the iris makes the pupil smaller and lets less light into the eye. In dim light, the pupil becomes larger and admits more light.

In a camera, the rays of light pass through a lens and are brought together at one point on the film, called the focus. Lens and film must be the right distance apart if the photograph is to be clear (see page 335).

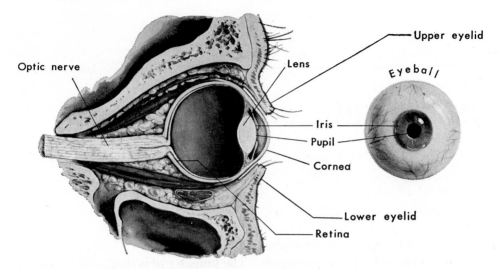

Optic nerve

Lens

Upper eyelid

Eyeball

Iris

Pupil

Cornea

Lower eyelid

Retina

What parts of the eye can be seen from the outside? How is the eye protected?

In the eye, light passes through a lens just behind the pupil and is brought to a focus on the retina. In the retina, light waves are changed into nervous impulses, which pass over the optic nerve to the brain. If a person is to see clearly, his lens must be of the proper strength and must be at the right distance from the retina.

The eyeball is hollow. The spaces within it are filled with a substance something like jelly. This substance is clear and allows light to pass through to the retina.

The eyes at work and at rest. Most people have learned that long periods of reading and writing make their eyes feel tired. The reason is that tiny muscles inside the eyeball must contract whenever you look at something near at hand.

These muscles within the eyeball relax when you look at something in the distance. Looking out the window or at something far off allows the eyes to rest. If you have much studying to do, it is a good plan for you to look away from your book every few minutes or at the end of each page.

Other muscles outside the eyeballs move the eyes up and down and from side to side. They act very rapidly. In 5 minutes of reading, the eyes may make a thousand movements (see Chapter 6).

Muscles that move eyeball

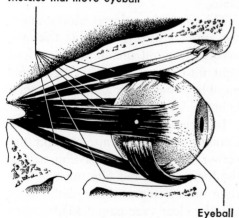

Eyeball

DEFECTIVE VISION

A photograph may be spoiled by too much or too little light, by a dirty or cloudy lens, by not having the camera in focus, or by a defective film or plate. In the human eye, vision may be blurred by similar defects.

Injury or infection of the cornea and iris. Injury or disease sometimes leaves scars on the cornea, which do not allow light to enter the eye. For this reason, dust or cinders in the eye must be handled carefully. Usually, closing the eye for a few moments without moving the eyeball will cause tears to accumulate and flush out the dust or cinder. Rubbing the eye is likely to scratch the cornea by pushing the hard particle across it or into it. Using dirty fingers or a dirty handkerchief adds the danger of infection. (Review the first-aid measures given in Chapter 4 for the care of the eyes.)

When the cornea is scarred or cloudy, it can sometimes be replaced by clear tissue from another person's eye. There are "eye banks" in some large cities, where corneas are collected for this purpose.

Infection of the iris sometimes prevents adjustment of the pupil to varying amounts of light. The infection may come from the cornea or from other parts of the body through the blood stream.

Clouding of the lens. Vision may be blurred or lost because the lens becomes so cloudy that light cannot pass through it. This condition is called cataract.

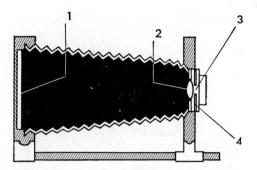

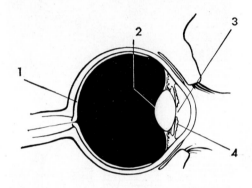

1 - Photographic film / Retina
2 - Lens
3 - Opening / Pupil
4 - Diaphragm / Iris

The human eye compared with a camera.

Some cataracts result from injury or disease. The most common kind, however, occurs in older persons and is known as senile cataract. The cause of this is not known but, apparently, is related to the process of growing old.

In the past, a cataract was considered a hopeless sentence to blindness for the rest of a person's life. Now, a simple but delicate operation can restore useful vision to about 97 percent of the people with cataract.

Retina too close to, or too far from,

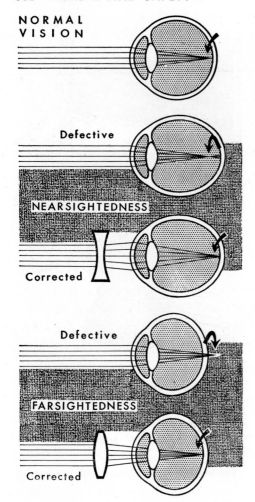

NORMAL
VISION

Defective

NEARSIGHTEDNESS

Corrected

Defective

FARSIGHTEDNESS

Corrected

the lens. Most eye defects result from defects in the shape of the eye.

A common cause of eyestrain is that the eyeball is too short from front to back. Because of this, rays of light, even from distant objects, do not focus on the retina unless the little muscles inside the eye are contracting. This condition is known as farsightedness.

If the eyeball is too long from front to back, vision is blurred, and no action of the muscles within the eye can clear it. This is known as nearsightedness.

In some persons, curved surfaces of the eye are not regular. Some rays of light may be focused on the retina, others not. This condition is astigmatism.

Children are ordinarily farsighted in infancy, but their eyeballs become longer as they grow older. Most children have eyeballs of proper length by the time they reach the fourth or fifth grade. Some reading difficulties among children in the early grades are probably related to farsightedness and the eyestrain it causes when close work, such as reading or writing, is done.

Damage to retina, nerves, and brain. The retina is so well protected that, when it is damaged, the damage usually comes from within. In persons with high blood pressure, bleeding may occur from small blood vessels in the retina and blur the vision.

Diseases, such as syphilis, and poisons, such as wood alcohol, sometimes injure the optic nerve, so that impulses cannot pass over it to the brain. Diseases or injury may damage the vision center in the brain and make it impossible for the person to become conscious of the impulses that come in from the eye.

Changes in the lens. As a person grows older, the lenses in his eyes become stiff, and it is no longer easy to see things close at hand. Sometime in middle age, most people start wearing glasses for reading or, if they al-

Look at the large circle at the bottom with each eye. If all the lines appear to be the same width and color, you have no astigmatism. The four circles at the top show how the spokes of a wheel may look to people with four different kinds of astigmatism.

ready wear glasses, begin wearing bifocal lenses, in which the lower part of the lens is for close work, and the upper part is for seeing things at a distance.

Crossed eyes. A common defect that occurs because we have two eyes instead of one is crossed eyes, or squint. The scientific term for this defect is strabismus.

There are six tiny muscles on the outside of each eyeball that move it. When a person fixes his eyes on an object, all of these muscles must be in exact balance. If one pulls harder than another, that eye is pulled too far in one direction or another. The two eyes then are not fixed on the same object (see Chapter 6).

Most babies appear cross-eyed when they are learning to use their two eyes together. This should cause no concern, unless the condition continues after the baby is a year old.

When strabismus occurs, it is of the greatest importance to have the condition corrected as early as possible. One reason for this is that the child will lose clear vision in one eye if the squint continues. Another reason is that crossed eyes are likely to make a child so sensitive about his appearance that he cannot make friends and cannot live a happy childhood.

Strabismus sometimes occurs when one eye is more farsighted than the other. This makes that eye work harder for clear vision, especially during close work. The strain may be so great that the muscles which correct the farsightedness may stop working. That eye then will not focus on the book or other near object, and squint will result. Cross-eyedness is most marked when a person is tired.

A crossed eye usually turns in. Strabismus includes also the cases of eyes turning up or down or out. Exercises, glasses, and operations are all used in treatment of strabismus.

HOW WELL DO YOU SEE?

Most schools and colleges test the vision of students. This probably should be done every year. Many times, people are thought to be stupid or lazy, when the real difficulty is that they cannot see well. The person himself feels discouraged and inferior when he fails again and again to do what other people do.

The test most commonly given is one in which the person to be tested stands 20 feet from a card and reads letters of different sizes on the card (see Chapter 26). If he can read the letters most people can read, his vision is said to be 20/20. If at 20 feet he can read only the larger letters, which people with good vision read at 40 feet, his vision is reported as 20/40. This record is not a fraction and does not mean "one-half vision."

This kind of vision testing is not accurate, but it picks out most of the persons who should have more careful eye examinations. It fails completely to pick out persons who are farsighted. This is because farsighted persons correct their vision reflexly by contracting the muscles within the eyeballs.

Eyestrain. A report of 20/20 vision does not prove that a person has good vision. He may be seeing clearly only because the muscles in his eyes are contracting. This is likely to cause eyestrain. If reading makes his eyes red and puffy, or gives him a headache, if it makes him feel tired and cross, or if he has frequent eye infections such as sties, these are symptoms of eyestrain. He should have a careful eye examination no matter what his record on a vision test shows.

WHO SHOULD WEAR GLASSES?

Glasses improve vision because they contain lenses that balance the defects of the eye itself. Thus, they enable people to see more clearly, and they relieve eyestrain in persons with astigmatism or farsightedness.

To find who should wear glasses requires skill and careful examinations. The eyes of most people can make adjustments for minor defects and will do better without glasses. On the other hand, some persons show eyestrain from what seems a small defect and need the help of glasses, especially for close work.

Eyes are always changing, especially during youth and middle age. This means that examinations must be repeated, every few months in some cases, every few years in others. Glasses that no longer fit may be as harmful as no glasses at all.

Making examinations. For an examination, you should go to a good eye specialist, not just to a store that has glasses for sale. A physician who specializes in care and diseases of the eye is called an oculist or an oph-

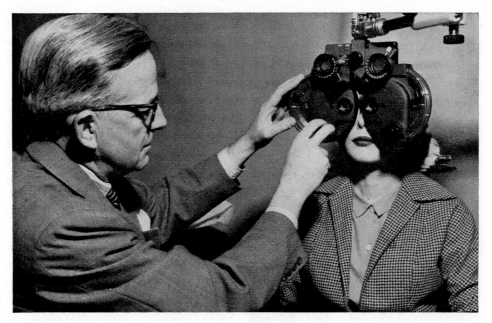

Making an eye examination and fitting glasses. (Courtesy Better Vision Institute)

thalmologist. He examines eyes and, if the patient needs glasses, gives him a prescription for them. This prescription is then filled by an optician. The optician grinds the lenses and makes the glasses.

Another group of specialists who make eye examinations are called optometrists. Optometrists are not physicians, but they have had training in making eye measurements and fitting glasses.

There are other persons who make a living by persuading people that they have poor vision and by selling them glasses. Customers go to them because they think they will get free examinations and inexpensive glasses. Glasses are never inexpensive if they are the wrong glasses.

Care of glasses. It is surprising how many people will have careful examinations of their eyes, get glasses, and then fail to wear them. If glasses are needed, it puts a strain on the eyes to do without them. It takes a little trouble to get them out of a pocket or out of a purse, but a little trouble is a very small price to pay for better vision.

It is surprising, too, how many people are careless about cleaning their glasses. They wash their faces two or three times a day and their glasses two or three times a year. It is easy for a person not to notice dirt on his own glasses, but every bit of dust and dirt shuts out light needed for seeing.

The frames of glasses, as well as the lenses, need care. Crooked frames may throw the lenses out of line. This is especially important for people with astigmatism.

Goggles, good lighting, and space in which to work are all eye safeguards. (Courtesy San Francisco Unified School District)

COLOR BLINDNESS

Color blindness is a condition in which the nerve endings in the retina are not sensitive to all the colors. This defect is hereditary. About one man in 25 and one woman in 200 have some degree of color blindness. However, a woman whose father is color blind may transmit, or pass on, the defect to her sons without herself showing it. This is one reason why people sometimes say that hereditary characteristics "skip generations."

Complete color blindness is rare. The most common form is inability to tell red from green. A color-blind driver tells the difference between red and green traffic lights by differences in their brightness. He also learns that the top light means "Stop" and the bottom light means "Go."

Color blindness may be a dangerous handicap in some situations, especially if a person does not know that he is color blind. Tests for color blindness may be included in physical examinations in schools and for employment in industries.

BLINDNESS

It has been estimated that there are 100,000 blind persons in the United States and that 50 percent of these cases could have been prevented. The most important causes of blindness are injuries, infections, and poisons. In addition to the blind, there are several million persons with very poor vision.

Eye injuries. Many cases of blindness are caused by carelessness when children throw sticks and stones or sharp pointed playthings, such as darts and arrows. They do not want to hurt other children, often do not even aim at them, but sometimes what they throw reaches another child's eyes. Small children's play must always be supervised, because they are not wise enough to know what is dangerous. Parents and other adults must see that playthings do not have sharp points and that such articles as knives and ice picks are kept out of reach.

In persons of high-school age, shotguns, rifles, and even air rifles cause many cases of blindness in one or both

This woman is reading Braille with her fingers. (Courtesy American Foundation for the Blind)

eyes. "Rough-housing" and "horse-play" are also the cause of many eye injuries.

Firecrackers sometimes cause blindness, as well as severe burns, when they are tossed about carelessly. This is one reason why they have been banned in many places.

Injuries to eyes of workers occur sometimes when metal is filed or sawed, and bits of metal fly into the eyes. Strong light, such as that given off in welding, may injure optic nerves. Prevention depends on using goggles and screens.

Eye infections. Forty or fifty years ago more than one-fourth of all blindness in this country was due to infection with the gonococcus organism. This usually occurred at the time of birth. Now, laws require that a special solution be placed in the eyes of all newborn infants. This kills the gonococcus organism. Blindness from this cause has almost disappeared since these laws have been in effect.

Trachoma is a virus infection that results in blindness if the person does not get early medical treatment. It is spread from person to person by hands, towels, wash basins, and other objects that have been contaminated with eye discharges from a person who has the disease.

Poisons and blindness. Among the more common poisons that may produce poor vision or complete blindness are tobacco, wood alcohol, and quinine.

Many people use tobacco for years,

and their eyes do not seem to be harmed by it. In others, the eyes tire easily, using the eyes causes headaches, and ability to see becomes less and less. These symptoms occur most commonly in pipe smokers who smoke most of the day, or cigar smokers who smoke half a dozen or more cigars a day. Drinking alcohol makes the symptoms worse.

Wood alcohol is a poison that causes blindness in most persons who drink it. Sometimes it is put into "bootleg" liquor.

Quinine is well known in the treatment of malaria. Many people know that it sometimes causes ringing in the ears, dizziness, and partial deafness. Blindness occurs less often but may be more serious. People should not take medicines containing quinine without medical advice.

Educating the blind. So much of our education comes by way of our eyes that it is hard to understand how one can get along without them. Blind people are educated through their ears and through their fingers. The principal means of instruction is through a method of reading and writing by touch. This method is called Braille. Paper is pricked by sharp instruments in tiny patterns, which stand for the letters of the alphabet. A blind person "reads" by running his fingers over these patterns.

The only difference between blind persons as a group and others is that the blind cannot see. They can be useful and happy members of society when given an education.

Sight-saving classes. Many people have a little vision but not enough to allow them to carry on their regular schoolwork. They are put into special classes called sight-saving classes. As the name shows, the purpose of these classes is to help children save all the sight they have and put it to good use. Children in sight-saving classes learn to read from large type. They learn to typewrite, so that they will not have to use their eyes for writing. They join the regular classes for discussions, singing, and physical education and carry on all the usual activities at home and outside of school with their friends.

KEEPING EYES BEAUTIFUL AND USEFUL

The eye has been called the "mirror of the soul." It twinkles with good nature, sparkles with joy, softens with love, hardens with anger, stares with fright, and clouds with despair. Many people with homely features are made beautiful by eyes that reflect interest, good nature, and pleasing personality.

Color of eyes. The color of the eyes is in the iris. It is determined by heredity. A parent with brown eyes may transmit to his or her children substances (genes) that make for brown eyes or for blue eyes.

A parent with blue eyes transmits to his children only substances (genes) that make for blue eyes. Therefore, if both parents have blue eyes all their children will have blue eyes. Eyes that are not strictly brown or blue represent various mixtures of brown and blue.

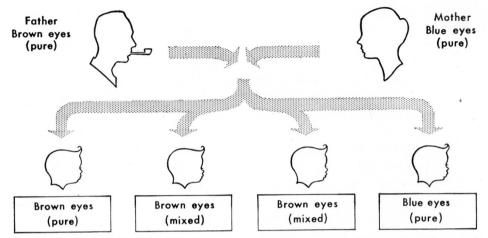

Father
Brown eyes
(pure)

Mother
Blue eyes
(pure)

| Brown eyes (pure) | Brown eyes (mixed) | Brown eyes (mixed) | Blue eyes (pure) |

This illustration shows first and third generations in inheritance of eye color. All second generation offspring would have brown eyes mixed.

Attractive eyes. Color and shape of eyes are not the most important things in making people's eyes beautiful or homely. General health, mental attitude, and choice of colors in clothing and cosmetics are of even greater importance.

A sick person's eyes are dull; a healthy person's eyes are clear and shining. Rest, good food, and exercise in the out-of-doors improve circulation, muscle tonus, and general good health. These do more for eyes than preparations sold in the beauty shop or drugstore.

Being happy and interested in people and things gives a sparkle to eyes that is very attractive. This is one of the outcomes of good mental health.

Clothing of the proper color can bring out hidden beauty in eyes. Cosmetics are less important but when properly applied they can give a pleasant frame to the eyes. They should never, of course, be put into the eyes (see Chapter 10).

Inflamed eyes. If you have a "good crying spell," your eyes become red and swollen. Cold water on your face and eyes and a brisk walk are usually all that is necessary to restore your eyes to their natural appearance.

Dust and exposure to sunlight often cause itching and redness. Or itching may be caused by an allergy. Never rub an itching eye. Find what causes the itching and care for that.

Inflammation of the lining of the eyelid and covering of the front of the eyeball is called conjunctivitis. This may occur with a common cold and usually clears up in a few days. Warm water with a little salt in it (1 tablespoonful of salt to 1 quart of warm water) or boric acid solution will make the eyes feel better and do no harm. Other eyewashes or eyedrops should be used only if prescribed by a physician.

"Pink eye" is a type of conjunctivitis that spreads easily from person to person in a family or in a school. Keep your hands away from your eyes and use only clean wash cloths and towels, and you can feel reasonably safe from infection.

A sty is a pimple-like infection on the margin of the eyelid. Sties occur most frequently with eyestrain.

Protection from strain. Some general rules for the care of the eyes may be gathered from earlier parts of this chapter.

Eyes tire more easily when the body as a whole is tired. They should not be used for close work during illness or for some time afterward. They should be protected from strong light during infectious diseases, especially measles and influenza. For people who read and study a great deal, rest by looking at some distant object every few minutes is helpful.

Good lighting is important when you read, write, sew, or do any other kind of close work. When you read and study, good type and good paper will help prevent eyestrain (see Chapter 23).

Reading in bed often produces eyestrain, because the book is not held in a proper position and the lighting is poor. Reading on a moving train or bus is tiring, because the position of the book is constantly changing and the small muscles of the eyes must make constant adjustments. The light, too, is likely to be unsteady.

Goggles are useful to protect the eyes from dust and wind as well as to prevent injuries in many occupations. Tinted lenses reduce the glare of the sun in summer and of the snow in winter. Inexpensive colored glasses are usually not made of clear glass and often cause strain and headaches. Good tinted lenses are carefully made of good glass. They may be ground by an optician to fit a person's prescription if he wears glasses.

Reading with strong sunlight shining on the page or looking directly at or near the sun is always hard on eyes. Even with tinted glasses on, a person should never lie on the beach and look up at the sky. The eyes of babies lying in buggies or pens out of doors should always be shaded.

Eyes should be tested regularly. If the tests show defective vision or if symptoms of eyestrain appear, a person should seek the best advice possible. In the case of vision, the best service is none too good.

THE EAR

Sound waves travel through the air somewhat as ripples travel on the surface of a lake when you throw in a stone or dip an oar. Sound waves travel about $\frac{1}{5}$ mile per second. A person can tell about how far off a flash of lightning has been by counting the seconds between the flash and the peal of thunder and dividing by 5.

Did you ever debate whether a tree falling in a forest where no one heard it made a sound? The fall, of course, would start sound waves. But sound waves do not become sounds until they reach the brain. There would, therefore, be no sensation of sound if no one heard it.

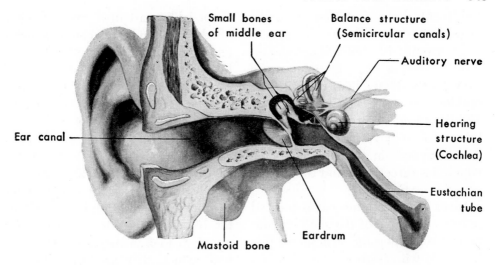

Small bones of middle ear

Balance structure (Semicircular canals)

Auditory nerve

Ear canal

Hearing structure (Cochlea)

Eustachian tube

Mastoid bone

Eardrum

How is the ear protected? What parts of the ear can be seen from the outside?

Outer ear. The ear consists of three parts: the outer ear, the middle ear, and the inner ear. The outer ear is the part that we can see and feel, plus the ear canal leading into the head. At the end of the ear canal is the eardrum, a thin membrane stretched tightly across the canal. This separates the outer ear from the middle ear.

Sound waves are caught by the outer ear and directed down the ear canal. Cupping the hands behind the ears catches more sound waves and enables us to hear more distinctly. Dogs and many other animals get the same effect by raising their ears.

Middle ear. The middle ear is a small cavity in the bones of the skull, just inside the eardrum. It contains three small bones that are delicately joined together and arch across the middle ear. Sound waves in the ear canal make the eardrum vibrate. The tiny bones then carry the waves across

the middle ear to a membrane that separates it from the inner ear.

Opening into the middle ear is the Eustachian tube from the pharynx, or back of the nose and throat. The Eustachian tube admits air to the middle ear and balances the pressure on the eardrum. When you swallow, the Eustachian tubes to your two ears open and allow the air pressure in the middle ear to be adjusted.

Anyone who has ridden in an airplane, or even in a fast elevator, knows the unpleasant sensation he feels in his ears. This is caused by the sudden changes in pressure on the outside of his eardrums as the airplane or elevator goes up or down. Swallowing or yawning opens the Eustachian tubes and allows the pressure on the inside of the eardrums to become the same as the outside pressure.

When the mucous membrane of the nose is swollen, as in a cold, the Eustachian tubes may be blocked. This results in discomfort and impaired hearing until the tubes again open.

Unfortunately, infectious organisms, as well as air, sometimes go up through the Eustachian tubes to the middle ears. (Look back at Chapter 13 for a discussion of the Eustachian tubes and colds.) They may go on to the air spaces in the mastoid bone, which lies directly behind the ear.

Inner ear. The inner ear is located in the solid bone of the skull. It contains two important structures: one has to do with hearing; the other has to do with the sense of balance, or equilibrium.

The part concerned with hearing, the cochlea, is filled with fluid and contains nerve endings. Movements of the tiny bones in the middle ear set up waves in the fluid and these in turn start nervous impulses over the auditory nerve. In the brain, these nervous impulses are understood as sounds (see Chapter 23).

Sound waves may also reach the inner ear through the bones of the skull. Hold a spoon between your teeth and tap it with your fingernail. Then hold it in one hand and tap it again. The sound is much louder when the spoon is held between the teeth, because some of the sound waves are carried through the bones of the skull. Many hearing aids depend upon this fact. They can be used if the inner ear and nerve are in good condition.

The part of the inner ear concerned with equilibrium consists of three small canals. These are called the semicircular canals, because each is shaped like part of a circle. Each is filled with fluid and contains nerve endings. Changing position of the head changes the pressure in the semicircular canals. This sets up nervous impulses to the brain and enables you to keep your balance.

Disturbance of the semicircular canals causes dizziness. Sea sickness, car sickness, and air sickness are due chiefly to the effect of motion upon this organ of equilibrium (see Chapter 16). In some diseases, the semicircular canals or the part of the brain with which they are connected are disturbed, and dizziness results. Quinine and certain other drugs have the same effects.

DEFECTIVE HEARING

Hearing can be disturbed by blocking the sound waves or the nervous impulses anywhere along the line from outer ear to brain.

Wax in the outer ear canal. Wax is always present in the ear canal in small quantities. As more is formed, the old is pushed to the outside.

Occasionally, wax accumulates and hardens. It may cover the eardrum and keep sound waves from reaching it. Excess wax can usually be removed by squirting warm water gently into the ear canal with a rubber bulb or an eye dropper. If this is not successful, a physician should be consulted.

Hard instruments, such as hairpins and toothpicks, should never be put into the ear. They may puncture the eardrum or they may carry infectious organisms into the ear. The old saying, "Never put anything smaller than your elbow into your ear" is worth remembering.

Inflammation of the middle ear. Most hearing defects result from infection in the middle ear. Infection may reach the middle ear through a broken eardrum. Most commonly, however, infection travels up the Eustachian tube from the nose and throat.

Swelling in the middle ear interferes with hearing by preventing the tiny middle-ear bones from moving and carrying sound waves. This is the reason it is often hard to hear during a cold.

In children, the Eustachian tubes are shorter and straighter than in adults, so infections travel up them more easily. Sometimes, an abscess forms in the ear. This may break the eardrum. A discharge, chiefly pus, from the abscess then appears in the outer ear.

Unfortunately in the past, abscessed ears or "running ears" were considered something almost every child must have. So, too, were the earaches that resulted from pressure in the middle ear. As soon as the discharge stopped or "dried up," the ear was forgotten. Many times, the infection had not been cured but lingered on in the middle ear or spread into the mastoid bone. Operations to open up the mastoid bone were fairly common.

Fortunately, the new drugs, peni-

cillin and the sulfonamides, are effective in curing ear infections. Operations to drain infections in the middle ear and mastoid are seldom necessary any more.

A broken eardrum sometimes interferes with hearing, sometimes not. A small opening at one side of the drum will allow it to move as sound waves strike it, just as it did before it was broken. A large hole in the center of the eardrum will probably make it useless.

Repeated minor infections of the middle ear thicken the membrane and make it difficult for the little middle-ear bones to move. Infections, such as scarlet fever, may do the same thing and leave a person with defective hearing for the rest of his life.

Damage to the inner ear, nerves, and brain. A few diseases, such as syphilis and meningitis, may reduce hearing by damaging the inner ear, the nerves, or the brain. So, too, may toxins, such as diphtheria toxin, and harmful drugs in the blood stream.

As persons grow older, changes take place in the inner ear that make it impossible for them to hear as well as they did when they were younger. They lose especially the ability to hear high notes.

HOW WELL DO YOU HEAR?

Hearing should be tested every few years. Audiometers, which are instruments for testing hearing, are provided in many schools (see Chapter 26). Or teachers may use a watch, a

This girl is having her hearing tested by means of an audiometer. The tester can make the sound louder or softer, higher or lower. The girl makes a sign whenever she hears a sound. (Courtesy Bell Telephone Laboratories)

tuning fork, or a whispered direction to find which students in their classes cannot hear as well as others. It is more difficult to discover the persons who do not hear well than it is to find those who do not see well.

It is important to find hearing difficulties early. In many cases, the defect can be helped by finding and caring for infections in the middle ear, nose, throat, or sinuses.

Children and young people who do not hear well are sometimes thought to be lazy or dull. In some cases, instead of being dull, they are the brightest students in a class and have managed to keep up with the class in spite of not hearing.

THE DEAF AND HARD OF HEARING

It is estimated that there are in the United States at least 3 million people with such poor hearing that they should have special education and medical care. Many of these do not know that there is anything wrong with their hearing.

Causes of deafness. Certain kinds of deafness are hereditary. Some of these appear in children. Others appear when the persons are adults.

Most deafness is due to the same conditions in the middle ear that cause minor defects in hearing. Severe damage to inner ear, nerves, and brain may also result in deafness.

Hearing aids. Deafness is usually not complete. The person can hear loud noises and can understand what people say if they speak slowly and clearly. In these cases, hearing aids can be fitted, which make sounds louder, much as the loudspeaker does in a radio.

In other cases, hearing aids make use of bone conduction; that is, the sound waves pass around the ear

This boy is almost completely deaf. The earphones help him a little to hear his teacher's voice and his own. He is learning to speak chiefly by imitating the way his teacher uses her lips, tongue, and cheeks. (Graphic House)

rather than through it. In still other cases, tiny nylon bristles take the place of the tiny bones in the middle ear and conduct sounds across the middle ear.

The fitting of hearing aids should be done by an otologist, or ear specialist. He will study a person, find where the interference with hearing is, and advise the kind of hearing aid that will be most useful. The condition of the inner ear and the amount of bone conduction that can be counted on are especially important.

Educating the deaf. The deaf and those who have severe hearing handicaps are educated through their eyes. A manual, or hand, alphabet has been developed, so that people can "talk" to a deaf person by using their hands to spell out words. Deaf people learn also to see what a person says by watching his lips. The study of lip reading needs to be started early,

which is another reason for trying to discover deaf children when they are young. It is suggested that mothers of deaf babies learn how to teach lip reading to their children.

One problem in working with deaf children is their own speech. Most people learn to speak by hearing other people speak and hearing how well they imitate, or copy, them. A deaf person cannot hear the speech of others or his own imitation. It is astonishing that people with little or no hearing ever learn to speak well enough to be understood.

Deaf persons tend to become depressed, shy, irritable, and dependent. People say things they cannot understand, then blame them or make fun of them for not understanding. The result is unhappiness and emotional disturbance.

Deaf people must, first of all, be helped to understand their own problems and the possibilities of success that life holds for them. Lip reading, hearing aids, and speech can open up a new world. There are many kinds of jobs that deaf persons can hold that will make them useful in the community. There are many hobbies they can develop that will help them to be happier and better poised.

CARING FOR THE EARS

The chief enemy of hearing is infection, especially infections that travel up the Eustachian tubes to the middle ears. These can be prevented to some extent by removing diseased tonsils and adenoids, curing sinus infections, and blowing the nose gently so that organisms are not forced up into the ears.

Loss of hearing from diphtheria can be prevented by immunizing people so that they will not develop diphtheria (see Chapter 24). Syphilis should be discovered and treated long before it reaches the stage where it affects hearing.

Most otologists think swimming and diving are not dangerous for persons with healthy ears if they are careful. Water should not be allowed to get into the Eustachian tube, because it may cause irritation of the lining of the middle ear. Jumping feet first into the water, allowing water to get into the nose while the head is under water, and blowing the nose hard after coming out of the water, all tend to force water up into the ears.

Whenever a person has even a slight cold, he should keep his head out of water in swimming and should not dive. A person with damaged eardrums or one who has had a mastoid operation should ask the advice of his physician on how to keep water from entering his ears.

SO WHAT?

Almost everything you do or learn depends upon seeing and hearing; and

Your eyes and ears are wonderful and delicate instruments; yet

Millions of persons have poor vision or hearing or are blind or deaf because of carelessness or ignorance; and

Some of these conditions begin in childhood and progress if not properly treated;

So, it is well worth while to learn how to take care of these priceless treasures and to put your mind on doing what will keep them functioning at their best.

CHECKING UP

1. How is the eye like a camera?
2. Draw a diagram of the eye. Locate on it the cornea, iris, lens, retina, eye muscles (two kinds), and optic nerve.
3. Trace light waves from an object in front of the eye to the retina. What happens in the retina? Where do you actually "see" the object?
4. What is the function of the muscles inside the eyeball? How can you rest these muscles? What is the function of the muscles outside the eyeball?
5. What is the shape of the eye in farsightedness? in nearsightedness? in astigmatism? How do glasses help a person to see better?
6. How can damage to the cornea be avoided? What are "eye banks"?
7. What is a cataract? When do most cataracts develop? What can be done about them?
8. As a person grows from babyhood to old age, what changes occur in his eyes?
9. Why do most middle-aged people need glasses for reading?
10. Why should crossed eyes be corrected as early in life as possible?
11. What is eyestrain? How can it be prevented?
12. What does a record of 20/20 on a vision test mean? 20/40? 20/80?
13. Why may a farsighted person be reported as having normal vision in a vision test?
14. What kinds of specialists examine eyes and make glasses?
15. How should a person who wears glasses care for them?
16. How does inheritance of color blindness compare with inheritance of hemophilia (Chapter 11)?
17. What are the chief causes of blindness? List ways of preventing blindness.
18. Make a list of rules for caring for the eyes. Tell why each is important.
19. Draw a diagram of the ear. Locate on it the ear canal, eardrum, ear bones, Eustachian tube, mastoid, semicircular canal, cochlea, auditory nerve, outer ear, middle ear, inner ear.
20. A boy shouts your name. Trace the sound from its start in his mouth to its reception in your brain. Where do you actually "hear" the sound?

21. Why does swallowing when you go up or down in a fast elevator make your ears feel more comfortable?
22. How is the Eustachian tube related to development of deafness? to infections of the mastoid bone?
23. What are "running" ears? Why are they dangerous?
24. Where can sound waves or nervous impulses be blocked as they go from the outer ear to the brain? How can they be blocked?
25. What is the organ of equilibrium? Where is it located? How does it function?
26. Make a list of common causes of poor hearing. How can poor hearing from these be avoided?
27. How is hearing related to development of speech?
28. What is an audiometer?
29. What is an otologist?
30. Make a list of rules for caring for the ears. Tell why each is important.
31. How can the blind and deaf be educated? What provisions should be made for educating children with defective vision and hearing?

THINGS TO DO

1. Ask a butcher for a beef eye or for several sheep, calf, or pig eyes. Look for the muscles on the outside of the eyeball. Cut a flap in the top of the eyeball so that you can look down into the eye. Find the lens, the pupil, the retina. Take out the lens. Look through it at the type in a book. Does it magnify, that is, make the type seem larger? Study a model of an eye.
2. Look through reading glasses or magnifying glasses. Find where you must hold them to read most clearly.
3. Examine a camera. Find the opening through which light enters the camera, the lens, the place where the film is placed. Take a picture with the camera out of focus, have it developed, and see how blurred it is.
4. Ask the school nurse or your teacher to test the vision of members of the class.
5. Ask a blind person to show the class one of his books and how he takes notes in Braille. Can you feel the patterns he pricks in the paper?
6. Shut your eyes and try to go from one corner of the room to another.

7. Study the model of an ear. Locate your own mastoid bones.
8. One or two students might undertake, as a special project, to find the eardrum and ear bones in the skull of a calf, lamb, or young pig.
9. Ask the school nurse or your teacher to test the hearing of members of the class.
10. Ask a person who wears a hearing aid to tell you about it.
11. Look up the manual alphabet in an encyclopedia and report on it.
12. Put your hands over your ears and see how well you can read the lips of other members of the class.

CHAPTER 21   Stimulants and Narcotics

People take on many strange habits, but few are so strange and so widespread as the use of tea, coffee, tobacco, and alcohol. The taste of these is not pleasant, at least to the beginner. The money spent on them is staggering in amount. Most people know that they are better off without them.

Yet people continue to use tea, coffee, tobacco, and alcohol. They spend money for them that could be better used for other things. What is it that makes them so attractive and gives them such a hold on so many people?

COFFEE AND TEA

We do not know how or when coffee and tea came to be used as drinks. The plants from which they are made are unrelated and grow in different parts of the world. They are bitter to the taste and contain no food nutrients.

Yet coffee and tea are used in every corner of the civilized world and form the major source of income of several countries. In the United States and the Scandinavian countries, the use of coffee averages 400 or more cups per adult per year. In England, Canada, and the Orient, tea is preferred to coffee and is used even more widely.

Caffeine. Both tea and coffee contain a drug called caffeine. Caffeine in small amounts is a mild stimulant; that is, it speeds up bodily activities. Some people take coffee in the morning to wake them up and give them a "lift" in starting the day. If they have had enough sleep, this probably does them little harm. If, however, a person is tired and needs rest, he should not take coffee. To do so is like whipping a tired horse to make him go faster. The stimulant makes a person forget that he is tired, but it does not get rid of the fatigue products in the blood or leave him any more ready for work or play (see Chapter 6).

Caffeine increases the amount of urine secreted by the kidneys. It makes the heart beat faster and increases blood pressure. In many people, it increases peristalsis and may even cause diarrhea.

Effects of tea and coffee. Many people are able to use tea or coffee for many years without showing ill effects. On the other hand, some persons are so sensitive to caffeine that 2 or 3 cups per day of tea or coffee will cause nervousness, sleeplessness, headaches, inability to think clearly, dizziness, and indigestion. These persons should avoid tea and coffee altogether.

All physicians agree that children and young people should not drink tea or coffee. One reason is that tea and coffee tend to crowd milk out of the diet and, hence, deprive growing teeth and bones of the calcium that milk provides. Another reason is that growing tissues should not be interfered with by drugs. Heart, reproductive organs, and endocrine glands, as well as bones, are all going through many changes in the early teens. Their functioning should not be disturbed by drugs.

Tea- and coffee-drinking are habits that do nobody any good but give many people pleasure without doing them much harm. The same cannot be said for the use of tobacco, alcohol, and narcotics.

TOBACCO

First experiences with tobacco are almost always unpleasant, and sometimes result in illness. Yet many persons keep trying it, because they want to be good sports or wish not to appear different from their friends and associates. In time, many learn to like it and continue its use throughout life.

Some people chew tobacco; some breathe it in as snuff; but the great majority smoke it in pipes, in cigars, or in cigarettes. Tobacco has no food value and supplies no human need. What is there about it that makes it so popular?

Nicotine. Tobacco contains a powerful poison called nicotine. When this is absorbed into the blood stream, it affects the nervous system. It takes very little pure nicotine to cause acute poisoning and death. The reason that users of tobacco do not die is that the amount of nicotine that they absorb at any one time is below the seriously toxic level.

When tobacco is used as snuff, more nicotine is absorbed than when the tobacco is smoked or chewed. Chewing results in greater absorption of nicotine than does smoking. There is more absorption from smoking a pipe than from a cigar, and more from a cigar than from a cigarette.

Probably every smoker absorbs some nicotine. The amount varies with the kind of tobacco used, since some kinds of tobacco contain less nicotine than others.

Some people breathe smoke down into their lungs. This is known as inhaling. Persons who inhale when they smoke absorb more nicotine than those who do not.

When smoke is drawn through a holder, some nicotine is caught in the holder. When a person smokes a fresh cigarette, the smoke must pass through the cigarette and loses some of its nicotine along the way. Smoke from cigarette butts, then, contains more nicotine than smoke from whole cigarettes.

Illness from tobacco. The beginning smoker often shows symptoms of nicotine poisoning. Even habitual smokers sometimes show the same effects. These symptoms include dizziness, faintness, rapid pulse, cold clammy skin, and sometimes nausea, vomiting, and diarrhea.

Over a period of time, smoking causes headaches, sleeplessness, and irritability in some people. Occasionally, excessive use of tobacco damages vision or hearing.

Effects upon the heart and circulation. The heart rate increases after smoking. In one group of young people studied, the average increase was 21 beats per minute. Sometimes, the heartbeat is irregular and there is pain in the chest.

Smoking causes the small arteries to contract, or become smaller. This contraction cuts down the flow of blood through them and results in a lowering of the temperature of the skin. This occurs in habitual, as well as in beginning, smokers. In a study of 100 persons, smoking a single cigarette caused an average drop of 5.3 degrees Fahrenheit in the temperature of the fingers and toes.

When the small arteries contract, the heart must work harder in order to force blood through them. This causes an increase in the blood pressure. Smoking a single cigarette will cause this increase in most persons.

All these facts seem to show that smoking puts additional strain on the heart and circulation. Persons with damaged hearts or high blood pressure should think carefully before increasing the work of their hearts by smoking.

Effects upon digestion. In most people, smoking reduces the appetite and dulls the senses of taste and smell. Thin, nervous persons often improve in health when they stop smoking.

A cigarette, a cigar, or a pipe after a meal helps some nervous people to relax and, thus, may aid digestion. In others, smoking causes indigestion and constipation. Many physicians report that patients with ulcers of the stomach are made worse by smoking.

Cigarette cough. Heavy smokers are often troubled with chronic coughing. This is probably due to irritation by the cigarette smoke of the membranes that line the nose, throat, and bronchial tubes.

The brown stain left by cigarette smoke is not nicotine, which is colorless, but tobacco tar. Both nicotine and this tobacco tar are irritating.

Smoking always causes more or less throat irritation, and many smokers are continually searching for brands of tobacco that are less irritating than the one they are using.

Tobacco and physical activity. High-school and college coaches forbid smoking by candidates for athletic teams. The effects of tobacco upon the heart and circulation, upon the lining of the respiratory tract, upon digestion, and upon the nervous system add up to a clear-cut argument against smoking for anyone who wishes to be at his best physically. Some athletes lose games for their teams because they sneak cigarettes when the coach is not around.

Certain people think that tobacco relieves fatigue. This may be because nicotine causes an increase of sugar in the blood, and more sugar means more fuel for the muscles. After a brief time, however, the fatigue is greater than before.

Tobacco and mental activity. Several studies of high-school and college students show that smokers make poorer marks on the average than nonsmokers. On the other hand, many brilliant students and distinguished scholars are regular smokers. It may be that smokers are more likely to waste time that they should put on their studies than are nonsmokers.

Tobacco smoking and length of life. Several years ago a scientific study of the effect of smoking upon the length of life was made by Professor Raymond Pearl, of Johns Hopkins University. He started with persons 30 years of age, some of whom were nonsmokers, some moderate smokers, and some heavy smokers. The results of Professor Pearl's study are summarized in Table 7.

To smoke or not to smoke. Many young people face the problem of whether or not to smoke before they are really ready to make an independent decision. It is a problem that calls for a long view of what one wants in life and for a willingness to look at facts, not at people's opinions or clever advertising.

Certainly, no thoughtful person would decide to smoke before all the organs of his body are fully developed. Anything that interferes with appetite, digestion, and heart action is more harmful during the period of active growth than after growth is completed.

People differ a great deal in their rates of development. The law considers a person fully responsible at 21; some people are well developed earlier than this, some later. In many states, it is against the law to sell tobacco to persons under 21.

Adolescents are able to deal with facts and reasons, though they do not always choose to do so. It is easy to "follow the leader" and to do some things that are suggested by careless

Table 7. Tobacco Smoking and Length of Life

Age	Nonsmokers	Moderate smokers	Heavy smokers
30	100,000	100,000	100,000
Still living at age			
40	91,546	90,883	81,191
50	81,160	72,436	62,699
60	66,564	61,911	46,226
70	45,919	41,431	30,393
80	21,737	19,945	14,498

people or people who wish to sell something. It is harder but more worth while to look for facts and then to decide independently what to do in terms of a good mind and a well-developed body. Smoking is one of the points on which many adolescents must take responsibility for themselves. One point they must bear in mind is that it takes far more time and effort to change a habit once formed than it does to avoid the habit in the first place.

ALCOHOL

Alcohol is a well-known drug contained in alcoholic beverages. Many people do not realize that for about three-quarters of a million persons in this country drinking has become a serious illness known as alcoholism. This makes it one of the major health problems of today, a far greater problem even than tuberculosis.

In addition to the persons suffering from alcoholism in its extreme form, that is, the alcoholics, there are some 3 million others who are classified as excessive drinkers. They drink so much that their work, their home life, and the happiness of themselves and others are interfered with.

Broken homes, poverty, accidents, and crime are the direct results of the drinking of alcohol. It is small wonder that many people are shocked at what alcohol does to individuals and to society. Every intelligent person should know something about the problem and put his mind to work at solving it.

Alcoholic beverages. Light wines and beers have been used as drinks since the earliest days of recorded history. Both are made by fermentation, which is the action of certain yeasts and bacteria on the sugars and starches in fruit and grain. Light wines contain 8 percent to 16 percent alcohol. Beer contains less alcohol (see Table 8). Beer, however, is usually drunk by the bottle, wines in smaller amounts.

Stronger beverages are made by distillation. In distillation, substances containing small amounts of alcohol are heated; the alcohol goes off as a gas and is then changed to a liquid by cooling. Brandy, whisky, and gin contain about 50 percent alcohol. Most drunkenness is the result of drinking these strong beverages, either alone or mixed with soda water or fruit juices.

Table 8. Usual Amount of Alcohol in Various Beverages

Beverage	Percentage of alcohol by volume
Distilled liquors	
Whiskies	
Gins	
Brandies	40 to 50
Cordials or liqueurs	
Mixed drinks	
Highballs	12 to 20
Cocktails	30 to 35
Fermented liquors	
Heavy wines (with alcohol added)	19 to 22
Light wines	8 to 16
Beer	4.5

Absorption of alcohol. Alcohol is absorbed directly from the stomach and small intestine into the blood. It is absorbed most rapidly when taken on an empty stomach and in the concentrated form of whisky, brandy, and gin. It is absorbed more slowly when taken along with food or in a drink that contains a good deal of water or fruit juice.

Effects of alcohol on the brain and nervous system. The alcohol in the blood reaches all the organs in the body and probably has some effects on all of them. Its greatest effect, however, is upon the brain.

Many people think that alcohol is a stimulant (see Chapter 7). This is incorrect. Alcohol dulls the nerve centers of the brain that are concerned with judgment, attention, memory, and self-control. The drinker feels overconfident, stimulated, and acts impulsively. This is particularly true when the drinker is active and is in the company of other people. If he sits quietly alone, the only effects of the alcohol he has drunk may be mental depression and sleepiness.

The amount of alcohol necessary to produce these effects in an average person begins at about ⅓ ounce. This is the amount contained in ⅔ ounce of whisky. A bottle of beer or an ordinary highball or cocktail contains more than this amount.

If the drinker takes larger amounts of alcohol, he usually becomes loud and talkative, affectionate or quarrelsome. He no longer thinks of what other people think of his conduct or what he may think of it later. He is apt soon to become dizzy and light-headed. He is slower in his actions. His muscular coordination is disturbed. This results in an unsteady or staggering gait. Walking along a line is one test of being sober.

Drinking still more alcohol leads to paralysis of one nerve center after another. Finally, unconsciousness results. On awakening, the individual usually feels uncomfortable and irritable. He is extremely thirsty, has a headache, and may suffer from nausea and vomiting. These ill effects usually last 24 hours or more.

Alcohol and physical efficiency. No responsible coach permits drinking by athletes in training. Successful athletes avoid liquor, because they know that alcohol interferes with muscular coordination.

No one would want to be operated upon by a surgeon who had been drinking or to ride in an airplane if the pilot had taken a drink before starting. The bus driver and the railroad engineer are others to whom we entrust our lives and who are not allowed to reduce their efficiency by drinking.

Alcohol and driving. The automobile has done much to make a person who drinks a problem, not only to his family and himself, but also to the whole community. Modern automobiles are made for drivers who are in full control of themselves, who can make the right decisions, and who can act quickly. A person who has taken even a small drink cannot do this. He is a menace on the highway, since he usually feels unlimited confidence in his ability to drive his car fast and skillfully.

Persons who have been drinking are involved in automobile accidents responsible for about 7500 deaths and a quarter of a million nonfatal injuries each year (see Chapter 3). *People who drink should not drive.* Others should not allow themselves to be driven by a person who has taken even a little alcohol.

Other effects of alcohol on the body. Alcohol causes the blood vessels of the skin to expand. This results in flushing and gives a false feeling of warmth. Actually, the body is losing heat and becoming colder.

The continued use of large quantities of alcohol may result in loss of appetite and indigestion. Heart, liver, and kidneys may be severely damaged. Damage to the nervous system may lead to one kind of psychosis, or insanity. The end-result in many cases is invalidism and early death.

Social and economic effects of alcohol. Accidents due to alcohol are only one of the ways in which alcohol becomes a social problem. Crimes such as stealing and murder are high among drinkers who have lost their powers of self-control.

Persons who drink to excess are unreliable as workers. They cannot be trusted to handle machinery, and they cannot be counted on to work regularly. This means usually that only the poorest jobs are open to them and that they are the first to be discharged in hard times.

Families in which most of the money is spent for alcohol cannot provide clothing, food, housing, and medical care for their members. Illness and death rates are high. In many cases, the children must be cared for through public funds.

The effects of alcohol upon mental health are even more striking than upon physical health. Alcoholics lose their standards of conduct. As parents, they cannot develop wholesome attitudes in their children. Many homes are broken, many children become delinquent, many persons suffer shame and unhappiness as the result of alcoholism in parents, brothers, or sisters, or children.

Why people drink. It is estimated that some 50 million people in this country use alcoholic beverages. This is about two-thirds of the adult population. The amount of money they spend for liquor is staggering—almost $3½ billion in 1955.

But some people spend nothing for alcohol, others much more than they can afford. Why do they do it?

There are various reasons. Some people start to drink for companionship, or because they are not strong enough to refuse when liquor is offered to them. Some drink because they like the taste of alcoholic beverages or the relaxation and relief from worry that alcohol seems to give them for a time. Others drink to overcome feelings of insecurity or inferiority or

One out of five fatal accidents involves a driver or a pedestrian who has been drinking. The driver who has taken a drink cannot put on his brakes quickly; the pedestrian cannot get out of the way. (Courtesy National Safety Council)

to forget disappointments and failures. Others mistakenly think that they are more alert and have more original ideas when they drink.

Many of these drinkers take alcoholic beverages only occasionally, in small, or moderate amounts. The danger is that occasional, moderate use may gradually lead to more frequent and less moderate drinking. It is safe to say that every drunkard began as an occasional, moderate drinker, that no drunkard ever deliberately started out to be a drunkard.

Alcohol is habit-forming. Some 3 or 4 million persons in this country are classed as heavy drinkers. They get drunk from time to time, or they consume large quantities of liquor every day. They feel that they can stop when they wish but most of them never do. Life-insurance companies tell us that, as a group, these heavy drinkers die earlier than other people.

A certain number of heavy drinkers go on to become chronic alcoholics. These are sick people—sick both mentally and physically. They may have started to drink for various reasons; they go on drinking because they are slaves of the habit.

The person who reaches this stage can rarely, if ever, go back and become a moderate drinker. A sufferer from alcoholism cannot handle liquor —liquor will always handle him. Either he gives up alcohol entirely or he sinks lower and lower until he dies.

It is impossible to tell who out of a

group of moderate drinkers will go on to become an alcoholic. This is the reason why many people believe that the only safe way for an individual to deal with alcohol is never to take the first drink. It is an important reason why it is dangerous to offer a drink to someone else or in any way to put pressure on anyone to drink.

How does an alcoholic get that way? The story of J.C. gives some details about the development of an alcoholic.

J.C. was reared in a good home with educated parents and a secure income. He was intelligent, had a pleasing personality, and made friends easily. During his early years, he was told by his parents about the evils of liquor, told that "nice people" do not drink, and told that if he wanted to be a real fellow he should not drink. In high school, J.C. was popular and made good marks. Then he saw others drinking and some of them were, in his opinion, "nice people."

After leaving high school and going to college, J.C. found that a large number of the students who were "nice people" had, on occasion, a few sociable drinks at parties. J.C. wanted to belong, to be "one of the group," so he, too, took drinks when he was offered them. To his amazement, he found that alcohol made him feel more at ease and seemed to add zest to the party. The girls looked prettier, the music sounded better, and his concern about tomorrow's examination flew out of his mind.

J.C. used liquor with reasonable control while in college and for a few years after entering business. However, by the time that he acquired a home and family, he had also acquired a regular habit of using liquor in his business associations, his social activities, and sometimes at home to pep him up after a hard day, to celebrate joyous occasions, or to help forget unpleasant ones.

After a time, J.C. became concerned about his drinking, because he was no longer able to stop after one or two drinks and would frequently end up drunk and sorry. He grew less careful in handling his business affairs; in fact, he had harsh words with his friends and his wife about his excessive drinking and its effect on his business.

Then, J.C. discovered that when he took one drink it caused a craving for more and that he could not resist this craving, even though he wanted to do so. He tried "going on the wagon" but soon felt that he must have "just one more drink" or he would die; he took the drink and ended up drunk. When he became conscious again he felt very ill, took more liquor to relieve his illness, and became as drunk as he had been on the previous day.

Carrying over a drinking spree to the following day became a part of his drinking habits, and it was not long before he lost the respect of his business associates and his friends. Yet J.C. could not realize what was happening to him, since alcohol was in control of his brain. Everybody around him could see with their sober minds what was taking place, but J.C.

could not see through the alcoholic haze that dimmed his thinking.

J.C.'s family and friends begged him to quit drinking. His physician told him that if he continued to drink he would be dead in a short time. J.C.'s reaction was that all these people were against him, that they were trying to take away his only "true friend"—alcohol. J.C., who had started drinking socially to be one of the "nice people," was now a victim of the disease of alcoholism. In the eyes of the community, he was a "drunk," a useless and stupid person who should be locked up where he could do no harm.

Prevention of alcoholism. The simple way to prevent alcoholism would be for no one to take the first drink. And that is what many people are able to do. However, our social culture puts difficulties in the way of many people who might otherwise follow this advice. The movies, the stage, novels, advertisements, and social columns in newspapers, all show the lighter side of drinking and all seem to make drinking a routine part of life.

This is a problem for the generation now in its teens to tackle seriously. Many changes in our way of living have made the use of alcohol a different and more serious problem today than it was for older generations. In the past, people did not know as much about the effects of alcohol; the automobile and other machines have only recently made drinking a very important safety problem; advertising in many different forms has become a new pressure in our lives.

As with tobacco, alcohol is more dangerous to growing tissues than to older ones. Habits formed in early years are harder to change than those made later. A grown-up emotional attitude is one of caution about things that are truly dangerous. The stronger a person is, and the more independent, the better able he is to look at all sides of the alcohol question. For many persons, the time to stop is before they begin.

OTHER HABIT-FORMING DRUGS

Certain widely used drugs, such as caffeine, nicotine, and those given to produce sleep, leave a person feeling nervous and "let down" when he cannot get them (see Chapter 7).

Far more dangerous, however, than any of these are certain drugs called "habit-forming." These drugs cause a person who uses them to crave larger and larger doses, until he comes to the point where he is taking enough to kill an ordinary person. The irresistible craving for more of these drugs is the result of changes in his body and in his personality.

The most important habit-forming drugs are alcohol, the opiates, cocaine, and marijuana. Alcohol is discussed separately in this chapter, since it is so widely used as a beverage.

Drug addicts. Certain drugs are called narcotics, because their chief effect is to relieve pain and produce sleep. They are valuable in medicine.

Physicians, however, must always use these drugs carefully, lest patients become dependent upon them.

Persons who use narcotics regularly are called drug addicts. Their craving for drugs governs their lives. They will beg, steal, and sacrifice their homes, their jobs, and their families to get money to satisfy their craving. More than 50 percent of the inmates of jails and correctional institutions in the City of New York are users or sellers of drugs. The proportion is probably about the same in other places.

A United States law makes it illegal for anyone to sell these drugs without a license and without a physician's prescription. Addicts, therefore, have to depend upon illegal channels for their drugs. An unscrupulous "dope peddler" can get from an addict $10, $20, $30, or more per day to keep him supplied with the drug he craves.

Opiates. Opium comes from a kind of poppy grown chiefly in Asia. The dried juice forms a gummy mass that is used for smoking; powdered, this becomes the drug opium. Morphine, codeine, heroin, and several other drugs are made from opium and are called opiates.

Of these, by far the most important medically is morphine. Physicians use morphine in small doses to deaden pain and produce sleep. Its dangerous habit-forming properties are never forgotten by the physician, however; he is careful not to prolong its use to the point where his patient is dependent on the drug.

Codeine is the least dangerous of the commonly used opiates, because it is least likely to cause the formation of a habit in the patient. This makes it a useful drug in the hands of physicians.

Heroin is the most dangerous habit-forming drug known. The dangers of this drug are so great that some years ago the Congress passed a law forbidding both its manufacture and sale in this country. Even physicians cannot prescribe its use.

Cocaine. Cocaine is a bitter drug obtained from the leaves of the coca tree, a native of South America. It blocks the passage of nervous impulses, so it is used as a local anesthetic.

Cocaine is one of the worst of the habit-forming drugs. Its first effects are excitement and a feeling of strength and alertness. Continued use causes nervousness, sleeplessness, and loss of physical and mental efficiency.

Marijuana. *Cannabis indica*, commonly called marijuana, or hashish, is obtained from the flowering top of Indian hemp. This plant grows wild in many parts of the world, including the United States. (Hemp is used commercially for the manufacture of twine, rope, bags, and clothing.) The drug *Cannabis* has no medicinal value. It is smoked as "reefer" cigarettes, chewed, or drunk by addicts.

The effects of marijuana are almost entirely on the central nervous system. It produces a dreamy state in which the person is only partly conscious. His ideas are disconnected and uncontrollable. He may have a feeling of well-being and excitement; or he may sink into a depression. He may commit acts of violence without being completely aware of what he is doing. Continued use of the drug damages the mind permanently.

Causes of addiction. There are several ways in which people get started in the use of narcotic drugs. Usually, the drugs are first supplied free by a peddler who expects later to make a handsome profit from a person who develops the habit.

In some communities, young people of high-school age are the target for activities of peddlers and "narcotic rings," who count on young people having many years in which to be slaves of the drugs and of the people who supply them. Federal narcotic agents tell us that it is common practice for narcotic peddlers to offer drugs to boys and girls of high-school age to "give them a lift" so they can enjoy an evening's fun. There are many instances in which one boy or girl has been given drugs and has then taught the drug habit to friends.

A study of 25 drug addicts between 17 and 21 years of age convicted in the Chicago courts during 1951 revealed that the drug habit usually started with the smoking of marijuana followed by a change to heroin after an interval varying from 1 month to 2 years.[1] The age at which the habit was started ranged from 13 to 19 years.

The following is a typical story of

this group: F.R. was 20 years of age and single. He was graduated from high school at 18 and immediately started work. He started smoking marijuana while he was a senior in high school, because his friends smoked and he wanted to be like them. After a year he "tried out" heroin with a friend, because, he said, he thought it would give him a new experience. Once he started taking the drug he was "hooked," and every thought became centered on securing money for it. To the psychiatrist who talked with him in connection with his arrest, he seemed evasive, insincere, unreliable, weak, and ineffectual.

YOUNG PEOPLE AND THE USE OF STIMULANTS AND NARCOTICS

Chapter 2 points out that young people in their teens are in process of taking over responsibility for their own actions and their own futures. Parents usually can keep babies and young children in many cases from doing harm to themselves; they can give advice and assist adolescents, but they cannot make their decisions for them. Problems of smoking, drinking, and, to some extent, using narcotics are young people's own problems. Whether they do the right thing or the wrong thing will affect their lives

[1] Harry R. Hoffman, Irene C. Sherman, Fannie Kreictsky, and Forrestine Williams. "Teen-Age Drug Addicts Arraigned in the Narcotic Court of Chicago," *Journal of the American Medical Association*, Vol. 149, p. 655, June 14, 1952.

and the lives of the children they will have in the future.

These problems are all tied up with many other aspects of life—getting the most for your money, building a good mind in a strong body, understanding the many kinds of social pressures, realizing the part automobiles and other machines play in our lives, setting standards and ideals and living up to them, developing will power, and not letting other people down. Older people and books can teach facts. It is up to the younger generation to use those facts in managing their lives.

SO WHAT?

Coffee and tea are widely used as beverages; and

Tobacco is smoked, chewed, or sniffed by millions of people; and

Alcohol, although definitely habit-forming and dangerous, is used by many persons; and

Opium, morphine, heroin, cocaine, marijuana, and similar narcotic drugs make slaves, invalids, and criminals out of thousands of boys and girls each year;

So, you as an intelligent person should

Know about these substances and their effects upon the body and upon health; and then

Decide whether or not to use any of them and, if so, under what conditions and with what limitations.

CHECKING UP

1. What is the difference between a stimulant and a narcotic?
2. Give two reasons why growing boys and girls should not drink coffee.
3. What drug do coffee and tea contain?
4. Why are high-school and college athletes not allowed to smoke?
5. Make a list of the facts favorable to smoking; the facts unfavorable to smoking.
6. Alcohol makes a person feel warm and self-confident. Explain how alcohol produces these effects.
7. What is the difference between an alcoholic and a moderate drinker? Why can an alcoholic rarely become a moderate drinker?

8. How do people become alcoholics?
9. What are the effects of alcoholism on an individual? on his family? on the community in general?
10. What conditions in our lives today make alcoholism more dangerous and difficult to deal with than it was 50 years ago?
11. Name the important "habit-forming" drugs.
12. What drug is forbidden by law to be manufactured or sold in this country? Why did the Congress pass this law?
13. What drugs are manufactured from opium?
14. What changes take place in a drug addict?
15. Why are young people of high-school age specially sought as customers by "dope" peddlers?

THINGS TO DO

1. Collect and discuss articles on nicotine, alcohol, and other drugs.
2. Look for the pressures in your community that push people into smoking or drinking. (Radio, television, newspaper and billboard advertisements, campaigns, talks, movies, and so forth.) Are there pressures in the opposite direction? (Some towns have been trying in recent years to cut down the drinking and driving at New Year's.) Ask the police department what they know of the problem and how they try to meet it.
3. Find the amount of money spent each year by the American people for tobacco and for alcohol. Compare with the amount spent for education and highways. Make graphs of these figures and display them on bulletin boards where all the students can see them.
4. Make a study of advertising of all kinds in one magazine; in two or three newspapers; in buses or streetcars; on billboards. Remember that an advertisement is aimed at getting you to buy something or to do something. How many advertisements do you find that seem to tell all the important facts? How many tell some of the facts? How many tell or suggest what is not true? How many include ideas that have nothing to do with the product being advertised? How do advertisements get your attention? Ask a social-studies teacher to discuss propaganda analysis with your class.
5. Find what are the laws in your state about selling tobacco and alcohol and other drugs to young people. What are the reasons for such laws?

CHAPTER 22   Chemical Regulators

of the Body

Earlier in this book (Chapters 5 and 18), the nervous system is called the master control system of the body. And so it is. Sometimes, you use this control deliberately, as when you watch a traffic signal and cross the street on the green light. Sometimes, control is unconscious, as when in running, nervous impulses go out to make your heart beat faster.

Another kind of unconscious control is by hormones, the secretions that are manufactured by the endocrine (ductless) glands. Hormones are internal secretions that pass directly into the blood.[1] They are sometimes called "chemical messengers." They do remind one of busy messengers carrying word from place to place of what is happening elsewhere in the body.

Hormones have a great influence on many processes of the body, such as

keeping warm, using sugar properly, growing hair on the face, storing fat, and even growing tall. The old tales of giants and dwarfs probably started as tales about people with oversupplies or undersupplies of certain hormones (see Chapter 6). Most of the "giants" and "dwarfs," "bearded ladies" and "living skeletons" in sideshows are persons whose endocrine glands do not function as those of other people do.

POSITION OF THE ENDOCRINE GLANDS

The endocrine glands are located in the head, the neck, and the trunk. Some endocrine glands have been studied carefully; a great deal is known about their hormones. Others are hard to study; only a little is known about their hormones.

Endocrine glands in the head. The pituitary gland is located in the head.

---

[1] Hormones are sometimes called internal secretions, and endocrine glands are sometimes called glands of internal secretion.

368

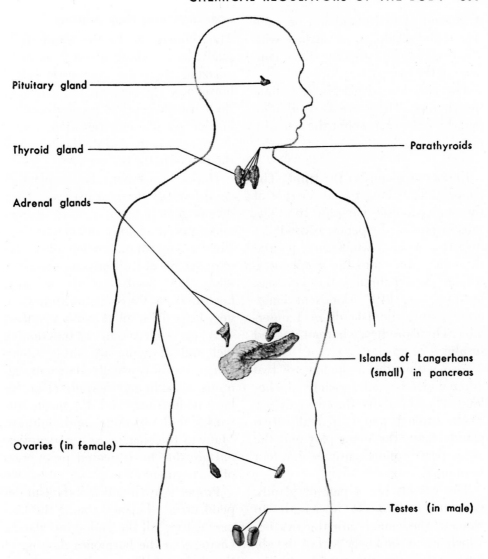

Pituitary gland

Thyroid gland

Parathyroids

Adrenal glands

Islands of Langerhans (small) in pancreas

Ovaries (in female)

Testes (in male)

Endocrine glands produce hormones, which go directly into the blood and are carried to all parts of the body. Hormones help to control and to relate the various activities of the body, so that a person acts as a single organism and not as a set of independent organs.

It is really two glands, one in front of the other. Each produces its own hormones. The whole pituitary is only about ½ inch long. In spite of its small size, its hormones control many other glands and influence many bodily processes. For this reason, the pituitary is sometimes called the master gland.

Endocrine glands in the neck. The thyroid gland is located in the neck.

A portion of this gland lies on each side of the windpipe, or trachea, with a narrow band of thyroid tissue connecting the two parts.

The parathyroid glands lie behind the thyroid. There are two or more parathyroids, each about the size of a pea.

Endocrine glands in the trunk. The pancreas lies along the lower side of the stomach (see Chapter 16). The greater part of the pancreas produces digestive juices, which are poured through a duct into the small intestine. Scattered through the pancreas, however, are little islands of endocrine tissue, the Islands of Langerhans. These produce a hormone called insulin.

Also within the abdomen are two adrenal glands, each 1 inch to 2 inches long. They lie above the two kidneys. Each adrenal gland is really two glands, since the inner part and the outer part produce entirely different hormones.

The gonads are a pair of glands, each an inch or so in length. In women, the gonads are the ovaries, which are in the lower part of the abdomen. In men, the gonads are the testes, which are in a little pouch outside the abdomen. Ovaries produce eggs, and testes produce sperms. In addition, both are endocrine glands and produce hormones that influence the development of the secondary sexual characteristics during adolescence as well as a variety of physiological and emotional processes throughout life (see Chapters 2 and 5).

HORMONES AND THEIR ACTIONS

The human body is wonderfully made, and nothing about it is more amazing than the chemicals called hormones. The very small amounts of these substances that are produced influence circulation, digestion, reproduction, growth, and the health of all the tissues in the body.

Hormones cannot take the place of good food, or sleep, or exercise. They do not fight infections. They do not make a person happy and courageous. They are useful only when all the organ systems of the body are receiving what they need and are in good health. Then, these chemical messengers help them all to work together.

When each organ is functioning well and all organs are acting in unison, a person is usually alert and vigorous, his skin and eyes are clear, his hair is lustrous, and he meets the world with courage and interest. Many of the changes as a person gets old are due to decreased production of the hormones.

Proper growth and metabolism depend upon a balance among the hormones from all the endocrine glands. Changes in the hormones may upset this balance. The results may be so slight that they are not important. Or they may have extremely serious effects on the individual's growth and health.

The hormone from the thyroid. A child who lacks thyroxin, the hormone from the thyroid, does not grow properly. His skin is thick, his hair is dry and dull, he is usually too fat, he has

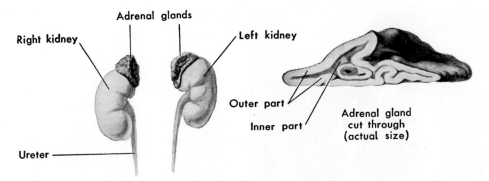

Cortisone is one of the hormones produced in the cortex, or outer part, of an adrenal gland; adrenalin is one produced in the medulla, or inner part.

trouble keeping warm, he is slow in his actions and in his thinking. Such a person is called a cretin.

Years ago, certain parts of the world contained many cretins. Nowadays, they are rare, because as soon as the condition is recognized, the patient can be treated and cured with extracts from the thyroid glands of animals.

Another important scientific discovery is that iodine is essential for the proper functioning of the thyroid gland. This iodine must come from food or water. If the body does not get enough iodine, the thyroid gland enlarges. This occurs most commonly in areas away from the sea coast. Sea water contains iodine, and sea foods contain enough iodine so that people who eat sea foods usually get the iodine they need. Where there is little iodine in food or drinking water, people usually get the needed iodine from iodized salt (see Chapter 8).

An enlargement of the thyroid is called a goiter. This may be due to insufficient iodine in food and drink or to any one of several other causes.

Thyroid hormone influences the rate of activity in all the body cells. If there is a question of whether a person is producing too much or too little thyroxin, he is given a basal metabolism test (see Chapter 8). If there is an oversupply of hormone, as occurs with some goiters, the work of the cells is speeded up. A person with too much thyroxin remains thin, no matter how much he eats, since the food is used rapidly; he feels warm even in cool weather; he is apt to be nervous and jittery and to shift quickly from one thing to another.

On the other hand, when there is too little thyroid hormone, the work of the cells is slowed. The person tends to become fat; he feels chilly; he moves slowly.

Of course, all these symptoms may be due to other causes than the thyroid. A person should not try to decide what is wrong with himself but should go to a physician who can make the needed tests.

The hormone from the parathyroids. Secretions from the parathyroids are

A giant and a midget compared with average-sized men. (Wide World)

mone is probably important in all these uses of calcium.

The hormone from the pancreas. The hormone from the pancreas is called insulin. When too little insulin is produced, the body cannot use carbohydrates properly (see Chapter 16). The result is the disease known as diabetes.

Sometimes, people say "the blood turns to sugar" in diabetes. This is not true. The blood does, however, contain more sugar than is usual, because the sugar is not taken out of the blood and used by the cells.

Because of the excessive amount of sugar in the blood, sugar appears in the urine. Finding it there is one of the tests used in finding cases of diabetes (see Chapters 17 and 26).

Today, most people with diabetes are able to work and lead successful lives. They reduce the amounts of carbohydrates and fats that they eat and they take injections of insulin to make up for what they do not produce in their own glands.

Hormones from the adrenal glands. One of the hormones from the adrenals is called adrenalin. It is sometimes known as the "fight hormone" or the "emergency hormone."

When a person is angry or afraid, more adrenalin is produced. Adrenalin makes the heart beat faster, raises the blood pressure, increases muscle tonus in the skeletal muscles, adds to the amount of sugar in the blood, and decreases the activity of the digestive tract. These changes make the body

necessary for the metabolism of calcium in the body. Beyond this fact, we know little of the function of the parathyroids.

Calcium is used in the building of all tissues, especially bones and teeth. Calcium in the blood makes it possible for the blood to clot in the case of a cut. A balance of calcium and other substances in the blood is necessary for the healthy functioning of muscles and nerves. Parathyroid hor-

ready for action of some kind, perhaps fighting, perhaps running away, perhaps doing something that the person would not have the strength to do if he were not excited. Impulses over the autonomic nervous system bring about much the same results (see Chapter 18).

Physicians use adrenalin in many ways. You may have read newspaper reports of "bringing a person back to life" by injecting adrenalin into his heart after it had stopped beating. Adrenalin can be used in cases of shock or suffocation to stimulate the circulation of the blood. Sometimes, it is given to relieve congestion in acute attacks of hay fever and asthma (see Chapters 13 and 14).

Adrenalin is produced by the inner part of the adrenal glands. Other hormones are produced by the outer part, or cortex. Some of these hormones we have known for a long time; others we are only beginning to get acquainted with. Cortisone is mentioned earlier (Chapter 6) for its usefulness in the treatment of arthritis. ACTH is produced by the pituitary gland but it acts by making the cortex of the adrenal glands secrete more cortisone.

Hormones from the ovaries and testes. Ovaries and testes grow like other organs of the body, starting before a girl or boy is born. They grow very slowly and do not start to produce eggs and sperms until puberty, around 12 or 13 in a girl, 14 or 15 in a boy. At about the same time, the endocrine tissue in the ovaries and testes starts producing hormones.

Hormones from the pituitary. So far in this discussion, it may have seemed that each gland and each hormone acts by itself in the body. This is far from the truth. Probably, all hormones interact with one another. If one gland must be chosen as the "master gland," however, it would be the pituitary.

The pituitary produces a number of hormones. One is necessary for growth. An overproduction of this hormone may cause bones to grow too long and too large (see Chapter 6). Another hormone makes smooth muscle contract.

Other pituitary hormones act upon the thyroid and, perhaps, upon the parathyroids. Recently, there has been work showing the relationship of the pituitary hormone ACTH to the activity of the adrenal glands. That is, ACTH, which means anterior corticotrophic hormone, stimulates the adrenal glands to produce cortisone. This gives great, though temporary, relief to many persons who suffer from arthritis, asthma, and certain other conditions (see Chapter 6).

Importance of knowing about hormones. Most people do not need to worry about their hormones. Keeping the body in good health usually means healthy glands.

It is important, however, to know that sometimes physicians can make a lot of difference in a person's health and happiness by giving him the right amounts of the right hormones. This is true when a person has diabetes and needs extra insulin. It is also true when a person's thyroid is not functioning properly. Most hormones for human use are obtained from the glands of animals.

Another reason why it is important to know something about hormones is that such knowledge keeps a person from expecting too much of them. Sometimes people foolishly say, "You are what your glands are." It would be better to say, "Your glands are a part of what you are."

SO WHAT?

The structures called the endocrine glands are interesting, important, and mysterious; and

Too much activity by these glands causes giantism, excessive growth of hair on the body, and some kinds of goiter; and

Too little results in diabetes, lack of development, dwarfism, and stupidity;

So, it is important that these glands function properly and in balance with one another; and

It is interesting to know something of how they affect your body and of the new discoveries scientists are making about them; and

It is necessary to realize how important hormones are and how dangerous it is to use them except under the supervision of a physician.

CHECKING UP

1. What are hormones? What kind of gland produces hormones?
2. Why is it important to know something about hormones?
3. How does the action of the nervous system compare with the action of hormones in controlling the processes of the body?
4. Where is the pituitary gland located? the thyroid? the parathyroid glands? the adrenal glands? the pancreas? the ovaries and testes?
5. What hormone is secreted by the pancreas? What is its function? Why is it used in treatment of diabetes?
6. What mineral is necessary for the proper functioning of the thyroid gland? What foods supply this mineral?
7. What is the function of the thyroid gland?

8. Where is adrenalin produced? What changes in the body does adrenalin bring about? How do these changes help us to act quickly in emergencies?
9. Give an example of hormones from one gland reacting with those from another gland.
10. Why is the pituitary gland sometimes called the "master gland" of the body?
11. Give three names for the kind of gland that produces hormones.
12. What is the function of the parathyroid glands?
13. Which hormones influence the development of secondary sexual characteristics?

THINGS TO DO

1. Ask the public-health officer whether there is iodine in your drinking water. Ask your grocer how much iodized salt he sells.
2. Read in an encyclopedia about goiter regions in the Alps and other places. Report to the class.
3. Find how many cases of diabetes occur in your community.
4. Locate the endocrine glands on anatomical models.
5. Listen to voices of children, young people, and older people. Can you guess the approximate ages of the speakers? Can you tell the difference between boys' voices and girls' voices?
6. Collect from newspapers and magazines accounts of research on hormones and report on these accounts.

CHAPTER 23 Environment and Health

Your environment includes everything around about you—air, light, sound, water, soil, other people, and animals, as well as the countless things that men have built and manufactured. Some of these make it easier for you to live and enjoy life. Some are harmful. Man has been able to develop civilization because he has been able to learn about his environment, to use some forces in the environment for his benefit, and to protect himself against forces that might harm him.

Every chapter in this book contains some discussion of how your environment influences you for better or worse. This chapter suggests ways in which the people living in your community, and you as an individual, can make your environment more healthful and more comfortable.

AIR

The factor in your environment to which you are most closely and continuously exposed is the air. From birth until death, you are completely surrounded by air and are constantly taking it into and expelling it from your lungs (see Chapter 14).

Air pressure. At sea level, air exerts a pressure of about 15 pounds on every square inch. You do not feel this, because the pressure within your body equals the air pressure outside. Air is lighter on mountains than at sea level; it is lighter at sea level than in deep mines and tunnels.

The human body adjusts to moderate changes in air pressure without difficulty. Men who work in deep mines or tunnels must make the change gradually from ordinary air pressure to the pressure of the place where they are working. They usually go through a series of rooms, each with a little greater air pressure than the one before it. Returning from work, they must spend a little time in each room becoming adjusted to less air pressure. If they go too rapidly from one pressure to another, they may become dizzy, feel severe pain, develop nosebleed, and even become unconscious. These are symptoms of the bends, or caisson disease.

With the perfection of airplanes that fly at high altitudes, low air pressures are beginning to have health importance. Pressurized cabins are airtight cabins that make it possible to keep the same air pressure, no matter how high a plane flies.

Oxygen and carbon dioxide in the air. The difficulty of breathing at very high altitudes is caused partly by the small amount of oxygen in the air. Airplanes carry tanks of oxygen to keep the air in pressurized cabins provided with enough oxygen.

Under ordinary conditions, there is always more than enough oxygen in the air for people to breathe. Most people do not know this. They think that "bad air" has too little oxygen or too much carbon dioxide in it.

As with oxygen, ordinarily the amount of carbon dioxide in the air need not be considered. Outdoor country air contains about 4 parts of carbon dioxide in 10,000 parts of air. Air in the crowded parts of cities may contain 10 to 20 parts of carbon dioxide in 10,000 parts of air. The carbon dioxide in homes and office buildings rarely exceeds 20 parts in 10,000 parts of air. To have harmful effects upon the body, it would have to be 25 times to 50 times as great as it is.

It is true that people can die from too little fresh air. It is not true that they die from lack of oxygen or from too much carbon dioxide (see Chapter 14). They die because the moisture and the heat become so great that their bodies cannot get rid of excess heat. Ventilation is chiefly important

These pictures show the effects on human beings of too little heat, the correct temperature, and too much heat.

in making it easier for the skin to regulate the temperature of the body by giving off heat to the air and by evaporation of perspiration (see Chapter 10).

Temperature. For schools and homes, a temperature of 68 degrees to 70 degrees Fahrenheit has been found comfortable for work and healthful for most people. Stoves and radiators should be placed so that the whole room is heated, not just the small area near the source of heat. In radiant heating, a popular new

These people are quite comfortable in their pressurized cabin, even though they are 20,000 feet above the ground. (Courtesy United Air Lines)

method, the heating pipes or wires are spread through the walls and floors so that warmth and comfort are provided everywhere in the room.

A few years ago people became very interested in cold fresh air, even for persons ill with pneumonia and tuberculosis. It has been found, however, that pneumonia patients treated in cold rooms are more likely not to get well than those treated in rooms at usual room temperatures.

Most of our thinking has been done with regard to heating houses and making them comfortable in winter, but we can be very uncomfortable in summer, too. Homes, schools, and public buildings can now be equipped

with cooling devices for summer use at reasonable cost.

Humidity. Moisture in the air, or humidity, is measured in terms of how much moisture the air can hold, compared with what it already has. Thus, "90 percent humidity" means that the air can take up only 10 percent more water. If you perspire when the humidity is 90 percent, the perspiration cannot evaporate as rapidly as you pour it out on your skin. Then you say that you "feel sticky." People feel very uncomfortable in hot, humid air; the heat makes them perspire, but the humidity keeps the perspiration from evaporating and cooling them.

This picture shows how smog looks in a factory area. Smog results from a combination of smoke with fog. Smog may irritate human eyes and breathing passages. (Courtesy E. I. du Pont de Nemours Co.)

On the other hand, perspiration evaporates quickly in dry air, thereby cooling the body even on a hot day. Very dry air makes the mucous membranes feel dry and irritated. Air with humidity around 50 percent, that is, air containing about half the moisture it is possible for it to hold, seems most comfortable.

To control humidity in houses, heated air is sometimes sprayed with water before being sent through heating ducts and registers. Placing pans of water on radiators or growing plants in heated rooms increases the humidity slightly but usually not enough to do much good.

Air in heated rooms is often uncom-

fortably dry. A heated room on the coldest day in winter may be as dry as the Sahara.

Air movement. A third factor in good ventilation is movement, or circulation, of the air. If the air does not move, each person warms up the layer of air close to his skin. Perspiration evaporates into this, until the person is covered with a blanket of hot, moist air, which will not allow further evaporation. If the air is moving, this warmed, moistened air is continuously being pulled away and replaced by cooler, drier air.

The movement of air should be gentle. One of the best methods of

Temperature 80°F
Humidity 20%

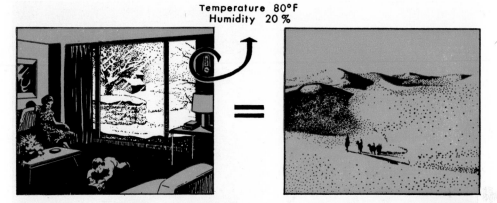

It is hard to think of a room in the middle of a cold winter as being like a desert. Both the room and the desert in this picture have a temperature of 80 degrees Fahrenheit and a humidity of 20 percent. A combination of high temperature and not enough moisture in the air makes most people very uncomfortable.

ventilating is to open windows on one side of the room at both top and bottom. Cool air comes in at the bottom, is warmed as it flows across the room, floats up along the opposite wall and across the ceiling, and goes out as warm air at the top of the window.

Air-conditioning. The conditioning of air is an attempt to provide clean air of the temperature and humidity in which people are most comfortable and can work most efficiently. Air is first filtered and washed to remove smoke, dust, and other substances from it. It is warmed or cooled as needed, has moisture added to it or taken from it, and then is circulated gently.

Many types of air-conditioning are now being offered for sale. Some are effective; others are worthless. In new buildings, air-conditioning machinery is often built in for the whole building. Units for individual rooms are less satisfactory, although some of these can improve the condition of the air considerably. For homes of moderate size, the simplest and, in general, the most satisfactory method of air-conditioning is to combine the air-conditioning with a warm-air heating system. With such a system, the air can be filtered, warmed, and moistened in the winter and filtered, cooled, and dried in the summer.

WHAT THE AIR CONTAINS

Air is a mixture of gases: nitrogen (about 78 percent), oxygen (21 percent), carbon dioxide (0.4 percent), and traces of other gases. Most air contains some moisture also. In addition, gases of many kinds are always being poured out into air—from every smokestack, from every chimney, from every automobile exhaust, from every bonfire, from every gas stove. Around some factories and in streets crowded with automobiles, these gaseous wastes are in the air in great quantities, and people and other animals breathe them in with every breath. Most of them do no harm in small amounts. Some are dangerous in large amounts. And a few are harmful even in very small amounts.

Carbon monoxide. Poisoning from carbon monoxide is discussed in Chapter 11. Carbon monoxide may be produced by incomplete burning of gas in defective or improperly adjusted appliances. Therefore, it is important to be certain that gas stoves, gas furnaces, gas water heaters, and other home appliances are in perfect condition. It is generally desirable for a gas room heater to have an outside flue.

Carbon monoxide itself has no odor, but there usually are other substances mixed with it which can be smelled. Sometimes, however, carbon monoxide is produced so slowly that people do not notice it, become drowsy from it, and drop off to sleep—a sleep that may be their last one.

Automobile engines produce some carbon monoxide in their exhaust gases. This is not important when there are only a few cars on an open road. But when many cars are crowded together or are stopped, especially in a closed space like a tunnel, the carbon monoxide and other gases from their engines are enough to cause illness and perhaps death. Ventilation of tunnels is an important problem for the engineers who build them and keep them in order. Tunnels under

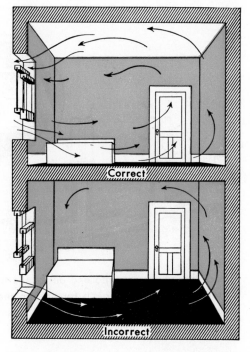

Trace the air currents in these diagrams. Which arrangement of the open windows gives the best ventilation? Can you explain why? Remember that cold air is heavier than warm air and tends to sink, while warm air rises.

rivers are especially dangerous, because the exhaust gases are heavy and tend to run down to the lowest part of the tunnel.

Everyone knows that a person should not run an automobile engine in a closed garage. Every so often, however, some foolish person tries to warm up his automobile on a cold morning with the door closed, occasionally with a fatal result.

Gases from factories. In the past, no one thought much about it when, as sometimes happened, all the plants around a factory died. Now, we know

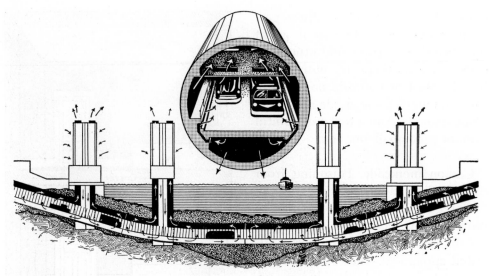

Trace the air currents into and out of the tunnel by following one set of arrows. In the inset, notice that fresh air is forced into the lower part of the tunnel, below the automobiles, and that used air containing gases from the exhaust pipes is sucked into the upper part of the tunnel.

that whatever kills the plants is probably harmful to human beings, too.

The problem of gases from factories is growing every year. For one thing, we are constantly building new factories and running them day and night. Not all gases coming out of factory smokestacks are harmful, but the more factories, the more chances that some of the waste gases are harmful.

A second problem of today is that we are using many new chemicals and are not always sure exactly what waste gases are being formed or whether they are harmful. Not long ago, a number of persons died in one factory community from gases that the owner of the factory did not know were dangerous.

Smoke and smog. In some cities, smoke is listed as the number-one community problem. Combined with fog, it makes what is called smog. Smog is like a thick, dirty blanket that lies over everything, shuts out the sunlight, makes houses gray and grimy inside and out, and may irritate eyes, noses, sinuses, and lungs. In some cities, several tons of soot fall each year on every square mile.

One person in a community cannot fight smog alone. It is a public-health problem, that is, one which all the people in a community, the public in general, must attack together.

It is possible to take the solid particles out of smoke before it is allowed to go out of the chimneys. This costs money, and sometimes the owners of factories do not want to, or cannot afford to, spend this money. Sometimes, leaders in a community are so

These sandblasters are wearing special suits and masks to protect them from the flying pellets that are used to clean the scale from the big tank. (Courtesy Standard Oil Co., N.J.)

anxious to have new factories built that they do not care whether smoke is controlled or not.

This makes the smog problem a difficult one. It is cheering to know that some places seem to have solved it. Other places can do the same if their people will work hard enough at the problem.

"Dusty trades." Some businesses are called "dusty trades" because the workers produce dust as they work. This is true for sand-blasting, stone-cutting, coal-mining, and metal-grinding and polishing.

In the past, workers in these trades always breathed in quantities of the fine particles with which they were working. Some they coughed out, but as the years went by, a solid layer would settle in their bronchi and lungs. The lungs of some old coal miners have so much fine soot in them that it seems almost impossible for them to get enough oxygen. Some kinds of dust cause definite diseases of the lungs. Others irritate the lungs and make it easier for infections to develop.

One answer to this problem is to build hoods over working places and draw away the dust with forced drafts. Wetting down the walls and floor is a help in some kinds of work. In some situations, the only answer to the problem is for the workers to wear masks.

It is the responsibility of the owners to provide the safeguards that will

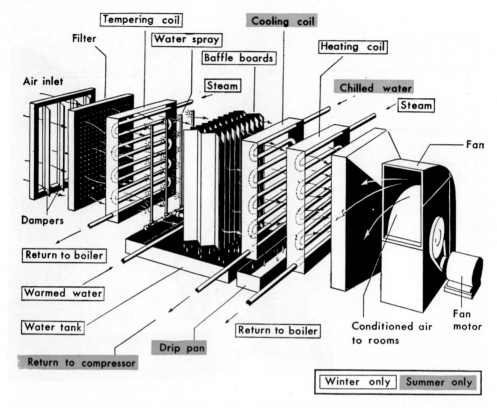

An air-conditioning unit that can be used to cool the air in summer and warm the air in winter.

take the dangers out of dusty work. It is the responsibility of each worker to use the masks or hoods or whatever safeguards are provided, even though these may be uncomfortable and awkward.

Pollens and microorganisms in the air. At certain seasons of the year, the air in both city and country contains a variety of pollens from grasses, trees, and other plants. These make people who are sensitive to them miserable with hay fever or asthma. About 5 per-cent of the population fall in this group (see Chapters 13 and 14).

Sufferers from hay fever and asthma long ago discovered that they could secure relief by traveling, during the pollinating season, to regions where the pollens to which they are sensitive do not occur. Filtering the air, as in modern air-conditioning, removes most of the pollen. Many hay-fever and asthma sufferers can be quite comfortable if they spend their working and sleeping hours in rooms supplied with filtered air.

Bacteria and viruses are always being breathed and coughed and sneezed out of people's noses and throats and lungs. Most of them are

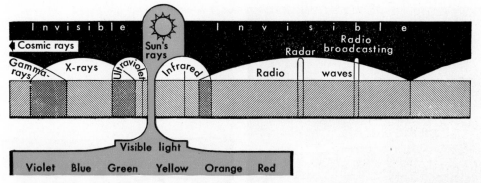

The electromagnetic spectrum. Electromagnetic rays are of different lengths. The ones we can see we call light waves. What other waves or rays in this diagram have you heard about? Are they longer or shorter than light waves? In the lower part of the diagram, the light waves are spread out to show the colors in the light spectrum. At which end of the rainbow are the longest light waves?

soon killed by sunshine or dry up and become harmless.

When the air is moist or dusty and there is no sunlight, bacteria and viruses may live in the air for hours or for days. This may occur in crowded halls or theaters where many people are breathing and coughing out moisture and microorganisms.

So many infectious diseases are spread through the air that there have been many attempts to disinfect or sterilize the air. Unfortunately, this is difficult to accomplish and as yet no methods of any real usefulness have been developed.

LIGHT

Light consists of waves of energy that travel through space at the rate of 186,000 miles per second—a little more than a million miles per minute. Through the day, most of the light about us comes from the sun, but one of the ways human beings have

changed their environment is by developing artificial lights—candles, lamps, and electric lights—that can be used at any time.

Light waves, or light rays, are of different lengths. Of the rays in sunlight, only about 13 percent are visible to the human eye. The longest rays to which the nerve endings in the human eyes are sensitive produce a sensation of red, the shortest violet, with blue, green, yellow, and orange between.

Infrared rays. About 80 percent of the rays in sunlight are longer than the visible red rays. These rays are called infrared and produce heat. Infrared rays coming in contact with the body give a feeling of warmth, stimulate the flow of blood in the skin, relieve pain, and bring relaxation.

Light colors or white reflects the infrared rays, while dark colors absorb them and allow them to pass through to the other side of the colored object.

Here is the same classroom with poor lighting and with good lighting. With poor light, it looks dreary and forbidding; with good light, it looks cheerful and as if you could work well in it. (Courtesy General Electric Co.)

This is the reason that light-colored clothing is cooler than dark-colored clothing and, hence, more comfortable to wear on days when the weather is warm.

Ultraviolet light and sunbaths. About 7 percent of the rays in sunlight are shorter than the visible violet and are called ultraviolet rays. When the sun is directly overhead, more ultraviolet rays reach the earth than at other times. Smoke, dust, and fog reduce the amount of the sun's rays that reach the earth but interfere most seriously with the ultraviolet rays. Even window glass shuts out most of the ultraviolet rays in sunlight.

Ultraviolet rays have more effect on health than do the other rays in sunlight. They act on certain oils in the skin to produce vitamin D and, thus, prevent rickets (see Chapter 8).

Too much exposure to sunlight, however, causes severe sunburn and illness. For this reason, sunbaths should be short at the beginning of the season, not more than 5 minutes twice a day. They usually may be safely lengthened 5 minutes each day for a week. Thereafter, the amount of tanning or sunburn should govern the length of sunbaths. It is not necessary to expose the entire body to ultraviolet light in order to obtain the beneficial effect from it.

Always protect your eyes when you are out in the sun. Be sure to keep babies shaded when they face the sun in their carriages outdoors or when they are in strong light inside a building.

Tanning screens out some of the ultraviolet rays and, thus, protects the body against the irritating effects of sunshine. But it also interferes with the formation of vitamin D (see Chapter 10).

Ultraviolet rays destroy bacteria. Exposing bed clothing or materials handled by sick persons to sunlight for 2 hours in the middle of the day kills most microorganisms. Ultraviolet rays are sometimes used to disinfect water in swimming pools. Attempts have been made, and with some success, to kill microorganisms that float in the air of schoolrooms, offices, and operating rooms by exposing the air of these rooms to ultraviolet rays.

Lighting rooms. A well-lighted room is bright and cheerful; a poorly lighted one is gloomy and depressing. Good lighting increases our ability to work rapidly and without discomfort. It also decreases accidents.

Light on surfaces is measured in foot candles. One foot candle is the light received from a candle of ordinary size 1 foot away. Six foot candles is the light from six candles at a distance of 1 foot. An unshaded, 75-watt gas-filled electric bulb provides 9 foot candles of light at a distance of 3 feet, 2 foot candles at a distance of 6 feet, and about ½ foot candle at a distance of 12 feet.

In rooms where no close work is being done, 1 to 3 foot candles of light may be enough. Classrooms and libraries should have at least 10 to 15 foot candles on the desks and tables. Recent research seems to show that 30 foot candles may be even better

Two pin-to-wall lamps against a light background give this student excellent lighting conditions. When walls are dark and reflect very little light, buy or make one of the popular pin-up boards and place it above your desk. The board shown here is 3 feet high and about desk width. The lamps are 30 inches apart and light the entire desk top. Each lamp contains a 6-inch plastic diffusing bowl and a 100-watt bulb. The shades are light in color and blend with the background; hence, they are not disturbing to the eye. When you use lamps like these, hang them so that the lower edge of the shade is 15 inches above the desk. (Courtesy Better Light Better Sight Bureau)

for schoolroom tasks. For drawing or sewing, 20 to 100 foot candles of light should be provided. More light must be provided in a room with dark walls and ceiling than in one with light walls and ceiling.

The shade, or reflector, over a lamp or an electric bulb makes a difference in the amount of light given off. Some very handsome shades absorb almost all the light. The stamp of approval of the Illuminating Engineering Society (I.E.S.) on a lamp means that it is properly designed for giving off light.

Strong light and glare. It is important to have enough light when you read or study, but too much light injures the eyes. Never let the sun shine directly on your book when you are reading. Never look directly at the sun or even at the sky close to it. Wear an eyeshade or a hat when you play in bright sunshine (see Chapter 20).

A baby's eyes need special attention, since a baby cannot take care of himself. Sometimes a baby is left in his carriage for hours at a time looking straight up at a bright sky. This often makes him uncomfortable and cross and may damage his eyes.

Electric lights indoors should be shaded or placed where they do not shine directly into people's eyes. In lighting a room, much of the light should be indirect; that is, the light should shine on the ceiling and be reflected back into the room. Indirect light is soft and lights up the whole room. For reading or close work, additional light can be centered over the work. For writing, light should come over the left shoulder of right-handed persons, over the right shoulder of left-handed persons, to avoid shadows.

Light seems stronger when it is seen alongside dimmer light. For example, light coming through a crack in a dark window shade seems very bright. Light from an unshaded lamp, glossy paper, polished furniture, a shiny blackboard, clean white snow, or the gleaming hood of an automobile causes eyestrain, because the eyes cannot adjust to the strong light and at the same time to the dimmer light from other objects. Any light strong enough to disturb vision is called glare. Indoors, contrasts in brightness can be avoided by care in painting and decorating, by having light-colored surfaces on desks, and by doing away with blackboards that are too dark or too shiny.

In night driving, there is often a glare from on-coming headlights. Many night accidents are caused by failure of drivers to see clearly under these conditions, either because headlights are too strong or because the driver's eyes do not adjust quickly enough. Vitamin A in the diet is related to ability to adjust to changes in amount of light (see Chapter 8).

Books and blackboards. Many studies have been made to find the size of type, the kind of paper, and the colors of ink and paper that make reading easy on the eyes. Some kinds of type, especially italics and Early English, are more difficult to read than type with simple lines and no shading. Fuzzy lines and lines that are not evenly dark in color are hard to read.

Size of type is measured in points, 72 points to an inch. For books for young children, 24-point type is recommended. For older people, 10-point type is considered good. For easy reading, there must be enough

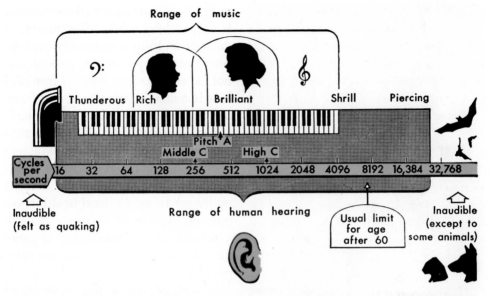

The wavelengths of low sounds are long; the wavelengths of high sounds are short. Most speech sounds are in the range 2000–4000 cycles per second.

distance between letters and between lines.

Paper should be dull surfaced so that it does not reflect light and cause glare. Paper should be thick enough so that the type does not show through. Black type on paper that is slightly off-white gives good contrast. White type on black paper might be even easier to read but is harder to keep clean.

Blackboards in older schools often reflected so much light when they were clean that teachers and children suffered from eyestrain and headaches. On the other hand, so much chalk dust often settled on the blackboards that it was hard to read anything written on them. Modern blackboards do not reflect light and are easy to keep clean. Many are dark green instead of black. Pale yellow

chalk may show up better on these than white chalk.

SOUND

When anything moves back and forth, or vibrates, it starts pressure waves through the air. The nerve endings in our ears are sensitive to certain of these waves and we "hear" them as sounds. There are longer and shorter waves, however, to which we do not respond. Some animals can hear sounds that human beings cannot; that is, they are sensitive to sound waves to which human ears do not respond.

Effects of noises. Extremely loud noises, such as the shooting of cannon, may cause such violent changes in air pressure that they break the ear-

These blocks of a soundproofing material on the ceiling will soak up loud and unpleasant noises. (Courtesy Dant and Russell Sales Co.)

work. People differ greatly as to what is a disturbing noise. What may keep one person from working may not disturb another person. A person may not be conscious of what is troubling him but may become tired and irritable when he must work with noise going on around him. This is partly a matter of habit formation: you can become accustomed to some noises and actually miss them when they are no longer there. General health is important, also: an ill person, especially a person with a headache, is much more sensitive to noises than are other people.

Music interferes less with work than talking or other noises. Music may shut out other disturbing noises and thus aid concentration. Stores, restaurants, and some industrial shops find that low music is pleasant for both customers and employees. Students sometimes find that soft music on the radio helps them to study. The difficulty comes in trying to keep the music low and in not letting attention wander from a difficult problem to the pleasant music.

drums of a person near at hand and may damage both middle and inner ears (see Chapter 20). Long-continued noises, such as those of engines, may also damage the ears, even though the eardrums are not injured. Airplane pilots sometimes show loss of hearing after flying for several months or years.

Noises that are not loud enough to do damage may still cause fatigue and interfere with a person's ability to

Sound-deadening. Schoolrooms in the past were often very noisy. Traffic noises from the street, the ringing of bells, the slamming of lockers, footsteps and talking in the halls, made a series of interruptions. Blackboards, floors, windows, and walls all reflected sound. What was true for schoolrooms was true for many shops and stores and even some libraries and homes.

In recent years, architects have paid more attention to sound-proof-

Here water is being sprayed into the air to allow oxygen and sunshine to kill the bacteria in it. This form of water purification is called aeration. (Courtesy San Francisco Water Dept.)

ing, or sound-deadening. New auditoriums, libraries, and schools are constructed in a way to keep noises at a minimum. For old buildings, there are on the market a variety of materials that can be applied to ceilings and walls to reduce the amount of sound. Soft drapes on the windows and walls will absorb sound. Rearranging furniture in a room can help to make a room less noisy.

WATER

Over the years, drinking water has been the most serious source of epidemic diseases (see Chapter 25). Today, the public water supplies of most communities in this country are so well cared for that we rarely give thought to the safety of the water we drink. But everyone should know how important it is to continue safeguarding water supplies, even though it sometimes seems expensive. Whenever a community becomes careless about its water, there follows an epidemic of typhoid or some other disease.

Sources of water supplies. For public-health purposes, water supplies may be divided into two general groups: surface and underground. Surface-water supplies are obtained from lakes and streams. Water from these sources is not considered safe for drinking unless purified. Underground-water supplies are from wells and springs. Water from these sources is usually safe, if they have not been contaminated by surface water or drainage.

Water purification. The water supplies of large communities are usually

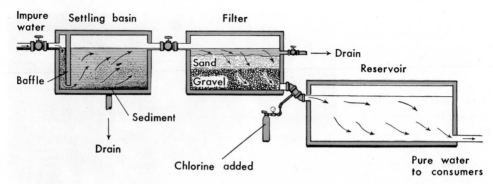

Impure water Settling basin Filter Drain Reservoir Baffle Sand Gravel Sediment Drain Chlorine added Pure water to consumers

Equipment for purifying water by filtration.

obtained from lakes and streams and must be purified. The usual method of water purification is as follows:

1) Water is taken from the source of supply and is pumped to a settling basin. Here it stands until most of the larger particles of dirt settle out. They carry some bacteria down to the bottom of the basin.

2) From the settling basin, water passes to filters. These usually consist of about 3 feet of sand and gravel, with the fine sand on the surface. As the water passes through these layers, almost all the particles of dirt, the coloring matter, and many of the bacteria are filtered out and left on the sand. At intervals, the filters themselves are cleaned.

3) As the water leaves the filters, chlorine, usually in the form of a gas, is added to the water to destroy any bacteria that may have passed through the filters. If the source of the water supply is badly contaminated, chlorine is added before, as well as after, filtration.

Safeguarding our underground-water supplies. Underground-water supplies

are obtained from wells that are dug, bored, driven, or drilled and from springs. Wells in limestone subsoil may be polluted by seepage from cesspools or privies at a distance, since limestone does not make a good filter. Wells in other kinds of subsoils are usually safe if the wells are located at least 50 feet from cesspools or privies. Common defects of underground-water supplies are these:

1) Location of the well or spring where it may be flooded by surface water during periods of high water

2) Leaks in well casings and covers and poor drainage away from the well at the surface

3) Location of the pump in a pit so close to the well or spring that surface water collects and seeps into the well or spring

4) Connection of the well pit with the sewer or drainage system

Public-health officers will provide owners of small wells and springs with directions for locating, constructing, and operating their water supplies. It may be necessary to call on a public-health engineer to assist with complicated water problems.

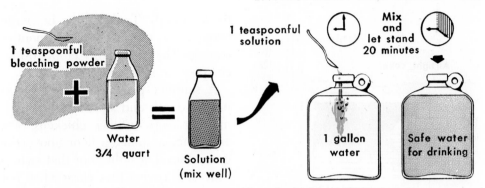

1 teaspoonful bleaching powder

+

Water
3/4 quart

=

Solution
(mix well)

1 teaspoonful solution

Mix and let stand 20 minutes

1 gallon water

Safe water for drinking

How campers may provide safe drinking water.

Safe water for campers. Campers or travelers must sometimes use water that they cannot be sure is safe for drinking. This water can be made safe by boiling it for a few minutes or by treatment with bleaching powder or chlorinated lime. Boiling drives off the dissolved air, with the result that the water has a flat taste. Shaking the water in a bottle, stirring it with an eggbeater, or exposing it to the air overnight will correct this. If water is cooled with ice, the ice should be placed around the container, not in it.

Chlorinated lime in water gives off chlorine and, hence, may be used to disinfect drinking water. A simple method of using chlorinated lime to disinfect small quantities of water is:

1) Add a level teaspoonful of bleaching powder (about 3–5 grams) to 3 measuring cups of water (1 cup is 8 ounces).

2) After the powder is thoroughly dissolved and mixed, add 1 teaspoonful of this solution to 1 gallon of water or 15 drops to 1 quart of water.

3) Mix thoroughly and allow to stand for at least 20 minutes before use.

Waste disposal. Disposing of human wastes is the most important problem in keeping water supplies safe. In towns, sewage systems collect wastes from homes and from industries and carry them to a place where they can be discharged. They are often dumped into a river, a lake, a bay, or the ocean. If the water into which the sewage is discharged is to be used for drinking or for swimming, the sewage should be treated in a way to get rid of the microorganisms it carries.

Sometimes treatment of sewage is no more than a settling process. Solid particles drop to the bottom of the settling basins and carry down with them most of the microorganisms. The liquid part then drains off into a river or some other body of water. More complete treatment of sewage consists of settling, then exposure to air to permit the oxygen and ultraviolet rays to destroy bacteria, filtration through layers of sand and gravel, and finally treatment with chlorine. The liquid that drains off after such treatment has no color or odor and is not in any way dangerous to health.

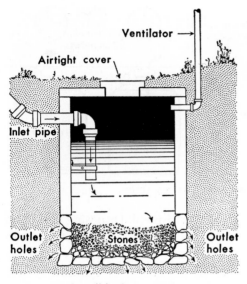

A well-built cesspool.

Where there are no sewage systems, cesspools, chemical toilets, or privies are used. A cesspool is really a small settling basin. A common type of cesspool is built something like a well. The sides are made of bricks or stones laid with spaces between them. Liquids pass out into the surrounding soil through these spaces. Solid particles sink to the bottom of the cesspool. Bacteria act on the sewage to break it into small bits that dissolve in the liquid. If cesspools are far enough away from the source of water supplies, they provide a satisfactory method of disposing of sewage.

Chemical toilets may be used inside the house if there is no sewage system connected with the house. They are also used in airplanes. A chemical toilet consists of a jar or an iron tank. Wastes are received into a strong solution of caustic soda, which disinfects the material and changes it to a liquid. Tanks may be large enough to permit several month's storage. They are finally emptied into cesspools or into scavenger wagons.

A sanitary privy requires a pit of proper depth and size, a tight building that keeps out flies, chickens, rats, and other animals, a floor above the ground level, a tight door that swings shut, seat covers that close when not in use, and screens over all openings. A privy need not be elaborate or expensive but it must meet these conditions of sanitation and decency. County and state departments of public health will provide directions for building privies to anyone who needs help.

SOIL

Plants that serve as food for human beings and other animals are built largely from the materials in soil. If the soil contains all the chemical elements necessary for health and growth, people have a good chance for health (see Chapter 5). If the soil lacks certain elements, people will be unhealthy. It has been known for many years that soils containing little iodine produce foods with inadequate supplies of this mineral element. Work is now being done on the relationship of phosphorus and other minerals in the soil in certain places to the health of people who eat foods from those soils. Farmers are trying to put into the soil fertilizers that not only allow plants to grow large but provide materials for building needed nutrients (see Chapter 8).

Soil sometimes contains organisms that produce disease. Most of these organisms reach the soil in intestinal discharges of human beings and animals (see Chapter 16). Except for organisms like tetanus, which gets into the body through wounds, and hookworms, the larvae of which enter the body through the skin, practically all the organisms from soil that cause disease reach human beings through contamination of food or drink. Protection of food is discussed in Chapter 9.

OTHER FACTORS IN THE ENVIRONMENT

Other people and animals and all the things human beings have manufactured and built are important parts of our environment. How you respond to them or how you use them will often make the difference between health and happiness, between illness and discomfort. People, for example, are part of your environment and can be a source of great help and satisfaction to you. A person with a cold can be a source of much unhappiness, unless you know how to avoid infection with the viruses he is discharging.

Animals are important parts of our environment. They are of great use as sources of food and clothing. Insects play a large part in pollinating flowers and, thus, contribute to our food supply as well as to our pleasure. Rats, flies, and mosquitoes, on the other hand, are common carriers of disease organisms (see Chapter 25).

An automobile is an example of a manufactured article in our environment that carries possibilities for both health and injury (see Chapter 3).

MAN AND HIS ENVIRONMENT

Human beings show their ability to control their environment very dramatically when they build pressurized cabins that allow people to fly to great heights, or build submarines that carry men comfortably deep into the ocean. It is even more important that they control the factors in their everyday environment, so that people in general can live healthier and more useful lives. You as an individual must do certain things for yourself, but there are other things one individual cannot do. The whole community must cooperate in such problems as providing safe water supplies and in making regulations about such matters as building houses, quarantine, and food-handling.

SO WHAT?

All your life you breathe air, you drink water, you eat food, and you are in contact with people and things in your environment; and

Some of these things contribute to good health and comfort, while others may cause disease;

So, you can live a more comfortable and more healthful life if you know how these things influence health; and then

Use this knowledge to the advantage of yourself, your family, and your community.

CHECKING UP

1. What are the three most important factors in ventilating a room?
2. Why do you feel more uncomfortable when the air is hot and moist than when it is hot and dry?
3. How is humidity measured?
4. How can many pollens be removed from the air?
5. What methods are being used in an effort to remove bacteria and viruses from the air?
6. Why should you open the garage doors before starting an automobile engine?
7. Which light rays have the greatest effect on health? in what ways?
8. What precautions should a person take when he takes sun-baths?
9. What is a foot candle? How many foot candles are desirable for reading or studying?
10. What is the advantage of indirect lighting?
11. What is glare? How can it be avoided?
12. How do noises affect health and efficiency?
13. Why are surface-water supplies considered less safe than underground-water supplies?
14. What are the steps in water purification? Of what value is each step? How can sewage be made safe?
15. How can campers make sure of a safe water supply?
16. Make a list of problems discussed in this chapter that an individual may do something about by himself. Make another list of problems that are public-health problems.

THINGS TO DO

1. If smog is a problem in your community, find out from the public-health department or the chamber of commerce what is being done about it.
2. Find what changes have happened in your community in the last 10 years that influence the contents of the air. Consider

such things as new factories, number of automobiles, new houses.

3. If you live near a tunnel used by automobiles, find how it is ventilated.

4. Keep a record of the temperature in your classroom. Read the thermometer every hour through the school day for 2 or 3 days. Do this in the fall, in the winter, and in the spring. Read the thermometer at the level of your nose. Is the temperature too high or too low?

5. Ask a science teacher to show the class how to use a wet- and dry-bulb thermometer, or hygrometer. Find the humidity in your classroom. Do this on a warm day, on a rainy day, and on a windy day. Is the humidity high or low?

6. Study the circulation of air in your classroom. Use smoke from a candle or from punk to show air currents. Try first with all the windows closed. Open windows at the top only; at the bottom; at top and bottom; on one side of the room; on two sides of the room. Which arrangement of window openings gives best circulation and no drafts? Are there "dead" spots in the room, with no air movement?

7. Give a special report on modern air-conditioning. If possible, visit a building with air-conditioning. What is the temperature? the humidity? How is the air circulated?

8. Find how your school is heated and ventilated. If the school is large, ask to see the heating and ventilating machinery. Is the humidity controlled? Is the air cleaned and recirculated? How are chalk dust and dust controlled?

9. If you know people who have asthma, find out the cause in each case, if you can, and list the causes.

10. Study the lighting in your classroom, in the school library, in your study hall. Is the area of the windows one-fourth or more of the floor area? Do the students or does the teacher face the light? From which direction does the light come for students who are writing? Is provision made for left-handed students?

11. Borrow a light meter and find how many foot candles of light are available at each desk. Make a diagram of the room showing the foot candles of light at various places. (The lighting company may give you assistance with this project.)

12. Make a diagram of the lighting in the place where you study at home. Can you improve it?

CHAPTER 24 How We Resist Disease

Boys and girls in high school have had many experiences with the diseases that we call "diseases of childhood." Almost everyone has had chicken pox. Most people have had measles: "red" measles or German measles or both. Many have had mumps and whooping cough. Some have had scarlet fever and diphtheria.

People used to think that these diseases were just part of growing up. They thought diseases just "happened" and that probably children should have them early and "get them over with."

Now, we know that it is not good for children to have these "childhood" diseases, or any other diseases. Young bodies need all their energy for growing properly. Diseases sometimes prevent tissues and organs from growing and developing as they should.

These diseases do not just "happen." They are caused by tiny organisms that are spread from one person to another. This chapter tells something about the organisms that cause disease and about some of the ways we can protect ourselves against them.

ORGANISMS THAT CAUSE DISEASE

Chapter 16 contains a brief discussion of tapeworms and hookworms and the diseases they cause in the human body. Most of the organisms that cause disease are smaller than worms, too small to be seen except under a microscope. Hence, they are called microorganisms. They are the smallest known forms of life.

It was only in the 1870's and 1880's that Louis Pasteur, a Frenchman, first proved that microorganisms cause disease. This was one of the most important discoveries ever made. It marked the beginning of our modern methods of preventing disease.

Kinds of infectious organisms. The most common kinds of infectious organisms are bacteria, fungi, protozoans, spirochetes, and viruses.

Bacteria are one-celled plants. They vary considerably in size, but all of them are much too small to be seen with the naked eye. In form, bacteria may be rod-shaped, spherical, or spiral-shaped.

Fungi are plants that are more complex than bacteria. The most common kinds of fungi are yeasts and molds. You know the yeast plants that are used to make bread rise and the molds that grow on old bread, fruit, and other foods. A few fungi cause infections.

Protozoans are larger than bacteria but are still microscopic. They belong to the animal kingdom.

Spirochetes are corkscrew-shaped microscopic organisms.

Viruses are smaller than bacteria. They are sometimes called ultramicroscopic, because they cannot be seen with the aid of an ordinary microscope. Most of them, however, can be seen and studied with a very powerful microscope called an electron microscope. Viruses are so small that they will pass through porcelain filters, which filter out bacteria. For this reason, they are sometimes called filtrable viruses.

A small electron microscope. (Courtesy Radio Corporation of America)

How microorganisms cause diseases. Microorganisms must have food. Most of the ones that cause diseases are parasites; that is, they get their food from other living things.

We think of these parasitic organisms as enemies, because they make us ill. Yet, they are merely keeping themselves alive. Unfortunately, they usually interfere so seriously with human life processes that either they or we must perish. Either we kill the parasitic organisms and get well, or they kill us.

Getting into the body. To produce disease, the microorganisms must establish themselves and multiply within the human body. The organisms that cause typhoid fever, dysentery, and cholera enter the mouth with food and drink and settle in the intestinal tract. The influenza virus and whooping-cough bacteria settle in the respiratory tract. Tetanus (lockjaw) bacteria live in deep wounds; they are usually carried in on whatever causes the wound.

Once the organisms are established in any part of the human body, they spread into surrounding tissues. Blood and lymph may carry them to all parts

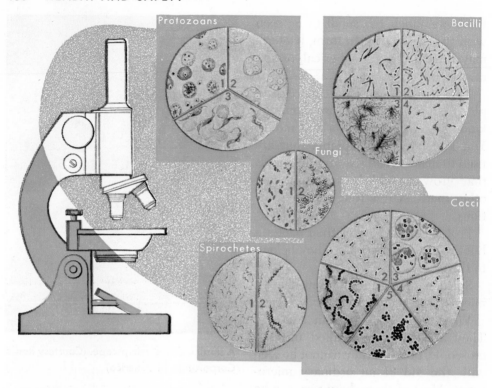

Microorganisms you can see through an ordinary microscope. Protozoans that cause (1) malaria; (2) amebic dysentery; (3) African sleeping sickness. Bacilli that cause (1) tuberculosis; (2) diphtheria; (3) typhoid fever; (4) tetanus. Fungi: (1) yeasts; (2) molds. Spirochetes that cause (1) trench mouth; (2) syphilis. Cocci: (1) streptococci; (2) pneumococci; (3) gonococci; (4) meningococci; (5) staphylococci.

of the body. For example, typhoid fever starts as an infection in the small intestine, but after a few days typhoid bacteria enter the blood stream and are carried all over the body. Most streptococcal infections start in the throat, but the streptococci (a kind of bacteria) may move up the Eustachian tube and cause infection of the middle ear, or down the respiratory tract and cause pneumonia; or they may get into the blood stream and set up infections in other parts of the body. When organisms get into the blood, the infection is said to have become blood poisoning.

While the organisms are beginning to multiply, they cause no symptoms of the disease. This period of time is called the incubation period. The incubation periods of different diseases range from a few hours for certain intestinal or eye infections to several years for various generalized diseases such as leprosy. A person who develops measles can be quite certain that he got the infection 14 days before his first symptoms occurred. The incubation period of whooping cough varies from 7 to 21 days; for scarlet

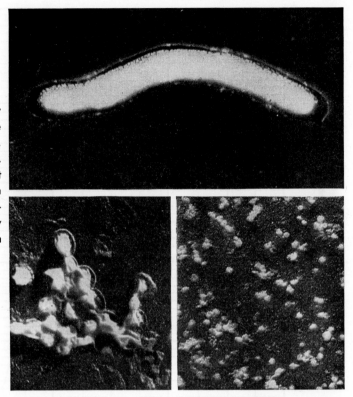

Organisms as shown by the electron microscope and magnified 9300 times. (Top) Tubercle bacillus. (Bottom left) Virus that causes lung infection in cats. (Bottom right) Influenza virus. (Courtesy American Public Health Association)

fever, from 2 to 5 days; for smallpox, from 7 to 16 days.

Toxins. Some disease organisms cause damage by producing poisons, or toxins, which injure or kill the cells. In Chapter 9, it is pointed out that botulinus organisms themselves are harmless but that they produce a deadly poison. Diphtheria and tetanus (lockjaw) organisms also produce toxins.

OUR DEFENSES AGAINST INFECTION

Fortunately for us, the human body has some good defense weapons against infection. We constantly come in contact with many kinds of disease-producing organisms, but usually we

are not made ill by them. A disease develops only when there are large numbers of organisms, too many for the body to destroy quickly, or when the organisms are so vigorous that they overcome the body's usual defenses, or when the body's defenses have become weakened for some reason.

Skin and secretions of the body. The skin is the body's first line of defense, since very few organisms can get through healthy unbroken skin or mucous membranes. Many of the secretions of the body, such as perspiration, tears, nasal secretions, saliva, and gastric juice are slightly antiseptic; that is, they tend to destroy microorganisms.

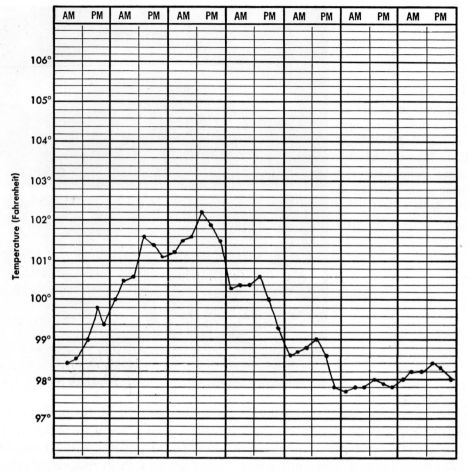

Fever chart. How high did this person's temperature go? How much did the temperature vary during any one day? At what time of day was it usually highest?

White blood cells. A second line of defense is provided by the leucocytes, or white blood cells (Chapter 11). These destroy microorganisms. A person usually has from 5000 to 9000 white blood cells in each cubic milli- meter of blood. This means 400,000 to 500,000 in each drop of blood. In some infections, this number may in- crease 3, 4, or 5 times. In others, how- ever, notably those caused by viruses and by the bacteria of typhoid fever, tuberculosis, and whooping cough, the number of white blood cells usu- ally decreases rather than increases.

Fever. A third defense of the body against infections is the development of fever. Any rise above 99 degrees Fahrenheit is considered fever. Within limits, this is helpful, not harmful, in combating infection. A low body temperature with a severe infection shows that the body is not responding to the infection as it should.

There are two reasons why fever is helpful. One is that most disease-producing organisms are less active at high temperatures than at normal body temperature. The other is that the body fights infection better when the temperature is raised slightly. High temperatures, above 105 degrees Fahrenheit, may be dangerous in that the cells of the body cannot carry on their essential activities well at these temperatures. This is true also when the temperature stays high for several days, even though it does not reach 105 degrees. Temperatures above 110 degrees Fahrenheit are usually fatal.

Antibodies. The most effective means of combating infection is the body's production of chemical substances that counteract the disease organisms. These substances are called antibodies. They circulate in the blood stream and act against the organisms causing the infection. Antibodies are formed against a specific disease and act only against that disease. That is, antibodies for typhoid destroy typhoid bacteria but do not destroy the virus that causes measles. Antibodies for smallpox destroy the virus of smallpox but do not destroy the bacteria that are the cause of whooping cough.

In diphtheria and tetanus, the antibodies destroy the poison, or toxin, produced by the organisms. Such antibodies are called antitoxins.

When a person has enough anti-

bodies to fight off an infection, he is said to be immune to that disease or to have an immunity against it.

IMMUNIZATION

Everyone knows that, after a person has had a disease like chicken pox or scarlet fever, he will probably not have that same disease again. From studying the development of immunity, scientists have learned how to produce immunities for certain diseases without the person ever having had the infection.

Most persons have been given "shots" against such diseases as smallpox and diphtheria. A better term than "shots" is injections that result in immunization. Their purpose is to protect, or immunize, people against smallpox and diphtheria.

Active immunity. When a person makes his own antibodies, he is said to have an active immunity to that disease. This may result from an attack of the disease. Sometimes, a person produces antibodies and, thus, builds an active immunity through coming in contact with small numbers of disease organisms again and again, never enough at any one time to give him the disease.

The body can also be stimulated to produce antibodies against certain diseases by the injection of dead or weakened organisms or small amounts of their toxins. This results in an active immunity without the dangers involved in an attack of the disease. This kind of immunization is called

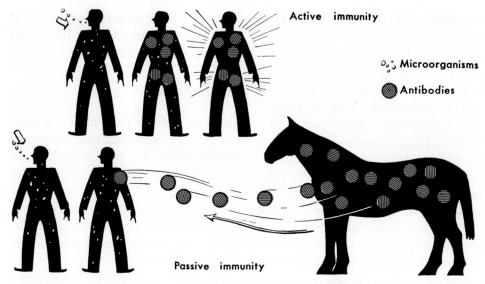

Active immunity: (1) Microorganisms only. (2) Person receives microorganisms or vaccine. (3) Person makes own antibodies, which destroy microorganisms. Passive immunity: (1) Microorganisms only. (2) Person does not make his own antibodies but is given them from some other person or animal.

vaccination. The material injected is called a vaccine. Vaccines are used to protect people against smallpox, diphtheria, typhoid, tetanus, whooping cough, and certain other diseases.

Passive immunity. Another form of immunization is the injection of antibodies obtained from the blood of an immune person or an immunized animal. The immunity that results is called passive immunity, because the person immunized does not produce his own antibodies. He receives them from some other person or animal that has actively produced them.

How long does immunity last? The immunity that follows an attack of smallpox, measles, typhoid fever, and

a few other diseases is usually lifelong, though occasionally individuals may have even these diseases more than once. Immunity against influenza, the common cold, and various streptococcal infections is of short duration. Hence, these are the diseases people have over and over again.

Active immunity produced by vaccination provides protection against possible exposure to disease sometime in the future. The duration of such immunity varies from less than a year in the case of influenza to a considerable number of years for tetanus and smallpox.

Passive immunization provides immediate protection against a disease to which the person has been exposed. The protection that it provides is pres-

People waiting to be vaccinated against smallpox in New York during the 1947 emergency. (Courtesy Department of Health, State of New York)

ent immediately but lasts only a few months. An example of this is the injection of diphtheria antitoxin to protect a child who has been exposed to diphtheria. Passive immunization is used, too, to aid a person in recovering from a disease. Diphtheria antitoxin is given to a person ill with diphtheria to increase the immunity he is building for himself.

THE CONQUEST OF SMALLPOX

The cause of smallpox is a virus. When a person has smallpox, the virus is present in his nose and throat and in the pus from little sores, called pustules, on his skin. The virus may reach a well person through contact with material from these pustules or on droplets breathed out by the sick person.

Many years ago, smallpox was considered a children's disease, just as chicken pox, whooping cough, and measles are considered children's dis-

eases today. Hardly anyone reached adult life without having had it.

Before the days of vaccination, smallpox was a very dangerous disease. Of every 100 people who got smallpox, 20 or 30 died. It has been estimated that 60 million people in Europe died of smallpox during the eighteenth century. The disease was brought to this country soon after Columbus discovered America. It is believed that half of the American Indians died of it within a few years.

Jenner's work. In England in the eighteenth century, it had been noticed that many persons who worked with cows got a disease called cowpox and were then immune to smallpox. An English physician named Jenner tested this belief in 1798. He first vaccinated a boy with cowpox and then tried to infect him with human smallpox. No disease resulted.

Cowpox is probably closely related to smallpox. The virus causing cowpox produces a mild infection in human beings, which causes the body to build up antibodies. These antibodies protect against smallpox as well as against cowpox.

Vaccination today. Smallpox vaccine is obtained from healthy calves that have been infected with cowpox. A very small amount of vaccine is introduced into the skin, usually of the arm of the person to be vaccinated. In a few days, the skin becomes red and swollen, and a single pustule develops. This should be kept dry. It should not be touched, because of the danger of infection. Usually, no bandage is necessary.

Everyone should be vaccinated every 5 or 10 years or whenever he has been exposed to smallpox. If a person follows this program, each vaccination will cause little inconvenience but will maintain his immunity to smallpox. It is a good plan to give a child his first vaccination before he is 1 year old, and the second at the time he enters school.

There is no question but that vaccination prevents smallpox. In many countries of the world and in certain states of this country, all school children must be vaccinated. In such countries and states, smallpox is practically unknown.

The greatest vaccination campaign ever undertaken was conducted in New York in the winter of 1947. More than 5 million persons were vaccinated within 2 weeks after the mayor of the city urged everyone to be vaccinated. The reason for the appeal

was the occurrence of several cases of a very severe type of smallpox. This campaign limited the outbreak to 12 cases and 2 deaths. This is a remarkable accomplishment. In 1901, when the city had less than half its present population, 1859 cases and 410 deaths occurred before a similar smallpox epidemic was brought under control.

Some people believe that vaccination is dangerous. Most stories of bad aftereffects go back to early days when not so much was known about vaccinations and they were not as carefully done as they are today. Millions of vaccinations were done in the Army and Navy during World War II with not a single record of a serious result. Certainly, the risk is small compared with the protection that vaccination gives.

Epidemics. Some smallpox infections are mild; some are severe. Epidemics of smallpox occur when the citizens of a community have become careless about vaccination. When most of the cases are mild, people neglect being vaccinated. Then, if a severe form of the disease appears, they are not protected.

This happened in the winter of 1924–1925. A severe type of smallpox was brought into this country and several epidemics occurred. In Minneapolis alone during December and January, there were about 1000 cases of smallpox with 300 deaths. The 1947 epidemic in New York might have been even worse, except for the prompt vaccination of many millions of citizens.

DIPHTHERIA

Not many years ago, diphtheria was one of the most serious diseases of childhood. Epidemics were frequent and from 25 percent to 40 percent of those infected died. Now, some communities have almost stamped out the disease by immunizing all babies.

The cause of diphtheria is a bacterium, which usually multiplies in the throat, causing a severe sore throat. A toxin is produced and spreads through the body by way of the blood stream. This toxin acts chiefly upon the muscles of the heart, causing heart failure, or upon the nervous system, causing paralysis.

How diphtheria spreads. Diphtheria bacteria are carried in discharges from the nose and throat of persons sick with the disease. Sometimes, organisms are spread in nose and throat discharges of people who are well themselves but carry the diphtheria bacteria in their throats. Such persons are diphtheria carriers (see Chapter 25).

Moisture containing the organisms may reach a well person on handkerchiefs, cups, glasses, forks, and spoons. Boiling water or exposure to sunshine will kill the organisms. Occasionally, they get into milk, where they may live for days. Pasteurization will kill them. Careful handling of milk and milk containers will prevent bacteria from sick persons or carriers from getting into the milk.

Conquering diphtheria. Since 1892, we have known about passive immunization with diphtheria antitoxin. This is useful when a person has the disease or has been exposed to it. By the use of antitoxin, the death rate from diphtheria was reduced from between 25 and 50 deaths to 6 or 7 deaths in every 100 cases.

Today, diphtheria toxoid is used for immunization. Toxoid is made from the toxin of diphtheria but is not poisonous. The injection of toxoid stimulates the body to produce its own antitoxin and, thus, to develop an active immunity. Toxoid should be given to persons who have not been exposed to diphtheria; they will be protected by it for several years.

All children should be immunized against diphtheria before they are 1 year old. After that, they should be tested for immunity before entering school, again about the time of going to junior high school, and whenever there is an epidemic.

Schick test. The test for immunity to diphtheria is the Schick test. A tiny amount of toxin is injected into the skin. If the person is immune, no change occurs in the skin. This is called a negative reaction.

If the person is not immune, the toxin causes redness and swelling around the point of injection. This is called a positive reaction. A person with a positive reaction should be given toxoid injections to immunize him.

Diphtheria is thought of as a children's disease. However, many older persons are not immune. Such persons may get the disease if they are ex-

DIPHTHERIA DEATHS IN THE CITY OF NEW YORK (1880-1950)

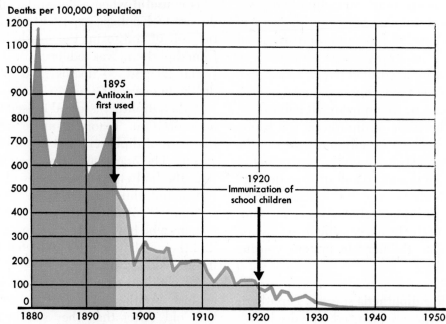

Deaths per 100,000 population

1895
Antitoxin
first used

1920
Immunization of
school children

posed to the infection. If diphtheria is present in a community, everyone should be Schick tested and, if the reaction is positive, be immunized.

Between 1000 and 2000 people, mostly children, still die of diphtheria every year in the United States. Most of these deaths are unnecessary. Most communities provide Schick tests and diphtheria immunizations at little or no cost. These are often offered in school. Fathers and mothers must see to it that their children are protected. Junior- and senior-high-school students can take some responsibility for their own immunizations.

WHOOPING COUGH

Whooping cough is the most serious of the childhood diseases. It causes many deaths among young babies.

The cause of whooping cough is the whooping-cough bacterium. The early symptoms of the disease are those of an ordinary cold. In about a week, severe coughing develops accompanied by a gasping struggle for breath. The disease gets its name from the prolonged breathing sound after the cough.

Spread of whooping cough. The whooping-cough bacteria are in the secretions of the nose and throat from the very beginning of the symptoms. Coughing throws the organisms into the air on drops of moisture. This is the usual way in which they reach other persons.

It is difficult to prevent the spread of whooping cough. One reason is that most people think of it as an ordinary cold at first. In this stage, it is

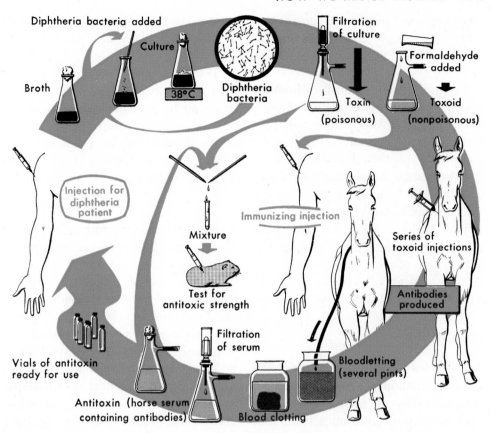

The production of diphtheria toxoid is shown along the upper arrow. First, broth is prepared. Diphtheria organisms (*bacillus diphtheriae*) are put into the broth. These organisms grow and produce toxin. The toxin is separated from the bacteria, treated so as to make it nonpoisonous, and stored at a low temperature until needed. Small amounts of the toxoid are injected into a horse. The horse develops an active immunity to diphtheria by producing antitoxin. The horse's blood is tested from time to time over a period of weeks to find how much antitoxin his been produced. Blood (several pints) is drawn from a vein in the horse's neck. To give this much blood does not injure the horse any more than it injures a human being to give a pint for the blood bank. The blood clots. The liquid, or serum, contains the antitoxin. Various amounts of serum containing antitoxin are mixed with toxin, and the mixtures are tested on guinea pigs to find how much antitoxin is in the serum. The tested serum is put in carefully labeled tubes to be distributed to physicians' offices, hospitals, clinics, and drugstores.

rarely recognized. In fact, many mild cases are never diagnosed; these spread the whooping-cough bacteria to others.

It is particularly important to protect babies from whooping cough. Safeguarding them against exposure to colds and other respiratory infections is one means of preventing whooping cough as well as various other diseases.

Immunization against whooping cough. Whooping-cough vaccine is made of dead whooping-cough bacteria. Most vaccinated children are completely protected. Those who do get the disease after vaccination usually have it in a much milder form than unvaccinated children.

Vaccination against whooping cough is recommended during the first year of life. Reinforcing, or booster, doses of vaccine are frequently given at 2 or 3 years of age.

TETANUS

Tetanus is the scientific name for the disease commonly known as lockjaw. It is caused by the tetanus bacterium. This bacterium gives off a toxin that acts upon the nervous system to cause violent muscle spasms. The jaw muscles are among the first ones affected, hence the name lockjaw.

Spread of tetanus. The belief that stepping on a rusty nail in the garden may result in tetanus has a scientific basis. It is not that the rust causes the tetanus or that the nail is important. Rusty nails, however, are likely to be dirty nails and dirt may contain tetanus organisms.

Tetanus bacteria commonly live in the intestinal tracts of horses. They leave the intestinal tract in the wastes and may be found in barnyards, fields, and gardens in which manure is used

as a fertilizer. Therefore, garden dirt is especially likely to contain tetanus organisms.

While tetanus bacteria stay alive in dirt, they do not grow and produce toxin so long as they are exposed to air. In a deep wound, such as one made by stepping on a nail, they are shut off from the air and have a chance to grow. They will not develop in clean, surface wounds.

Immunization against tetanus. We have two kinds of immunization against tetanus, just as we have two kinds against diphtheria. Antitoxin can be used to give immediate protection. This is very useful if given very soon after a wound occurs, before toxin has damaged nerve tissues.

The value of tetanus antitoxin was clearly shown in World War I. Battle wounds are often deep, and when battles are fought in fields that have been fertilized for generations there are many infections with tetanus. In October, 1914, no antitoxin was used, and 32 out of every 1000 wounded British soldiers developed tetanus. By giving antitoxin to all wounded men, the rate was reduced to two cases per 1000 wounded. In the American Army in World War I, the rate was cut to two per 10,000 wounded, or only 36 cases among 176,132 wounded men.

Between World War I and World War II, tetanus toxoid was developed. Small injections of toxoid produce an active immunity which gives protection for 5 to 10 years.

Toxoid was given to all American servicemen in World War II. As a result, only four cases of tetanus developed among the more than 10 million men in our armed forces.

It is now recommended that all children be given tetanus toxoid and a small booster dose when there is need.

MEASLES

Measles is often thought to be a mild disease, but it is a serious disease in infancy. Measles sometimes leaves defects in eyes, ears, kidneys, and other organs. The possibility of death from measles is 17 times as great for a baby as for a child of 6.

Preventing exposure to measles. The cause of measles is a virus. The virus is spread by discharges from the nose and throat. Early symptoms are like those of a cold. It is in this stage that the disease is most easily passed on to other persons. If you keep away from anyone who has symptoms of a cold, you help to prevent exposure to measles. Be sure not to go near babies if you have symptoms of a cold.

Immunization against measles. When it is known that babies have been exposed to measles, they can be given blood, or the dried immune substances in blood, from someone who has had measles. The blood contains antibodies, and this condition gives a passive immunity. Immunization is usually not given to older children and adults, since the disease is usually mild at those ages.

If injections are given within 5 days

after exposure, the disease is usually prevented. If they are given from the fifth to the eighth day, a mild form of measles may develop. Injections after the eighth day usually give little or no protection. The protection from such injections lasts only a short time but is usually long enough to safeguard a child during an epidemic. Each year that an attack of measles can be postponed means lessened danger to the child.

German measles. German measles is a different disease from measles, and it is confusing to call the two by the same name. No immunization has as yet been developed against German measles, but this is of no great importance, since German measles is usually a mild disease.

OTHER IMMUNIZATIONS

Vaccines for yellow fever, bubonic plague, cholera, and typhus fever are given to all members of the military services who are sent to parts of the world where these diseases are common. Immunization against tuberculosis is used in some places, where exposure to infection is practically certain to occur (see Chapter 25). Immunization against typhoid fever is recommended for travelers. Immunization against influenza sometimes seems to have value in times of epidemic.

Typhoid fever. The bacterium that causes typhoid fever is carried from a sick person to a well one in water,

PROGRESS IN CONTROL OF FIVE DISEASES

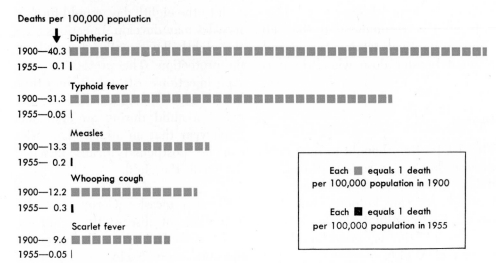

Deaths per 100,000 population

↓ Diphtheria
1900—40.3
1955— 0.1

Typhoid fever
1900—31.3
1955—0.05

Measles
1900—13.3
1955— 0.2

Whooping cough
1900—12.2
1955— 0.3

Scarlet fever
1900— 9.6
1955—0.05

Each ■ equals 1 death per 100,000 population in 1900

Each ■ equals 1 death per 100,000 population in 1955

We have made remarkable progress in the control of certain infectious diseases since the beginning of the century.

milk, or food. The disease has been almost wiped out in the United States by sanitation (see Chapter 25).

In addition, however, it is possible to use a typhoid vaccine to build up an active immunity against the disease. The vaccine consists of dead typhoid organisms. It is widely used by the Army and Navy in places where safe food and water are not always available.

Few people in ordinary life think it necessary to be immunized against typhoid fever. This is reasonable when it is known that the water, food, and milk supplies are safe. On the other hand, when a person is traveling, typhoid vaccination is cheap insurance against a serious disease.

Influenza. Influenza is caused by a virus. From this virus, a vaccine has

been prepared. Millions of men in our armed forces were given this vaccine during the last years of World War II. It seemed to protect against influenza in about three-fourths of the cases. This vaccine has not been widely used among the civilian population, but it has been used in some cities and in some colleges during epidemics. At present, vaccination against influenza is not as useful as we would wish, because epidemics of influenza may be caused by different kinds or types of influenza virus, against some of which the present vaccine does not protect.

Influenza and the milder disease called grippe are infections of the respiratory tract. The symptoms are headache, backache, fever, chills, weakness, sore throat, and cough. Most patients with influenza recover in 3 to 4 days, although weakness and cough may last for some time.

The great danger from influenza is not the disease itself but the pneumonia that so often follows it. Pneumonia occurs most frequently among persons who remain up and about while ill with influenza. The most valuable advice that can be given to patients with influenza is "go to bed when you have any fever and stay there until you are completely recovered." Other measures are helpful but should be prescribed by a physician for each individual patient.

WHAT IMMUNIZATION MEANS

If a man of a century ago could visit us today, he might think we were practicing magic when we protect people against disease by the tiny injections used in immunizations. It is hard to realize all that the development of immunization has meant. We can now be protected against some of the most dreaded diseases of the past and are hopeful that the future may provide us with effective vaccines against pneumonia, the common cold, rheumatic fever, and many other serious and important diseases.

SO WHAT?

One of the greatest achievements of medical science has been the prevention of communicable diseases; and

The control of many of these diseases has been made possible by the development of vaccinations or other immunizations; and

Many diseases, such as smallpox, diphtheria, typhoid fever, cholera, tetanus, which used to cause hundreds of thousands of deaths each year, now can be prevented; and

There are many misunderstandings concerning the values and the dangers of vaccinations;

So, every intelligent person and future parent should

Understand how immunizations and vaccinations act and what their values and their limitations are; and

Insist upon being protected against those diseases to which one may be exposed and against which a safe and reliable vaccination is available.

CHECKING UP

1. What are the most common kinds of infectious organisms? Describe each kind.

2. What is a toxin? Name three infectious organisms that produce toxins.
3. What is the incubation period of a disease? Of what value is it to know incubation periods of common diseases?
4. How do infectious organisms get inside the human body?
5. How does your body protect itself against infections?
6. What is fever? In what ways is fever helpful?
7. What is a vaccine?
8. What does it mean when we say that antibodies are specific in their action?
9. Which lasts the longer, active immunity or passive immunity? Which takes effect immediately? In active immunization, who produces the antibodies? In passive immunization, where do the antibodies come from? When babies are immunized against smallpox, diphtheria, and whooping cough, is their immunity active or passive?
10. What is toxoid? Toxoids are used in immunizing against what diseases?
11. What does the Schick test show?
12. What is a carrier? How are carriers important in spreading diseases?
13. Copy the following chart in your notebook. Fill in the information asked for. Allow room to add the names of other diseases.

Disease	What is the cause?	How is the disease spread?	How can the disease be prevented?	What are other important points about the disease?
Diphtheria				
Influenza				
Measles				
Smallpox				
Tetanus				
Typhoid fever				
Whooping cough				

14. Add poliomyelitis to the list of diseases. Look in Chapter 18 for information about poliomyelitis.

THINGS TO DO

1. Prepare some agar plates (or ask the biology teacher to pre-pare some for you). Rub your fingers over one; shake a pow-der puff over one; let a fly walk over one; put a drop of clean fresh milk in one; put a drop of milk that has stood in an open container for some time in one. Put the plates in an incubator or near a radiator for 24 to 48 hours and examine the colonies of bacteria that have grown. (Most of these are harmless, but some may be harmful. Ask the biology teacher how to sterilize the agar plates.)

2. Examine under the microscope slides showing various kinds of bacteria.

3. Ask the public-health department what information is given to parents about immunizations. How are these provided in your community? Ask the school nurse what immunizations are provided for school children.

4. Obtain statistics from your city or state health department about diseases in your city or state. Make graphs to show:

   a) Smallpox cases during the last 20 years

   b) Typhoid cases during the last 20 years

   c) Typhoid cases in each month of last year. Is there an in-crease during the summer? Can you explain such an in-crease?

   d) Diphtheria cases and diphtheria deaths among children; among older persons

   e) Tetanus in World War I and in World War II

   f) Measles among babies; among older persons

   g) Whooping cough among babies; among older persons

5. Make a list of the diseases each person in the class has been immunized against.

6. Give special reports on diphtheria in your grandparents' times; the work of Jenner; the 1947 epidemic of smallpox in New York; the influenza epidemic of 1918–1919; the work of Pas-teur.

CHAPTER 25 Controlling the Spread

of Disease Organisms

Before people knew that epidemic diseases are caused by microorganisms, the diseases were often blamed on evil spirits or witches. Some people thought epidemics were punishments for wrong-doing.

Even then, however, certain careful observers believed that the diseases were spread from person to person. In the Middle Ages, the rulers of Venice realized that epidemics of bubonic plague, or the "black death," often followed the arrival of sailors from foreign countries. They ordered that ships with cases of illness, or "pestilence," aboard be held in the harbor 40 days before being permitted to dock. Thus, we get the modern word *quarantine* from the Latin word meaning forty. The purpose of quarantine is to keep a sick person from infecting others with his organisms.

Infected or poisonous air was often believed to be a cause of disease. Firing cannons and building bonfires were supposed to purify the air. The fear some people have of night air goes back to the belief in "bad air."

The causes of disease and how our bodies are made immune to them are discussed in Chapter 24. In this chapter, you will learn how organisms pass from one person to another. For some communicable diseases, we have no practical immunization; our best methods of control consist in stopping the spread of organisms from sick persons to well ones.

SOURCES OF INFECTION

The microorganisms that cause diseases of human beings all come directly or indirectly from other human beings or other animals. In some cases, disease-producing microorganisms come from people who are actually sick from the disease. Sometimes, a person has a mild, unrecognized case of the disease and is up and about spreading the microorganisms to others. In other cases, microor-

416

ganisms come from a person who is just coming down with the disease and does not know what he has. In still other cases, a well person who has recovered from the disease continues to carry and discharge the disease-producing microorganisms from his body. People in this last group are called carriers.

Chains of infection. A chain of infection is the pathway by which an organism goes from one person to another. A chain of infection may be short or long, direct or indirect.

Some chains of infection are short. Most disease-producing organisms die quickly on leaving a person, unless they can immediately find a living place in another person. This is true for colds, influenza, and measles.

Some chains of infection are long. Tuberculosis organisms will live for weeks in dust. Typhoid organisms may live for months in water or air. Tetanus organisms may stay alive for years in dirt.

A chain of infection starts when the organisms leave the body of the person who is the source of infection. If the organisms live in the nose, throat, or lungs, coughing, spitting, sneezing, and even talking spread them far and wide through the air. If other persons breathe them in, these organisms get a new chance to grow.

Coughing or sneezing on one's hands or putting fingers in the mouth make it possible for organisms to get on the fingers. Unless a sick person washes his hands often, everything he touches spreads infection. And since

A short chain of infection.

we frequently touch objects that contain infectious organisms, our fingers are likely to carry infection to our noses and mouths. It is, therefore, important to keep fingers out of the mouth and to carefully wash your hands before eating or preparing food.

The organisms that live in the digestive tract leave the body in intestinal wastes, or feces. If these organisms get into water or milk or on food, well persons may take them into their mouths and develop the disease. Typhoid fever and cholera are examples of diseases spread in this way. Fingers that are soiled with wastes from the digestive tract often play an important part in carrying organisms to food and water or to spoons, cups, glasses, and food containers.

If the organisms live on the surface of the body, they may reach another person by direct contact. Skin diseases are often spread in this way. Kissing gives organisms that happen to be on the lips a chance to reach another person's lips.

Insects and other animals play a part in spreading disease organisms. Flies may pick up microorganisms from garbage, feces, or discharges from the mouth and carry them to

One way to prevent the breeding of mosquitoes is to fill ponds with dirt. Another way to get rid of mosquitoes is to spray swampy areas with poison dust or DDT. (Courtesy U.S. Public Health Service)

other people's food and drink. Cockroaches and rats may do the same thing, though these animals do not travel as far as do flies. Ticks, lice, and fleas carry some disease organisms. Getting rid of these pests is one way to break chains of infection and to control spread of disease.

In diseases such as malaria and yellow fever, the disease-producing organisms must live for a time in the body of certain kinds of mosquitoes. This makes a complicated chain of infection. The reasonable way of controlling these diseases is to kill as many mosquitoes as possible and to protect people from their attacks by screens.

INFECTIONS THAT ENTER THROUGH THE NOSE AND THROAT

More disease-producing microorganisms enter the body by way of the nose and throat than by any other channel. You have already studied some of the diseases that are contracted in this way: namely, rheumatic fever (Chapter 12), colds (Chapter 13), poliomyelitis (Chapter 18), meningitis (Chapter 18), smallpox (Chapter 24), diphtheria (Chapter 24), whooping cough (Chapter 24), measles (Chapter 24), German measles (Chapter 24), and influenza (Chapter 24).

Other diseases whose microorganisms enter through the nose and throat are chicken pox, mumps, scarlet fever, pneumonia, and tuberculosis. Since these diseases are spread chiefly by discharges from the nose and throat, they are difficult to control.

Chicken pox. Chicken pox is a mild disease that almost everyone gets during childhood. The cause is a virus that is spread by discharges from the nose and throat and from the sores that occur on the skin.

Occasionally, a case of chicken pox seems serious and is mistaken for smallpox. What is more dangerous is that a mild case of smallpox is sometimes thought to be chicken pox.

Mumps. Mumps is caused by a virus that usually settles in the salivary glands and causes swelling and soreness. Usually, one attack of mumps leaves an immunity against a second attack, but this is not always true. Mumps is one disease that usually is less severe and leaves fewer aftereffects in children than it leaves in adults.

Scarlet fever. The cause of scarlet fever is a round bacterium, the streptococcus. It grows on the tonsils and throat, causing sore throat, fever, and aching. A rash develops in most patients. Complications and aftereffects, such as infections of the sinuses, of the middle ear, and of the kidneys, are common.

Years ago scarlet fever was so severe that 10 to 20 persons died out of every 100 who got the disease. Now, most cases are very mild. Sometimes, such mild cases are called scarlatina. This is unfortunate, because these persons really have scarlet fever, and a person who gets infected from them may have a severe attack. Scarlet fever may be spread, not only by persons who have a rash, but also by persons who are carriers with no symptoms of the disease at all.

Scarlet-fever microorganisms some-

The large round metal shield is a guard to keep rats from crawling along the lines that tie the ship to the pier. (Courtesy U.S. Public Health Service)

times get into milk from a person who is a mild case or a carrier and who works on a dairy farm or in a creamery. In milk, scarlet-fever organisms not only live but multiply rapidly. Consequently, serious epidemics of this disease may occur from contaminated milk.

Scarlet-fever organisms produce a toxin that causes the rash. It is possible to test for immunity by injecting a little of this toxin into the skin. If redness develops at the point of injection, the person is not immune to scarlet fever. This is called the Dick test.

Vaccination against scarlet fever is possible but seldom used. This is true chiefly because scarlet fever is now

Some communicable diseases are transmitted from infected people through food prepared by them.

such a mild disease that immunization against it is not considered necessary. Penicillin and the sulfonamides are very useful in the treatment of scarlet fever and its complications.

Pneumonia. Pneumonia is an infection of the lungs that may be caused by various organisms, pneumococci, streptococci, tuberculosis bacteria, and even some viruses. It is, therefore, not a single disease. All types of pneumonia, however, are communicable; the organisms are spread in discharges from the lungs and throat. Patients with pneumonia should, therefore, be isolated to prevent the organisms that cause the disease from spreading to other persons.

Many pneumonias follow other diseases, such as measles, whooping cough, or influenza. The prevention of these pneumonias depends upon the prevention of the other diseases, or, failing that, on early and proper care of them.

Death rates from pneumonia are especially high in babies and old people and in persons weakened by fatigue, alcohol, chilling, poor nutrition, or other diseases. Vaccines have been tried at various times for the prevention of pneumonia, but as yet none of real value has been developed. In recent years, treatment with such drugs as penicillin, aureomycin, and the sulfonamides has cut the death rate from pneumonia to less than one-half of what it was before these drugs were developed.

One problem in checking pneumonia is the fact that there are many carriers. In fact, there are many more healthy persons carrying pneumonia organisms in their noses and throats than there are persons ill with the disease.

TUBERCULOSIS

Tuberculosis has been called the "Captain of the Men of Death," because in the past, it caused many more deaths in this country every year than any other disease. Today, this killer has dropped down to ninth place as a cause of death in the United States. Yet it still takes more than 15,000 lives a year and kills more persons between the ages of 15 and 45 years than any other communicable disease. In most countries of the world, it is still the leading cause of death. And even in this country, the number of cases of tuberculosis is not declining nearly as rapidly as the number of deaths from tuberculosis.

Cause of tuberculosis. People used to believe that the "white plague," as tuberculosis was called, was caused by a mysterious poison in the air. This belief did not satisfy a German physician by the name of Robert Koch. He gave up his medical practice and spent all his time and money studying tuberculosis.

With his microscope, Koch found tiny organisms in the lungs of a person who had died of tuberculosis. He injected some of these into animals. Many of the animals became sick and died. When Koch examined their lungs, he found the same kind of rod-shaped bacteria as he had found in the lungs of human beings. The first step in the war against tuberculosis was won—the enemy was known.

Today, we start with the knowledge that tuberculosis is caused by tubercle bacteria. These bacteria may infect any organ of the body, but they settle most often in the lungs. Tubercle bacteria have tough, waxy coverings. This makes it possible for the organisms to live for long periods of time outside the body.

How tuberculosis is spread. Every person who develops tuberculosis gets it from some other person or, occasionally, from an animal with the disease. Tuberculosis is spread usually in the following ways:

1) Through the sputum, or droplets of moisture, from the lungs of a person with active tuberculosis. Such

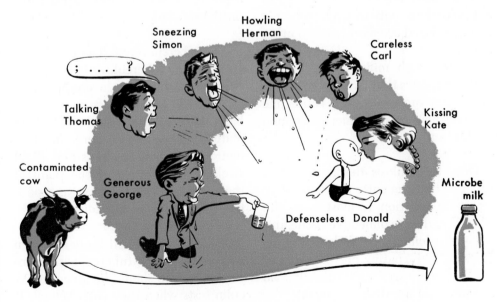

How tuberculosis organisms may be spread from one person to another.

droplets of moisture are sprayed into the air during coughing, sneezing, and talking. If a person comes in contact with this spray, he may breathe in some of the organisms carried by the droplets of moisture and, thus, catch the disease.

2) Through kissing. A tuberculous patient may spread the organisms directly by kissing.

3) Through dust. If the organisms are spit out, they may mix with dust on the floor or on the ground. They may be dried and carried by the air to a person who may breathe them into his body. A child, crawling about the floor or playing on the ground, may pick up some of the organisms on his fingers or on his toys and carry them to his mouth.

4) Through objects of common use, such as water glasses, dishes, forks and spoons, or bed linen. Any objects that have touched the lips of a tuberculous patient and have not been sterilized are dangerous to other persons.

5) Through milk. Unpasteurized milk from cows that have tuberculosis may carry organisms that cause one form of the disease, formerly common in children.

How tuberculosis develops. When tubercle bacteria enter the body, they set up an infection. In most cases, the body lays down connective tissue and walls of calcium around clumps of organisms. This coating prevents spread of the organisms and, usually, no symptoms of the disease appear.

If the tuberculous infection is not walled off, it tends to destroy surrounding tissues. In the lungs, actual cavities appear. The farther such infection goes, the harder it becomes to give successful treatment for the disease. Early diagnosis is therefore of great importance.

Unfortunately, this disease frequently does not produce symptoms until the infection is well developed. And this may take months or years. Even then, the symptoms may be nothing more than suggestions that something is wrong—a continual "all in" or "tired out" feeling, loss of weight, poor appetite, persistent hoarseness. More definite symptoms are a cough that "hangs on," spitting of blood, pains in the chest, and rises of temperature in the afternoon.

All these symptoms may be due to other causes than tuberculosis. But when they occur, a person should see a physician without delay, just to be on the safe side.

The tuberculin test. The test for infection with tuberculosis is the tuberculin test. In this test, a small amount of protein obtained from tubercle bacteria is injected into the skin. This material is known as tuberculin. If infection is present, redness and slight swelling will appear at the point of the injection. This is known as a positive tuberculin, or Mantoux, test.

In a negative test, no redness appears. This shows that there has been no infection with tuberculosis organisms. Children should be given tuberculin tests when they enter school. If the test is negative, they should be

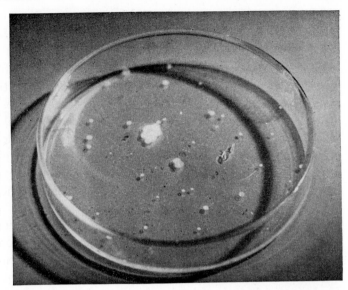

Dust, powder, or some other substance carrying bacteria was spread over agar in the plate shown here. Each bacterium grew and divided many, many times to form a colony. Each bacterium is too small to be seen with the naked eye, but the colonies of bacteria can be seen. The plate is about 4 inches across. (From the "Health Education" Series. Mc-Graw-Hill Text-Films)

tested yearly. Repeated negative tests show that the child has not yet been infected.

A positive test shows that the body has been made sensitive to the proteins of the tuberculosis organisms. Almost always this is the result of infection. A positive test does not show whether a person has an active case of tuberculosis; he may have safely walled off the organisms and still he will show a positive test.

X-ray examinations. Everyone who has a positive tuberculin test should have an x-ray examination immediately and every year thereafter. An x-ray shows shadows in the chest. To a trained physician, these shadows are significant. Progress of the disease can be read in the size and location of the shadowed spots.

Recent developments in x-ray machines make it possible to take as many as 1000 pictures per day with a single machine. Many schools, colleges, and industries are using these machines to make regular x-ray examinations of all students and employees. The United States Public Health Service and the tuberculosis associations have taken chest x-rays of almost all the inhabitants of several cities in this country.

Treatment of tuberculosis. Before Koch's discovery, a diagnosis of tuberculosis was a death sentence. Thousands of tuberculosis victims who easily could have been cured were literally murdered by being given the wrong kind of care.

In 1873 a young New York physician, Dr. Edward Livingston Trudeau, found tuberculosis organisms in his own sputum. He left his work, his friends, and his family and went off alone to a cabin in the Adirondack Mountains—to die. But young Dr. Trudeau did not die; instead he regained his strength and finally his health.

Having survived the disease himself, Dr. Trudeau wanted to help others. He bought a little red cottage and made it into a hospital. He gave other patients what he had had himself, fresh air, rest, good food, and plenty of sunshine. Today sanatoriums for the care of patients with tuberculosis are found from coast to coast. Patients by the thousands go into these sanatoriums, not to die, but to be cured.

The essentials of successful treatment are early diagnosis, nourishing food, rest, and good medical and nursing care. Climate is of little importance. Most patients who travel about looking for the right climate would do better to enter a good sanatorium near their homes.

No drugs have as yet been developed that are completely satisfactory in the treatment of tuberculosis. Scientists have long been searching for a drug that will destroy tuberculosis organisms and be harmless to man. Streptomycin is helpful for some patients. Other drugs, some recently developed, are also beneficial.

Putting infected lungs to rest by means of pneumothorax and surgical removal of infected portions of lungs (Chapter 14) are valuable methods of treatment for certain patients.

Taken together, modern drugs and surgery represent great advances in the successful treatment of patients with tuberculosis. Their greatest usefulness, however, is in connection with the other well-established methods of treatment.

Prevention of tuberculosis. A person should, of course, avoid associating with people who are known to have tuberculosis and are spreading organisms. He should not use articles, such as drinking glasses, that have been used by the sick person and so might spread disease organisms. He should avoid the possibility of getting tuberculosis from infected cattle by using only pasteurized milk from tested cows. Finally, good general health helps maintain resistance against this disease.

Vaccination against tuberculosis. A vaccine called BCG has been used in Europe for several years as a protection against tuberculosis. The vaccine consists of a very weak strain of tu-

Flies are an important link in some chains of infection.

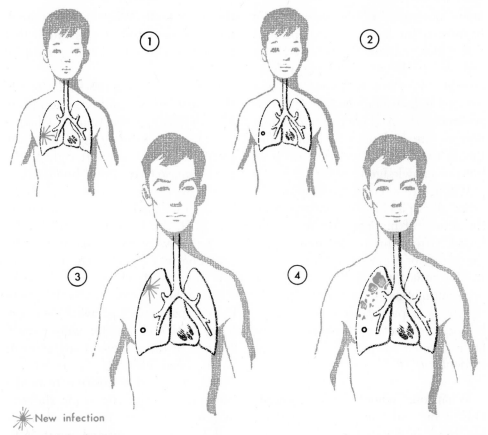

※ New infection

o Healed infection

Primary infection (1) often escapes notice and (2) heals quickly, leaving a small scar. Secondary infection (3) reinfection in later years is dangerous if the person's resistance is low and he receives many organisms. (4) Cavities form when diseased lung tissue breaks down.

berculosis organisms from cattle. These organisms, when injected into human beings, cause a mild infection. It is hoped that this mild infection will cause the body to build up a resistance against tuberculosis organisms, thus enabling it to resist severe infections.

Studies of the value of this vaccine are being made in a number of places. The general opinion among physi-cians is that it may be useful in reducing tuberculosis among people who are repeatedly exposed to the disease—for example, among children of parents who have tuberculosis and among physicians and nurses who often work with tuberculous patients.

Let's wipe out tuberculosis. We have all the scientific information necessary to wipe out tuberculosis. We know the cause of the disease. We have tests for finding which persons and which animals are infected. We can avoid danger of infection from animals. We can successfully treat persons with tuberculosis if it is discovered early. And we can find which persons are a danger to others and isolate them. What we must do is to put our knowledge to work.

When a tuberculin test is positive, especially in a child or young person, the source of his infection should be found. Often, this is someone within the family or a close friend in school. In the home, it may be grandfather or grandmother who has a chronic cough, or a parent, or a maid, or a brother, or a sister. In school, it may be a teacher, a janitor, or another student.

What one school survey showed. D.E. is big and husky-looking but he has been in a sanatorium since his freshman year in high school. His father died of tuberculosis when D.E. was a small child. D.E. should have been checked regularly, but his mother was busy making a living and did not remember the warnings that had been given her. D.E. was given a tuberculin test in the seventh grade and was found to have a positive reaction. Arrangements were made for him to be x-rayed, but he did not go for the examination. Two years later, D.E. went to his physician complaining that he was tired. X-rays showed active tuberculosis in his lungs. He entered a sanatorium and is being given treatment, with no great success. But

this is not all. When D.E.'s schoolmates were tested, it was found that he had spread infection to almost all of them.

G.H. was given a tuberculin test in the ninth grade and was found to have a positive reaction. He had a chest x-ray examination. The x-ray picture did not look quite right to the physician, so G.H. stayed home to rest and was given a number of tests. These tests finally showed definitely that G.H. did have active tuberculosis. So he went to a sanatorium. Because he was found early, treatment was successful. He is now back in school, a healed case, perfectly safe to his companions. And what is more, when G.H.'s classmates were tested, not one of them showed any signs of having been infected.

A.B. also had a positive test. She was x-rayed regularly while she was in school, because the school nurse and her mother insisted on it. A.B. thought this was silly. She was married as soon as she was graduated, moved out to a farm, and was very happy. Only a few years later, however, she had to leave her three little children and go to a sanatorium for treatment of active tuberculosis of her lungs. She had been too occupied with other things to remember that she had been told to be checked regularly.

DISEASES ACQUIRED BY CONTACT

You have seen how certain skin diseases such as boils, impetigo, scabies, ringworm, pediculosis (Chapter 10),

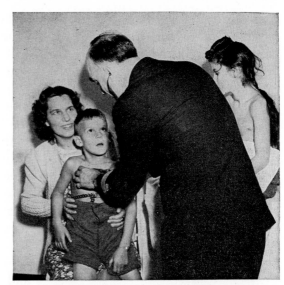

Persons from other lands may bring diseases into this country. Here an officer of the United States Public Health Service examines a foreign mother and her children before allowing them to leave the ship. (Courtesy U.S. Public Health Service)

are usually spread by direct or indirect bodily contact. Two other diseases of real importance that are spread in a similar manner are syphilis and gonorrhea. These diseases are caused by microorganisms and are spread from person to person. If not properly treated, they may pass from parent to children at or before birth, but they are never hereditary.

Syphilis. The cause of syphilis is a spiral-shaped microorganism called a spirochete. At the point that it enters the body, a small sore appears. This sore disappears in a few weeks, and the person may think that the organisms are gone, and the illness cured.

The spirochetes, however, get into the blood stream and spread all over the body. They then usually settle in one or more organs and may stay there for months or years without causing symptoms. During this time, they are destroying tissues, and by the time symptoms appear it may be too late for treatment to be successful.

The body builds antibodies against the syphilis spirochetes. The Wassermann test or one of its variations is a test for the presence of these antibodies. A positive reaction on a Wassermann test shows that there is an infection somewhere in the body.

Many states have laws requiring that people planning to be married take Wassermann tests. If these tests are positive, the applicants can be given treatment. Penicillin gives excellent results in the treatment of syphilis.

Syphilis is like tuberculosis in that we know the cause, we know how the organisms are spread, we have a good test for infections, and we know a great deal about treatment. The disease continues to be a problem because people in general do not know or do not use this information.

Gonococcus infections. The cause of gonococcus infection is a spherical bacterium, the gonococcus. In the past, gonococcus infection was a common cause of blindness, because the organisms sometimes got into babies' eyes at the time of birth. Now, most states require that a drug be put into the baby's eyes at birth. This destroys any gonococcus organisms that are present.

Gonococcus organisms may live for a long time in the body without causing symptoms. Treatment with certain of the newer drugs has been very successful when given by a competent physician.

DISEASES ACQUIRED THROUGH FOOD AND DRINK

The organisms that cause typhoid fever, dysentery, cholera, and many other intestinal diseases enter the body with food or drink. They live in the digestive tract and leave the body with the feces. They usually reach the food or drink of other people on fingers, flies, or in water. Before the days of refrigeration and pasteurization of milk, many people suffered with intestinal infections, and many babies died of intestinal infections, which they got from milk.

Typhoid fever. Typhoid fever is caused by bacteria that set up an infection in the intestinal tract and then enter the blood stream to be carried throughout the body. It is 2 to 3 weeks after these organisms are taken into the body before they have multiplied to the point that symptoms occur.

In the past, typhoid fever was an exceedingly important epidemic disease. Throughout this country in 1900, there were 300 deaths from typhoid fever for each 1 million of population. Its control has been one of the great achievements of modern medicine and public health. By 1955, the number of deaths had dropped to less than one for each 2 million of the population.

Sanitation has been our chief weapon in fighting typhoid fever. In the Army, immunization has been used, also. The results have been even more surprising than in the civilian population. During the Spanish American War, 19,265 out of every 100,000 men got typhoid fever, and 1463 of these died. During the 4 years of World War II, only three men in every 100,000 got typhoid fever and only 29 deaths occurred in the whole Army of almost 10 million men.

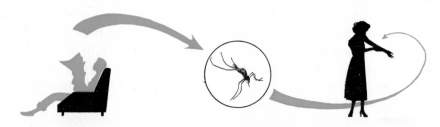

Some chains of infection depend on mosquitoes or other blood-sucking animals.

In spite of this record, there were in 1956 in the United States about 1700 cases and 50 deaths—needless deaths—from typhoid fever. Therefore, we must remember that sources of infection still exist. All sewage must be considered infectious. All rivers that pass through cities must be considered dangerous. Milk or milk products should be pasteurized or boiled, unless they have been produced under extraordinarily safe conditions. Drinking water from sources not known to be safe should be sterilized by boiling or by use of chlorine (see Chapter 23). Travelers should probably be immunized against typhoid (see Chapter 24).

Typhoid carriers. Today most outbreaks of typhoid fever are caused by typhoid carriers. These are individuals who are perfectly well but carry the organisms in their bodies and discharge them in their feces. One or 2 percent of the people who recover from typhoid fever become carriers of typhoid bacteria for years or for life.

"Typhoid Mary" is the name given to one of the most famous typhoid carriers. She worked as a cook in a New York family for several years. In 1901, she developed typhoid fever. She recovered, but a month later the laundress in the family became ill with the disease.

Mary went to work in another family. Soon, seven members of this household were ill with typhoid fever. Mary took another job. Here, within 3 weeks, four servants became ill. Mary moved to another family, and

six members developed typhoid fever.

About this time, the public-health authorities began to suspect that Mary was a carrier. However, she moved on to at least two other households before anything was done. In 5 years, "Typhoid Mary" was the known cause of 26 cases of typhoid fever.

During a period of 3 years, Mary was kept under observation in a hospital. She had not committed a crime, however, so could not be kept in isolation. She disappeared and was not found for 4 years. In 1914, she was engaged as a cook in a hospital. Twenty-five cases of typhoid occurred within a few months. Mary again disappeared. Later, she was found under an assumed name.

The story of "Typhoid Mary" shows very well what carriers should and should not do. They should keep in touch with physicians, since often the condition can be cleared up. They should not handle food or dishes. They should be unusually clean in their habits, especially with regard to hand washing.

People should keep the danger of carriers in mind in hiring cooks and patronizing restaurants. The work of health officers in supervising food handlers deserves support by all, since we cannot always protect ourselves individually.

Dysentery. There are at least two types of dysentery, but the prevention is much the same for both. The organisms are carried in food and drink that have been contaminated by feces of

Airplanes travel so fast and so far that harmful organisms from one place may easily be carried to another place. Here an airplane stewardess sprays an insecticide through the interior of an overseas plane before it lands in the United States. (Courtesy U.S. Public Health Service)

patients or carriers. Both types are more common in the tropical countries than elsewhere, but both occur in the United States.

Prevention depends chiefly on providing safe drinking water. Travelers in tropical countries should also avoid raw fruits and vegetables, unless they are sure they are safe.

Cholera. The organisms that cause cholera are spread almost entirely through drinking water. Over the centuries, cholera has counted its victims by the millions, but today it exists only in India, China, and other countries that do not have the benefits of modern sanitation. Travelers to these parts of the world are advised to be immunized against cholera.

DISEASES TRANSMITTED BY MOSQUITOES

A number of diseases are transmitted from person to person or from an animal to a person by mosquitoes. The most important of these diseases are malaria and yellow fever.

The organisms that cause malaria and yellow fever are quite different but have one thing in common—they must live for part of their lives in mosquitoes. For human beings, this means that the chain of infection in these diseases is from sick person to mosquito to well person. Destroying mosquitoes is the easiest way to break this chain.

Malaria. In human beings, the tiny organisms that cause malaria live inside the red blood cells. A person with malaria usually has a severe chill every day or two followed by a high fever. During this time, many blood cells are destroyed. Malaria is rarely fatal, but persons with the disease are half-sick all the time.

Malaria is one of the oldest diseases known. The Romans noticed that it occurred in swamps and lowlands. They also noticed that people who were outdoors at night were most likely to develop the disease. Therefore, they gave it the name malaria, meaning bad air. Now, we know that the mosquito that carries malaria flies at night. People get the disease because they are bitten by these mosquitoes, not because they breathe damp night air.

Malaria is carried only by the *Anopheles* mosquito. It lives chiefly in tropical climates, but there are many places in the United States where *Anopheles* mosquitoes occur. As a result, malaria is, or could become, common in those regions. The disease lasts indefinitely in some people.

Preventing malaria depends upon (1) getting rid of places where mosquitoes may breed, by draining swamps and not allowing stagnant water to collect in barrels and troughs; (2) destroying mosquito larvae with oil, insecticides, or fish; (3) making blood examinations of persons living in malarial districts to find which ones are infected; (4) screening houses and in every way possible keeping mosquitoes away from people at night; (5) giving quinine or atabrine to persons with malaria and others who may be bitten by *Anopheles* mosquitoes.

Yellow fever. The story of the conquest of yellow fever is a dramatic one. Now, the disease is of importance only in a few tropical regions.

Yellow fever was first known as Yellowjack. It drove white men out of the tropics. For many years, yellow fever made it impossible to dig a canal across the Isthmus of Panama. From time to time, it invaded the United States, causing epidemics and great loss of life.

Then Dr. Walter Reed and several Army men went to Cuba to study the disease. A few people thought it might be carried by mosquitoes, but this had not been proved. In Cuba, several of the men wore the clothing and slept in beds that had been used by people who had died of yellow fever. The men were carefully screened from mosquitoes. Not a single one of them became ill.

The other men lived in a clean sanitary room and had no contact with any yellow-fever patients or any of their belongings. They did, however, allow themselves to be bitten by mosquitoes that had bitten yellow-fever patients. Six of these seven men developed yellow fever. This experiment showed definitely that mosquitoes carry yellow fever. These are not the same kind of mosquitoes as those that carry malaria.

During World War II, men going into the tropics were immunized against yellow fever. In most communities, immunization is not necessary. Destroying the places where mosquitoes breed and screening houses will control the disease.

DISEASES SPREAD BY OTHER INSECTS AND LARGER ANIMALS

There are many diseases that human beings get from animals, but only a few of the most important can be discussed here.

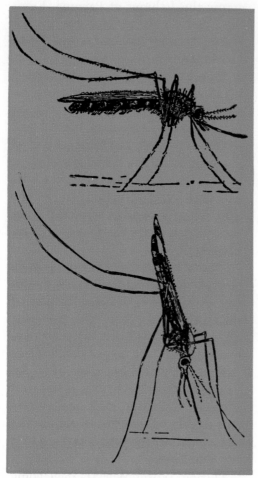

(Top) The common, or *Culex,* mosquito. Its sting can cause much itching, but it does not transmit disease. (Bottom) The *Anopheles* mosquito transmits the organisms that cause malaria. Notice the difference between this mosquito and the *Culex.* (Courtesy American Museum of Natural History)

Typhus fever. Typhus fever, which is spread by the body louse, is an ever-present disease in countries with poor living conditions and low standards of personal cleanliness. During wars, when many people are driven from their homes and live under overcrowded and insanitary conditions, serious epidemics of this disease frequently occur. In years past, this disease has been called camp fever, jail fever, and ship fever. Keeping clean and getting rid of body lice will control epidemic typhus fever.

Bubonic plague. Bubonic plague has been known for centuries. Epidemics in Europe from the sixth century to the seventeenth century caused untold numbers of deaths. One epidemic called the "black death" killed about one-fourth of the total population of Europe.

Bubonic plague is usually a disease of rats. The cause is a microorganism that is carried from rat to rat by fleas. On the West coast of the United States, the disease is now common among the ground squirrels.

Sometimes, fleas carry the organisms to human beings. In human beings, the disease may cause pneumonia and may then be spread by discharges from the throat and lungs. The death rate among people with plague is high.

The best way to control plague is by controlling rats. The number of rats in cities and upon farms is enormous. It is estimated, for example, that there are 20 million to 30 million rats in one section of New York alone.

Plague is common in crowded parts of the world, such as India. These places may seem far away, but fast ships and airplanes have brought them close to the United States. Infected rats from other countries may bring in the disease. People who have the organisms but have not yet developed symptoms also may bring in

THE CONQUEST OF DISEASE IN THE CITY OF NEW YORK (1800-1950)

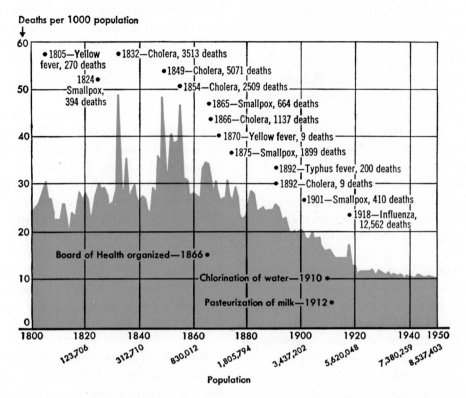

Deaths per 1000 population

- 1805—Yellow fever, 270 deaths
- 1824—Smallpox, 394 deaths
- 1832—Cholera, 3513 deaths
- 1849—Cholera, 5071 deaths
- 1854—Cholera, 2509 deaths
- 1865—Smallpox, 664 deaths
- 1866—Cholera, 1137 deaths
- 1870—Yellow fever, 9 deaths
- 1875—Smallpox, 1899 deaths
- 1892—Typhus fever, 200 deaths
- 1892—Cholera, 9 deaths
- 1901—Smallpox, 410 deaths
- 1918—Influenza, 12,562 deaths

Board of Health organized—1866 •

Chlorination of water—1910 •

Pasteurization of milk—1912 •

Population: 1800, 123,706; 1820, 312,710; 1840, 830,012; 1860, 1,805,794; 1880, 3,437,202; 1900, 5,620,048; 1920, 7,380,259; 1940, 8,537,403

Population

the disease. Plague and other diseases are, thus, problems of international travel and international trade.

Rabies. Rabies is one of the important and dramatic diseases of medical history. It is a disease chiefly of dogs. The cause is a virus. This virus is in the saliva of infected animals and is carried to other animals and to human beings by the bites of these animals. In both human beings and animals, rabies is almost always fatal.

The virus travels along nerves, from the bite to the brain, and may take from 2 to 10 weeks or even longer to reach the brain. When the brain becomes infected, the person or animal usually becomes very excited. This is

the reason that dogs with rabies are commonly called "mad" dogs. They run about and snap at anything they meet. Later, paralysis develops. When the muscles of swallowing are paralyzed, the animals cannot drink water. This gives the name hydrophobia, meaning fear of water, to the disease.

The best method of preventing rabies is to muzzle dogs or to vaccinate them against the disease. Vaccination of dogs is required in some places.

If a person is bitten by a dog, the dog should *not* be killed. It should be isolated and watched. If it has rabies, it will show symptoms and probably die within 2 weeks.

A person who has been bitten should report immediately to a physician who will decide whether he should be given the Pasteur treatment at once or wait until it is known whether the dog really has rabies.

The Pasteur treatment is an immunization against rabies. Pasteur knew that rabies does not develop immediately after a bite by a "mad" dog. He found that he could inject tiny amounts of weakened virus into animals after they were bitten and stimulate them to build antibodies. By the time the virus from the bite reached their brains, they had so many antibodies that the disease did not develop.

For a long time, Pasteur was unwilling to try his treatment on human beings. Then one day a Mrs. Meister brought her 9-year-old son, Joseph, to him. The boy had been bitten in 14 places by a "mad" dog. She knew he was doomed to die unless Pasteur could save him.

So, on the night of July 6, 1885, Pasteur made the first injection of weakened rabies virus into a human being. Every day for 2 weeks the boy was given an injection. Then Joseph Meister went home, a laughing healthy youngster. He was the first of thousands to be saved from death by the Pasteur treatment.

The Pasteur treatment, however, is long and expensive and does not always protect human beings who have been bitten from rabies. Our best hope for breaking this chain of infection is by protecting dogs from rabies.

Rocky Mountain spotted fever.
Rocky Mountain spotted fever occurs in various wild animals and is spread from animal to animal and from infected animals to people by ticks. It is most important in the western parts of the United States but may occur wherever ticks are found.

Tularemia. Tularemia is called "rabbit fever" because it is found chiefly among wild rabbits. Ticks and blood-sucking flies carry the disease to human beings. Hunters or cooks may be infected by handling dead rabbits that have had the disease. It may be avoided by not touching weak animals and those found dead, by handling dead animals with rubber gloves, and by cooking wild game until the meat is thoroughly done.

Brucellosis. Brucellosis is also called undulant fever, Malta fever, and Bang's disease. It may be caught directly from infected cows, pigs, or goats or indirectly through milk. The disease causes many deaths among animals. It is rarely fatal in man but may cause fatigue, weakness, and a low fever over many months. Prevention depends upon care in handling sick animals and upon pasteurization of milk.

Psittacosis. Psittacosis, or parrot fever, spreads to human beings from parrots, parakeets, love birds, and sometimes canaries and pigeons. A person who buys a bird he does not know about should keep at a distance and not make a pet of it for 2 or 3 weeks. If it remains well during that time, he can be reasonably sure that the bird is not infected with the virus that causes psittacosis.

CONTROLLING COMMUNICABLE DISEASES

After a person develops a disease, all we can do is to help him get well quickly and with few or no after-effects. It is like wiping up spilled milk instead of preventing the spilling.

Chapter 24 shows how people can be immunized against some diseases, so that even if they pick up the organisms they will not become ill. This chapter shows how we control some diseases by stopping the spread of the organisms from a sick person to a well one. To do this, we must know what the organism is and what pathway it uses in leaving one person and reaching another.

By these two methods of control, we have made almost unbelievable progress. Yet, much remains to be done. Many people are ill, many people die, unnecessarily. How can such illness and death be prevented?

We need more knowledge. But, most of all, we need to use all the knowledge we have. Physicians, nurses, hospitals, public-health officers, and clinics can help, but they cannot do the whole job. Control depends on every person's knowing how diseases are spread and then doing his share in preventing their spread—for himself and for his family, his school, and his community.

SO WHAT?

The enormous reduction in deaths and illness from communicable diseases has been a magnificent achievement, yet communicable diseases are still widespread and some of them are very serious, especially among children; and

Communicable diseases are all caused by microorganisms that a person gets directly or indirectly from another person or an animal; and

Tuberculosis, one of the communicable diseases, is a leading cause of death among teenage boys and girls;

So, be certain that you

Know about these diseases, the microorganisms that cause them, how they are spread, and how they can be prevented; and then

Use this knowledge to protect yourself, your family, and your neighbors from them.

CHECKING UP

1. What is meant by a chain of infection? Give an example of a short chain of infection; of a long chain of infection; of one that involves another animal.
2. What does a negative tuberculin test mean? Explain why a positive tuberculin test may not mean that a person has an active case of tuberculosis.
3. Should persons with negative tuberculin reactions be given chest x-rays? Should persons with positive tuberculin reactions be given chest x-rays? How often should a person be given a chest x-ray?
4. Why is it important to try to find cases of tuberculosis before symptoms of the disease appear?
5. What important diseases are carried by mosquitoes?
6. What is the Pasteur treatment?
7. Why are diseases that are spread through discharges from the nose and throat especially hard to control?
8. List the diseases discussed in this chapter. Add them to the chart you prepared for Chapter 24 and give the information called for about them.

THINGS TO DO

1. Make posters showing chains of infection for diseases that are spread by direct contact; by nose and throat discharges; by intestinal discharges; by insects and other animals.
2. Find whether any of the diseases discussed in this chapter occur in your community. Make a special study of these.
3. Write the tuberculosis association in your county or state for information, pamphlets, posters, and films about tuberculosis. Help with the Christmas Seal sale and other projects. How many in the class have had a tuberculin test? an x-ray? Ask the school nurse, public-health department, or the tuberculosis association how the others can be tuberculin tested or x-rayed.
4. Ask the public-health department how water and milk are protected in your community. Visit the public-health laboratory to see the examination of water and milk. Find whether food handlers are examined and whether they are given instructions about cleanliness and handling of food.
5. Make a list of rules for people who go camping, showing how they can be sure their water and milk are safe.

6. Give special reports on DDT and other insecticides.
7. Give special reports on Pasteur's work on rabies; on Koch's discovery of the cause of tuberculosis; on Walter Reed's experiments; on the life of Trudeau.
8. Make a survey of the schoolgrounds and the neighborhood in which you live, to find breeding places of mosquitoes. Get information from the agency for mosquito control, if there is one, in your community.
9. Find what immunizations men in the Army and Navy are given.
10. Find regulations about dogs in your community. Is the community well protected against rabies?
11. Make maps of the world and of the United States, showing where the diseases discussed in Chapters 24 and 25 are commonly found.

CHAPTER 26   Your Health Inventory

Wise automobile owners have their cars checked after every 1000 miles or so of driving. Usually, nothing is seriously wrong. The owner is merely playing safe. Sometimes, a worn part is found and replaced before it breaks. The examination costs a few dollars, and the repair job costs a few dollars more. A little time and a little money may prevent an accident out on the road that would wreck the car and the people in it and cost thousands of dollars.

The human body is more complicated than any automobile. Surely, it should be given as much care as a fine piece of nonliving machinery is given.

Life-insurance companies have found that regular checkups help their policy-holders to live longer. A careful examination will discover defects and diseases in their early stages, when they are most easily controlled.

It is recommended that children be examined every 6 months. Young adults should be given examinations once a year or at least once in 2 years. After the age of 50 or 60, and some-

times earlier, people should be given examinations 2 or 3 times yearly.

Every chapter in this book contains information that will help you understand better how a health inventory is made. References to previous chapters are included here for your convenience. Read the section on the health inventory in Chapter 7. You are ready now for a fuller discussion than you were when you first read that chapter.

WHAT YOU CAN LEARN FROM YOUR HEALTH INVENTORY

You are still in the growing period of life. Your health inventory will tell you about the stages of development of your various organs. How far toward adulthood are you? Are you as tall as you may expect to be?

There are certain minor ailments you may learn how to deal with. Are you too thin or too fat? Do you have round shoulders? Do you tire easily? Do you have many colds and sore throats?

It should not surprise you to find

that your past health may affect your health today and tomorrow. Did the diseases you had as a baby or a small child damage your heart or lungs or kidneys? Which diseases are you immune to? Has your diet always been good enough to build healthy bones and teeth?

Then, there is the future to consider. Remember, you can expect to live longer than any generation before you. Is there anything in your family history that should put you on your guard against poor hearing, diabetes, or high blood pressure? If you are strong and husky now, what can you do to be sure you will still be healthy when you are 30 or 50 years old?

Don't be afraid of finding something wrong. Some people are so afraid that there is "something wrong" with them that they will not go to a physician or a dentist for a checkup. This is part of the "running away" from problems that was discussed in Chapter 19. It is a foolish attitude, for two reasons.

First, most people have nothing seriously wrong with them. The main purpose of a health inventory is not to find how poor a person's health is but to find how good it is and how to make it better.

Second, if something is found to be wrong, the person has a chance to put his attention on doing something about it, instead of worrying about a dozen other ailments he thinks he might have. Finding exactly what the problem is and attacking it intelligently are good for mental health and peace of mind.

WHO SHOULD MAKE YOUR HEALTH INVENTORY

If you have a family physician, he will already have information about you and your family. Then, your regular checkup will consist of bringing your previous records up to date.

If you have no family physician, you must choose the best and most trustworthy medical adviser you can find. (Chapter 28 gives some suggestions for making such a choice.) It will take him longer to make an examination, since he will have to spend time finding out about your past health and the health of your family.

What goes into the record of your health inventory? Many physicians divide their records into five parts: family history, personal history, results of laboratory examinations, results of tests and measurements, and other physical findings.

FAMILY HISTORY

The first person you meet in a physician's office is probably his office nurse. She asks your name, age, birthday, and address and writes these at the top of your record card.

Then, the nurse or the physician asks about the health of your parents, your brothers and sisters, your grandparents, and perhaps your aunts and uncles and cousins. These questions are not just a matter of idle curiosity. The answers give the physician information about your heredity and about the environment in which you grew up.

Your physician will ask about your personal and family health history. (Courtesy Department of Health, City of New York)

It is unfortunate that most of us know so little about the health of our ancestors. Looking forward, we can do our own children and grandchildren a good turn if we keep and pass on to them our own health inventories.

Hereditary characteristics. It is often said that if a person wants to have a long life, the most important thing to do is to choose long-lived ancestors. Heredity has a good deal to do with long life, with good health, and with certain kinds of poor health.

Many cases of allergies, diabetes, sick headaches (migraine), color blindness, nearsightedness, and hemophilia are hereditary conditions. If one person in a family has diabetes, it does not mean that everyone else in that family will have diabetes. However, the tendency to diabetes is present in that family. There is always the chance that other persons in the family will have inherited the same tendency.

High blood pressure, certain kinds of anemia and epilepsy, and other conditions seem to be hereditary in part. If these conditions appear in a person's family stock, he is more likely than most other persons to develop them.

Knowing which hereditary characteristics, good and poor, are present in your family is a protection for you. Your physician can tell you how to prevent the development of many undesirable conditions. If the members of your family usually live to be very old, he can advise you how to build good health for all those probable years to come.

Family exposure to disease. Your physician will want to know whether any members of your family have had tuberculosis. Tuberculosis is not a matter of heredity but of exposure to the organisms that cause the disease. If one of your relatives has had tuberculosis, it may mean that you have been exposed to the disease. Your physician will then be especially interested in giving you a tuberculin test, an x-ray, and perhaps other tests to find whether the organisms have a foothold in your body. (See Chapter 25 for a discussion of tuberculosis.)

PERSONAL HISTORY

Your health in the future will, in part, be the result of what has happened to you in the past and your ways of living in the present.

Past health and development. Your physician will want to know about your birth and babyhood. When did you get your first tooth? When did you learn to walk? Did you have feeding problems? (If your parents kept a Baby Book for you, it contains valuable information about your development.)

What diseases have you had? Some diseases that you may have had, such as measles and whooping cough, usually mean protection against future attacks. Others, such as rheumatic fever and scarlet fever, may have injured kidneys, heart, or other organs. Your physician keeps this in mind when he makes your physical examination later. A person who has had tuberculosis usually carries tuberculosis organisms all his life and must be careful about his health and nutrition if he is to keep this infection under control

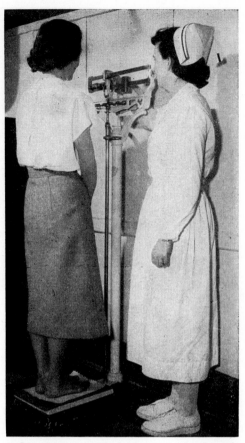

Your physician will want to know how much you weigh and how tall you are. (Courtesy Department of Health, State of New York)

(see Chapter 25). Hay fever, asthma, migraine headaches, and some other diseases often occur again and again (see Chapters 13 and 14). Your physician wants to know whether you have suffered from any of these.

Immunizations and tests for immunity. The physician will certainly ask when you were first vaccinated against smallpox and whether you have been revaccinated within the last few years. He will want to know whether you were immunized against

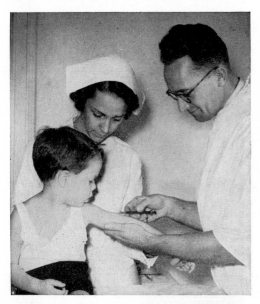

This boy is receiving an inoculation against diphtheria. (Courtesy U.S. Public Health Service)

diphtheria and whether you have been given the Schick test to determine your present state of immunity (see Chapter 24). If you were immunized against diphtheria, were you given toxoid or antitoxin?

When you were a child, were you given tetanus toxoid to immunize you against tetanus? Have you been given booster doses since then? And were you ever given tetanus antitoxin?

What about tuberculin tests? If your tuberculin test is now positive, how old were you when it became positive? Have you had x-rays of your chest? How recently? When?

Have you been immunized against whooping cough, scarlet fever, typhoid fever, or any other diseases? When?

It is not easy to remember all this information. For this reason, it is wise for parents to keep a record showing the dates of immunizations and tests. You are now old enough to take over the responsibility of keeping up the record.

Health habits. What do you usually eat for breakfast? for lunch? for dinner? between meals? Does the food you eat add up to a diet that contains the right amounts of protein, vitamins, minerals, and roughage for a boy or girl of your age? Are you eating enough or too much? (Look back at Chapter 9.)

How much exercise do you get? how much rest? When do you go to bed and when do you get up? Do you sleep soundly? Are you a worrier or do you accept things pretty much as they come, doing the best you can with each situation? (See Chapters 7, 18, 19.)

Answers to these questions may give you an answer to your own health problems and show you how to write a prescription for better health for yourself. However, your physician has had wider experience and training and will make suggestions that would not occur to you.

Other personal information. You will be asked a number of questions that may seem to have little or nothing to do with your present health: Have you ever had earaches or a "running ear"? How many colds do you have in a year? Do you ever feel dizzy? Do you have to stop and pant after you run upstairs? What kind of

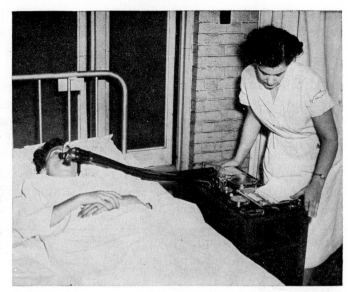

A test for basal metabolism is given when the person is resting quietly. The technician finds how much oxygen the patient uses in a minute for each pound of body weight. This shows how much he needs for breathing, heart beat, and muscle tonus when at rest. When he moves his demands for oxygen are, of course, greater than when he is resting. (Courtesy Mount Sinai Hospital, New York)

appetite do you have? Do you ever have stomachaches? Did you ever have convulsions?

These and many more questions are not important when you take them one by one. Taken together, the answers may suggest something that your physician will wish to study further. All these facts tell him something about the fascinating puzzle that is yourself.

LABORATORY EXAMINATIONS

A complete health inventory includes a urine examination, a blood examination, a tuberculin test and, if the tuberculin test is positive, a chest x-ray. If the physician suspects that your heart is not functioning properly, he may ask for an electrocardiogram. If there is a question about how your body is using food or about the functioning of your thyroid gland, he will ask for a basal metabolism test. If he

wonders whether you have reached your adult height or how much longer you may expect to go on growing, he may ask for x-rays of the bones of your legs. For older persons, he may want to make some special examinations for cancer.

Urine examination. For a urine examination, the physician usually asks for a sample of urine collected early in the morning. Sometimes, he wants to know how much urine is formed in one day and asks you to collect the urine for a whole day.

In making an examination of the urine, the physician or laboratory technician usually first finds how much water is in the urine and what other substances are dissolved in it. A large amount of water in the urine suggests that the person has been drinking large amounts of liquid, or that his kidneys are damaged, or that his pituitary gland or some other organ of the body is not functioning properly.

Sugar occurs in the urine when there is an oversupply of sugar in the blood, due usually to having eaten too much sugar or to diabetes. Diabetes can best be controlled in its early stages. This is one reason why it is important to have regular urinalyses (see Chapter 17).

A urinalysis also includes a test for albumin, a kind of protein. Albumin in the urine shows that the kidneys are not functioning properly and are allowing albumin to escape from the blood.

When urine is allowed to stand awhile, a layer of material settles to the bottom of the container. This sediment is examined under the microscope. White blood cells usually indicate an infection somewhere along the urinary tract: in the kidneys, ureters, bladder, or urethra. The presence of other kinds of cells may show injuries or diseased conditions in these organs.

Blood examinations. Examination of the blood includes an estimation of the amount of hemoglobin, a count of the red blood cells and of the white cells, and a Wassermann test. For these tests, the physician pricks your ear or your finger to get a few drops of blood and takes a small amount of blood from a vein in your arm. He does this so quickly and skillfully that you hardly know he is doing it.

To get oxygen distributed to all your cells, you must have enough red blood cells, and those cells must carry a rich supply of hemoglobin (see

Chapter 11). If your physician finds that you are anemic, he will try to find the cause and give proper treatment.

The number of white cells in the blood is increased by some infections and toxins (poisons) and decreased by others. If you have the usual 5000 to 8000 or 9000 white cells in each cubic millimeter of blood, this suggests that you are free of infection. If there are more or fewer than this number, your physician will suspect an infection somewhere—in teeth, tonsils, appendix, or some other organ —and will try to find it.

The Wassermann test is a test for the presence or absence of syphilis (see Chapter 25). This disease is so serious that it is advisable to give the test to everyone, even though only a few persons will be found to be infected. Many states now require this test for both partners before a marriage license can be issued. Many states, also, require that physicians arrange for a Wassermann test to be made on all prospective mothers.

Tests are sometimes made on the blood for other substances, such as hormones, antibodies, digested foods, and infectious organisms, especially those that cause malaria. Since the blood carries materials all over the body and receives materials from all the organs, tests of the blood may suggest trouble anywhere in the body.

Tuberculin test and chest x-ray. You may have had a tuberculin test. It is very simple. Your physician injects a tiny amount of tuberculin into the skin of your forearm and asks you to come back in a day or two so that he can see whether the test is negative or positive (see Chapter 25). If it is negative, he will tell you to have another one in 6 months or a year.

If the tuberculin test is positive, the physician will take a chest x-ray or send you to an x-ray laboratory for one. If the chest x-ray shows any suspicious shadows, he will make tests of sputum, stomach contents, and blood.

An x-ray of the chest can give valuable information, not only about the lungs, but also about the heart, lymph nodes, blood vessels, and esophagus. The x-ray picture, however, merely shows shadows against a light background. To have any value, it must be properly taken and must be studied by an expert.

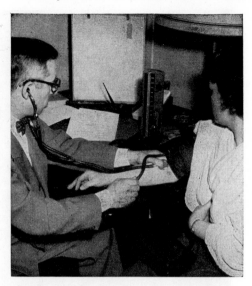

Measuring blood pressure. (Courtesy Department of Health, State of New York)

SPECIALS TESTS AND MEASUREMENTS

The physician will "take" your temperature, count your pulse, "take" your blood pressure, weigh and measure you, and test your vision and hearing.

Temperature. You have had your temperature "taken" many times, so this part of the examination will not be new to you. The physician will shake the mercury down in a thermometer and then place the mercury bulb under your tongue for a few minutes (see Chapter 5).

In infants, temperature is measured by a rectal thermometer placed in the rectum, which is the lower end of the large intestine. Rectal temperature is usually about a degree higher than mouth temperature. This is because the air in the nose and mouth carries away some of the body heat.

Pulse rate. Your physician will probably count the rate of your pulse while the thermometer is in your mouth. Exercise and excitement both cause an increase in the pulse rate (see Chapter 12). For this reason, a physician does not "take" the pulse at the beginning of an examination or when his patient seems nervous and excited.

The usual pulse rate is often said to be about 72 for men and 80 for women. These are average figures. Some healthy people have higher pulse rates; others have lower pulse rates. In general, the pulse rate decreases with age. In adults, a pulse rate over 100 may have some signifi-

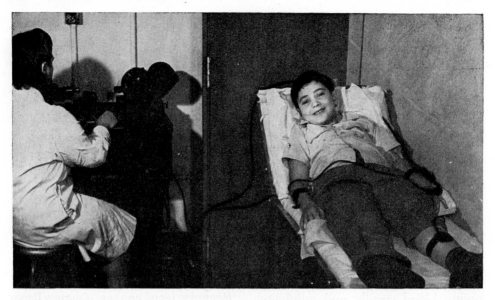

This boy's physician asked to have an electrocardiogram made. Here the boy lies quietly while a record is made of electrical changes in his heart as it contracts and relaxes. (Courtesy Department of Health, City of New York)

cance. In young children, a pulse rate over 100 may be quite usual.

Knowing how your pulse compares with that of other persons is not very important. It is important to know what is your usual rate and how it changes over the months and years. This means repeated tests.

Blood pressure. Blood pressure, like the pulse rate, is affected by exercise and excitement. The physician, therefore, will measure your blood pressure when you are quiet and resting.

To "take" your blood pressure, the physician wraps a hollow rubber tube, or cuff as it is called, around your upper arm. Then he pumps air into the cuff until the pressure is great enough to stop the flow of blood in the arteries. He can tell when the flow of blood is stopped by feeling the pulse in your wrist or listening to the flow of blood by means of his stethoscope. You can feel the pressure of the cuff on your arm, but it is not heavy enough to hurt.

The smallest amount of air pressure in the cuff that will stop all flow of blood during the heartbeat is a measure of the systolic pressure. The pressure that stops the flow of blood between heartbeats is the diastolic pressure (see Chapter 12). The instrument for measuring blood pressure is called a sphygmomanometer, *sphygmo* meaning pulse, and *manometer* meaning an instrument for measuring.

Blood pressure frequently increases as people grow older. Repeated tests will give the record of changes over a

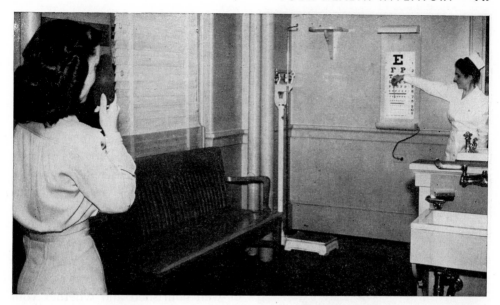

Reading this eye chart at a 20-foot distance is one procedure used in testing vision. (Courtesy General Electric Co.)

period of years. This record is useful in showing whether there are sudden increases or decreases in blood pressure.

Height and weight. Records of height and weight should be started in infancy and continued throughout life. Little children should be measured and weighed every month, older persons every 3 to 6 months.

We know that human beings grow according to a general pattern, though each person follows this pattern at his own rate (see Chapter 9). The purpose of keeping your record of height and weight through the growing years is to find *your own* rate of growth. Changes from this may be normal, or they may be signs of disturbances in metabolism.

The weight record has a somewhat different meaning for older people. Increases in weight are undesirable after 30 or 35. Decreases in weight lead to suspicion of changes in endocrine balance, infection, or a poor diet, unless, of course, the person has been dieting to take off weight.

Vision. Your health inventory should include a test of how well you can see and whether you can do ordinary close work without eyestrain (see Chapter 20). Your physician may test your vision in his office, or he may suggest that you go to a specialist, that is, an oculist, for a complete eye examination.

Tests of vision should be made at least every year. You should be given a color vision test at least once in your life, and the result should be a part of your permanent record.

Looking through the pupil into the interior of the eye often gives your physician information about the health of your whole body. (Courtesy Better Vision Institute)

Hearing. Hearing tests should be made at least once a year. Your physician may give you an audiometer test in his office. Or he may give a watch or whisper test and refer you to a specialist for a more careful audiometer test if he thinks it desirable (see Chapter 20).

PHYSICAL FINDINGS

In making physical examinations, physicians often wish that they could take the human machine apart and put it back together again, as a jeweler does a watch. As it is, they must be satisfied with learning what they can by (1) looking at the outside of the body and as far as they can into openings such as nose and ears, (2) feeling the surface of the body and the outlines of organs under the skin, (3) listening to sounds from within the body.

General examination. Before starting your physical examination, your physician will ask you to take off most of your clothing and will give you a gown to wear. This gives him a chance to look, feel, and listen without being disturbed by layers of cloth and leather. He will make a quick estimate of your posture, the development of your muscles, whether you look thin or well nourished and whether your fat is well distributed over your body. He will feel your shoulder and upper arm to see how firm the muscles are and how thick the layer of fat under the skin is. He will look at your skin to see whether it is smooth, pink, and free from infection.

Examination of the head. Physicians usually start a physical examination at the head. They feel hair and scalp; examine eyes to see whether they are clear, move smoothly together, react to light, and have no dark circles under them. Your physician may throw a beam of light through the pupil of your eye and look at the surface of the retina. This is not a test of vision but of the health of the tissues of the eyes. It may tell a good deal about the health of your whole body.

The physician will look into your ears to see whether they are clogged with wax and whether the eardrums look pink and healthy and have no signs of discharge from the middle ear. These are not tests of hearing but of the health of the ears.

General inspection tells the physician whether a person breathes through his nose or his mouth. Looking into the nose shows whether there is discharge and infection and whether there is any obstruction to breathing (see Chapter 13).

Examination of the mouth includes finding whether the teeth are clean, how many of the permanent teeth have erupted, and how many teeth are decayed, missing, or filled. This examination does not take the place of examination by a dentist, but a health inventory should include a general estimate of the health and development of the teeth. The physician also looks at the shape of your jaws and may refer you to an orthodontist if your teeth do not meet properly (see Chapter 15).

Looking in the mouth gives the physician a chance to see whether the mucous membranes are pink and whether the tongue is coated. He will flatten your tongue with a wooden tongue depressor and look as far down your throat as possible to see whether it appears healthy.

He will feel behind and below your ears to see whether the lymph nodes are enlarged (see Chapter 12). He will run his fingers across the front of your neck to find the size of the thyroid gland (see Chapter 22).

Examination of the chest. The physician observes the shape of your chest, its movements in breathing,

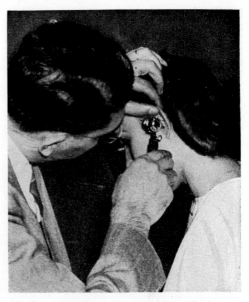

Through a special instrument, your physician can see a long way into your ear. This is one of many special tests that are part of a general physical examination. (Courtesy Department of Health, City of New York)

and the heartbeat against the chest wall. He taps your chest and listens to the sounds of the tapping over the lungs. He listens to the breath sounds through his stethoscope.

Tapping the chest (percussion) and listening through a stethoscope (auscultation) help the physician find the size and shape of your heart. He listens to the sounds made by the heart valves as they close and by the blood flowing through the valves (see Chapter 12).

This physical examination of the chest gives information to be added to that shown by the chest x-ray.

Examination of the abdomen. Your physician can feel the size and shape

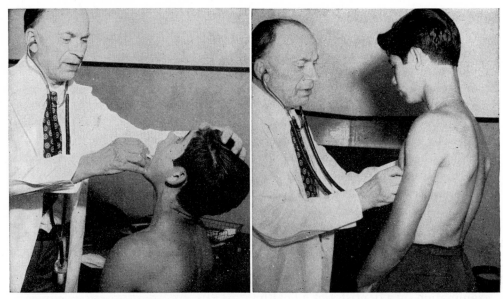

(Left) Examining mouth and throat. (Right) Listening to the sounds of the heart and lungs by means of a stethoscope. (Courtesy Department of Health, City of New York)

of many organs in the abdomen through the layers of skin and muscle. He will try, also, to find whether there are points of tenderness; these may indicate infection.

Examination of the limbs. The general survey includes an estimate of the straightness of arms and legs, and their size in relationship to the trunk and to each other. The physician will test your reflexes by tapping with a little rubber hammer just below the knee and above the elbow (see Chapter 18). He will look at your hands and nails, feet and toes. Examination of feet is especially important (see Chapters 6 and 7).

OTHER HEALTH EXAMINATIONS

The health inventory described in this chapter is a fairly complete one and takes considerable time. It is the kind of examination a physician makes in his private office with the aid of laboratory technicians. Its aim is to discover as many as possible of a person's health assets and liabilities.

School health examinations are shorter and usually do not include laboratory tests. Teachers or nurses weigh and measure children and give vision and hearing tests. They should make daily inspections of students for signs of possible illness or defects. Physicians examine hearts and lungs and decide whether children are ill or have defects.

Most life-insurance companies give examinations to persons applying for policies. The interest of the companies is chiefly in finding defects, as of heart or kidneys, or diseases, such as tuberculosis, which make a person a poor risk for life insurance.

Various industrial and business firms give examinations to people they employ. These examinations aim chiefly at finding whether the person can do the work required. Certain industries require good eyesight, for example. Sometimes, x-rays of the chest are made to find whether a person has tuberculosis, which he might spread to other employees. There is seldom any effort to find what illnesses a person had as a child or what his family background is like.

A person cannot rely on school health examinations, or on insurance or employment medical examinations, for a health inventory. Everyone should have a careful examination by his own physician once a year, or oftener if the physician advises it.

THE FINAL SCORE

The person most interested in your health inventory is you. Your physician will bring together all the information he is able to gather about you, will study it, and tell you what are your strong points and what are your weak ones. Most people have reasonably good health, but very few people are healthy in all respects. You may find that you would be happier and more efficient if you made a few changes in your way of living, ate more foods containing a particular vitamin, for example, or rested a little in the middle of the day, or wore glasses for reading.

The physician's job is done when he makes recommendations based on his expert training and his good judgment. Carrying out these recommendations is your job. Recall that the early teens are the healthiest years of life. Now is the time to build strong bodies and healthy attitudes toward life that will carry you on into the sixties and seventies, or even the eighties and nineties.

SO WHAT?

Everyone likes to check up, from time to time, on what he owns and how much money he has in the bank; and

Health is the most valuable possession you can have; and

It is possible by means of a health inventory to find out how your health is today and what the prospects are of health in the future; and

On the basis of this information there frequently are things you can do to improve your health;

So, remember what a health inventory is and how you can use it to insure yourself the best possible health in the years ahead.

CHECKING UP

1. What is the purpose of a health inventory?
2. When a physician makes a health examination of a person, why does he ask questions about that person's family?
3. What kinds of questions does a physician ask about a person's own past health? Why?
4. What tests are included in a urinalysis? What does each show?
5. What tests are included in an examination of the blood? What is each designed to show?
6. What special tests and measurements are usually included in a health examination? Why is each included?
7. How does a physician examine the head? the chest? the abdomen?
8. What is the purpose of the kind of health inventory described in this chapter? How is this purpose different from the purpose of a health examination given in school? How is this purpose different from the purpose of an examination given by life-insurance companies? by business firms?

THINGS TO DO

1. Ask a physician to tell the class about health inventories as he gives them.
2. Study the record form used for health examination at school. Compare it with the examination discussed in this chapter.
3. Find what kinds of examinations are given by life-insurance companies; by industries and businesses in your community.
4. Ask your parents and grandparents to tell you what they know about the health of their parents and grandparents.
5. Make a record, with dates, of the illnesses you have had. Record which immunizations you have had; whether you were given toxoid or antitoxin against diphtheria and tetanus; which tests you have been given. Put this information in good form, so that you can add to it in the future and refer to it when needed.
6. Make a graph of your height and weight, going as far back as you have any records. Leave room for future records.
7. Collect any information you can about tests of vision and hearing that you have had in the past.

CHAPTER 27 Opportunities for Service
in the Field of Health

Have you been thinking about what you will do after you leave school? Perhaps you have wondered whether you would like to be a doctor or a nurse. Have you thought of all the other persons that are needed today to keep people healthy? How much do you know of the opportunities that are open and of the training you must have if you decide to work in this field?

Almost any boy or girl who wants to be of service to other people can find a place in the field of health. Training for certain kinds of jobs is long and expensive, but for others only 1 or 2 years of training after high school is required. In some places, scholarships are open to young people who are intelligent and need financial help. The work is often hard and is usually not as dramatic as it is made to seem in storybooks. But there are many opportunities to make a comfortable living.

The Armed Services need men and women in every kind of health work and will give some of you the chance to extend your education and to serve your country at the same time. Best of all, for the right persons, helping people to be strong and healthy is interesting work and brings rich satisfactions.

MEDICINE

The number of physicians in this country is greater in relationship to the population than in any other country of the world. In spite of this, there are plenty of opportunities for men and women with good training. In rural districts, especially, there are more openings than there are physicians to fill them.

In general, physicians hold a respected place in the community and receive incomes that allow them to live comfortably. Very few become wealthy.

The medical course is long and ex-

453

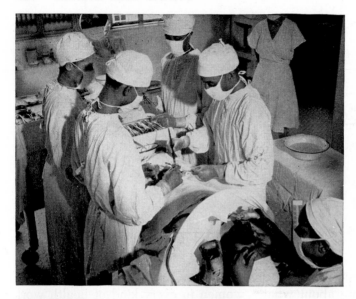

(Top) Surgery is a highly skilled specialization in the field of medicine. (Bottom) Physicians who specialize in work with babies and small children are called pediatricians. (Courtesy U.S. Public Health Service)

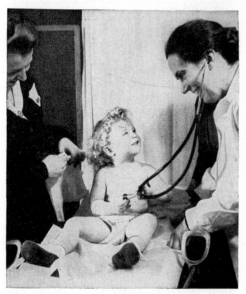

pensive. Boys and girls who wish to go into it should choose good foundation courses in high school, including mathematics, biology, chemistry, and physics. Physicians need to understand human relationships, so students should take courses in the social sciences and in literature. They should develop wide cultural and recreational interests, in art, music, games, and handicrafts, since their work will become more and more specialized and allow little time later for these.

After high school, a physician's preparation includes at least 3 years of college, 4 years in medical school, and 1 or more years in a hospital, working under the supervision of older physicians. Many physicians go into specialized fields of medicine, such as surgery, psychiatry (see Chapter 19), otology (see Chapter 20), or endocrinology (see Chapter 22). If a physician wishes to become a specialist, he usually works for 3 or more years in hospitals and clinics.

Most physicians engage in the private practice of medicine. However, there are other opportunities open to them, in research, in teaching in medical schools, in public-health work, in industry, in government service, and in public and private clinics. What-

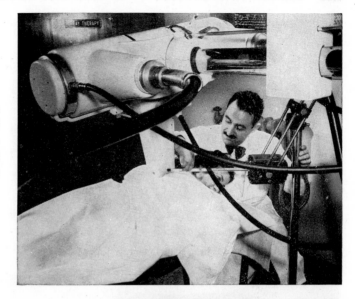

Physicians who specialize in work with x-rays and radium are called radiologists. (Courtesy Michael Reese Hospital, Chicago)

ever he does, a physician must always devote a great deal of time to study of new developments in his field.

DENTISTRY

Another profession devoted to health services is dentistry. The training of a dentist resembles that of a physician but is usually shorter.

A dentist must have knowledge about the teeth and the mouth and learn to handle a wide variety of delicate tools. Dentists may specialize in the removal of teeth, the correction of malocclusion, diseases of the gums, and mouth surgery.

Most dentists engage in the private practice of dentistry. There are also opportunities for them in the Armed Services, in public health, in schools and colleges, and in hospitals.

Dentists make a comfortable living, and there is an urgent need for more dentists in many parts of the country.

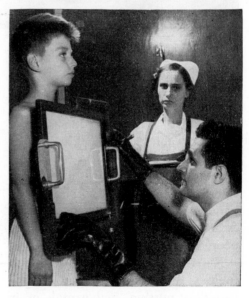

It is estimated that we need 1½ times our present number of dentists to give needed dental care to Americans.

NURSING

In the care of the sick, the nurse is the teammate of the physician. She

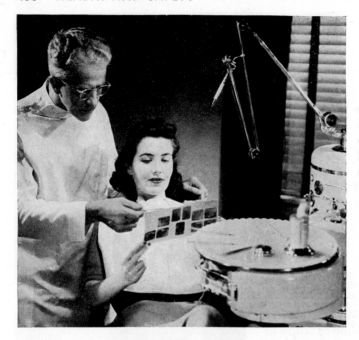

Dentistry demands skill in handling tools and in using x-rays. (Courtesy American Dental Association)

looks out for the patient's welfare and comfort, supervises his diet, keeps a constant check on his condition, and reports all this to the physician. Without well-trained nurses, modern medical care would be impossible.

The nurse acts also as a friend and companion, who brings cheer and courage into the sickroom. No two patients are alike, so nursing is never dull for those who are interested in people.

Nursing offers a variety of opportunities. A nurse may engage in private-duty nursing, in hospitals or in homes. Or if she prefers a position with a regular salary, she may be a hospital nurse, a nursing supervisor, or a teacher of nursing. She may specialize in surgical nursing, care of mental patients, care of children, or care of the aged. She may become a school nurse, an industrial nurse, a

visiting nurse, or a health-department nurse. Furthermore, a nurse's training is valuable in running one's own home and caring for children.

At present, there are three types of preparation for nursing. In one type of program, the student spends about 2 years in college, taking general courses including basic courses in science. She then spends 2 to 3 years in a hospital. At the end of this period, she receives a college degree and her certificate in nursing. Most public-health nurses and supervising nurses have this kind of preparation.

In the second type of program, the student goes directly from high school into a hospital school of nursing. The course is usually 3 years in length. Most of the time is spent on subject matter and practice directly related to nursing. This prepares a girl for bedside nursing in institutions and in homes. She may, however, take further work in more specialized fields of nursing.

In the third type of program, after high school the student spends 9 to 18 months in hospital training and becomes a nonprofessional, or practical, nurse. She works mainly with chronic, convalescent, or mildly ill persons or she serves in hospitals under the supervision of professional nurses.

Salaries and working conditions for nurses are as good as those in most other fields. The increase in the number of hospitals and developments in medical and surgical treatments have increased the need for nurses. Industrial medicine and public-health activities have opened new fields for nursing services. The Armed Services need nurses at home and overseas. Together, these add up to a need for many more nurses than are now being trained.

Although we usually think of nursing as women's work, there are demands for men nurses, also. These usually are nonprofessional nurses, employed to care for men patients, especially in mental hospitals. The Army and Navy give training in this field to some men, and certain kinds of training are available in hospitals.

MEDICAL TECHNOLOGY

Many recent advances in medicine are possible only because of advances in laboratory skills. Physicians must trust trained technicians to give them information on what may be life-and-death matters to patients.

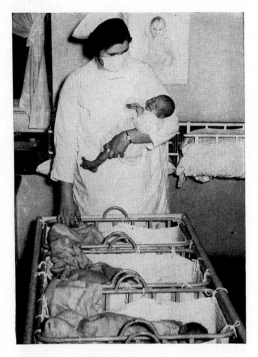

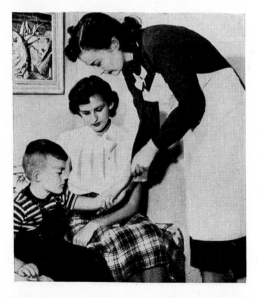

Nurses work with many kinds of people. (Top) A registered nurse in a hospital nursery. (Bottom) A public-health nurse makes a home visit. (Courtesy U.S. Public Health Service)

Veterinarians care for the health of animals. (Courtesy American Veterinarian Medical Association)

A medical technician prepares blood smears and other slides to be examined under a microscope. This girl is also trained as a medical secretary. (Courtesy Colby Junior College)

The medical technician "matches" blood and, thus, finds which persons can give blood to a patient who needs a blood transfusion. He stains thin slices of tissue removed in an operation, so that the physician can tell whether a lump is a cancer or a harmless growth. He photographs the electrical record of the heart's action (by using an electrocardiograph) and, thus, enables the physician to learn more about the condition of a patient's heart. He finds which micro-organisms are present in infections. He makes basal metabolism tests, and he may take x-rays.

Many universities give a 4-year course in medical technology. Positions are found in hospitals, clinics, research laboratories, physicians' offices, and in industries. Earnings on the average are above those in other professions that call for the same amount of training and ability. There are far more positions open than there are trained technicians to fill them.

In the past, most medical technicians have been women, although men are now entering the field. Positions in medical technology are responsible ones. They give opportunities for interesting work to persons who are careful and accurate and wish to be of service.

PHYSICAL THERAPY

Heat, cold, light, water, electricity, massage, and exercise are often used to make patients more comfortable and to hasten their recovery. The use of these agents in treatment is known

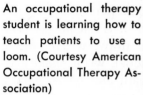

An occupational therapy student is learning how to teach patients to use a loom. (Courtesy American Occupational Therapy Association)

as physical therapy (see Chapter 6).

Physical therapy is not new. Everyone who ever rubbed a bumped elbow or dipped a burned finger into cold water or sat in front of a fire when he was chilled was using physical therapy. We know more today about the effects of cold, heat, massage, and other physical agents on the human body, and it is possible to use them more successfully than ever before.

Treatment with these physical agents is given by physical therapists. They work only under the direction of physicians, as do nurses and medical technicians.

A number of colleges and universities now give 4-year courses for the preparation of physical therapists. Students study the structure and functioning of the human body, since they must be able to understand the conditions of the patients with whom they will work. Physical therapists learn how to use ultraviolet and infrared lamps, how to give deep heat treatments (diathermy), how to use hot and cold water in whirlpool baths and contrast baths. They learn the kinds of exercise and massage to give patients at various stages of their recovery.

Physical therapy is especially useful in the treatment of injured and crippled persons. In many cases, they can leave the hospital in a much shorter time than would have been possible without physical therapy. Getting a patient back to a useful life is known as rehabilitation.

OCCUPATIONAL THERAPY

A person must have something to do while he is ill, and especially while he is getting well. The longer his ill-

A pharmacist knows how to mix chemicals and handle drugs of all kinds. (Courtesy American Association of Colleges of Pharmacy)

ness and convalescence, the more important it is for him to have something to occupy his mind, to interest him, and to lead him toward a useful life when he is well.

Occupational therapy refers to any activity that hastens recovery and helps a patient back to a useful life. The activity may be either mental or physical. Physical therapy puts the emphasis on making the patient physically fit, so far as this is possible. Occupational therapy improves the person's outlook on life and gives him the skills he needs to lead a happy, useful life after he leaves the hospital.

Occupational therapy has been used most successfully with persons who have been injured. Their rehabilitation may include learning to walk, to play games, and to earn a living. Occupational therapy is also useful in the treatment of patients with mental illnesses, tuberculosis, heart disease, arthritis, and paralysis of all forms. It has been used in helping deaf and blind persons.

When a patient is flat on his back in bed he can draw, weave, braid, read, study, model, write, make baskets, or play card and board games. When he becomes able to move about, he may garden, build furniture, do folk dancing, write and produce plays, sing and play musical instruments, and play ball games. Working and playing in a group breaks down the feeling of being shut off and develops a sense of contributing to others. This is important for everyone but seems to be especially important for the mentally ill.

Occupational therapy may help a patient get ready to earn a living. A patient may be able to go back to his old job, or he may have to learn entirely new skills. A shoemaker, for example, who develops tuberculosis may expect to become a shoemaker again when he recovers. A carpenter, however, who develops tuberculosis may need to learn a new trade that will not take him out in bad weather. A blind person or a cripple often has to prepare himself to work at something quite different from what he did before he was blinded or crippled.

Many colleges and universities offer training in occupational therapy to both men and women. The courses include study of the human body and the many conditions in which occupa-

Teachers have many opportunities to teach children how to care for their health. (Courtesy Kansas City, Missouri, Public Schools)

tional therapy is useful. Part of the training of therapists is an internship in a hospital. Here is a field with wide opportunities for young people, especially those who like to do things with their hands.

PHARMACY

Medicine and *drug* are two words with much the same meaning. Both refer to substances used in the prevention and treatment of disease. Pharmacy means the preparation of drugs, or medicines.

In the past, we had only a limited number of drugs: a few chemicals, such as mercury and arsenic, and a few medicines prepared from plants, such as castor oil and digitalis. The pharmacist, or druggist, prepared these drugs and sold them in his drugstore.

Now we have an almost limitless number of medicines. There are drugs that destroy or check disease-producing organisms; hormones; vitamins; substances that relieve pain and produce sleep; laxatives; antiseptics; and drugs that act on the heart and relax muscles.

Drugs are still sold in drugstores, along with a large number of other things—ice cream, candy, pencils, postcards, magazines, cosmetics, toys, cigarettes, films. Certain drugs are sold as freely to the public as are candy and magazines. These drugs include laxatives, vitamins, antiseptics, headache remedies, and other preparations that probably can do little harm when taken or used in moderate quantities.

Other drugs cannot be bought except when a physician writes a prescription for them. These include the drugs that are strong enough to relieve severe pain, such as morphine; drugs that have an effect on the heart, such as digitalis; hormones; new drugs such as penicillin whose action is not yet completely known; and others that may do damage if not used properly.

The person in the drugstore who fills a physician's prescription is required by law to be a pharmacist with special training and a state license to prepare drugs. There are also openings for pharmacists in the factories and laboratories of companies that manufacture drugs.

Many universities offer 4- or 5-year courses for the training of pharmacists. The courses include study of chemistry, the manufacture of drugs, and the filling of prescriptions.

EDUCATION

Health is only partly the responsibility of physicians, hospitals, public-health officers, and their helpers. Patients must know how to make use of health services and how to cooperate in their own treatment. People must know how to prevent illness by eating properly, avoiding infections, exercising and resting, having regular checkups, and obtaining early treatment for diseases. Teaching them to do all of these things is an important aspect of preventive medicine.

There are opportunities for health teaching to all age groups. In elementary school, children learn to like the proper foods, keep reasonably clean, wash their hands, use their own drinking glasses and toothbrushes, and keep away from other children who have the sniffles. In the upper grades, children begin to learn why they should do these things. In high school and college, there are special classes in health, biology, physical education, first aid, and nutrition. In schools for adults, there are classes in care of children, home nursing, foods and nutrition, and other aspects of health. There are opportunities for teaching the blind, deaf, crippled, and mentally defective how to live well in spite of their handicaps.

Preparation for teaching is given in universities and colleges. Many states require 4 years of college work for elementary-school teachers and 5 years for high-school teachers. The first 2 years are usually filled with courses in social studies, science, literature, art and music, languages— courses designed to give teachers a broad general education. The later years contain courses aimed at giving teachers understanding of how children develop and how people learn. For high school teachers there are opportunities in biology, nutrition, physical education, and coaching.

The salaries of teachers are not high but are steady and increase with experience. Usually, there is provision for retirement and health insurance.

Teaching offers unusual opportunities for men and women who like to work with people. It calls for patience and willingness to look into the future, to the years when students will be using what they have learned, in caring for themselves and their families.

OTHER FIELDS RELATED TO HEALTH

Osteopathy is a form of medical practice, the training for which is patterned after the training that is given in medical schools. The relationship of normal structure to normal function is stressed with emphasis on physical manipulations and adjustments. There are six colleges of osteopathy in the United States, each of which requires a minimum of 2 years of college work for admission. The course in the osteopathic college lasts for 4 years and is followed by a period of internship and sometimes by further work in a field of specialization.

Chiropractic is a form of treatment based on spinal adjustments. Special schools of chiropractic offer courses that range from 6 months to 2 years in length, following graduation from high school.

Optometrists test people's vision and, in many instances, prescribe glasses. Several universities offer 4-year courses in optometry.

A chiropodist, or podiatrist, diagnoses and treats minor ailments of the human foot. He also prescribes correct shoes. There are six approved colleges of chiropody in the United States, which offer 3- and 4-year courses.

Modern medical care is so complex that many people, in addition to those already discussed, contribute to it. Medical secretaries are in demand for work in physicians' offices and in hospitals. They learn to use the technical terms needed in medical forms and reports.

Medical social workers work in public clinics and hospitals, with patients and their families. Psychiatric social workers assist with the financial

A dietitian prepares for a public program. (Courtesy American Dietetic Association)

A sanitary engineer discusses with a farmer the proper methods for making well water safe. (Courtesy U.S. Public Health Service)

and family problems of the mentally disturbed.

Psychologists give tests of intelligence and personality. They also assist people who are confused and mentally upset.

Dietitians plan meals for patients with special food needs, for children, and for old people.

Sanitarians inspect houses, eating places, packing plants, and markets to see that regulations about health are being obeyed. Sanitary engineers are trained chiefly in engineering. They install and maintain water works and sewage-disposal plants.

Public-health engineers serve on the staffs of national, state, and local health departments as specialists in all aspects of environmental health.

Atomic medicine. Research in atomic medicine is a growing field. Atomic energy is already in use for the diagnosis and treatment of certain types of cancer. It also has greater possibilities in the study of fundamental problems of health and disease. For example, certain chemical substances can be made radioactive and then their passage throughout the body and their utilization by the cells of the body carefully studied. Such studies have great potential value for the improvement of human health.

MORE KNOWLEDGE MAKES MORE JOBS

In the days of your grandparents, there were only a few kinds of jobs in the health field. However, as human beings learn more and more about keeping well, more and more kinds of opportunities open up for a lifework in this field. Every job is important. One person cannot know everything or do everything that is needed. It takes teamwork to keep people healthy. If you are interested, you should be able to find a place and a job that will fit your own abilities.

SO WHAT?

Many boys and girls think that they would like to be physicians, dentists, nurses, or other health workers; and

Modern health services, both preventive and curative, offer many opportunities for interesting and rewarding careers to young men and young women interested in these fields; and

Some of these careers require many years of education and training, while others are less demanding;

So, it is well to know what sort of preparation is required for the various health professions; and

If you are interested in a career in this field, to select the profession in which you are most likely to be happy and successful.

CHECKING UP

1. Make a list of all the kinds of work listed in this chapter. Answer the following questions about each.
   a) How long is the training?
   b) How does a person obtain the needed training?
   c) What kind of work does the person do after he has received his training?
   d) Are there chances for advancement to better jobs? Are there chances for specializing?
   e) Is the field crowded, or are there plenty of places for well-trained people?
2. Add other kinds of work. For example, the work of oculists (ophthalmologists), optometrists, and opticians was discussed in Chapter 20.
3. If you have special interest in a kind of work in the health field that is not discussed anywhere in this book, add it to the list and see what you can learn about it.

THINGS TO DO

1. Ask people who are working in the field of health to tell the class about their jobs and about the necessary preparation for them. Choose one kind of work in this field that seems interesting to you and one that seems uninteresting. Give reports to the class on why you think you would like the one and dislike the other.
2. Consult catalogs from colleges and universities to find what preparation they give for work in the field of health. If you are interested in one of these, which courses should you take in high school?
3. Give special reports on the needs and opportunities for physicians, nurses, medical corpsmen, physical therapists, public-health engineers, and other health personnel in government service.
4. Look at the lists of questions you made at the beginning of the year. Do you have the answers to them all? If there are still some unanswered ask your teacher, the school nurse, or a physician how you can get the answers.
5. Look at the lists of health problems you made at the beginning of the year. Do you still think they are the most important problems? Do you want to add any? take any away?

CHAPTER 28   Health Services for

All People

There are times in life when medical care becomes more important than anything else. One such time is when we enter the world; another is when we are about to leave it; another is when illnesses or accidents strike.

Providing good medical care today is much more complex than it was in the past. The family physician used to be the only one concerned in most cases of illness. He came to the home carrying his instruments and his medicines in his "little black bag." Sometimes, a nurse was called in to help, but usually the family or neighbors provided nursing care.

Today, the situation is different. Minor ailments are still cared for in the home, but the diagnosis and treatment of many illnesses must be carried on in physicians' offices, clinics, or hospitals.

Health services today are concerned with the prevention of disease even more than with its cure. Giving toxoid to keep healthy children from developing diphtheria is not so dramatic as giving antitoxin to a child who is dying of diphtheria, but it is much better to prevent a disease than to try to cure it.

CHOOSING A HEALTH ADVISER

Almost every community contains a number of people who are ready to give advice about health. Each person must choose whom of these he will trust, for himself and his family. Perhaps the two points of greatest importance in making such a choice are the knowledge and the honesty of the persons considered.

However, choosing a well-trained and honest health adviser is just the beginning of good health care. The person seeking care must be a good patient. He should know the importance of careful examinations and allow time for them, and he should not expect the impossible.

The family doctor. Few persons in society have been as much beloved as

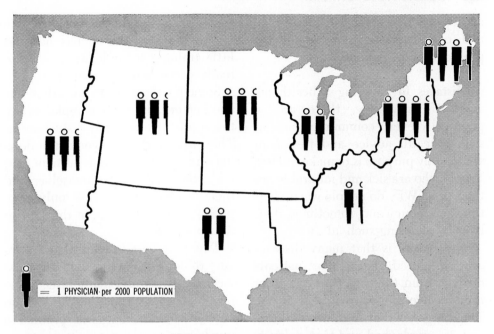

The number of physicians in relation to population shows sharp regional differences.

the "family doctor." There is an old proverb that says: "In illness the physician is a father; in convalescence, a friend; when health is restored, a guardian."

Now, as in the past, the family physician is the person who knows the family and each member in it and can be depended on in an emergency. In addition, he gives his patients regular examinations when they are not ill, advises them about diet, exercise, and immunizations, and cares for minor ailments before they become serious.

The family physician calls on laboratory technicians to make blood counts, take x-rays, and examine sputum, urine, and feces. He decides when a patient should go to a hospital or obtain the care of medical specialists. His patients remain his spe-

cial charge, even when they are in a hospital under the care of specialists; he takes responsibility for them until they are well.

Medical specialists. Medical science has grown so rapidly that one person cannot learn all that is known in the field. Specialists devote years to study of one part of the human body or to perfecting skills in diagnosis and treatment.

There is frequent need in every community for specialists in the fields of surgery, care of children, care of eyes and teeth, and so on. Occasionally, the highly skilled services of a brain surgeon or a specialist in internal medicine or children's diseases may mean the difference between life and death. The family physician gives advice on when specialists are needed and consults with them about the problems of his patients.

Mistakes in choosing a health adviser. Unfortunately, there are in practically every community persons selling health advice and treatment whose only purpose is to make money. People who are sick and miserable are their prey. Why do people waste their time and money and, sometimes, their lives by choosing such advisers?

One reason is that many diseases are self-limited; that is, most patients recover from them in time, whether they receive proper treatment or not. The danger is that serious conditions may be overlooked and that delay in proper treatment may result in permanent damage to heart, kidneys, or other organs of the body.

Other patients have chronic illnesses, which seem better at times and worse at others. Arthritis is one such disease. So, too, are various diseases of the heart, digestive tract, and kidneys. A well-trained physician may tell the patient that he will have ups and downs, that he can be made more comfortable but not really cured. A more ignorant adviser may give him treatments and claim a cure when improvement occurs. Later, when a relapse occurs, it is blamed on stopping the treatments, and the patient hopefully starts a new series.

Other "cures" are cures of diseases that never existed. It is easy to cure a "pneumonia" that is nothing more than mild influenza, or an "appendicitis" that is only indigestion. Some-

times, the adviser is entirely sincere in his advice, because he has had too little training to understand what is really wrong with the patient.

Some people go from one adviser to another because their complaints are the result of emotional disturbances. They may feel improvement following almost any kind of treatment that takes their minds off themselves and their troubles. But this is only temporary, and these people drift on to someone else.

There are certain ailments that are very difficult to diagnose. It may take weeks of study and many tests. Some people become impatient and go to another adviser who will promise a quick cure.

HOSPITALS

Hospitals in the past were often looked on as places to avoid. The situation is different now.

Modern medical care makes use of operating rooms, laboratories, and x-ray equipment. These cannot be taken to the patient in his home, so the patient must be taken to them.

It is easy for physicians and specialists to cooperate in hospitals. Nurses and technicians are always available.

In many homes, there is not room to care for a sick person. In cities, many people live in small apartments; in rural communities, the trend is toward smaller houses. Hospitals provide a place for members of the family who are ill.

There are no servants in most

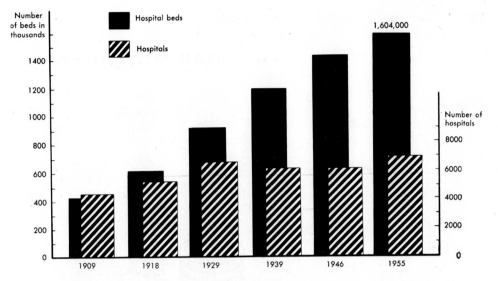

Increase in hospitals and hospital beds in the United States 1909–1955.

homes; many wives are employed outside the home; and mothers with young children are kept extremely busy. If someone becomes ill, there may be no one in the home who can give the time needed to care for a sick person.

Most hospitals for the care of patients with mental illness and with tuberculosis are provided by the government. Many people buy hospital insurance so that they can afford to go to hospitals when they are ill. All this means that hospitals are much more commonly accepted than they were in the past. In many communities, almost all babies are now born in hospitals.

In 1955, more than 21 million persons were admitted as patients to hospitals in this country. This means about one person out of every eight during this one year. It is estimated that to take care of our needs there should be one hospital bed for every 100 people.

CAN PEOPLE AFFORD GOOD MEDICAL CARE?

Medical care today costs more than it did in the past. Are the costs too high? Can people pay them?

Modern medical care makes use of many highly trained persons—physicians, nurses, laboratory technicians, hospital employees. Laboratories, hospitals, and offices cost money to build, equip, and maintain. All this makes illness expensive.

One way, however, to look at the cost of anything is in terms of what the money buys. Modern medical care costs money. Is it worth it?

The answer is that people live longer and are healthier today than ever before in the history of the world. Modern medical care is partly responsible for this. Are life and health

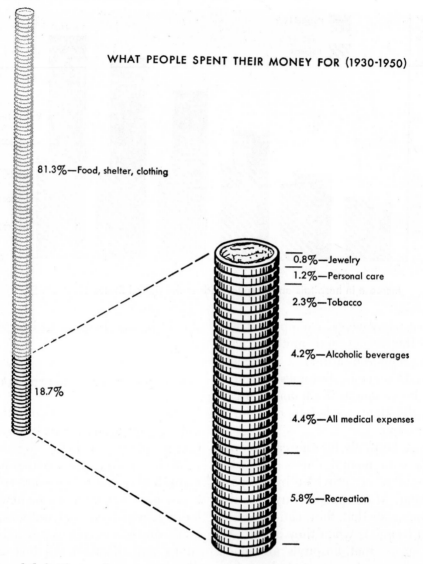

WHAT PEOPLE SPENT THEIR MONEY FOR (1930-1950)

81.3%—Food, shelter, clothing

18.7%

0.8%—Jewelry
1.2%—Personal care

2.3%—Tobacco

4.2%—Alcoholic beverages

4.4%—All medical expenses

5.8%—Recreation

worth while? If so, they are worth paying for.

Many people have money enough to pay for good medical care but spend it for other things. Government reports show, for example, that the American people each year spend more than twice as much for tobacco as they spend for the services of physicians and dentists. Many people spend more for candy, cosmetics, chewing gum, and movies than for all kinds of medical care.

Some people think that they are spending money for health when they are actually wasting it. The nation's drug bill is enormous, but much of it is for pills and lotions and advertised products that cost money and do little or no good. Many people try to treat

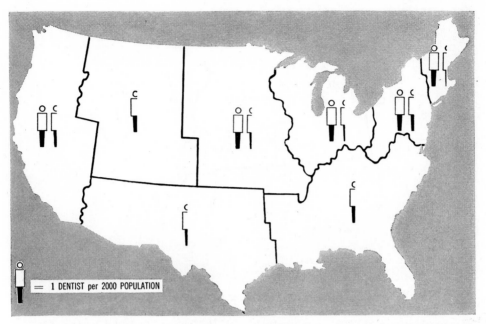

The number of dentists in relation to population also shows regional differences.

their own ills, because they are afraid it would cost too much to go to a physician. Frequently, such people spend several times as much money on useless "medicines" as they would need to spend for the services of a well-trained physician.

Planning ahead for health care. If people were sick as often as they are hungry, they might budget for medical expenses, just as they budget for food. But illness comes unexpectedly. When it does strike, it may wreck the family finances.

Many people meet the cost of illness simply by saving a little each week or each month. Just as a family saves money to buy an automobile or a television set, so they may save for hospital and physicians' and dentists' bills. Some families keep a sum of

money in the bank, to provide for health emergencies. Other people prefer insurance plans.

Insurance plans. Many millions of people carry insurance against the costs of hospital care with the Blue Cross hospital insurance plan or with a regular insurance company. Other insurance plans, such as Blue Shield, cover the fees of physicians and surgeons. It is more difficult to set up medical care in insurance plans than hospital insurance schemes, but sound programs are being developed in increasing numbers, and millions of persons now carry this protection.

In this country, accident and sickness insurance is sold by many commercial insurance companies that set their rates so as to yield a profit to the company. Other plans are set up

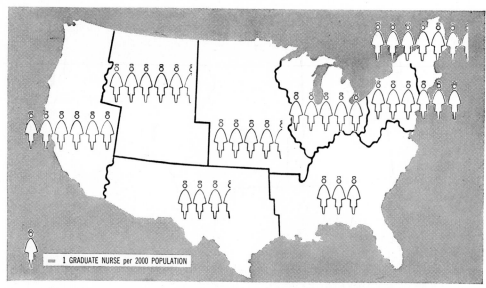

= 1 GRADUATE NURSE per 2000 POPULATION

Note the regional differences in number of nurses in relation to population.

by organizations that do not make a profit on the insurance sold. This is true for the Blue Cross and Blue Shield programs. Many industrial and labor organizations have their own nonprofit plans for health insurance.

By means of these experiments and programs, the American people are working out plans to make it possible for everyone to meet the costs of good medical care.

PUBLIC-HEALTH SERVICES

Where people live widely scattered, health is largely an individual matter. If one person who lives far from other people has a communicable disease, he puts very few other people in danger. If his well is not safe, the water is used only by his family and his stock.

In a thickly populated community, one person is constantly in contact with other people and, therefore, can give infections to them and receive infections from them. Many people share public water and milk supplies. Rules about quarantine, care of food and water supplies, and sewage disposal are all aimed at controlling the spread of communicable diseases among large groups of people.

There are other problems to which we give public attention, because everyone is concerned with them and because they demand more money than individuals can provide. Research in control of poliomyelitis is one example.

Public-health departments. In the cities, counties, and states of this country, there are public-health departments whose job it is to promote the health of all citizens. In the federal government, the United States Public Health Service is concerned

A public-health quarantine officer and other government inspectors board an arriving ship in New York Harbor. (Courtesy U.S. Public Health Service)

with the health of the whole nation.

One job of public-health departments is to control communicable diseases. Sanitation and quarantine are aspects of public control of communicable diseases.

Many public-health departments have divisions concerned with the health of special groups in the population—mothers and babies, school children, and, in recent years, the aged. Health instruction and advice are given to people in these various groups. These people also receive information on where they can go to secure treatment when they become ill.

Another important job of public-health departments is to keep our vital statistics. That is, they keep track of how many babies are born and how many people die. They know what the causes of death are from day to day, week to week, and year to year. They know where epidemics are occurring and how they are spreading.

They give us a picture of the health of the nation as a whole and show us what problems we are conquering and what problems we are neglecting.

Health departments can force people to do certain things, for example, to get rid of rats or to keep dirt from food that is to be sold. For the most part, however, their job is to educate people to know what they as individuals should do and to want to do it. In some states, for example, vaccination against smallpox is compulsory. In other states, public-health agencies cannot force people to be immunized. They try to make people understand that they should be immunized and make it easy for them to do so.

Other governmental agencies. In every community there are other public agencies concerned with health. Hospital care and medical treatment must be provided for people who cannot pay for them. In some communities, the welfare department takes this

A local health-department officer is taking swab samples from glasses in a restaurant. These samples will be tested for the number of bacteria. (Courtesy U.S. Public Health Service)

responsibility or there may be a separate division of hospitals.

In the national government, in addition to the United States Public Health Service, a number of other departments and bureaus are concerned with health. For example, the health of mothers and babies and the safeguarding of working minors are the special responsibility of the Children's Bureau. A special Congressional Act provides care for crippled children. The Department of Agriculture has a school lunch program. The Armed Services give complete medical care to servicemen and women and provide some care for their families. The Bureau of Indian Affairs gives health services to Indians on reservations.

Voluntary health agencies. Voluntary health agencies are supported by gifts. The Red Cross is a voluntary agency that is closely affiliated with our national government. It works with the Armed Services, but it also sends help all over the world, wherever there is need. Floods, famines, earthquakes, bombings, epidemics, all leave people sick and hungry. The Red Cross tries to provide whatever is needed—food, clothing, medicine, immunizations, hospital care. Every year people are asked to give money to support the Red Cross. In time of emergency, they may be asked for special gifts of food, clothing, or money.

Other well-known voluntary agencies are concerned with controlling tuberculosis, poliomyelitis, cancer, and heart disease. Still others are interested in the needs of special groups, such as crippled children, the blind, the deaf, babies, and veterans. There are visiting-nurse associations, which provide nursing care for patients in their homes. Safety councils are concerned with accident prevention.

Voluntary agencies can change from one program to another as needs change. Often they show a community what should be done and then turn the work over to agencies supported by taxes. For example, the National Tuberculosis Association for many years provided hospitals and medical care for tuberculosis patients. Now, this association devotes its energy to finding new cases and to educating people about tuberculosis.

World Health Organization. The World Health Organization is one of the agencies of the United Nations. It attempts to study health problems of the whole world—for example, care of mothers and babies and control of tuberculosis and malaria.

HEALTH IN INDUSTRY AND BUSINESS

People in industry and business have their own health problems. One reason for our laws about hours of work and minimum wages is that we do not want anyone to work so long that his health is in danger, and we want everyone to have money enough for good food, a good home, and medical care.

Most industries and business firms give vacations and sick leaves with pay. In many states, employees and employers share the costs of insurance against accidents on the job. The federal Social Security plan and various kinds of old-age benefits help older people to have health care. Many labor unions have their own programs for providing health care, hospitalization, and sick benefits to members and their families.

Laws about safety and health. Certain industries have special hazards. Mining, for example, involves dangers of cave-ins, fires, gases, and floods. In metalworking, there are dangers involved in working with furnaces and hot metals. Dangerous chemicals are used in some factories. Certain trades expose workers to dust, to gas fumes, or to sparks. There is always a danger from careless use of machines.

Laws provide that these hazards be reduced as much as possible. Laws, however, cannot solve the problem. Workers must understand the hazards and must be willing to do their share in protecting themselves and others. It is easy to become careless, to forget to wear protective masks, to light a match where there may be inflammable gases, to take dangerous short cuts, to look away from machinery in operation, and to do some of the hundred and one things that may cost an injury or a life.

Laws also provide for the sanitation of factories and of workers' camps. Water must be safe, sewage must be properly disposed of, rest rooms must be provided, and ventilation must be adequate. In addition, many industries provide rest periods for workers, hot lunches in clean, quiet lunchrooms, health examinations, and x-rays.

Young people at work. Special protection is thrown about the work of young people. They are not as strong as grown men and women, so laws limit the kinds of work in which they may be employed, their hours of labor, and the time of day when they may work, and require special rest periods. Where the things made in a factory are sold outside the state, there are federal regulations that the employer must follow. These are usually more strict than local or state regulations. In other words, the whole nation is concerned with protecting the health of young workers.

In many states, it is illegal to hire persons younger than 15 or 16 in most industries. This regulation usually does not apply to farm work, messenger service, and selling newspapers. Young people injured in these occupations are not protected by the laws that safeguard workers in other occupations.

MAKE AMERICA STRONG AND HEALTHY

Health today plays a large part in the affairs of every community. Our taxes support public-health agencies that deal with the health of all of us. We make laws to protect our health. We give money to agencies to work on special problems, such as poliomyelitis, heart disease, and cancer. And we spend millions of dollars for medical care.

Yet there is more to be done. We need more information about how to keep people healthy. But, even more important, we must make better use of the knowledge already available to each and every one of us. The diamond mine of good health, "life's greatest treasure," is within our reach. Let us not pass it by.

Never has our country been in greater need of strength and clear thinking. Each one of us has a responsibility to contribute to this by personally keeping strong and healthy and by taking part in activities that will make for a healthier and stronger community and nation.

SO WHAT?

Many kinds of medical and health services are needed for the prevention of disease and for medical care; and

Some of these services we can provide for ourselves, while others can be provided only by groups of people working together; and

Many people do not make good use of the health services that are available to them;

So, it is in your interest to be informed about the health services of your community and to help develop, support, and use these services so that everyone will get the most out of them.

CHECKING UP

1. What are the two most important characteristics to look for in a health adviser?
2. What is the relationship of a family physician to his patients? What is the relationship of a family physician to medical specialists?

3. What assistance in caring for the sick do modern physicians have that physicians in earlier times did not have?
4. What are some of the reasons people waste their money and time on poor health care?
5. What are the advantages of caring for sick people in hospitals rather than in their homes? Are there disadvantages?
6. What is health insurance? Why is it difficult to plan ahead for health care? List different methods for providing health insurance.
7. What are the jobs of public-health departments?
8. What is the United States Public Health Service?
9. How are governmental health agencies supported financially? How are voluntary health agencies supported? List some governmental health agencies; some voluntary health agencies.
10. Why will laws alone do little to improve the health of persons in industry? What more is needed?
11. Under what conditions is a factory subject to federal laws? Which laws—local, state, or federal—are usually most strict about providing healthful and safe working conditions?
12. What are some of the laws regulating the work of young people? Why have these been passed?

THINGS TO DO

1. Make a survey of the health facilities in your community. Find how many physicians there are; how many medical specialists. Find the number of dentists. Are some of them specialists? Find the number of hospitals and hospital beds. Are there special hospitals for the tuberculous and the mentally disabled?
2. What is the population of your community? Divide the population by the number of physicians to find the ratio of physicians to population. Find the ratio of dentists to population; the ratio of hospital beds to population. Do there seem to be enough physicians, dentists, and hospital beds?
3. Ask older people how illness was handled when they were young. Compare the length of life and infant mortality in those days and now.
4. Ask someone from the health department to talk about the work of his department. Ask for health-department bulletins. Try to get from them a picture of health conditions in your

community. What are its problems? What are the chief activities of the health department?

5. Ask your city or county health department what kind of health care is given to persons who cannot pay for it in your community. How are the handicapped cared for?

6. Give special reports on the work of your state department of health; the United States Public Health Service; the World Health Organization; the Crippled Children's Act; the Children's Bureau.

7. Make a list of the voluntary health agencies in your community (Red Cross, Tuberculosis Association, Safety Council, Cancer Society, and others). Visit their headquarters. Find what they do in the community and how they are financed. Find how you can give assistance.

8. Visit a hospital; an x-ray laboratory; a medical laboratory. How many people work in each? What do they do?

9. List the principal industries in your community (consult the Census reports and chamber of commerce). What special hazards are associated with each?

10. Visit factories or other industrial plants. How is the health of the workers safeguarded?

11. Ask a social-studies teacher how you can find the state and federal laws on child labor and young workers. How is their health protected?

12. Study the health program in your school. How are epidemics controlled? Are the students given health examinations? Are the grounds, gyms, halls, and laboratories safe? Do the students have a chance to obtain good lunches? Ask teachers of biology, home economics, physical education, and other subjects how they contribute to the health program.

13. Ask an insurance company what are the costs of insurance compared with costs of accidents, illness, and hospitalization. Study the Blue Cross plan for hospitalization (or any other plan available in your community). Find whether insurance plans are available that pay for physicians' services. How much are the fees in these plans? What do they provide? Can families with ordinary incomes afford them?

14. Give special reports on government health insurance in England, Sweden, and other countries.

For Further Reading

CHAPTER 1

Atkinson, Donald T. *Magic, Myth, and Medicine.* The World Publishing Co., Cleveland, 1956.

Marriott, Henry J. L. *Medical Milestones.* The Williams & Wilkins Co., Baltimore, 1952.

National Midcentury Committee for Children and Youth, Inc. *As Children Go, So Goes the Nation.* 160 Broadway, New York.

Ruck, F. L. and others. *People Are Important.* Scott, Foresman & Co., Chicago, 1941.

Rusk, Howard. "The State of the Union's Health," *New York Times Magazine,* July 22, 1956.

Winslow, C. E. A. and Grace T. Hallock. *Health Through the Ages.* Metropolitan Life Insurance Co., 1 Madison Ave., New York.

CHAPTER 2

Crawford, J. E. and L. E. Woodward. *Better Ways of Growing Up.* Muhlenberg Press, Philadelphia, 1948.

Crow, Lester M. and Alice. *Adolescent Development and Adjustment.* McGraw-Hill Book Co., Inc., New York, 1956.

Duval, Evelyn M. *Keeping Up with Teen-Agers.* Public Affairs Committee. 22 East 38 St., New York.

Gallagher, J. Roswell. *Understanding Your Son's Adolescence.* Little, Brown & Co., Boston, 1951.

Josselyn, Irene M. *The Adolescent and His World.* Family Service Association of America, 192 Lexington Ave., New York, 1952.

Moore, B. W. and D. M. Leahy. *You and Your Family.* D. C. Heath & Co., Boston, 1948.

Neugarten, Bernice L. *How You Grow, Junior Life Adjustment Booklet.* Science Research Associates, 57 West Grand Ave., Chicago, 1951.

Spock, Benjamin. *The Common Sense Book of Baby and Child Care.* Duell, Sloan & Pearce, New York, 1946. Also in Pocket Book edition.

CHAPTER 3

American Automobile Association. *Sportsmanlike Driving,* 2d ed. Pennsylvania Ave. at 17 St., Washington, 1948.

Dearborn, Ned H. and Bill Andrews. *Your Safety Handbook, Junior Life Adjustment Booklet.* Science Research Associates, 1952.

Herschensohn, H. L. *It Wasn't My Fault.* American Medical Association, 535 North Dearborn St., Chicago, Illinois, 1940.

International Harvester Co. *Farm Accidents.* 180 North Michigan Ave., Chicago.

Metropolitan Life Insurance Co. *How's Your Driving.*

——. *Safety Begins at Home.*

National Commission on Safety Education. *High-School Driver Education: Policies and Recommendations.* National Education Association, 1201 Sixteenth St., N.W., Washington, 1950.

National Safety Council. *Accident Facts.* 425 North Michigan Ave., Chicago. (Published every year)

U.S. Public Health Service. *Swimming,*

Health Information Series No. 7. Department of Health, Education, and Welfare, Washington.

Yahraes, Herbert. *Make Your Town Safe.* Public Affairs Committee.

CHAPTER 4

American National Red Cross. *Youth on Guard against Accidents, Workbook-Textbook.* Washington 13, 1947.

American Red Cross First Aid Textbook for Juniors. The Blakiston Co., New York, 1949.

Boy Scouts of America. *First Aid and Rescue Methods.* 2 Park Ave., New York.

Children's Medical Center. *Accident Handbook.* 300 Longwood Ave., Boston.

Federal Civil Defense Administration. *Emergency Action to Save Lives.* Superintendent of Documents, Washington, July, 1951.

Metropolitan Life Insurance Co. *What to Do While Waiting for the Doctor.*

U.S. Public Health Service. *Home Care of the Sick, Health Information Series No. 21.* Department of Health, Education, and Welfare, Washington.

Wheatley, George M. "The Public Health Problem of Accidental Poisoning," *American Journal of Public Health,* August, 1956.

CHAPTER 5

Beck, L. F. *Human Growth.* Harcourt, Brace & Co., New York, 1949.

Clendening, Logan. *The Human Body.* Alfred A. Knopf, New York, 1945.

Gesell, Arnold and Katherine Walden. *How a Baby Grows.* Harper & Bros., New York, 1945.

Johnson, Dallas. *Facing the Facts about Cancer.* Public Affairs Committee.

Pfeiffer, John. *Genetics—The Science of Heredity.* Public Affairs Committee.

U.S. Public Health Service. *Cancer: What to Know, What to Do about It, Cancer Series No. 1.* Department of Health, Education, and Welfare, Washington.

CHAPTER 6

American Medical Association. *Wonder Stories of the Human Machine: The Framework (Bones).* 1939.

——. *Wonder Stories of the Human Machine: The Running Gear (Muscles).* 1939.

Blakeslee, Alton L. *Arthritis—And the Miracle Drugs.* Public Affairs Committee.

Jenkins, Patricia. *Arthritis—The Story of Compound E.* American Medical Association, 1939.

——. *The Facts about Arthritis.* American Medical Association, 1950.

Lautmann, M. F. *Preventing Arthritis.* American Medical Association, 1949.

CHAPTER 7

Fluck, Paul H. *So You Can't Sleep?* American Medical Association, 1950.

Hein, Fred V. *Johnny Makes the Team.* American Medical Association, 1948.

Lewin, Philip. *Sitting Pretty.* American Medical Association, 1950.

Lile, Letha O. *Sleep: How Much Do We Know about It? Today's Health.* American Medical Association, Dec., 1951.

Richmond, Julius B. *Your Health Handbook, Junior Life Adjustment Booklet.* Science Research Associates, 1953.

Riedman, Sarah R. *The Physiology of Work and Play.* Dryden Press, New York, 1950.

Scott, Ruth B. *Your Posture Is Showing.* American Medical Association, 1949.

U.S. Public Health Service. *Care of the Feet, Health Information Series No. 4.*

Department of Health, Education, and Welfare, Washington.

CHAPTER 8

Agriculture Handbook No. 8. *Composition of Foods: Raw, Processed, Prepared.* Superintendent of Documents, Government Printing Office, Washington, 1950.

Borsook, Henry and William Huse. *Vitamins for Health.* Public Affairs Committee.

Bureau of Human Nutrition and Home Economics. *Nutrition, Up-to-Date: Up to You.* U.S. Department of Agriculture, Washington, 1950.

Roberts, Lydia J. *The Road to Good Nutrition.* U.S. Children's Bureau, Department of Health, Education, and Welfare, Washington.

CHAPTER 9

Amidon, E. P., D. E. Bradberry, and V. V. Drenckhahn. *Good Food and Nutrition for Young People and Their Families.* John Wiley & Sons, New York, 1946.

Bureau of Human Nutrition and Home Economics. *Food for Families with School Children.* U.S. Department of Agriculture, Washington, 1951.

——. *Food Values in Common Portions.* U.S. Department of Agriculture, Washington, 1951.

Leverton, Ruth M. *A Girl and Her Figure.* National Dairy Council, Chicago, 1955.

Metropolitan Life Insurance Co. *Food for the Family.*

Rowntree, Jennie. *The Problem of Food.* Public Affairs Committee.

U.S. Office of Education. *A Selected List of Nutrition and School Lunch Materials, Misc. 3392.* Department of Health, Education, and Welfare, Washington, 1951.

U.S. Public Health Service. *What Every Person Should Know about Milk, Supplement 150 to Public Health Reports.* Department of Health, Education, and Welfare, Washington.

CHAPTER 10

American Medical Association. *Wonder Stories of the Human Machine: The Body Finish (Skin).* 1939.

Block, Maxine. *Are Hormone Creams a Skin Game?* American Medical Association, 1949.

Cole, Harold N. *The Skin in Health and Disease.* American Medical Association, 1951.

Conley, V. L. "Grooming Aids for Young Men," *Today's Health,* April, 1955.

Goldsmith, N. R. *Acne, the Tragedy of Youth.* American Medical Association, 1948.

Kaufman, S. M. *Superfluous Hair and Acne.* American Medical Association, 1946.

Levin, Oscar L. and Howard T. Behrman. *Your Hair and Its Care.* Emerson Books, New York, 1945.

Smith, Austin. *Cosmetics, Facts and Fancies.* American Medical Association, 1947.

U.S. Public Health Service. *Poison Ivy, Health Information Series No. 65.* Department of Health, Education, and Welfare, Washington.

——. *Ringworm, Including Athlete's Foot, Health Information Series No. 6.* Department of Health, Education, and Welfare, Washington.

CHAPTER 11

American National Red Cross. *The Story of Blood.* Washington, D.C. 1951.

Blakeslee, Alton L. *Blood—Your Gift of Life.* Public Affairs Committee.

Cohn, E. J. "Blood and Blood Derivatives" in *Serving through Science.* United States Rubber Co., 1230 Avenue of the Americas, New York, 1946.

Matson, G. Albin. *Some Facts about Rh.* Minneapolis War Memorial Blood Bank, 1914 LaSalle Ave., Minneapolis.

CHAPTER 12

American Medical Association. *Healthy Hearts.* 1947.

——. *Wonder Stories of the Human Machine: The Engine (Heart).* 1939.

Blakeslee, Howard. *Know Your Heart.* Public Affairs Committee.

Crosby, Alexander L. *Your Blood Pressure and Your Arteries.* Public Affairs Committee.

Marvin, H. M. and others. *You and Your Heart.* Random House, New York, 1950.

U.S. Public Health Service. *Heart Disease, a Story of Progress, Public Health Service Publication No. 17.* Department of Health, Education, and Welfare, Washington.

Yahraes, Herbert. *Rheumatic Fever— Childhood's Greatest Enemy.* Public Affairs Committee.

CHAPTER 13

Metropolitan Life Insurance Co. *Respiratory Diseases.*

Rubber Manufacturers Association. *Ker-Choo and You.* 440 Madison Ave., New York.

Swartz, Harry. *Allergy: What It Is and What to Do about It.* Rutgers University Press, New Brunswick, N.J., 1949.

U.S. Public Health Service. *Allergy, Health Information Series No. 32.* Department of Health, Education, and Welfare, Washington.

Vaughan, Warren T. Rev. by J. Harvey Black. *Primer of Allergy,* 3rd ed. C. V. Mosby Co., St. Louis, 1950.

CHAPTER 14

American Medical Association. *Wonder Stories of the Human Machine: The Breather Pipes and Thermostatic Control (Lungs and Skin).* 1939.

CHAPTER 15

American Dental Association. *Attractive Teeth for Teen-Agers.* 222 East Superior St., Chicago, 1950.

Ast, D. B., and E. R. Schlesinger. "Fluoridation and Caries," *American Journal of Public Health,* March, 1956.

Gardner, W. M. *The Care of the Teeth.* American Medical Association, 1946.

Howe, P. R. *Our Food and Our Teeth.* American Medical Association, 1937.

Metropolitan Life Insurance Co. *For Good Teeth.*

U.S. Public Health Service. *Better Health for 5 to 14 Cents a Year through Fluoridated Water, Public Health Service Publication No. 62.* Department of Health, Education, and Welfare, Washington.

——. *Good Teeth, Supplement 149 to the Public Health Service.* Department of Health, Education, and Welfare.

CHAPTER 16

American Medical Association. *Wonder Stories of the Human Machine: The Fuel System (Digestion).* 1939.

Cannon, Walter B. *Digestion and Health.* W. W. Norton & Co., New York, 1936.

CHAPTER 17

American Medical Association. *Wonder Stories of the Human Machine: The Exhaust (Waste Removal).* 1939.

CHAPTER 18

American Medical Association. *Wonder Stories of the Human Machine: The Electric System (Nerves).* 1939.

Cannon, Walter B. *The Wisdom of the Body*. W. W. Norton & Co., New York, 1939.

National Foundation for Infantile Paralysis. *Poliomyelitis—A Source Book for High-School Students*. 120 Broadway, New York, 1952.

Rutstein, David. "How Good is Polio Vaccine," *The Atlantic*, February, 1957.

CHAPTER 19

Barry, Herbert, Jr. *The Mind in Sickness and in Health*. John Hancock Mutual Life Insurance Co., Boston, 1951.

Dimond, Stanley E. *You and Your Problems, Junior Life Adjustment Booklet*. Science Research Associates, 1952.

Duvall, Evelyn M. *Facts of Life and Love for Teen-Agers*, second edition. Association Press, New York, 1956.

Jenkins, G. G. and Joy Newman. *How to Live with Parents, Life Adjustment Booklet Series*. Science Research Associates, 1948.

Menninger, W. C. *Understanding Yourself, Life Adjustment Booklet Series*. Science Research Associates, 1948.

Miller, F. S. and H. H. Laitem. *Personal Problems of the High School Girl*, 2d ed. John Wiley & Sons, New York, 1945.

Neugarten, Bernice L. *How to Get Along with Others, Junior Life Adjustment Booklet*. Science Research Associates, 1953.

——, and Paul J. Misner. *Getting Along in School, Junior Life Adjustment Booklet*. Science Research Associates, 1951.

Peale, Norman V. and Smiley Blanton. *The Art of Real Happiness*. Prentice-Hall, New York, 1950.

Pratt, Dallas and Jack Neher. *Mental Health Is a Family Affair*. Public Affairs Committee.

Thorman, George. *Toward Mental Health*. Public Affairs Committee.

Ullmann, Frances. *Life with Brothers and Sisters, Junior Life Adjustment Booklet*. Science Research Associates, 1952.

Whiteside-Taylor, Katharine. *Getting Along with Parents, Junior Life Adjustment Booklet*. Science Research Associates, 1952.

Whitmer, Helen Leland and Ruth Kotinsky. *Personality in the Making*. Harper & Bros., New York, 1952.

CHAPTER 20

American Medical Association. *Wonder Stories of the Human Machine: Safety Devices (the Sense Organs)*. 1939.

DuBois, Cleo. *How to Save Your Eyes*. American Medical Association, 1945.

National Society for the Prevention of Blindness. *Crossed Eyes—A Needless Handicap*. 1790 Broadway, New York.

Phillips, Wendell C. and Hugh G. Rowell. *Your Hearing—How to Preserve and Aid It*. World Publishing Co., Cleveland, 1943.

U.S. Public Health Service. *Care of the Eyes, Health Information Series No. 64*. Department of Health, Education, and Welfare, Washington.

——. *How to Protect Your Hearing, Health Information Series No. 53*. Department of Health, Education, and Welfare, Washington.

Yahraes, Herbert. *What Do You Know about Blindness?* Public Affairs Committee.

CHAPTER 21

Buck, Robert N. "Why an Airline Pilot Quit Smoking," *Reader's Digest*, July, 1956.

Deutsch, Albert. *Narcotics*. Public Affairs Committee, 1952.

Kolb, Laurence. "Let's Stop This Narcotics Hysteria," *Saturday Evening Post*, July 28, 1956.

McCarthy, R. G. *Facts about Alcohol, Life Adjustment Booklet Series*. Science Research Associates, 1952.

Merrill, Frederick T. *Marihuana—The New Dangerous Drug*. Foreign Policy Association, New York, 1951.

Norr, Roy. "Cancer by the Carton." *The Reader's Digest*, Dec., 1952.

Riis, R. W. "How Harmful Are Cigarettes?" *The Reader's Digest*, Jan., 1950.

Spaulding, W. B. and J. R. Montague. *Alcohol and Human Affairs*. World Book Co., Yonkers, N.Y., 1949.

Steinhaus, Arthur H. and F. M. Grunderman. *Tobacco and Health*, 4th ed. Association Press, New York, 1948.

Weston, Paul B. *Narcotics U.S.A.* Greenberg Co., New York, 1952.

Yahraes, Herbert. *Alcoholism—A Sickness That Can Be Beaten*. Public Affairs Committee, 1952.

CHAPTER 22

Gregory, Jennie. *ABC of the Endocrines*. The Williams & Wilkins Co., Baltimore, 1935.

Yahraes, Herbert. *Good News about Diabetes*. Public Affairs Committee.

CHAPTER 23

American Journal of Public Health. *A Century of Progress through Sanitation*. New York, June, 1953.

Smiley, Dean F. and A. G. Gould. *Your Community's Health*. The Macmillan Co., New York, 1952.

U.S. Public Health Service. *Clean Water Is Everybody's Business, Public Health Service Publication No. 11*. Department of Health, Education, and Welfare, Washington, 1950.

——. *Environment and Health, Public Health Service Publication No. 84*. Department of Health, Education, and Welfare, Washington, 1951.

——. *Home Sanitation, Health Information Series No. 35. Public Health Service Publication No. 231*. Department of Health, Education, and Welfare, Washington, 1952.

——. *What Every Person Should Know about Milk, Supplement No. 150 to Public Health Reports*. Department of Health, Education, and Welfare, Washington, 1950.

CHAPTER 24

DeKruif, Paul. *Microbe Hunters*. Harcourt, Brace & Co., New York, 1926.

Hill, Justina. *Germs and the Man*. G. P. Putnam's Sons, New York, 1940.

Metropolitan Life Insurance Co. *Health Heroes—Edward Jenner*. 1926.

——. *Health Heroes—Louis Pasteur*. 1925.

CHAPTER 25

American Public Health Association. *Control of Communicable Diseases*. 1790 Broadway, New York, January, 1950.

Blakeslee, Alton L. *TB—The Killer Cornered*. Public Affairs Committee. 1952.

McCall, Marie. *The Long Adventure: Chapters in the Story of Tuberculosis Control*. National Tuberculosis Association, 1790 Broadway, New York, 1946.

Metropolitan Life Insurance Co. *Health Heroes—Robert Koch*. 1932.

——. *Health Heroes—Walter Reed*. 1926.

Perkins, James E. and Floyd M. Feldman. *You and Tuberculosis*. Alfred A. Knopf, New York, 1952.

Pyle, Marjorie M. *Help Yourself Get Well*. Appleton-Century-Crofts, New York, 1951.

Wilmer, Harry A. *The Lives and Loves of Huber and Tuber*. National Tuberculosis Association, 1949.

Zinsser, Hans. *Rats, Lice and History*. Little, Brown & Co., Boston, 1935.

CHAPTER 26

Crampton, C. Ward. *Live Long and Like It*. Public Affairs Committee.

Health Information Foundation. *The Multiple Screening Idea*. 420 Lexington Ave., New York.

Singer-Brooks, Charlotte. "Of What Value Are Health Inventories Filled Out by Parents?" *American Journal of Public Health*, June, 1952.

CHAPTER 27

American Dental Association. *Dentistry as a Professional Career*. 1953.

Kitch, Donald E. *Exploring the World of Jobs, Junior Life Adjustment Booklet*. Science Research Associates, 1952.

Lee, Roger I. *The Happy Life of a Doctor*. Little, Brown, and Company, Boston, 1956.

Lewis, Edith P. *Opportunities in Nursing*. Vocational Guidance Manuals, New York, 1952.

Metropolitan Life Insurance Co. *Health Heroes—Marie Curie*. 1937.

———. *Health Heroes—Florence Nightingale*. 1928.

Smith, C. R. "Medicine at a New Frontier," *Fortune Magazine*, July, 1956.

Stoops, Emery and Lucile Rosenheim. *Planning Your Job Future, Junior Life Adjustment Booklet*. Science Research Associates, 1953.

Williams, Harley. *The Healing Touch*. Charles C. Thomas, Springfield, Ill., 1951.

CHAPTER 28

American Medical Association. *A Doctor for Your Community*. 1953.

Council on Medical Service. *Voluntary Prepayment Medical Benefit Plans*. American Medical Association, 1953.

Health Careers Guide Book, National Health Council, New York, 1955.

Dunn, Halbert L. "Public Health Begins in the Family," *Public Health Report*, Washington, October, 1956.

Maisel, Albert Q. *Your Neighbor's Health Is Your Business*. Public Affairs Committee, 1952.

National Society for Medical Research. *How Will Biological-Medical Research Help Me to Live Longer?* 208 North Wells St., Chicago.

Pink, Louis H. *The Story of Blue Cross— A National Health Plan*. Public Affairs Committee, 1953.

Riis, R. W. "They Guard Our Food and Drugs." *The Reader's Digest*, June, 1952.

The President's Commission on the Health Needs of the Nation. *Building America's Health, Findings and Recommendations*, Vol. I. Superintendent of Documents, Washington, 1953.

———. *Services for Crippled Children, Children's Bureau Folder 38*. Washington, 1952.

U.S. Public Health Service. *The Public Health Nurse in Your Community, Public Health Service Publication No. 47*. Department of Health, Education, and Welfare, Washington, 1951.

———. *Guide to Health Organization in the United States, Public Health Service Publication No. 196*. Department of Health, Education, and Welfare, Washington, 1953.

Winslow, C. E. A. *The Cost of Sickness and the Price of Health. World Health Organization Monograph Series No. 7*. International Documents Service, Columbia University Press, New York, 1951.

Glossary

abdomen (ăb dō′mĕn). The abdominal cavity; the part of the body between the chest and the hips. It contains the liver, stomach, intestines, and other organs; it is sometimes referred to as the "stomach."

abscess (ăb′sĕs). A collection of pus.

absorbed (ăb sôrbd′). Taken into. For example, digested food is absorbed into the blood stream.

acne (ăk′nē). A skin condition marked by pimples and small red lumps, usually on the back, chest, and face. Acne often develops during the teens.

ACTH. A hormone secreted by the pituitary gland. It acts on the adrenal glands and is used in treatment of arthritis and other diseases.

acute (à kūt′). Severe but lasting a short time; for example, acute infection.

addict (ăd′ĭkt) (drug). A person who has developed the habit of using drugs and depends upon them for a sense of well-being.

adenoids (ăd′ė noidz). Two masses of lymph tissue that are located in the pharynx.

adolescence (ăd ô les′ĕns). The period roughly between the ages of 12 and 20; the time when children are growing into adults.

adolescent (ăd ô les′ĕnt). A boy or girl in the period of adolescence.

adrenal (ăd rē′năl) **glands.** Two endocrine glands that lie above the kidneys.

afferent (ăf′ēr ĕnt) **nerve.** A nerve that carries impulses toward the central nervous system.

air-conditioning. Cleaning air and adjusting its temperature and humidity, so that persons indoors will be comfortable no matter what the outside conditions are.

alcoholic (ăl kŏ hŏl′ĭk). (1) Pertaining to alcohol. (2) A person suffering from alcoholism; one addicted to the use of alcohol.

alcoholism (ăl′kŏ hŏl ĭz′m). An illness due to prolonged drinking of alcohol.

allergy (ăl′ēr jĭ). A condition of not being able to come in contact with certain substances without harmful effects. A person may be allergic to substances such as pollen or fur or certain foods, which are harmless to most people.

alveoli (ăl vē′ō lī) (*sing.* alveolus). Tiny air sacs that make up the greater part of the lungs.

amino (ă mē′nō) **acids.** End-products of the digestion of proteins; they are the building blocks from which the blood makes its own proteins.

anemia (à nē′mĭ à). A condition that results when a person's blood cannot carry enough oxygen for good health; it is caused by lack of hemoglobin. Nutritional anemia results from lack of iron in the diet. Pernicious anemia results from failure of the body to make enough red blood cells.

anesthesia (ăn ĕs thē′zhĭ à). Loss of sensation. Local anesthesia stops the pain impulses that come from one area, as from around a tooth. Spinal anesthesia is produced by injecting around the spinal cord a drug that blocks passage of impulses to the brain.

antibody (ăn′tĭ bŏd ĭ). A chemical produced in the blood that reacts against other substances, such as disease organisms or their toxins.

antihistamine (ăn tĭ hĭs′tȧ mēn). A drug used in the treatment of allergies; it is supposed to react against excess histamine in the tissues.

antiseptic (ăn tĭ sĕp′tĭk). A substance that kills microorganisms or keeps them from growing.

antitoxin (ăn tĭ tŏk′sĭn). Antibodies that destroy toxins.

aorta (ȧ ôr′tȧ). The large artery leaving the left ventricle of the heart. Branches from the aorta supply blood to all parts of the body except the lungs.

apoplexy (ăp′ȯ plĕk sĭ). Unconsciousness that results when small blood vessels in the brain are broken or are closed by a clot.

appendicitis (ă pĕn dĭ sĭ′tĭs). Infection of the appendix.

appendix (ă pĕn′dĭks) (vermiform). A small blind tube located where the small and large intestines join. (*Vermiform* means wormlike.)

artery (är′tĕr ĭ). A blood vessel that carries blood away from the heart.

arthritis (är thrī′tĭs). Swollen and painful joints.

artificial respiration (är tĭ fĭsh′ăl rĕs pĭ-rā′shŭn). The forcing of air into and out of the lungs of a person who has stopped breathing.

ascorbic (ȧ skôr′bĭk) acid. Vitamin C.

association (ă sō sĭ ā′shŭn) nerve cells. Nerve cells within the brain and spinal cord.

asthma (ăz′mȧ). An allergic condition in which the muscles in the walls of the bronchi contract and make it difficult for the person to breathe.

astigmatism (ȧ stĭg′mȧ tĭz′m). A condition in which the surfaces of the eye are not curved regularly.

astringent (ăs trĭn′jĕnt). A substance, usually containing alcohol, which is used on the skin in an effort to keep it from wrinkling.

athlete's foot. A common infection caused by a fungus. It usually occurs between the toes.

audiometer (ô dĭ ŏm′ė tēr). An instrument for testing hearing.

auricles (ô′rĭ k'ls). The two upper chambers of the heart. The veins empty into the auricles.

autonomic (ô tȯ nŏm′ĭk) nervous system. The part of the nervous system that carries impulses a person cannot deliberately control.

bacteria (băk tēr′ĭ ȧ) (*sing.* bacterium). Microscopic plants. Some bacteria cause illness or infection; most bacteria are harmless.

Basic Seven. Seven groups of foods, which together supply all the nutritional needs of the body.

BCG. Bacillus Calmette-Guérin; used as a vaccine against tuberculosis.

beriberi (bĕr′ĭ bĕr′ĭ). A disease caused by lack of thiamine (a vitamin of the vitamin-B complex).

bile (bīl). A bitter fluid secreted by the liver. Bile helps in the digestion of fats in the small intestine.

bladder. A baglike organ. The urinary bladder in the lower part of the abdomen stores urine. The gall bladder under the liver stores bile.

bleeder. A person suffering from hemophilia.

blister. A swelling filled with fluid, under the top layers of the skin.

blood bank. A store of blood that can be used in emergencies.

blood poisoning. An infection in the blood stream.

blood pressure. The pressure, or push, of the blood against the walls of the arteries. Systolic pressure is the blood pressure at the time of the heartbeat (systole). Diastolic pressure is the blood pressure between heartbeats (diastole).

blood types. Blood groups. An individual's blood is said to belong in one or another of these groups. Certain blood types will mix; others will not. It is important in using blood in a transfusion to know that the blood of the person who gives the blood will mix safely with that of the person who receives the blood.

blue baby. A baby born with certain defects in the heart or large arteries. As a result, not all of the blood reaches the lungs where oxygen is picked up and carbon dioxide is lost. The color of the blood and of the baby is therefore bluish.

boil. An infection in the skin, usually around the root of a hair.

booster. A small amount of vaccine or toxoid given to a person who already has some immunity, in order to increase and continue the person's immunity.

botulinus (bŏt̬ ṷ̈ li′nŭs) **organism.** The microorganism that produces a powerful poison (toxin) causing the disease, botulism. The organism lives in foods that are not properly canned.

bowel (bou′ĕl). Intestine.

brain. The part of the nervous system that is located in the head.

breathing. Getting air into and out of the lungs.

bronchus (brŏng′kŭs) (*pl.* bronchi, brŏng′kī). One of the tubes from the trachea to the lungs.

bruise. An injury in which the skin is not broken.

caffeine (kăf′ė ĭn). A drug contained in tea and coffee; a mild stimulant.

callus. A thickening of the skin caused by rubbing or pressure.

calory (kăl′ṏ rĭ). The unit in which energy value is measured. It is used in measuring the heat energy of foods.

cancer. A growth of cells that spread and destroy healthy cells.

capillary (kăp′ĭ lĕr ĭ). A tiny blood vessel that connects arteries to veins.

carbohydrates (kär bṏ hī′drāts). Sugars and starches; nutrients that provide energy.

carbon monoxide. A poisonous gas.

carbuncle (kär′bŭng k'l). A number of boils occurring together.

cardiac (kär′dĭ ăk). Referring to the heart.

caries (kâr′ĭ ēz) (dental). Tooth decay.

carotene (kăr′ṏ tēn). The yellow coloring found in yellow vegetables and fruits and in green vegetables. The human body changes carotene to vitamin A.

carrier. A person who carries disease organisms and may spread them to other persons but is not himself sick with the disease.

cartilage (kär′tĭ lĭj). Tough connective tissue; gristle. It forms parts of the skeleton.

cataract (kăt′a răkt). Cloudiness of the lens in the eye. It causes difficulty in seeing.

cell. A small mass of living stuff (protoplasm) containing a central part called the nucleus. All living things are made up of cells.

cellulose. A kind of carbohydrate that is not digested by human beings; the woody part of cereals, vegetables, and fruits.

central nervous system. The brain and spinal cord and nerves from these.

chain of infection. The pathway by which disease organisms go from a sick person to a well person.

chemical elements. The simple substances that make up everything, living and nonliving, in the world.

chlorine (klō'rēn). A poisonous gas often used to kill microorganisms in water.

cholera (kŏl'ĕr a). A serious disease caused by organisms that enter the body with food or drink. It is rare now in the United States.

chromosomes (krō'mŏ sōmz). Short threads found in cells. They are important in determining a person's heredity.

chronic (krŏn'ĭk). Lasting a long time—that is, a chronic infection or chronic fatigue.

cilia (sĭl'ĭ a). Microscopic threadlike projections from cells in the lining of the nose and other parts of the body. Cilia wave back and forth and push substances in one direction.

circulatory (sûr'kū la tō rĭ) system. Blood, blood vessels, and heart.

citrus (sĭt'rŭs) fruits. Oranges, grapefruit, lemons, and limes.

clinic (klĭn'ĭk). An institution, usually connected with a hospital, where patients who are not bedridden come for care.

clot. A jelly-like mass. Blood forms a clot when it is exposed to air. *To clot* means to thicken.

cocaine (kō kān'). A habit-forming drug obtained from leaves of the coca tree.

cocci (kŏk'sī). Tiny, spherical bacteria. There are many kinds of cocci—for example, pneumococci, streptococci, gonococci.

codeine (kō'dĕ ēn). A drug derived from opium. It carries practically no danger of habit formation and is used to reduce pain and to treat colds and coughs.

colic (kŏl'ĭk). A severe pain that occurs at short intervals, usually in the abdomen.

color blindness. An inability to see one or more colors.

communicable (kŏ mū'nĭ ka b'l) disease. A disease that spreads from one person to another.

compress (kŏm'prĕs). A pad applied to a wound to prevent bleeding or to some part of the body to relieve pain.

concussion (kŏn kŭsh'ŭn) of the brain. Injury to the brain, usually from a blow or fall.

conjunctivitis (kŏn jŭngk tĭ vī'tĭs). Swelling and redness of the eyes, usually due to mild infection.

constipation (kŏn stĭ pā'shŭn). A condition that results from failure to get rid of wastes from the large intestine. Bowel movements occur less often than is usual and are frequently painful.

contraction. Shortening of a muscle, causing movement.

convalescent (kŏn va lĕs'ĕnt). A person who is recovering from illness. Convalescence is the period of recovery from illness.

convulsion. Violent movements of the body; a spasm.

coordination (kŏ ôr dĭ nā'shŭn). The condition in which all parts of the body are under good control and act together harmoniously.

corn. A thickening of the skin caused by rubbing or pressure.

cornea (kôr'nĕ a). The transparent covering over the front of the eye.

coronary (kŏr'ŏ nĕr ĭ) blood vessels. The blood vessels of the heart. Coronary occlusion, or coronary thrombosis, is a closing of a coronary blood vessel, thus stopping circulation of blood in the walls of the heart.

corpuscle (kôr'pŭs'l). A tiny solid particle, cell, in the blood. Red corpuscles carry oxygen. White corpuscles fight infection.

cortisone (kôr'tĭ sōn). A secretion from the adrenal glands; a drug used in medicine.

coryza (kŏ rī'zȧ). A cold in the head.

cosmetics. Substances used to beautify the skin, hair, nails.

cretin (krē'tĭn). A person without enough thyroid hormone, thyroxin. A cretin has poor physical and mental development.

cuspids (kŭs'pĭdz). Teeth with single points or cusps; canine teeth.

dandruff. Scales formed among the hairs on the head.

deciduous (dė sĭd'ŭ ŭs) teeth. "Baby," temporary, or primary teeth.

dentrifrice (dĕn'tĭ frĭs). A paste, powder, or liquid used to clean teeth.

dentin (dĕn'tēn). The hard substance under the enamel of teeth; ivory.

deodorant (dē ō'dėr ănt). A substance used to stop body odor.

depilatory (dė pĭl'ȧ tō rĭ). A substance used to remove hair.

depressant (dė prĕs'ănt). A drug that lowers the rate of activity of an organ or of the whole body. Alcohol is a depressant.

dermatitis (dûr mȧ tī'tĭs). Inflammation of the skin. It may have many causes.

dermis (dûr'mĭs). The lower layer of the skin. The dermis contains the nerves, blood vessels, glands, hair roots, and smooth muscle cells.

development. Changing from a younger to a more adult form; becoming more complex.

diabetes (dī ȧ bē'tėz). A disease in which the body cannot use sugar properly. It is caused by failure to produce enough insulin.

diagnosis (dī ăg nō'sĭs). The process of deciding what disease or abnormal condition a person has. *To diagnose* means to make a diagnosis.

diaphragm (dī'ȧ frăm). The wall of muscle and connective tissue that separates the chest cavity from the abdominal cavity.

diarrhea (dī ȧ rē'ȧ). A condition in which bowel movements occur more often than usual, and the feces are watery.

diastole (dī ăs'tŏ lē). The period of relaxation of the heart. The heart fills with blood during diastole.

digestion (dĭ jĕs'chŭn). The process of changing food into substances that the cells of the body can use.

digestive juice. A fluid that digests food.

digestive system. The digestive tract and digestive glands; the parts of the body that have to do with digesting food.

digestive tract. The place where digestion occurs.

diphtheria (dĭf thēr'ĭ ȧ). A serious disease caused by the diphtheria organisms and spread by these organisms in discharges from the nose and mouth of a person who has the disease.

dislocation (dĭs lŏ kā'shŭn). Displacement of one or more bones in a joint.

distillation. The changing of a liquid into a gas by heating and then cooling the gas to form a liquid. Strong alcoholic drinks are made by distillation from material that contains small amounts of alcohol.

donor. The person who gives blood in a transfusion.

Dramamine (drăm'ȧ mēn). A drug used in treatment of sea sickness and other forms of motion sickness.

duct. A tube.

ductless gland. A gland without a duct to carry its secretions; another name for endocrine gland, or gland of internal secretion.

dysentery (dĭs'ĕn tĕr ĭ). An intestinal disease with severe diarrhea. It is caused by organisms that enter the body in food or drink.

eardrum. The membrane that is stretched across the ear canal. It separates the outer ear from the middle ear.

eczema (ĕk'sĕ mȧ). A common name for many different kinds of itching inflammations of the skin.

efferent (ĕf'ẽr ĕnt) nerve. A nerve that carries impulses away from the central nervous system.

egg cell. The reproductive cell produced by an ovary. An egg cell unites with a sperm cell to form a fertilized ovum, or egg.

electrocardiogram (ė lĕk trȯ kär'dĭ ȯ-grăm). A record of electrical changes that occur in the heart as it beats; it is made by an electrocardiograph.

elimination. The process of getting rid of, especially of waste products from the body.

emergency. A condition that needs immediate action.

emotion. A strong feeling—for example, anger or fear.

enamel. The smooth, hard outer layer of teeth.

endocrine (ĕn'dȯ krīn) gland. A gland that produces a hormone and pours it directly into the blood.

endocrine system. All the endocrine glands considered together.

enema (ĕn'ė mȧ). A treatment for constipation or to cleanse the lower bowel. In this treatment, warm water or some other liquid is put directly into the rectum.

energy. The ability to do work.

enriched flour. Flour that contains added vitamins and minerals to take the place of those that are lost in milling.

enteritis (ĕn tẽr ī'tĭs). Inflammation of the intestines.

enuresis (ĕn û rē'sĭs). The inability to control elimination from the bladder at an age when most children are able to do so.

environment. Everything around a living thing.

enzyme (ĕn'zīm). A chemical formed by living cells that causes changes in other substances without itself being used up or changed. Digestive enzymes are found in digestive juices and digest food.

epidemic (ĕp ĭ dĕm'ĭk). An unusual number of cases of a disease; rapid spreading of a disease.

epidermis (ĕp ĭ dûr'mĭs). The outer protective layer of the skin.

epiglottis (ĕp ĭ glŏt'ĭs). A fold of tissue that closes over the larynx when food or drink goes down the esophagus, or when one swallows.

epilepsy (ĕp'ĭ lĕp sĭ). A disease of the central nervous system, usually of unknown cause. The person loses consciousness briefly and may go into convulsions.

erupt (teeth). To appear above the gum.

esophagus (ė sŏf'ȧ gŭs). A tube from mouth to stomach.

Eustachian (û stā'kĭ ăn) tubes. Two tubes that lead from the pharynx to the middle ears.

evaporation. The passing off into the air as a gas. Evaporation of perspiration cools the skin.

excretory (ĕks'krė tō rĭ) systems. Parts of the body that get rid of wastes.

expiration (ĕk spĭ rā'shŭn). The act of exhaling; breathing out.

faint. A form of unconsciousness; swoon. Fainting occurs if too much blood leaves the head.

farsightedness. The condition in which the retina is too close to the lens of the eye. This makes it necessary for muscles inside the eye to be continuously contracted in order that a person may see clearly.

fatal. Causing death.

fatigue (fȧ tēg'). Weariness; feeling tired. Acute fatigue results from exercise. It is cured by rest. Chronic fatigue is a sign of general ill health.

fatty acid. A substance that results from the digestion of fats.

feces (fē'sēz). The undigested materials that are gotten rid of through the large intestine.

fermentation. The making of alcohol by the action of yeasts and bacteria on carbohydrates in fruits and grains; a method of making light wines and beer.

fertilization (fûr tĭ lĭ zā'shŭn). The uniting of egg and sperm.

fertilized egg. The cell formed when an egg cell unites with a sperm cell; the beginning of a new living thing.

fever. Body temperatures above 99 degrees Fahrenheit.

filter. A device that allows some substances to pass through and holds others back. A filter is used to purify water by removing dirt and bacteria. Filtration is the process of passing through a filter.

first aid. The first help that is given to a person who is sick or hurt.

fluorine (flōō'ȯ rēn). A chemical element. In the form of sodium fluoride, it is sometimes added to drinking water in an effort to prevent caries.

focus (pl. foci). (1) The center from which infection spreads. (2) The point at which rays of light meet after passing through a lens.

foot candle. A measure of light; the light received from a standard candle at a distance of 1 foot.

fortified margarine. Vegetable fat to which vitamin A has been added.

fracture. The breaking of a bone. In a simple fracture, the bone does not come through the skin. In a compound fracture, the end of the bone comes through the skin.

freckles. Spots of brown pigment in the skin. Freckles form as a result of exposure to sunlight.

frostbite. Injury caused by extreme cold.

fungus (fŭng'gŭs). One of a group of plants that have no green coloring (chlorophyll). Some tiny fungi (fŭn'jī) may cause infections, such as athlete's foot.

gall stones. Hard masses that sometimes form in the gall bladder.

gamma globulin (găm'ȧ glŏb'ŭ lĭn). A part of the blood plasma. It is used in the prevention and treatment of poliomyelitis, measles, and certain other diseases. It contains antibodies.

ganglion (găng'glĭ ŭn) (pl. ganglia). A mass of nerve cells.

gastric juice. The digestive juice that is secreted by glands in the walls of the stomach; it contains pepsin, rennin, and acid.

genes (jēnz). Parts of chromosomes. Genes are important factors in heredity.

germ. Common name for tiny living things, especially the ones that cause infection or illness.

gingivitis (jĭn jĭ vī'tĭs). An inflammation of the gums.

glands. Parts of the body that manufacture substances, or secretions, used by the body.

glare. Light strong enough to disturb vision. Glare results from too strong light or from too great contrasts in light.

glycogen (glī'kȯ jĕn). A carbohydrate called animal starch; it is formed from excess food and stored chiefly in the liver.

goiter (goi'tēr). An enlargement of the thyroid gland.

gonococcus (gŏn ȯ kŏk'ŭs). The bacterium that causes gonococcus infection. In the past, gonococcus infection was a common cause of blindness.

gray matter. Parts of the brain and spinal cord made up of cell bodies and nerve fibers without a white covering.

groin. The inner groove where the legs join the trunk.

grooming. Taking care of one's appearance.

"growing pains." Various pains in the legs and arms of children. They may be caused by infections and are not related to growing.

growth. Increase in size.

habit. An action a person has learned to do without thinking about it.

halitosis (hăl ĭ tō'sĭs). Unpleasant breath.

hay fever. A disease caused by sensitivity, or allergic reaction, to pollens; allergic rhinitis. It is marked by symptoms of a cold.

health. General well-being of mind and body.

health insurance. Insurance designed to pay part or all of the costs of care or treatment when a person is ill or injured. Sickness insurance, hospital insurance, and accident insurance are kinds of health insurance.

heart disease. A general term meaning any condition of the heart that weakens it.

heat exhaustion. A condition that results from exposure to heat, usually indoors.

hemoglobin (hē mȯ glō'bĭn). The red coloring matter in the red corpuscles; it carries oxygen.

hemophilia (hē mȯ fĭl'ĭ à). A condition in which the blood clots slowly or not at all.

hemorrhoids (hĕm'ȯ roidz). Piles; enlargement of the veins of the lower part of the large intestine.

heredity (hē rĕd'ĭ tĭ). (1) The characteristics a person receives from his ancestors. (2) The passing on of characteristics from one generation to another.

hereditary. Appearing in a family in different generations.

hernia (hûr'nĭ à). A rupture; condition that results when an organ is pushed through the wall of the abdomen.

heroin (hĕr'ȯ ĭn). An opiate. It is a dangerous habit-forming drug.

herpes (hûr'pēz). Inflammation and blisters of the skin. Cold sores, or fever blisters, near the lips are the most common form of herpes.

histamine (hĭs'tà mēn). A substance that is always present in the tissues of the body. It is thought that persons with allergies have unusually large amounts of histamine in their tissues.

hives. Small itching lumps on the skin. Hives result from an allergy to some substance.

homicide. The killing of one human being by another.

hookworm. A small worm that sometimes lives in the digestive tract. Persons with hookworms are usually anemic and may be stunted in growth.

hormones (hôr'mōnz). Chemicals produced by certain glands (endocrine, or ductless) and carried in the blood; some regulate growth and development.

humidity. Moisture in the air.

hygiene. Knowledge of how to keep well.

hypertension. Continued high blood pressure.

IQ Intelligence quotient; a person's score on an intelligence test (his mental age) divided by his age in years.

idiot. The lowest grade of mental retardation. Idiots remain like babies in intelligence all their lives.

imbecile. The middle grade of mental retardation. Imbeciles are persons who stay all their lives at the intelligence level of children aged 3 to 7 years.

immunity (ĭ mū'nĭ tĭ). Resistance against disease. Active immunity is an immunity for which a person builds his own antibodies against a disease. Passive immunity is an immunity in which a person is given antibodies produced by another person or animal.

immunize. To make a person immune.

impacted tooth. A tooth that is crowded against the roots of a nearby tooth and cannot erupt.

impetigo (ĭm pė tī′gō). A common infection of the skin.

incisors (ĭn sī′zẽrs). The cutting teeth. Central incisors are the four teeth at the front of the mouth, two in each jaw. Lateral incisors are the teeth next to the central incisors, two in each jaw.

incubation (ĭn kŭ bā′shŭn) **period.** The time between the entrance of disease organisms into the body and the appearance of symptoms.

indigestion. Any failure to digest food properly.

infantile paralysis. The common name for poliomyelitis.

infect. To introduce an infectious microorganism into the body.

infection (ĭn fĕk′shŭn). Causing of disease by introduction of infectious organisms.

infectious organism. An organism (living thing) that causes disease.

inferiority complex. The feeling that one is not as good as other people when there is no reason for such a feeling.

infest. To introduce animal parasites, larger than microscopic, onto or into a living thing.

infestation (ĭn fĕs tā′shŭn). The condition produced by animal parasites living in or on another living thing.

inflammation (ĭn flă mā′shŭn). A diseased condition marked by swelling, redness, and pain.

infrared waves. The rays in sunlight that are beyond the red end of the spectrum (rainbow) and not visible to the eye. They give a feeling of warmth.

inherit. To receive characteristics, such as hair coloring, from an ancestor by means of genes and chromosomes.

insanity. The legal term for a severe mental disorder. *Psychosis* is the medical term for the same condition.

insomnia (ĭn sŏm′nĭ a). Wakefulness when a person should be sleeping.

inspiration. The act of inhaling; breathing in.

insulin (ĭn′sů lĭn). The hormone secreted by the Islands of Langerhans in the pancreas. Insulin influences the use of sugar in the body.

intelligence test. A test designed to find how intelligent, or bright, one person is in comparison with other persons.

inventory. The careful description of a stock of goods, including the value of each piece. As used in this book, inventory refers to a person's finding his own assets and liabilities in terms of health.

iris (ī′rĭs). The colored band around the pupil of the eye. It changes size to control the amount of light that enters the eye.

irradiated food. Food that contains vitamin D as a result of exposure to ultraviolet light.

irritability (ĭr ĭ ta bĭl′ĭ tĭ). (1) Responsiveness to stimuli. (2) Impatience.

irritation. The condition of being unusually disturbed and sensitive.

Islands of Langerhans. Masses of endocrine cells, which secrete insulin, in the pancreas.

jaundice (jôn′dĭs). A condition in which the skin turns yellowish. Jaundice is caused by the presence of bile in the blood.

joint. A place where two bones are held together by connective tissue. In movable joints, the two bones move in relationship to each other, as in the fingers or hip.

jugular (jŭg'ù lẽr) **veins.** Two veins in the sides of the neck. They carry blood from the head.

kidneys. Two bean-shaped organs at the back of the abdomen. The kidneys remove certain waste products from the blood.

laboratory. A place with special equipment for use by trained workers in carrying on special work or experiments.

laboratory technician. A person trained in special skills, such as those needed in making various kinds of medical tests.

large intestine. The last few feet of the digestive tract.

larva (*pl.* larvae, lăr've̅). An early stage in the development of some insects, worms, and other animals.

larynx (lăr'ĭngks). The voice box, at the upper end of the trachea.

laxative (lăk'sȧ tĭv). Medicine that is taken to relieve constipation.

leprosy (lĕp'rȯ sĭ). A chronic infectious disease that affects primarily the skin and nerves. It is caused by the lepra bacillus and occurs most frequently in the tropics.

leukemia (lù kē'mĭ ȧ). A serious disease in which there is great increase in the number of white blood corpuscles (leukocytes).

leukocytes (lū'kȯ sīts). White blood corpuscles.

life-expectancy. The expected length of life at any age, based on the average length of life of other persons.

ligament (lĭg'ȧ mĕnt). A band of connective tissue that holds bones together at a joint.

lymph (lĭmf). Colorless fluid found in the tissues and in lymph vessels.

lymph nodes. Small structures along the lymph vessels. Lymph nodes kill disease organisms and manufacture white corpuscles. They are sometimes carelessly called lymph "glands."

lymphatic system. The lymph and the tubes or vessels that carry lymph back to the blood.

malaria (mȧ lâr'ĭ ȧ). A disease caused by a protozoan which must live part of its life in a mosquito. Thus, the disease is spread by mosquitoes. It causes "chills and fever."

malocclusion (măl'ȯ klo̅o̅'zhŭn). Failure of the teeth to close properly; due to crooked teeth or poorly formed jaws.

marijuana (măr ĭ wä'nȧ). A narcotic and habit-forming drug made from the hemp plant.

marrow. The soft material inside bones.

mastoid (măs'toid). A projection of bone behind the ear.

membrane (mĕm'brān). A thin soft layer of tissue lining or covering a part of the body.

meningitis (mĕn ĭn jī'tĭs). Infection of the membranes covering the brain and spinal cord.

mental conflicts. Confused feelings; wishing different things at the same time; being disturbed by ideas or wishes of which a person is ashamed.

mental disorder. A condition in which a person does not think, act, or feel as other people do.

mental hygiene. Care of the mind.

mental retardation. Incomplete mental development.

metabolism (mě tăb'ȯ lĭz'm). The building up and tearing down of protoplasm. Basal metabolism is the energy used by a person who is resting quietly. Basal metabolism rate (B.M.R.) is the amount of energy used by a resting person in 1 hour for each pound of body weight.

microorganism (mī krȯ ôr'găn ĭz'm). Living things so small they can be seen only by use of a microscope. Most are harmless; certain ones cause disease.

migraine (mī′grān) **headache.** Severe headache, sometimes called a "sick headache."

molars. The grinding teeth, at the sides of the mouth. There are twelve molars in the permanent set, three on each side of each jaw; there are eight molars in the deciduous set.

mold. A kind of fungus. It often grows on food stuffs, leather, and so forth.

mole. A dark-colored growth in the skin.

moron. A mentally retarded person who stays all his life at the intelligence level of children aged 7 to 12.

morphine (môr′fēn). A drug made from opium; medically the most important of the opiates; used primarily for the relief of pain; dangerously habit-forming.

mucous. Secreting mucus.

mucus. A thin, slightly sticky substance secreted by the cells that line the nose, throat, and other organs.

murmur (heart). A soft sound heard over the heart, sometimes due to failure of the heart valves to close tightly.

muscles. The parts of the body that cause movement. Striated, or voluntary, muscles are those that a person can deliberately control, for example, in arms and legs. Smooth, or involuntary, muscles are muscles around the digestive tract and blood vessels, not under deliberate control. Cardiac muscles are heart muscles.

narcotic (när kŏt′ĭk). A drug that relieves pain and produces sleep.

nasal septum. The wall that divides the nose into two long cavities from front to back.

nausea (nô′shė á). A feeling of being about to vomit.

nearsightedness. A condition in which the retina is too far from the lens of the eye. The result is that distant objects are not seen clearly.

nephritis (nė frī′tĭs). An inflammation of the kidneys.

nerve. A threadlike structure that carries impulses to and from the central nervous system.

nervous impulse. A message carried over a nerve from one part of the body to another.

nervous system. The brain, spinal cord, ganglia, and nerves; all the parts of the body that carry impulses from place to place.

niacin (nī′á sĭn) (or nicotinic acid). A vitamin in the vitamin-B complex.

nicotine (nĭk′ȯ tēn). A drug contained in tobacco.

night blindness. Difficulty in adjusting to seeing in dim light; often caused by lack of vitamin A in the diet.

nitrogenous (nī trŏj′ė nŭs) **wastes.** Wastes that contain nitrogen; chiefly urine.

normal. Used sometimes to mean the way something should be, for example, normal eyesight; sometimes with the meaning of average, for example, normal weight. *Abnormal* means not normal. *Subnormal* means below normal. *Supernormal* means above normal.

nostrils. The two outside openings of the nose.

nucleus (nū′klė ŭs). A small mass within a cell. Without the nucleus, a cell cannot live.

nutrient. A class of foods.

nutrition (nủ trĭsh′ŭn). The process by which food is taken into the body of a plant or animal and is used to keep the plant or animal alive.

occupational therapy. Activity designed to improve a person's outlook on life and give him useful skills.

oculist (ŏk′ủ lĭst). An ophthalmologist; a physician who specializes in the care of the eyes.

ophthalmologist (ŏf thăl mŏl'ô jĭst). An oculist; a physician who specializes in the care of the eyes.

opiate (ō'pĭ āt). A drug made from opium. Morphine, codeine, and heroin are opiates.

optic nerve. The nerve from the eye to the brain.

optician (ŏp tĭsh'ăn). A person with technical training who grinds lenses and makes glasses.

optometrist (ŏp tŏm'ė trĭst). A person trained in testing vision and fitting glasses.

organ. A part of the body made up of tissues and carrying out a special function—for example, the heart, the tongue.

organism. A living thing.

orthodontia (ôr thô dŏn'shĭ ȧ). The treatment of malocclusion.

orthodontist. A dentist who treats malocclusion.

otology (ō'tŏl ô jĭ). The branch of knowledge that deals with the ear and its diseases.

ovaries. Two organs in the lower part of the abdomen in the female. They produce eggs and also hormones that influence the development of secondary sexual characteristics.

oxidation. Uniting with oxygen. Oxidation results in the production of heat.

pancreas (păn'krė ăs). A large gland close to the stomach. It manufactures digestive juices (pancreatic juice) and a hormone (insulin).

pancreatic juice. A secretion from the pancreas that empties into the small intestine and contains enzymes which aid in the digestion of fats, starches, and proteins.

paralysis (pȧ răl'ĭ sĭs). Loss of power to move.

parasites. Organisms that live on, and get their food from, other living things.

parathyroid (păr ȧ thī'roid) glands. Small endocrine glands in the neck. They regulate the use of calcium in the body.

Pasteur treatment. Immunization against rabies. It is given to persons bitten by dogs suspected of having rabies.

pasteurize (păs'tēr īz). To heat a substance in order to destroy harmful bacteria. Pasteurized milk has been heated to about 140 degrees Fahrenheit for 20 minutes.

patient. A sick person.

pediculosis (pė dĭk ú lō'sĭs). A skin disease caused by lice (small, wingless insects).

pellagra (pĕ lā'grȧ). A disease due to lack of vitamin B, especially niacin, in the diet.

pelvis (pĕl'vĭs). (1) A basin-like cavity formed by the hip bones and the end of the backbone. (2) The bones about the pelvis.

penicillin (pĕn ĭ sĭl'ĭn). A drug produced by certain molds. It is useful in the treatment of many infections.

pepsin. An enzyme secreted by glands in the walls of the stomach. Pepsin helps to digest protein.

peristalsis (pĕr ĭ stăl'sĭs). Waves of contraction down the digestive tract.

perspiration (pûr spĭ rā'shŭn). Sweat; a salty fluid secreted by the sweat glands in the skin.

pharmacist. A druggist.

pharmacy (fär'mȧ sĭ). The preparation of drugs or medicines.

pharynx (făr'ĭngks). The space at the back of the nose and mouth.

phenol (fē'nōl). Carbolic acid.

physical therapy. The use of massage, heat, light, water, electricity, or exercise in the treatment of an abnormal condition.

physician. A doctor who has training in medicine.

pigment. Coloring matter.

pinworm. A threadlike worm that sometimes lives in the large intestine.

pituitary (pĭ tū′ĭ tĕr ĭ) **gland.** An endocrine gland in the head. The pituitary gland regulates a person's growth and has an influence on most of the other endocrine glands.

plasma. The liquid part of the blood. Dried plasma can be mixed with water and used in the treatment of shock.

pleura (plŏŏr′a̤). The membrane that covers the lungs and lines the cavities in the chest.

pleurisy (plŏŏr′ĭ sĭ). Inflammation of the pleura.

pneumonia (nŭ mō′nĭ a̤). An infectious disease in which the lungs are inflamed.

pneumothorax (nū mȯ thō′răks). Air in the thorax. In pneumothorax, one lung is collapsed and cannot be used for breathing.

poliomyelitis (pō′lĭ ȯ mī ĕ lī′tĭs). Infantile paralysis. A disease caused by a virus, which may kill the nerves and cause paralysis of muscles to which the nerves go.

polyp (pŏl′ĭp). A small grapelike growth.

posture. The way of holding the body while standing, walking, or lying.

prenatal. Before birth.

pressure point. The place where an artery can be pressed against a bone to stop bleeding.

privy (prĭv′ĭ). Outdoor toilet.

protective foods. Foods that contain proteins, minerals, and vitamins.

protein (prō′tĕ ĭn). A kind of nutrient needed for building protoplasm. Protein is contained in meat, fish, eggs, cheese, beans, and other foods. Complete proteins contain all the needed amino acids and come from animal sources. Incomplete proteins contain some of the needed amino acids and come from plant sources.

protoplasm (prō′tȯ plăz′m). The living stuff in all plants and animals.

protozoan (prō tȯ zō′ăn). A one-celled animal. Some protozoans cause disease —for example, malaria.

psychiatrist (sī kī′a̤ trĭst). A physician who specializes in the treatment of persons with mental disorders.

psychosis (sī kō′sĭs). The medical term for a severe mental disorder. *Insanity* is the legal term for the same condition. (*Pl.* psychoses.)

psychosomatic (sī kȯ sȯ măt′ĭk). Relating to mind and body considered together.

"ptomaine" (tō′mān) **poisoning.** An inaccurate term sometimes applied to intestinal disturbances. Ptomaines are poisonous substances in decaying food but rarely cause poisoning.

puberty (pū′bĕr tĭ). The time when ovaries and testes begin to produce eggs and sperm and hormones. Puberty occurs in most girls around 12 or 13, in most boys around 14 or 15.

public-health nurse. (1) A nurse who works for a public-health department. (2) A nurse with special training for educating and working with groups of people rather than with individual patients only.

public-health services. The care of public water supplies, public sewage disposal, quarantine, and other services which individuals cannot perform for themselves and which are carried on by the community as a whole.

pulmonary (pŭl′mȯ nĕr ĭ). Relating to the lungs.

pulp cavity. The space within a tooth containing nerves, blood vessels, and lymph vessels.

pulse. The beat or wave of pressure in the arteries that follows each contraction of the heart. The pulse beat is usually felt in the wrist.

pupil. The opening, in the front of the eye, through which light enters the eye. The pupil is round and appears black.

pus. Material in boils and other infections. It is usually yellowish and contains plasma, white blood cells, and bacteria.

pustules (pŭs'tụ̈ls). Small sores containing pus.

pyorrhea (pī ŏ rē'a). Infection of the gums, usually with the presence of pus.

quarantine (kwŏr'ăn tēn). Keeping persons who may have been exposed to a disease away from other persons during the incubation period of the disease; applied to ships that have had cases of disease on board; applied to isolating a sick person in his house and allowing no one to come in or out.

rash. A swelling and redness of the skin.

rectum (rĕk'tŭm). The lower part of the large intestine.

reflex (rē'flĕks). An action a person performs without having to learn it—for example, sneezing.

rehabilitation (rē ha bĭl ĭ tā'shŭn). Getting patients back to useful lives.

rennin (rĕn'ĭn). An enzyme in the gastric juice which curdles milk.

reproductive organs. The organs that have to do with the production of new individuals.

research (rė sûrch'). Careful study.

respiration (rĕs pĭ rā'shŭn). The exchange of oxygen and carbon dioxide. External respiration is the exchange of oxygen and carbon dioxide in the lungs. Internal respiration is the exchange of oxygen and carbon dioxide between the blood and the cells.

respiratory system. The nose, lungs, and passages between them; all the parts of the body that have to do with breathing.

response. An action following a stimulus.

retina (rĕt'ĭ na). The lining at the back of the eyeball where light rays set up nervous impulses that go to the brain.

Rh factor. A substance found in the blood of some persons and not in that of other persons. It is important in transfusions.

rheumatic (rōō măt'ĭk) fever. An infectious disease that often causes damage to the heart.

rheumatism (rōō'ma tĭz'm). A common name for painful joints and muscles.

riboflavin (rī bỏ flā'vĭn). One of the vitamins in the vitamin-B complex.

rickets. A disease due to lack of vitamin D. In rickets, the bones are soft and weak.

ringworm. Infection of the skin caused by fungi.

sac. A pouch, or baglike part, in a living thing.

salivary (săl'ĭ vĕr ĭ) glands. Digestive glands in the mouth, which secrete saliva.

sanatorium (săn a tō'rĭ ŭm). A hospital for the care of patients with a chronic disease such as tuberculosis.

sanitation. Making living conditions healthful.

scabies (skā'bĭ ēz). A skin disease caused by a tiny spider-like animal, the itch mite.

Schick test. A skin test for immunity to diphtheria.

scurvy (skûr'vĭ). A disease caused by lack of vitamin C in the diet.

secondary sexual characteristics. The characteristics, or traits, that make men appear different from women—for example, shape and voice.

secretion (sė krē'shŭn). A substance formed by some organ in the body.

semicircular canals. The small tubes in the inner ears, concerned with the sense of balance.

sensation. Feeling; being conscious of

something seen, heard, felt, tasted, or smelled.

sense organs. The eyes, ears, nose, tongue, and skin; parts of the body that receive stimuli.

shock. Weakness and failure of blood flow following injury.

sinuses (sī′nŭs ĕz). Hollow spaces in bones, especially those of the head.

skeletal (skĕl′ė tăl) **muscles.** The muscles attached to bones.

skeleton. The bony framework of the body.

skull. The bones of the head.

sling. A bandage used to support an arm or hand.

small intestine. The part of the digestive tract where digestion is completed and where digested food is absorbed; between the stomach and the large intestine. It is about 20 feet long in adults.

smog. A combination of smoke and fog.

sound-deadening. Reducing the amount of noise in rooms by using materials that absorb sound waves and by moving objects that reflect sound waves.

sperm cells. The cells produced by testes. A sperm cell unites with an egg cell to form a fertilized ovum, or egg.

sphygmomanometer (sfĭg mō mȧ nŏm′ė-tẽr). An instrument for measuring blood pressure.

spinal cord. The part of the nervous system contained within the backbone.

spine. The backbone.

spirochete (spī′rȯ kēt). A corkscrew-shaped microorganism. A few spirochetes cause disease.

splint. A thin piece of wood or other stiff material used to keep an injured bone from being moved.

sprain. Injury to ligaments, tendons, or muscles about a joint.

sputum (spū′tŭm). Material from the mouth. The term refers chiefly to saliva but may include mucus and pus.

sterile (stĕr′ĭl). Very clean; free from any organisms that might cause an infection.

sterile dressing. Very clean bandage or pad for use on a wound or infection.

sternum (stûr′nŭm). The flat bone, in the front of the chest, to which ribs are attached.

stethoscope (stĕth′ȯ skōp). An instrument through which a physician listens to sounds within the body, for example, in the lungs and heart.

stimulant. A drug that increases activity of an organ or of the body as a whole by acting on the nervous system. Caffeine is a stimulant.

stimulus (stĭm′ȗ lŭs). Something that brings about some action in a living thing—for example, hunger, a flash of light.

stomach (stŭm′ăk). The large saclike portion of the digestive tract, where food is stored and partly digested.

strabismus (strȧ bĭz′mŭs). A condition in which the two eyes do not work together. Crossed eyes is an example.

strain. (1) Great effort; excessive effort or stretching. (2) Injury caused by excessive effort or stretching.

streptococcus (strĕp tȯ kŏk′ŭs). A kind of bacteria, in the shape of balls, growing in chains. Many cases of sore throat and tonsillitis are caused by streptococci (strĕp tȯ kŏk′sī).

stroke. The common name for apoplexy.

suffocation (sŭf ȯ kā′shŭn). The inability to get enough air or oxygen; dying for lack of oxygen.

sulfonamides (sŭl fŏn′ȧ mīds). Sulfa drugs; used in treating many kinds of infections.

sty. An inflammation, like a small boil, on the edge of the eyelid.

sunstroke. Illness caused by direct exposure to sun.

superiority complex. Feeling that one is better than other persons when there is no reason for such a feeling.

surgery. Treatment of diseases or injuries by means of operations.

symptom (sĭmp′tŭm). A warning sign; a condition that shows the presence of disease.

syphilis (sĭf′ĭ lĭs). One of the venereal diseases, caused by a spirochete.

system. A combination of organs of the body, which carries on a series of related activities—for example, the digestive system.

systole (sĭs′tô lē). Contraction of the heart.

tanning. The formation of brown pigment in the skin after exposure to sunshine.

tapeworm. A long flat worm that sometimes lives in the digestive tract of a human being.

tartar (tär′tẽr). A hard deposit on the teeth.

tendon. A band of connective tissue that holds a muscle to a bone.

testes (tĕs′tēz). Two organs lying in a pouch outside the abdomen in the male. They produce sperm and also hormones that influence the development of secondary sexual characteristics.

tetanus (tĕt′a̍ nŭs). A disease commonly known as lockjaw, due to toxin produced by a microorganism.

thiamine (thī′a̍ mēn). Part of the vitamin-B complex.

thorax (thō′răks). The chest.

thymus (thī′mŭs). An organ in the chest, composed chiefly of lymph tissue.

thyroid (thī′roid) gland. An endocrine gland in the neck. It regulates the use of iodine in the body and has an important influence on growth.

tick. A small, spider-like animal. Certain disease organisms are carried by ticks.

tissue. A mass of cells that are all alike—for example, muscle tissue.

tonsils. Two masses of lymph tissue lo-cated in the side walls of the throat.

tonus. Continuous slight contraction of muscles.

tourniquet (toŏr′nĭ kĕt). A tight band tied around an arm or leg to prevent bleeding.

toxin (tŏk′sĭn). A poison produced by a living thing.

toxoid (tŏk′soid). A substance made from toxin but not itself poisonous. It is used in active immunization against diphtheria and tetanus.

trachea (trā′kĕ a̍). The windpipe.

trachoma (tra̍ kō′ma̍). A serious virus infection of the eyes. It may cause blindness.

training. Getting into good condition to do a job by following a program of regular rest, exercise, and meals.

transfusion (trăns fū′zhŭn). The transfer of blood from the blood vessels of one person into the blood vessels of another.

trench mouth. An infection of the mouth and throat.

trichina (trĭ kī′na̍). A tiny worm sometimes taken into the body in undercooked pork. It causes the disease trichinosis.

tubercle (tū′bẽr k′l) bacillus. The microorganism that causes tuberculosis.

tuberculin (tu̍ bûr′ku̍ lĭn) test. A skin test for possible infection with tubercle bacilli.

tuberculosis (tu̍ bûr ku̍ lō′sĭs). A communicable disease. It is usually located in the lungs but may attack any organ.

tumor (tū′mẽr). A swelling; a mass of cells. Some tumors are benign, that is, harmless. Some tumors (cancers) are malignant; that is, they tend to destroy life.

turbinates (tûr′bĭ na̍ts). Thin curved bones in the nose.

typhoid (tī′foid) fever. An intestinal disease caused by organisms that enter the body with food or drink.

ulcer. A sore on the surface or the lining of an organ.

ultraviolet light. Invisible rays in sunlight beyond the violet end of the spectrum (rainbow). Ultraviolet rays change certain oils in the skin to vitamin D. They also cause tanning.

umbilicus (ŭm bĭl′ĭ kŭs). Naval; scar in the front wall of the abdomen, where the umbilical cord was attached.

unconsciousness. The condition of not knowing what is happening around one.

undulant (ŭn′dụ̆ lănt) **fever** (brucellosis). A communicable disease usually of cows. It may spread to human beings who work with diseased cows or handle their milk.

uremia (ụ̆ rē′mĭ a). Poisoning caused by collection of waste products in the blood.

ureters (ụ̆ rē′tĕrs). Two slender tubes, one from each kidney. They carry urine to the bladder.

urethra (ụ̆ rē′thra). A tube that carries urine from the bladder to the outside of the body.

urinalysis (ụ̆ rĭ năl′ĭ sĭs). An examination of the urine.

urinary (ū′rĭ nĕr ĭ) **system.** The parts of the body that produce and get rid of urine.

urination (ū rĭ nā′shŭn). Eliminating urine from the bladder.

urine (ū′rĭn). Water and waste materials taken out of the blood by the kidneys.

vaccination (văk sĭ nā′shŭn). Giving vaccine to a person in order to stimulate him to build antibodies.

vaccine (văk′sēn). Killed or weakened disease organisms or small amounts of disease toxins.

valve. A fold or flap of tissue that prevents fluid from flowing backward. For example, valves in the heart and veins keep blood from flowing back.

varicose (văr′ĭ kōs) **veins.** Veins that are stretched and allow blood to collect above the valves.

vegetarians. Persons who eat no meat.

veins. Blood vessels that carry blood toward the heart.

ventilation. Supplying fresh air to a room, a mine, or some other closed space.

ventricles (vĕn′trĭ k'lz). The two lower chambers of the heart.

vertebrae (vûr′tĕ brē) (*sing.* vertebra). The small bones that make up the backbone.

virus (vī′rŭs). A living thing so small it cannot be seen through ordinary microscopes and will pass through porcelain filters. Some viruses cause diseases.

vital statistics. The records of births, deaths, causes of death, and other information about persons.

vitamins (vī′ta mĭns). Nutrients that are needed for good health but do not furnish energy.

warts. Small growths in the skin caused by a virus.

Wassermann test. A blood test for syphilis.

white matter. The parts of the brain and spinal cord made up of nerve fibers that have a white covering.

"wisdom" teeth. The third and last set of molars, located toward the back of the mouth.

xerophthalmia (zē rŏf thăl′mĭ a). A disease of the eyes caused by lack of vitamin A in the diet.

yellow fever. An infectious disease spread by mosquitoes. It is rare now in the United States but is common in the tropics.

Index

Abdomen, 117, 136, 259, 260, 267, 269, 270, 281, 370, 449–450
Accidents, 12, 18–40
  automobile, 19–26, 37–40, 360
  bicycle, 35
  burns, 26, 37, 38, 40
  drinking, 23, 37, 359–360
  drowning, 32–33, 36
  falls, 28
  farm, 30–32, 38
  fatigue, 123, 124
  firearms, 26, 39
  home, 26–29
  job, 29–30
  poison gases, 37, 40
  predicting, 36
  school, 33–35
  sports, 35–36, 39, 40
  suffocation, 28
  through the year, 36–40
Acid stomach, 261
Acne, 9, 168–170
ACTH, 98, 192, 373
Adam's apple, 232–233, 260
Addicts, drug, 363–365
Adenoids, 212, 228–229, 260, 350
Adolescence, 7–16, 86, 127, 150, 170, 210, 321, 324, 357–358, 365, 370
Adrenal glands, 370, 372–373
Adrenalin, 314, 315, 372, 373
Afferent nerve fibers, 291–292, 295
Air, 239–243, 376–385
Air-conditioning, 380
Air sickness, 270, 346
Alcohol, 124, 202, 261, 283, 336, 341, 342, 358–363, 420
  in driving, 37–40, 359–360
Alcoholism, 358, 360–363

Allergies, 174, 177, 217, 221, 225–228, 240–242, 304, 343, 440
Alveoli, 232, 233, 276
Amino acids, 137, 138, 259, 260
Anemia, 95, 190–191, 207, 273, 276, 306, 440, 444
Anesthesia, 291
Anger, 315
Ankles, 117, 120, 122
Antibodies, 403–404, 406, 427, 434, 444
Antihistamines, 174, 226–227
Antiseptics, 64, 223–224
Antitoxin, 403
  diphtheria, 405, 407
  tetanus, 410
Anus, 259, 276
Aorta, 204, 205, 208
Apoplexy, 52, 60, 208, 303
Appendicitis, 66, 190, 266, 268–271
Appendix, 265, 444
Appetite, 158, 304, 356, 357, 360
Arch supports, 121
Arches of foot, 119–122
Army standards of physical fitness, 14–15
Arteries, 78, 200, 201, 204, 281, 356
  bleeding from, 45–46
  blood pressure, 207
  pulmonary, 202
Arthritis, 97–98, 210, 373, 460
Artificial respiration, 47–49, 58, 59, 189, 235
Ascaris, 272–273
Ascorbic acid, 143–144
  (See also Vitamins, C)
Aspirin, 98, 174, 304
Asthma, 226, 240–241, 373, 384, 441
  (See also Allergies)
Astigmatism, 336, 338, 339
Astringents, 178

Athlete, 111, 112, 114, 142, 171, 357
  untrained, 105
Athlete's foot, 169, 171–172
Athlete's heart, 113
Athletics, 115, 151, 170, 357
  safety in, 35
Atomic medicine, 464
Atomic radiation, 95, 192
Audiometer, 347, 448
Auditory nerve, 346
Auricle, 199, 200, 204
Automobile accidents, 19–26, 37–40, 360
Autonomic nervous system, 102, 205, 267, 290, 293, 373

Backbone, 92, 119, 293
Bacteria, 72, 178, 233, 242, 265, 272, 276, 283, 285, 398–399
Bad breath, 220, 255
Baldness, 182
Bands on teeth, 253
Barbiturates, 127
Basal metabolism, 135, 280, 282
  test for, 371, 443, 458
Basic Seven Food Groups, 155, 156, 158, 159
Bath, 127, 168, 171, 222
BCG, 424–425
Beauty, 165, 183–184
Beauty treatment, 167–168
Bed, in relation to posture, 116, 118
  in relation to sleep, 125, 126
Beds, hospital, 469
Bends, 376
Beriberi, 141, 142
Bile, 262, 264
Birthmarks, 176
Blackheads, 170
Bladder, gall, 98, 264, 269
  urinary, 102, 281, 283, 284, 444
Bleeders, 192
Bleeding, 45, 51, 53, 60, 303, 336
  from arteries, 45–46
Blindness, 176, 335, 340–342
  color, 340, 440

Blister, 38, 56, 65, 169, 171, 173–175
Blood, 45, 47, 51, 76, 78, 84, 87, 103, 105, 111, 125, 138, 188–196, 199, 240, 253, 261, 263, 264, 273, 282–284, 300, 301
  circulation (see Circulation)
  corpuscles (see Corpuscles)
  types, 193
Blood banks, 193, 196
Blood poisoning, 51
Blood pressure, 103, 111, 114, 207–208, 210, 355, 356, 372, 446
Blood transfusions, 192, 196, 458
Blood vessels, 86, 102, 114, 115, 165, 168, 176, 199, 202–205, 234, 246, 266, 445
"Blue baby," 204
Body odor, 178–179
Body processes, regulation of, 139
Boil, 65, 169, 170, 426
Bones, 86, 92–97, 118, 119, 134, 138, 144, 150, 249, 355, 439
  marrow, 95, 191
Botulinus toxin, 159
Bowed legs, 97
  (See also Rickets)
Bowel movement, 266–267
Braille, 342
Brain, 79–82, 105, 122, 225, 288–308, 313, 315, 328, 333, 336, 348, 359
Brain fever, 303
Breakfast, 156, 158, 268
Breastbone, 92
Breathing, 125, 135, 234–241, 294, 300–302
  first aid, 47–49
Bright's disease, 283
Bronchi, 232, 233, 241, 383
Bronchial tubes, 356
Bronchitis, 222
Bruise, 13, 64, 105
Bubonic plague, 411, 416, 430, 432
Burns, 19, 26, 37, 38, 40, 56–57, 341
Butter (see Fat)

Caffeine, 124, 354–355

Calcium, 94, 97, 134, 138, 139, 155, 248, 249, 355, 372, 422

Calluses, 169

Calories, 135, 136, 150–151, 154

Cancer, 18, 87–89, 74, 175, 192, 268, 443, 464, 458
  danger signals, 88

Capillaries, 45, 78, 190, 201, 205, 207, 273, 282, 303

Car sickness, 270, 346

Carbohydrates, 134–136, 151, 161, 248, 259, 372

Carbon dioxide, 78, 204, 233–235
  action on respiratory center, 238–240
  in air, 377, 380

Carbon monoxide, 280, 381
  poisoning, 189

Carbuncles, 169–170

Cardiac muscle, 100, 103, 205

Caries, 248–252

Carotene, 140

Carriers, 407, 419, 420, 429

Cartilage, 94, 233

Cataract, 335

Cells, 72, 76, 79, 87
  cancer, 87–89
  nerve, 288, 290

Cellulose, 136

Central nervous system, 288, 291, 292, 301, 303, 364

Cesspools, 392, 394

Chairs and posture, 116, 118

Chapping, 169, 177

Charley horse, 105

Cheese (see Protein)

Chemical elements in human body, 71, 74, 76, 97, 249, 394

Chest, 92, 117, 233

Chest cavities, 234, 235, 237–238

Chewing, 245, 247, 254

Chicken pox, 169, 242, 246, 403, 405, 418–419

Childhood diseases, 398
  (See also names of diseases)

Chilling and colds, 223

Cholera, 277, 399, 411, 417, 428, 430

Chromosomes, 72

Cigarettes, 125, 356–358

Cilia, 215, 233

Circulation, 100, 103, 105, 110, 167, 199–210, 283, 294, 343, 370

Circulatory system, 73, 83
  effects of exercise on, 111, 114
  effects of tobacco on, 356, 357

Clot, blood, 45, 64, 138, 192, 208, 303, 372

Clothing, cleanliness, 172, 173
  relation to posture, 117, 118
  temperature control, 167

Cocaine, 363, 364

Cochlea, 346

Codeine, 364

Coffee, 127, 354–355

Cold sore (herpes), 175

Colds, 123, 144, 175, 217, 220–225, 242, 343, 347, 404, 413, 442

Colic, 66

Color blindness, 340, 440

Communicable diseases, 12, 13
  (See also names of diseases)

Concussion of brain, 60

Conjunctivitis, 343

Consciousness and brain, 298

Constipation, 13, 113, 123, 249, 266–267, 271, 272, 356

Contraction of muscles, 100, 138

Convulsions, 58, 60, 303, 443

Cooking, 160–161

Coordination, effects of exercise on, 113, 114, 119

Cornea, 333, 335

Corns, 169

Coronary occlusion, 210

Coronary thrombosis, 210

Corpuscles, 95, 188, 285, 444
  red, 138, 177, 189–192, 240, 264
  white, 189–190, 192, 212, 271, 402

Cortisone, 98, 373

Coryza (see Colds)

Cosmetics, 144, 173, 176–178, 225, 343
Cowpox, 405–406
Cramps, abdominal, 268
  muscle, 103, 105, 112
Creams, 168, 169, 174, 177
  (*See also* Cosmetics)
Cretin, 370–371
Crossed eyes, 102, 337–338
Cuts, 64

Dandruff, 181
Daydreaming, 311, 318, 319
DDT, 173
Deafness, 348–350
Dental defects (*see* Teeth)
Dentin, 245, 248
Dentist, training of, 455
Deodorant, 178–179
Depilatories, 179
Depressants, 124
Dermatitis, 173–174
Dermis, 165, 166
Diabetes, 170, 265, 282, 285, 372, 373,
  440, 444
Diaphragm, 234, 235, 237, 260
Diarrhea, 265–266, 268, 276, 355, 356, 371
Diastole, 201, 207
Dick test, 419
Diet, 114, 118, 133–162, 167, 223, 248–
  249, 255
  gaining weight, 151, 154
  reducing, 154, 158
Digestion, 2, 75, 100, 110, 112, 114, 137,
  142, 158, 259–277, 294, 356, 357
Digestive tract, 77, 82, 136, 177, 259–267,
  290, 372, 417, 428
  infections and infestations of, 272–277
Diphtheria, 160, 209, 220, 242, 347, 350,
  401, 403–405, 407–408, 418, 442
Dislocation, 55–56
Dizziness, 58, 346, 355, 356
Dramamine, 270
Dressings, sterile, 45, 51, 56, 65
Drinking (*see* Alcohol)
Drowning, 19, 32–33, 36–38, 105

Drugs, 124, 127, 222, 226, 241, 261, 291,
  300
  habit-forming, 358, 361, 363–366
Dwarfs, 96, 368
Dysentery, 277, 399, 428–430

Ear, 294, 301, 303, 333, 344–350
Earache, 66, 218
Eardrum, 390
Eating (*see* Diet)
Eczema, 173–174
Efferent nerve fibers, 292, 295
Egg cell, 73, 84, 373
Electric shock, 58
Electrocardiogram, 443, 458
Elimination, 110, 114, 280–286
Emergencies, minor, 44, 63–66
  what to do in, 44–66
Emotions, 82, 83, 103, 110, 306, 314–318,
  327
  and allergies, 226
  and circulation, 207
  and digestion, 267
Encephalitis, 303
Endocrine glands, 96, 138, 150, 368–374
Enema, 266
Energy from food, 76, 98–99, 133–138,
  150–154
Enuresis, 284
Enzyme, 139, 260–262, 268
Epidemic, 12, 13, 170–173, 221, 242, 391,
  406, 407, 411, 416, 419, 428, 430,
  431
Epidermis, 165, 166
Epiglottis, 260, 261
Epilepsy, 303–304, 440
Esophagus, 77, 260, 261, 269
Eustachian tube, 216, 218, 228, 260, 345–
  347, 350, 400
Excitement and sleep, 126, 127
Excretion, 84, 280–284
Exercise, 86, 105, 110–115, 122, 139, 165,
  167, 202, 267, 316, 445, 459
  eye, 338
  foot, 121

Expiration (*see* Breathing)
Eye, 79, 80, 86, 126, 178, 219, 294, 333–344, 411, 447, 448
  infections, 338, 341
  muscles, 102, 334, 337, 338, 344
  night blindness, 140
Eye banks, 335
Eyestrain, 123, 304, 336, 338, 344

Face powders (*see* Cosmetics)
Fainting, 58, 60, 204, 207
Falls, 19, 28, 63
Farsightedness, 336–338
Fat, 134–136, 151, 155, 255, 259, 262, 372
  storing, 150
Fatigue, 103, 115, 120, 122–125, 127, 142, 223, 304, 354, 357, 390, 420, 434
Fatty acids, 259, 260
Fear, 110, 314–315
Feces, 260, 264, 265, 272, 276, 277, 280, 302, 417, 429
Feet, 15, 117, 119, 223
Fertilization, 84
Fever, 79, 175, 202, 222, 225, 276, 282, 303, 304, 412, 419, 434
Firearms, accidents with, 19, 26, 36, 39
First aid, 44–66
Flat feet, 120
Fleas as carriers of disease, 418, 430, 432
Fletcherizing, 245
Flies as carriers of disease, 272, 277, 302, 395, 417, 428
Fluorine and teeth, 138, 249–250
Foci of infection, 98
Folic acid, 191, 192
Food, 85, 96–98, 110, 114, 117, 168, 300, 424, 428
  dangers in, 159–160
  protective, 159
  storage of, 160–161
  use of, in body, 74–75
  (*See also* Diet; Nutrition)
Foot candle, 387

Foot strain, 119–121
Fractures, care of, 52–55
  transporting persons with, 61–63
Freezing, 58–59
Freckles, 166
Friends, 323–324
Frostbite, 58–59
Fungi, 169, 171–172, 399

Gall bladder, 98, 264, 269
Gall stones, 264, 268
Gamma globulin, 196
Ganglia, 290
Gastric juice, 261–262, 270, 401
Genes, 72, 342
German measles, 398, 411, 418
Giants, 96, 368, 372
Gingivitis, 254–255
Glands, 81–82, 125, 288, 290, 292
  digestive, 78, 82, 260–264, 267
  endocrine (ductless), 82, 123, 135, 252, 355, 368–374
  oil, 169, 170, 177
  salivary, 260, 267, 401, 419
  sweat, 165–166
Glare, 388
Glasses, 338–339
Glycogen, 136
Goiter, 138, 371
Gonads, 370
Gonococcus infections, 341, 427–428
Goose pimples, 165
Gray matter (*see* Brain)
Grippe (*see* Influenza)
Grooming, 168, 176–184
"Growing pains," 209
Growth, 84–86, 357, 363, 370, 373, 438, 443, 447
  adolescence, 8–10
  cancer cells, 86–89
  cell, 72–73
  foods for, 137–138, 142–144, 146, 149–155
Gum boil, 253

Habit-forming drugs, 358, 361, 363–366
Habits, 16, 114, 128, 129, 150, 294–298, 311, 354–355, 390
  eating, 150, 268
  health, 442
  laxative, 266–267
Hair, 86, 165–166, 176, 180–182, 370
Hair removal, 179
Halitosis, 220, 255
Hangnails, 182–183
Hay fever, 226–228, 240, 241, 270, 373, 384, 441
Head injuries, 60
Headache, 13, 225, 226, 229, 304, 319, 342, 355, 356, 390, 412
  migraine, 304, 440, 441
Health examination (health inventory), 13, 127–129, 438–451
  (*See also* Physical examinations)
Hearing, 16, 86, 128, 293, 346–350, 356, 439
  test, 448, 450
Hearing aids, 348–350
Heart, 78, 81, 86, 92, 125, 135, 199–201, 290
  circulation in, 205
  effect on, of alcohol, 360
    of exercise, 111, 113, 115
    of tobacco, 354–356
  examination of, 445, 450
  spread of infection to, 225, 229
Heart disease, 16, 18, 97, 208–210, 269, 441, 460
Heart failure, 210
Heart murmur, 201
Heart muscle, 92, 103
Heart rate, 201–202, 445
Heat exhaustion, 57–58
Height-weight tables, 150, 151
Hemoglobin, 189–192, 204, 264, 444
Hemophilia, 192, 440
Hemorrhage, 47
Hemorrhoids, 266

Heredity, 72–73, 84, 96, 129, 182, 208, 252, 307, 311, 313, 340, 342, 348, 439, 440
Hernia, 106–107
Heroin, 364, 365
Herpes, 175
Hiccoughing, 239
High blood pressure, 283, 336, 356, 439, 440
High heels, 120
Histamine, 226
Hives, 169, 173–174, 177, 226
Hobbies, 316, 321, 324, 350
Home safety, 26–29
Homicide, 18, 19
Hookworms, 272–276, 395
Hormones, 8, 10, 82, 96, 103, 150, 252, 264, 368–374, 444, 461
Hospital insurance plans, 471–472
Hospitals, 468
  beds in, 469
  care in, 471
Humidity, 378–379
Hydrophobia, 433–434
Hypertension (*see* High blood pressure)

Idiots, 306
Imbeciles, 306
Immunity, 302, 403, 404, 407
  active, 403, 404, 410
  passive, 404, 405, 407, 410, 411
Immunization, 403–413
  against: bubonic plague, 411
    cholera, 411
    colds, 224
    diphtheria, 407
    influenza, 412
    measles, 411
    pneumonia, 420
    poliomyelitis, 302
    rabies, 433
    smallpox, 406
    tetanus, 410
    tuberculosis, 424–425

Immunization (*Continued*)
  against (*Continued*)
    typhoid fever, 412
    typhus fever, 411
    whooping cough, 410
Impetigo, 169, 171, 426
Indigestion, 123, 245, 268, 304, 355, 356, 360
Infantile paralysis (*see* Poliomyelitis)
Infected, definition of, 106
Infection, 56, 63–66, 95, 98, 110, 118, 123, 141, 166, 189–190, 209, 212, 220, 222, 228, 255, 266, 286
  acute, 217
  chronic, 217
  intestinal, 271, 276, 277
  of nervous system, 301
  secondary, 222
  sinus, 219, 221, 225, 242
  of skin, 169–171
  of teeth, 252
  of tonsils, 229
Inferiority feelings, 316, 317, 338, 360
Infestations, intestinal, 272–276
Infested, definition of, 106
Influenza, 18, 123, 124, 220, 221, 344, 399, 411–413, 417, 420
Infrared lamp, 459
Infrared rays, 385–386
Insanity, 301, 312–314, 360
Insect bites, 66
Insomnia, 126–127
Inspiration (*see* Breathing)
Insulin, 264, 265, 372, 373
Intelligence, 306, 307, 315
Intelligence quotient, 306–308
Intestinal infections, 272, 276, 277
Intestine, 102, 103, 106, 112, 260, 267, 288
  large, 77, 259, 265, 266, 273, 276
  small, 77, 78, 260, 262–263, 270, 359
Inventory, health, 13, 127–129, 438–451
Iodine, 71, 138, 139, 300, 371, 394
IQ, 306–308
Iris, 333, 335, 342
Iron, 71, 138, 155, 191, 192

Islands of Langerhans, 265, 370
Itch mite, 169, 172

Jaundice, 264
Jenner, Edward, 405
Job safety, 29–32
Joints, 55, 95–96, 119, 225
Jugular vein, 204

Kidneys, 16, 19, 76, 78, 79, 208, 225, 280–285, 354, 360, 411, 441, 443–444, 450
  circulation through, 205–207
Knees, 116, 117
Koch, Robert, 421, 423
Korea, 14

Large intestine (*see* Intestine)
Larynx, 232–233, 260
Laxative, 266–267, 270–272, 461
Lens, of eye, 333–337
  of spectacles, 339, 344
Leprosy, 400
Leucocyte (*see* Corpuscles)
Leukemia, 192
Lice, 169, 172–173, 418, 430
"Lie detector," 207
Life-expectancy, 16, 84
Ligaments, 55, 95, 116, 118–120
Light, 125, 128, 385–389
Lighting, 344, 387
Lip reading, 349, 350
Lipstick, 176
Liver, 136, 191, 192, 262–264
Lockjaw (*see* Tetanus)
Lungs, 76, 78, 79, 112, 168, 232–235, 237, 241, 242, 273, 280, 376, 383, 384
  circulation through, 202, 204
Lymph, 75, 78, 87, 138, 188, 253, 260, 399
Lymph nodes, 210–212, 228–229, 445, 449
Lymph vessels, 210–212, 246

Mad dogs, 433–434
Malaria, 430–431

Malocclusion, 252–255, 455
Mantoux test, 422
Margarine, 136, 141
Marijuana, 363–365
Marrow, bone, 95
Master control, 82–84, 368
Mastoid, 66, 222, 229, 346, 347, 350
Measles, 196, 242, 246, 344, 398, 404, 411,
    417, 420, 441
Meningitis, 303, 347
Mental conflicts, 317
Mental disorders, 312–314
Mental health, 1, 86, 103, 311–328, 343,
    360, 439
Mental retardation, 306–307, 312
Metabolism, 74, 78–79, 82
  basal (see Basal metabolism)
Microorganisms, 215, 233
  infectious, 49–50, 208, 220, 223, 224,
    229, 242
  (See also Infection)
Migraine, 304, 440, 441
Milk, 138, 160, 161, 167, 249, 355, 422,
  429
Mind, 306
Minerals, 134, 136, 138, 159, 160
Minor ailments, care of, 13, 44, 63–66,
  438
Moles, 89, 175–176
Morons, 306
Morphine, 364
Mosquitoes, 395, 418, 430–431
Mouth, 260
Mouth breathing, 218, 253
Mucous membrane, 216–219, 226, 345,
  379
Mucus, 215, 220, 225, 233
Mumps, 242, 419
Muscles, 81, 92, 98–107, 168, 261, 292,
  295
  involuntary (smooth), 102–103, 165
  voluntary (striated), 100, 102–103
  (See also Exercise; Fatigue; Tonus;
    and names of muscles)
Mushrooms, 159

Nails, 166, 182–183
Narcotics, 354, 363–366
Nasal cavities (see Nose)
Nasal membrane, 224, 225
Nausea, 58, 271, 276, 302, 356, 359
  (See also Dizziness; Vomiting)
Navel and hernia, 107
Nearsightedness, 336, 440
Nephritis, 283–284
Nerve center, 293
Nerves, 79–80, 142, 167, 246
  afferent, 291
  association, 292–293
  efferent, 292
  (See also Nervous system)
Nervous breakdown, 304, 306
Nervous impulses, 80, 364
Nervous system, 82, 123, 124, 288–308,
  311, 355, 359
  autonomic (see Autonomic nervous
    system)
  central (see Central nervous system)
Nervousness, 126, 144, 304, 355
Niacin, 141, 142
Nicotine, 125, 355–356
Night blindness, 140
Nitrogen, in air, 239, 380
  in food, 137
  (See also Chemical elements in body)
Nitrogenous wastes, 280
Noise, 125–126, 389–391
Nose, 78, 215–220, 223, 242, 255, 301–
  303, 449
Nose drops, 218–219, 222, 223, 225
Nosebleed, 64, 376
Nostrils, 215
  (See also Nose)
Nucleus (see Cells)
Nurses' training, 455–457
Nutrients, 300, 394
Nutrition, 133–162, 176, 420

Occupational therapy, training in, 459–
  461

Oculist, 338
Ophthalmologist, 339
Opiates, 363–364
Opium, 222, 364
Optic nerve, 334, 336
Optician, 339, 344
Optometrist, 339
Organisms, 72
  (*See also* Microorganisms)
Organs, 76
Orthodontia, 253
Otologist, 349, 350
Ovaries, 373
Overweight, 8, 14, 98, 150
Oxygen, 76, 78, 111, 189, 232, 300
  in air, 239–240, 377, 380
  (*See also* Breathing; Circulation)

Pain, 126, 293, 300–301
Pancreas, 262, 264–265, 370, 372
Paralysis, 141, 303, 359, 407, 460
  (*See also* Poliomyelitis)
Parathyroids, 370–373
Paratyphoid fever, 277
Pasteur, Louis, 398, 434
Pasteurization, 160, 407, 428, 434
Pediculosis, 172
Pellagra, 142
Pelvis, 94, 97
  in posture, 116, 117
Penicillin, 174, 222, 347, 420, 427
Pepsin, 261
Peristalsis, 260, 261, 266, 267, 269, 290,
    301, 355
Peritonitis, 270
Permanent waves, 181–182
Personality, 311–328
Perspiration, 58, 82, 83, 112, 138–139,
    166–167, 173, 377–379, 401
  and deodorants, 178–179, 220
  and ventilation, 377–379
Pharmacy, training in, 461
Pharynx, 215, 216, 225, 228, 260
Phosphorus, 97, 134, 138, 249, 394

Physical examinations, 89
  in athletics, 114
  before and after Pearl Harbor, 13
  before reducing, 154
  of school children, 14, 15
  (*See also* Health examination)
Physical therapy, 98
  training in, 458–459
Physician, 44
  training of, 453–455
Piles, 266
Pimples, 65, 168–170
Pink eye, 343
Pinworm, 272, 276
Pituitary gland, 96, 369, 373
Plague, 432–433
Plasma, 188, 196
Pleura, 234
Pleurisy, 234
Pneumonia, 18, 222, 400, 420, 424, 432
Pneumothorax, 237–238, 424
Poise, 321–322
Poison, 269, 300, 355
  and blindness, 341
  first aid for, 59
  in food, 159
  from gases, 37, 40
  (*See also* Toxins)
Poison ivy, 37, 66, 173–174
Poison oak, 37, 66, 173
Poison sumac, 66, 173
Poliomyelitis, 18, 19, 104, 192, 220, 242,
    269, 301–303
Pollens, in air, 384
  and allergies, 227–228, 240–241
Polyps, nasal, 219
Posture, 15, 100, 115–119
Prenatal period, 84–85
Pressure points, 46
Prickly heat, 174–175
Protein, 135–138, 159, 259, 261, 262
Protoplasm, 71–72, 74, 76, 125, 232, 259,
    280
Protozoans, 399, 430–431
Psittacosis, 434

Psychiatrist, 312
Psychosis (*see* Insanity)
Psychosomatic influence, 2
Ptomaine poisoning, 276
Puberty, 178, 373
  (*See also* Adolescence)
Pulse rate, 111, 113, 201–202, 204, 444–446
Pupil, 333
Pus, 64, 65, 172, 190
Pyorrhea, 254–256

Quarantine, 395, 416
Quinine, 341, 346, 430

Rabies, 433–434
Rash, 169, 177, 246, 419
Rats as carriers of disease, 395, 418, 432
Rectum, 266
Red blood cells (red corpuscles) (*see* Corpuscles)
Reducing diet, 154, 158
Reed, Dr. Walter, 431
Reflexes, 294–297, 450
Rennin, 261
Reproduction, 82, 370
  of cancer cells, 87
  of cells, 72
Respiration (*see* Breathing)
Respiratory center, 238, 240
Respiratory system, 77
Rest, 110, 114, 125–127, 167, 225, 424
Retina, 334–336, 340, 448
Rh factor, 193
Rheumatic fever, 18, 200, 208–209, 441
Rheumatism, 97–98, 249
Rhinitis, 227
Riboflavin, 141, 142
Ribs, 92
Rickets, 97, 144, 386
Ringworm, 169, 171–172
Rocky Mountain spotted fever, 430, 434
Rose cold, 227

Roughage, 136
Running away, 319–320
  from problems, 439
Running ears, 347
Rupture, 106–107

Safety, 18–40
  athletics, 35–36
  automobile, 20–26
  home, 26–29
  job, 29–32
  school, 33–36
  through the year, 36–40
  water, 32–33
St. Martin, Alexis, 262
Saliva, 245
Salivary glands, 260, 267, 401, 419
Salk vaccine, 302
Sanitation, 412, 428, 430
Scabies, 172
Scarlet fever, 160, 200, 209, 269, 347, 401, 403, 419–420, 441, 442
Schick test, 407–408
School safety, 33–36
Scurvy, 143
Sea sickness, 270, 346
Secondary sexual characteristics, 11, 82, 370
Seeing, 333–344
Semicircular canal, 346
Sensations, 291, 293
Sense organs, 288, 291
  (*See also* names of organs)
Sewage, 393–394, 429
Shaving, 175, 179, 180
Shock, 45, 51–53, 55, 56, 60, 63, 65, 196, 373
Shoes, and athlete's foot, 172
  choice of, 121
  corns caused by, 169
  and posture, 117, 118
Sight-saving classes, 342
Sinus, 209, 216, 218, 225
Sinus infections, 98, 200, 219, 222, 223, 225, 229, 253, 283, 304, 348, 350

Skeleton, 81, 92–97

Skin, 78, 144, 165–180, 280, 356, 360, 385–387, 401, 417

Skull, 92, 95, 293

Sleep, 112, 114, 116, 125–127, 223

Sleeping sickness, 303

Sling, 54, 55

Small intestine (*see* Intestine)

Smallpox, 401, 404–406

Smog, 382–383

Smell, 215, 219–220, 255, 293

Smoke, 386

Smoking, 355–358, 365

Snacks between meals, 158

Snuff, 355

Soil, 394–395

Sore throat, 97, 229

Sound, 389–391

Sound deadening, 390–391

Sound waves, 344, 346

Speech for the deaf, 349–350

Sperm, 73, 84, 370, 373

Sphygmomanometer, 207, 446

Spinal cord, 80, 92, 288, 290, 293, 294
  (*See also* Central nervous system)

Spine, 117

Spirochete, 398, 399, 427

Splint, 53–56

Sports, safety in, 35–36, 39, 46

Sprain, 55–56

Squint, 337
  (*See also* Crossed eyes)

Starches, 134, 136, 249, 260, 262, 282
  (*See also* Carbohydrates)

Sternum, 92

Stethoscope, 446, 449

Stimulants, 124, 354–355

Stimulus, 80–82, 125, 298

Stomach, 75, 77, 78, 102, 103, 260–262, 267, 269, 270

Stomach ache, 66, 270, 271

Strabismus (*see* Crossed eyes)

Strain, 55–56, 105

Streptococcus, 229

Streptomycin, 301

Stretcher, 54, 61–62

Stroke (*see* Apoplexy)

Sties, 338, 344

Suffocation, 28

Sugar, 249, 260, 282, 357
  (*See also* Carbohydrates)

Suicide, 18, 19

Sulfonamides, 174, 190, 222, 283, 347, 420

Sun baths, 386–387

Sunburn, 37, 38, 65, 166, 174

Sunlight, 144, 343, 344, 386, 424

Sunstroke, 57–58

Superiority feelings, 316–317

Sway-back, 116

Sweat (*see* Perspiration)

Swimming, 32–33, 37–38
  and ear infections, 350

Syphilis, 209, 301, 307, 336, 347, 427, 444

Systems, 76–82

Systole, 201, 207

Tanning, 166, 174

Tapeworms, 272, 276

Tartar, 254

Taste, 220

Taste buds, 260

Tea, 354–355

Tear ducts, 216, 218

Technician, medical, training of, 457–458

Teeth, 16, 138, 144, 209, 245–256, 449
  abscessed, 200, 253–254
  brushing, 250, 251, 254
  and diet, 248–249
  permanent, 247–248
  primary, 246–247, 252–253
  6-year, 247, 248
  12-year, 248
  wisdom, 248

Television, 126

Temper tantrums, 311, 315

Temperature, of body, 79, 445
  of room, 377–378

Tendons, 55, 100–101, 119, 120

Testes, 370, 373

Tetanus, 64, 394, 399, 401, 403–404, 410–411, 417

Thiamine, 141, 142, 300

Thorax, 233

Throat, 347, 348, 356

Thumb-sucking, 253

Thyroid, 138, 300, 369–371, 373, 374, 443

Thyroxin, 370–371

Ticks, 434

Tissues, 76–77

Tobacco, 125, 202, 341, 355–358

Tonsillitis, 15, 98, 118, 123, 200, 209, 222, 223, 229, 283, 302, 350

Tonsils, 228–229, 260

Tonus, 100, 103, 113, 117–119, 142, 146, 260, 372

Toothpastes, 251, 254

Tourniquet, 46–47

Toxins, 103, 122–124, 283, 300, 401, 403, 407, 409, 410, 419, 444

Toxoids, tetanus, 410, 411
   diphtheria, 407, 409

Trachea, 232, 233, 239, 261

Trachoma, 341

Training of athletes, 114

Tranquilizing drugs, 328

Transfusion, 192–193

Transportation of injured persons, 61–63

Trench mouth, 254

Trichina, 106, 272

Trichinosis, 106, 160

Trudeau, E. L., 423–424

Tuberculin test, 422–423, 426, 441, 444–445

Tuberculosis, 12, 18, 160, 220, 237–238, 282, 301, 306, 402, 411, 417, 420–426, 440, 441

Tularemia, 430, 434

Tumor, 87
   (*See also* Cancer)

Turbinates, 216

Type in books, 388–389

Typhoid fever, 160, 277, 391, 399, 402, 404, 411–412, 417, 428–429

"Typhoid Mary," 429

Typhus fever, 173, 430

Ulcer, 2, 268, 270, 356

Ultraviolet lamps, 459

Ultraviolet light, 97, 144, 166, 386–387

Umbilicus and hernia, 107

Unconsciousness, 59–60, 376

Underweight, 8, 14, 150, 158

Undulant fever, 160, 434

Uremia, 208, 284

Ureters, 281–284, 444

Urethra, 281, 283, 284, 444

Urinalysis, 284–285, 444

Urinary disturbances, 282–284

Urinary system, 280–282, 285, 286

Urine, 112, 139, 205, 277, 282, 354, 372
   examination (*see* Urinalysis)

Urticaria, 174

Vaccination and vaccines, 224, 302, 403–404, 406
   (*See also* Immunization)

Valves, of heart, 200, 209
   in veins, 204

Varicose veins, 205, 266

Vegetarians, 138

Veins, 78, 189, 201, 204, 205, 281
   bleeding from, 45
   pulmonary, 204
   varicose, 205, 266

Ventilation, 377–381

Ventricle, 199, 200

Vertebrae, 92, 94, 234

Virus, 175, 190, 221–223, 225, 242, 272, 276, 283, 301, 302, 399, 433

Vision, 14, 15, 293, 333–344, 356, 447
   test, 450

Vitamin pills, 144, 146, 161

Vitamins, 3, 74, 135, 136, 139–146, 154, 155, 159, 191–192, 223
   A, 139–141, 144, 155, 388
   B, 141–143, 155

Vitamins (*Continued*)
    C, 143–144, 155, 249, 254
    D, 97, 144, 155, 249, 386, 387
Vomiting, 268–271, 276, 304, 356, 359

Warming up, 111
Warts, 175
Wassermann test, 427, 444
Water, drinking, 391–393
    need for, 138–139
Water safety, 32–33
Wax in ear, 346
Weight, 150–154
Wells, 392
White blood cells (white corpuscles)
    (*see* Corpuscles)
White matter (*see* Brain)
Whiteheads, 170

Whooping cough, 220, 399, 400, 402, 404,
    408–410, 420
Windpipe (*see* Trachea)
World War II, Army standards, 13–15
    deaths in, 18
Worms, 272–276
Worry, 110, 117, 126, 270, 304, 315–316
Wounds, first aid for, 45, 49, 51
    small, 64
Wrinkles, 174

Xerophthalmia, 140
X-ray, of bones, 443
    of chest, 423, 441, 443–445
    of teeth, 255
    in treatment of cancer, 87
    in treatment of leukemia, 192

Yellow fever, 411, 418, 430, 431

Servings of Food for Different Kinds of Work

Light work	Moderate work	Heavy work
BREAKFAST		
Orange juice, ½ cup (Group 2)	Orange juice, ½ cup (Group 2)	Orange juice, ½ cup (Group 2)
Cereal, 1 oz and ½ cup milk (Groups 6 and 4)	Cereal, 1½ oz and ¾ cup milk (Groups 6 and 4)	Cereal, 1½ oz and ¾ cup milk (Groups 6 and 4)
Egg, 1 (Group 5)	Egg, 1 (Group 5)	Eggs, 2 (Group 5)
Toast, 1 slice and butter or fortified margarine (Groups 6 and 7)	Toast, 2 slices and butter or fortified margarine (Groups 6 and 7)	Toast, 3 slices and butter or fortified margarine (Groups 6 and 7)
Strawberry jam, 1 tbs	Strawberry jam, 2 tbs	Strawberry jam, 3 tbs
Coffee or tea for adults	Coffee or tea for adults	Coffee or tea for adults
Milk, 1 cup for children (Group 4)	Milk, 1 cup for children (Group 4)	Milk, 1 cup for children (Group 4)
LUNCH		
Cheese sandwich, 1 (Groups 4, 6, and 7)	Cream of potato soup, ½ cup (Groups 3 and 4)	Cream of potato soup, 1 cup (Groups 3 and 4)
Carrot and cabbage salad, 1 cup (Groups 1 and 2)	Cheese sandwich, 1 (Groups 4, 6, and 7)	Cheese sandwiches, 2 (Groups 4, 6, and 7)
Fresh or canned peach, 1 (Group 3)	Carrot and cabbage salad, ¾ cup (Groups 1 and 2)	Carrot and cabbage salad, 1 cup (Groups 1 and 2)
Cookie, 1	Fresh or canned peach, 1 (Group 3)	Fresh or canned peach, 1 (Group 3)
	Cookies, 2	Cookies, 3
Milk, 1 cup (Group 4)	Milk, 1 cup (Group 4)	Milk, 1 cup (Group 4)
DINNER		
Meat or nut loaf, 1 serving (Group 5)	Meat or nut loaf, 1 serving (Group 5)	Meat or nut loaf, 1 large serving (Group 5)
Creamed potato or turnips, ½ cup (Groups 3 and 4)	Creamed potato or turnips, ½ cup (Groups 3 and 4)	Creamed potato or turnips, ¾ cup (Groups 3 and 4)
Buttered spinach or kale, ½ cup (Groups 1 and 7)	Buttered spinach or kale, ¾ cup (Groups 1 and 7)	Buttered spinach or kale, ¾ cup (Groups 1 and 7)
Lettuce and tomato salad, 1 serving (Groups 1 and 2)	Lettuce and tomato salad, 1 serving (Groups 1 and 2)	Lettuce and tomato salad, 1 serving (Groups 1 and 2)
Dinner roll, 1 and butter or fortified margarine (Groups 6 and 7)	Dinner rolls, 2 and butter or fortified margarine (Groups 6 and 7)	Dinner rolls, 3 and butter or fortified margarine (Groups 6 and 7)
Pudding with fruit sauce, ½ cup	Pudding with fruit sauce, ¾ cup	Pudding with fruit sauce, ¾ cup
Coffee or tea for adults	Coffee or tea for adults	Coffee or tea for adults
Milk for children, 1 cup (Group 4)	Milk for children, 1 cup (Group 4)	Milk for children, 1 cup (Group 4)